Mechanical and Electrical

Equipment for Buildings

The Chase Manhattan Bank Building, New York, N.Y. (*Architects:* Skidmore, Owings and Merrill.)

Fourth Edition

Mechanical and Electrical Equipment for Buildings

William J. McGuinness

Professor of Architecture
Chairman, Department of Structural Design
School of Architecture, Pratt Institute
Partner, McGuinness and Duncan, Engineers

Benjamin Stein

Associate and Chief Electrical Engineer
Seelye, Stevenson, Value and Knecht,
Consulting Engineers

The Late **Charles Merrick Gay**

Professor of Architectural Construction
University of Pennsylvania

The Late **Charles De van Fawcett**

Professor of Electrical Engineering
University of Pennsylvania

JOHN WILEY & SONS, INC., NEW YORK · LONDON · SYDNEY

Library of Congress Catalog Card Number: 64-17149
Printed in the United States of America

Preface

Change is implicit in architecture. Only the adherence to beauty is timeless. The creative designer is alert to the needs of society and the evolvement of the material that he may use to fashion man's total environment. It is his trust to look beyond in anticipation of future social changes and to inspire and aid the technical advances they will demand. Variety in form and the elevation of the human spirit are his constant goals. He does not know repetition or conformity.

In the long history of the practice of architecture, major changes in the nature of *structure* may be bracketed in the relatively short period of a century. Accelerating as time passed, these changes have included the emergence of rolled steel sections, reinforced concrete, precast and prestressed concrete, increase and control of the strength of both concrete and steel, cable construction, lightly sheathed skeleton frames, folded concrete shapes and glued-laminated wood manufacture.

Within this century of rapid structural change has been a half-century that has marked the advent of an entirely new component of architectural design—mechanical and electrical equipment. Unlike structure which, even in primitive form, has always been inherently necessary in all shelter, the machinery for contemporary living was essentially nonexistent 50 years ago. The speed of its increase is well known. It is necessary to walk only a few steps to find electricity and communications instantly available. The distribution of hot and cold water and the parallel network of drainage piping encompass all habitable buildings. Vertical transportation is speedy and automatic, indoor climate is controllable at proximate locations, and lighting is highly efficient.

Architects adapted quickly to new structural forms as they became available. Adaptation to the organic demands of the amenities of modern living is presently an even greater challenge. In the era of advanced structural development, error (deplored by the best designers) consisted of using new structure to simulate old forms. In the current surge of mechanical and electrical demand, error, to be avoided, could lie in an attempt to preserve the charm of modern structure, free of the impact of modern equipment.

In the concept of good design, each service has its engineering efficiency, function, dignity, and balance, all qualities that resist attempts to hide or distort them. These services are part of the fabric of modern architecture.

In designing contemporary structures and communities, the architect must be equipped with engineering knowledge. He retains and directs the assistance of structural, mechanical, electrical, and acoustical engineers among his many other technical specialists. To collaborate well, the engi-

v

neers must know the objectives of architecture.

This book attempts to emphasize the interrelationship of architecture and engineering and to add to the technical knowledge of the architect and the architectural student. It is hoped that its use may assist engineers and engineering students to a better understanding of the total composition of an architectural design. It may aid those who have the important responsibility of building or operating modern complex structures to know the intentions and attitudes of the designers, part of whose work is here discussed.

The book includes sufficient data to aid architects and engineers in designing some mechanical and electrical systems. Mastery of these subjects suggests an entire library of appropriate literature. For this reason, lists of specialized and developed references are given in each section. A good knowledge of physics is assumed and no attempt is made to explain all of the physical principles involved.

The basic groundwork and method of approach of the original authors, Professors Charles Merrick Gay and Charles De van Fawcett, representing respectively architecture and engineering, has been faithfully retained, together with much of the material that relates to fundamental principles. Since change, however, is inescapable, an additional aim has been to report major developments that have occurred in the decade that has elapsed since the appearance of the third edition.

Stress has been placed upon the population increase and its effect upon the problem of obtaining pure water and disposing of wastes. The zoning of services in high-rise buildings has received more attention. New codes have been incorporated, notably the National Plumbing Code and the recent report of the Industry Heat Gain Joint Study Group. Changes in heating by hot water have been noted and one-pipe steam and vapor steam systems have been deemphasized. The use of steam, high-temperature hot water, and chilled water as district services in communities has been added. All reference to gravity heating systems has been eliminated. More space has been allotted to heating and cooling by air in subslab ducts. The subject of air distribution in general has been increased, especially as it relates to large buildings. Entirely new to this edition are the subjects of electric heating, the heat pump, and cooling by absorption.

The sections of the book devoted to lighting, wiring, and elevators have been completely revised and rewritten to bring the information presented up to date and to further the emphasis on the interrelation between architecture and engineering. This is particularly true of lighting design, where the book approaches lighting as an architectural medium to be utilized in spatial design. In addition, an entirely new section on sound and signals has been added to reflect the increasing importance of intrabuilding communications. Sufficient data are made available in tabular and graphical form to allow use of this volume as a handbook for some of the common problems encountered in design work.

The section on acoustics has been rewritten by W. Ranger Farrell of Bolt, Beranek and Newman, Inc., Consultants in Acoustics. It covers material which has been developed since the previous edition. The emphasis on room acoustics has been reduced and, instead, sound transmission, sound propagation, and acoustic criteria have been emphasized.

The authors express their sincere gratitude to all those who have so generously aided in this work by advice and information. Many of them are named here or are mentioned in the several sections of the book:—
Warren Bendixen, William Cleland, Raniero Corbelletti, Arthur Fox, Irving Gold, Dean Olindo Grossi, H. Seymour Howard, Jr., Arthur Johnson, Ivan Kittle-

son, Harold Matthiessen, Joseph McCann, Dr. Sidney Sussman, Willard Warren, John Woodworth.

Figures 10.2, 10.3*a*, 10.4*a*, 10.13, 10.14*a*, 10.15, 10.16 are reprinted by permission of the University of Illinois Small Homes Council from its copyright circulars *Fuels and Burners,* Index No. G 3.5 and *Heating the Home,* Index No. G 3.1. Other circulars in this series on home building are available for a small fee. For a list of publications, write to the Small Homes Council, Mumford House, University of Illinois, Urbana, Illinois. Figure 3.1 is adapted from the Standard for the Installation of Air Conditioning and Ventilating Systems of Other than Residence Type (NFPA No. 90A), copyrighted by the National Fire Protection Association.

We are especially grateful to our wives for their interest and assistance and to Margaret Kelly for the preparation of manuscript.

WILLIAM J. McGUINNESS
BENJAMIN STEIN

New York,
June 1964

Contents

1

Water

1. Uses of Water. Pure, potable water is one of the most vital of human needs. More essential on a short-term basis than food, it also serves human comfort and convenience in providing the means for washing, bathing, cooking, cleaning, and laundering. In the improvement of food production, irrigation has a measurable effect on the yield and quality of fruit and vegetables, just as the watering of livestock has on meat. The safety of building occupants and the protection of the material value of combustible structures and of the contents of both fireproof and nonfireproof buildings is enhanced when fire-hose standpipe installations and overhead sprinkler systems are standing ready to operate at any dangerous rise in temperature. The control of environmental comfort is often provided by circulating warm water for heat during the winter and chilled water for the removal of heat in summer. In the rapidly advancing field of climate control, water takes its place beside refrigerants, air, and other media for thermal exchange. Among the many other processes which involve the handling of water is the introduction of water vapor to the air or its removal in order to control relative humidity.

In the planning of buildings, the architect and engineer assume the responsibility of providing for adequate water supplies in the correct quantities, flow-rates, pressures, and temperatures with proper arrangements for changes and building expansion. The water must be palatable and bacteriologically pure. It is essential that its inherent chemical contents be controlled or modified to render it useful and to avoid clogging or corroding piping and equipment. Condensation of air-borne water vapor on the outside of cold-water pipes must be avoided. Controls must provide that sections of the building or its equipment can be valved off to permit repairs or changes. Valves, controls, and all equipment must be easily accessible with sufficient space for inspection and repairs. To avoid the encroachment of plumbing on the general esthetic design in the later stages of planning, both must be considered integrally from the first.

2. Sources and Qualities of Water. In its circuit of descending from the clouds to the earth's surface, accumulating in streams, rivers, and lakes, and returning by evaporation to the clouds, water changes in quality. The process of evaporation, conceived as low temperature boiling, is virtually one of distillation. It is evident that the best water is in the inaccessible vapor of the clouds. If it were possible to collect this water by

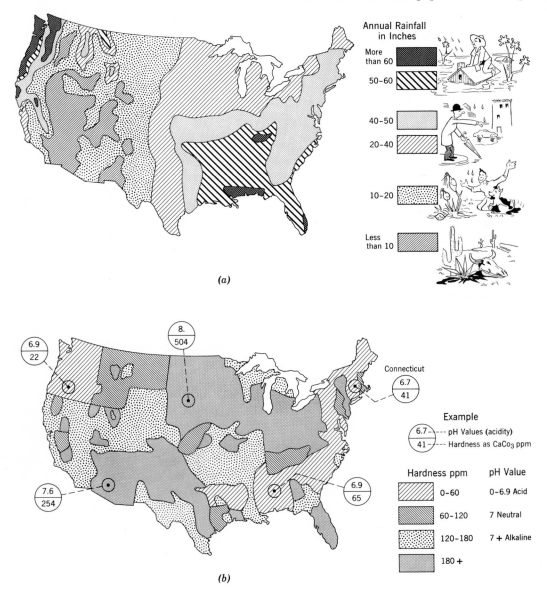

Fig. 1.1   Annual rainfall and typical examples of quality at selected locations. (*a*) Quantity.
(*b*) Quality: Treatment may be needed when pH is less than 7.0, a corrosive condition, or when
hardness as $CaCO_3$ exceeds 65 ppm. (*Progressive Architecture*)

condensing the vapor and catching it in a sterile cloud-pan directly below the clouds, most of our water problems would disappear. Instead, as the cloud vapor condenses to form rain, the drops passing through the denser parts of the earth's atmosphere acquire gases that cause an acid condition. Water caught at the earth's surface, though soft, will have a corrosive action on iron, due to the free carbon dioxide and oxygen that create the acid condition.

The rain is seldom caught directly for water supplies, but is permitted to become surface water in streams and lakes or even allowed to flow underground before being collected for use. When flowing over the earth it picks up organic impurities that may be dangerous to health. It may also acquire silt, odors, and, in summer, an undesirably warm temperature (see Fig. 1.2*b*). There is a mass of water flowing or standing beneath the earth's surface. The level of its surface is called the water table. As the surface water sinks through the soil to join this mass, its chemistry usually changes. Though it may remain acid and impure, especially when taken from shallow wells, it usually picks up minerals that are present in the

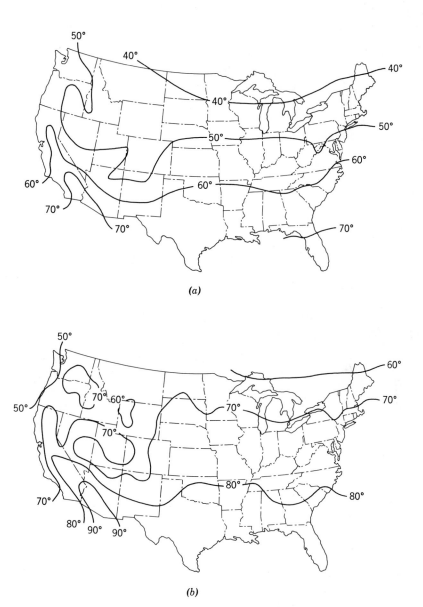

Fig. 1.2 Mean annual temperatures of well water and mean monthly temperatures of surface water during warm months. Degrees Fahrenheit. Adapted from records of the United States Geological Survey. (*a*) Temperature, ground water. Approximate temperature of water from nonthermal wells at depths of 30 to 60 ft. (*b*) Temperature, surface water. Approximate mean monthly temperature of water from surface sources for July and August.

earth and acquires a chemically basic (alkaline) quality. In this state of hardness it will not corrode metals, but will deposit its mineral content within pipes, often closing them completely.

During the process of descent to the underground water table, there may be other changes which are for the better. Long travel through the soil usually corrects the condition of organic impurity and renders the water safely potable for human consumption without the need for a chlorine purification process. The water also becomes cool, making it, in summer, more pleasant to drink than the warmer surface waters. When water reaches the sea, its high mineral content renders it unsuitable for almost all normal use. Sea water can be treated to make it usable, but the process is difficult and expensive. It is done on ships and in a few places where better water is in short supply. It is expected that the purification of sea water will become more important as an increasing population taxes

the normal water supplies, along with all natural resources.

Where rainfall is abundant, such as on the east and west coasts of the United States and north of the Gulf of Mexico, surface and shallow well supplies are generally available. In the central area of the country where the annual rainfall is less, water tables are lower and water has an opportunity to absorb more mineral content as it descends to these levels. In coastal regions water will often be found to have a low pH value, an index related to acidity. Such waters will attack ferrous pipes. The resulting rust, being many times bulkier than iron, may close the pipes in a few years. It will attack the zinc in brass pipe, finally causing holes to develop. Copper tubing is perhaps the best choice, and treatment to neutralize the acid condition should be considered. Hard waters (those having a total hardness in excess of about 65 ppm as is common in the central regions) will need treatment by a softening process; otherwise scale in the form of calcium deposits will form on the inside of any pipe without respect to its metal, finally closing it. These problems vary in degree and many supplies will not require treatment. It is also true that Fig. 1.1 represents only broad generalities in its statement of water availability and quality throughout the country.

A typical report of water analysis is shown in Table 1.1. With a total hardness of only 30 ppm, treatment for softening is not considered essential, but the low pH value of 6.6 indicates that the water must be classified as corrosive. The use of copper pipe and possible neutralization must be contemplated. It is evident that the architect will need the professional services of trained specialists to interpret the significance of these two items and the many others that appear on the report. Despite the conformity of the analysis in Table 1.1 with general conditions along the east coast (Fig. 1.1*b*), every proposed water source must be studied as an individual case and many sharp divergencies may be expected.

Table 1.1   Chemical Analysis of Water from a Private Well in Virginia

Quality		Parts per Million (ppm)
Total hardness	as $CaCO_3$	30
Calcium hardness	as $CaCO_3$	20
Alkalinity (Methyl Orange)	as $CaCO_3$	27
Alkalinity (Phenolphtalein)	as $CaCO_3$	0
Free Carbon Dioxide	as CO_2	13.5
Chlorides	as Cl	6
Sulfates	as SO_4	4
Silica	as SiO_2	19
Phosphates—normal	as PO_4	0
Phosphates—total	as PO_4	0.5
Iron—total	as Fe	1.6
Total dissolved solids		66
Turbidity or sediment		present
pH		6.6

From a report of Water Service Laboratories, Inc.

Impurities injurious to health are not usually tested as part of the general chemical analysis. County or other official health offices have strict jurisdiction over the use of waters that may be polluted. They will often provide free analyses to determine the biological qualities of such waters and will allow their use or require treatment for correction of impurities. Troubles generally arise when water sources are polluted by defective cesspools, septic tanks, and other sewage disposal systems, or by the proximity of organic matter or grazing animals. Detergents are now a source of contamination where sewage disposal and wells are close together. As areas become congested, the separation of sewage disposal centers and approved water sources becomes an important matter of public health.

3. Public Water Systems. The sources of water for most large cities are rivers and lakes. A small percentage of the total public water systems in the United States use ground water from deep wells. Figure 1.3 shows this kind of installation for a small community on Long Island, New York. The water is taken from the ground by multistage turbine pumps at depths of several hundred feet. The water is delivered to submerged pneumatic tanks at a pressure of about 80 psi. As water is demanded in the houses, the air under pressure in the upper part of the tanks forces it through the mains. No treatment of this water is necessary and none is provided. A neutral pH value and low mineral content make this a very satisfactory water. Quite a few systems of this type do not have any treatment; but some, where there is evidence of bacterial impurity, provide chlorination to correct this condition.

Water taken from rivers and lakes tends to be turbid (silty), warm in summer, and to contain harmful bacteria. It is often odorous, discolored, and acid. The treatment process shown in Fig. 1.4, which is for a big city, comprises six operations and three additions of chemicals. Mixing occurs after the first two additions of correctives.

Alum forms a coagulant which traps silt, foreign matter, and some impurities. Settling allows the heavier solids to drop to the bottom and filtration takes out the flocculated material resulting from the coagulating process. Chlorine kills bacteria and the combination of ammonia and chlorine assures a continuation of the sterilization process with a minimum of unpleasant chemical taste. Ferric sulfate, lime, and soda ash aid in the coagulation process. Finally, the water is passed through underground piping which cools it to more acceptable temperatures in summer. Figure 1.2 indicates a differential of 15° to 20° between ground water and the warmer surface water in summer at the same location. Figure 1.4 represents only one of many varied kinds of treatment programs.

The goal of most public treatment systems is to provide a pleasant, palatable water, free of harmful bacteria, silt, odor, unpleasant taste, and color. Some systems attempt to regulate the pH characteristics and some provide softening to reduce the total hardness. It becomes apparent that water is a controlled product. It may be fairly stated that for the many diverse uses of water in a big city, the water authorities *cannot* provide a product that is satisfactory to all users. For instance, if a city delivers a soft, though mildly corrosive, water, there may be some trouble with rusting of pipes. If this were corrected by the addition of lime to give it an alkaline nature, the extra hardness would play havoc with industrial and power boilers unless very costly private treatment were provided by those users. There is no clear middle ground and some consumers may always face the problem of private water treatment.

4. Private Water Systems. Farms and remote estates usually have their own private water systems. In rural and suburban areas where the progress of building is faster than the development of municipal water supplies or water companies, private sources must be sought. The elaborate treatment necessary for the use of surface waters or

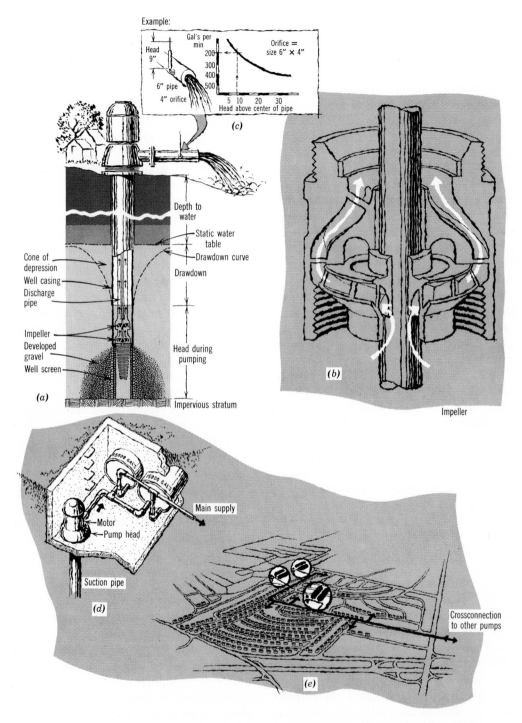

Example:

Head 9″

Gal's per min

Orifice = size 6″ × 4″

6″ pipe

4″ orifice

Head above center of pipe

(c)

Depth to water

Static water table

Cone of depression

Drawdown curve

Well casing

Drawdown

Discharge pipe

Impeller

Developed gravel

Head during pumping

Well screen

(a)

Impervious stratum

(b)

Impeller

Main supply

Motor

Pump head

Suction pipe

(d)

Crossconnection to other pumps

(e)

Fig. 1.3   *(a)* A turbine well-pump. *(b)* Its operation. *(c)* Measurement of its capacity. *(d)* and *(e)* Its use in supplying a small community with ground water. Capacities of turbine pumps range from 50 to 16,000 gal per min. (*Progressive Architecture*)

those in dug wells of the old type makes the use of driven or drilled wells preferred. Water from these sources usually has at least the advantages of purity, coolness, and freedom from turbidity, odor, and unpleasant taste. There is the possibility that any of these *may* be encountered in addition to acidity or hardness. Table 1.2 lists the possible problems with their causes, effects, and correction. Figure 1.7 illustrates some of the corrective processes.

When a client plans to build in a remote location, the architect and engineer will want to advise him about water problems even, if possible, before the purchase of the property. Quality-corrective measures can always be taken and pumping equipment purchased, but the amount of water that can be had from the ground, and the depth and cost of wells are all important considerations. There are some problem areas where wells several hundred feet in depth will yield as little as 5 gpm or nothing. The cost of drilling a number of exploratory wells may sometimes exceed the value of the property. Unfortunately, when such difficulties occur there is no guarantee of their solution. Conferences with neighboring owners, state and federal geologists, and with local well-drillers are all helpful. Many regions, of course, yield plentiful water, but the cost of the probable depth of the well should be considered.

When water is plentiful at levels less than 25 ft below the pump, a shallow-well pump such as that illustrated in Fig. 1.5 may be used. For water at greater depths a deep-well jet pump, shown in Fig. 1.6 would be suitable. For the largest installations, turbine pumps resembling the one in Fig. 1.3 may be used in connection with underground pneumatic storage tanks. There are many other types of pumping equipment available (see article 5), although for the larger capacities the turbine type is quite standard.

The well generally should be outside of the house to permit drawing up the pipes and the pump suction pipe for maintenance.

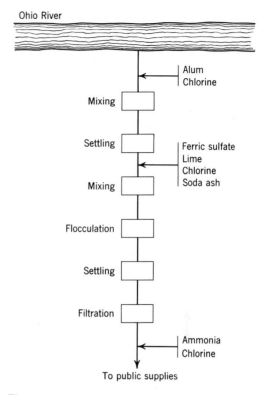

Fig. 1.4 An example of city water treatment. Treated water for the city of Cincinnati using river water as a source. From *Water Quality and Treatment,* 2nd edition, American Water Works Association, Inc.

Attention must be given to prevent freezing, to minimize pumping noises that may reach the house, and to provide for catching the moisture that may condense on the cold tank. There should be a drain to carry away water when the tank or the system is drained.

5. Pumping Methods. Well pumps with adjunct pneumatic tanks usually operate in response to the pressure in the tank, starting up when the pressure drops to about 20 or 25 psi, and shutting down when it has reached 40 or 50 psi. They are rated, as are all pumps, in gallons per minute (gpm) or gallons per hour (gph) and feet of "head." The latter is the number of feet in height that the water is lifted, being the sum of the suction lift, the discharge height above the pump, the number of feet equivalent to the pressure loss due to friction and

Table 1.2   *Water Quality Problems and Their Correction in Private Systems*

Item	Cause	Bad Effect	Correction
Hardness	Calcium and magnesium salts from underground flow	Clogging of pipes by scale, burning out of boilers, and impaired laundering and food preparation	Ion exchanger (Zeolite process)
Corrosion	Acidity, entrained oxygen and carbon dioxide, (low pH)	Closing of iron pipe by rust, destruction of brass pipe	Raising the alkaline content (Neutralizer)
Pollution	Contamination by organic matter or sewage	Disease	Chlorination by sodium hypochlorite or chlorine gas.
Color	Iron and manganese	Discoloration of fixtures and laundry	Precipitation by filtration through manganese zeolite (Oxidizing filter)
Taste and Odor*	Organic matter	Unpleasantness	Filtration through activated carbon (Purifier)
Turbidity*	Silt or suspended matter picked up in surface or near-surface flow	Unpleasantness	Filtration

* NOTE: These problems are not common in private systems using deep wells.

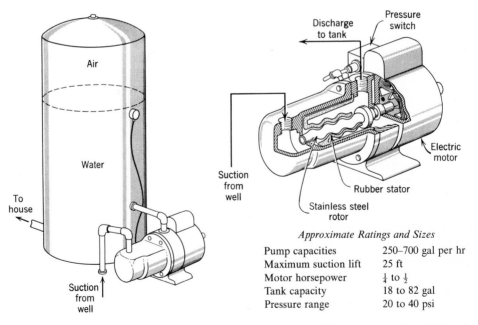

Approximate Ratings and Sizes

Pump capacities	250–700 gal per hr
Maximum suction lift	25 ft
Motor horsepower	$\frac{1}{4}$ to $\frac{1}{2}$
Tank capacity	18 to 82 gal
Pressure range	20 to 40 psi

Fig. 1.5   Shallow-well pump and storage tank for domestic water supply to a house. For well-lifts of less than 25 ft.

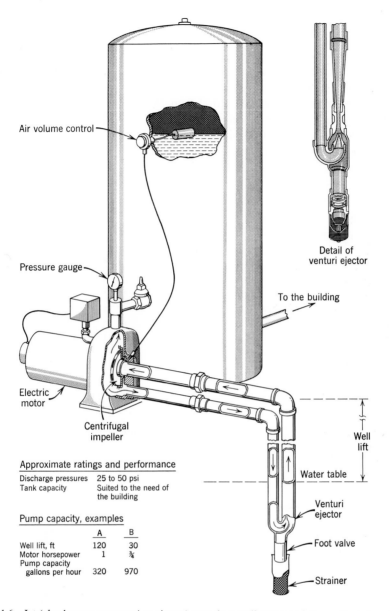

Air volume control

Pressure gauge

Electric motor

Centrifugal impeller

Detail of venturi ejector

To the building

Well lift

Water table

Venturi ejector

Foot valve

Strainer

Approximate ratings and performance

Discharge pressures 25 to 50 psi
Tank capacity   Suited to the need of the building

Pump capacity, examples

	A	B
Well lift, ft	120	30
Motor horsepower	1	¾
Pump capacity gallons per hour	320	970

Fig. 1.6   Jet (also known as venturi or ejector) type deep-well pump and storage tank for a house or small building. For well-lifts greater than 25 ft.

the number of feet equivalent to the fixture pressure. Conversions between head and psi may be made by the standard relationships. One foot of water exerts .434 psi and 1 psi will sustain 2.3 ft of head.

(a) *Shallow-Well Pumps.* Suitable pumps for use when the water level is not more than 25 ft below the pump are rotary (Fig.

1.5), shallow-well jet, and the reciprocating piston type. The first two each have a single moving part and smooth, continuous action. The rotary causes an axial motion of the water by the contact of helical rotor and stator. The shallow-well jet resembles the deep-well jet. A centrifugal impeller circulates the water which passes through the venturi *at the level of the pump,* including a suction in a single suction pipe. The reciprocating pump changes a rotary motion to a linear one and operates a piston and valves to create a suction. Its pulsations and multiplicity of parts make it less favored than the other two types. All of these pumps create a partial vacuum in the suction pipe. The real motive power is the atmospheric pressure acting through the ground on the water table forcing the water to rise in the vacuum (suction) pipe. The theoretical limit of lift is almost 34 ft but the practical limit is 25 ft.

(*b*) *Deep-Well Pumps.* For lifts greater than 25 ft it is necessary to place the lifting element below the water table in its lowered position during pumping. Suitable pump types are: deep-well jet (Fig. 1.6), submersible, turbine, and reciprocating. The jet or

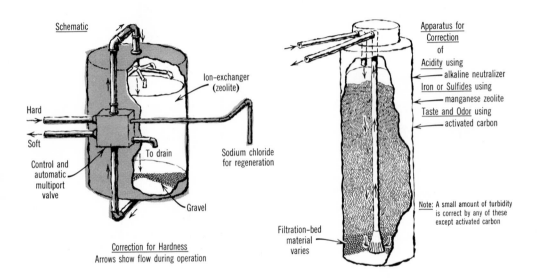

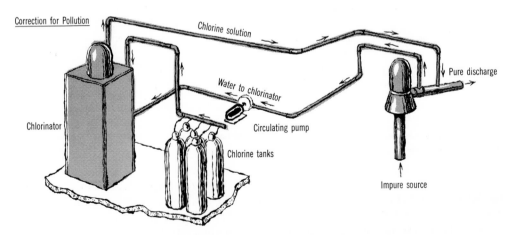

Fig. 1.7 Treatment systems for private water supplies. Hardness yields to treatment in an ion-exchanger. Soft water results. The hardness is deposited in the filter. The exchanger may be back washed and regenerated. Iron and sulphides are removed by manganese zeolite. Acid may be neutralized. Taste and odor may be removed by activated carbon. Impure supply may be corrected by chlorine gas as shown or, in smaller installations, by a hypochlorinator using a powder. (*Progressive Architecture*)

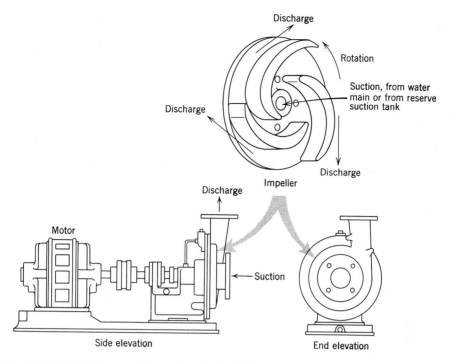

Fig. 1.8 Centrifugal pump. Frequently used to fill elevated house tank in penthouse or at intermediate mechanical floor.

venturi principle is used to create a high-velocity jet at which point the pressure is reduced, inducing a flow of water to join the stream. The upflow pipe is therefore larger than the downflow pipe. Water in both pipes is kept circulating by a centrifugal impeller. To operate, the water must be retained, because the impeller will not work well in air. This is done by a foot valve at the well bottom, a standard requirement in most pumping systems. The submersible is a narrow turbine-type pump with a slim electric motor, sealed and fastened to the bottom end of the turbine shaft, below the impellers. This whole unit is immersed in the well casing. Waterproof wires serve the motor and water flows *around* the motor in its path to the impellers. The moving element must be placed below the drawdown-point of the water table. The Turbine pump (Fig. 1.3) is the one usually chosen for high-capacity work. It may have 10 or more impellers, which, unlike the simple centrifugal impellers, also have a slope in the direction

of the axis shaft to give the water an upward dynamically induced motion. The reciprocating type, formerly much more used than at present, has a pumping mecha-

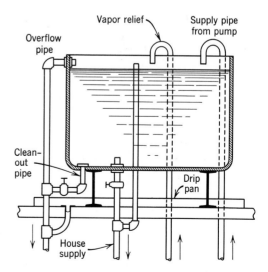

Fig. 1.9 House tank in elevated position for downfeed by gravity.

nism which operates a shaft that reaches below the water level. Valves are located at the bottom end to "lift" the water. As in the case of all reciprocating pumps, an air chamber must be used to smooth out the pulsations.

(c) *House Tank Supply Pumps.* For the purpose of filling elevated house tanks (Fig. 1.9), the centrifugal pump, directly connected to an electric motor, is the common choice (Fig. 1.8). Dynamic centrifugal motion of the water is caught in a housing with a discharge connection for the house supply pipe. The water enters axially and leaves tangentially. When the suction of such pumps might reduce the pressure in the city mains to the detriment of neighboring users, the suction side may be connected to a reserve tank which fills up between pumpings by gravity flow from the mains.

References

1. "The Industrial Utility of Public Water Supplies in the United States," Part 2, E. W. Lohr and S. K. Lowe, *Geological Water Supply Paper 1300.* United States Government Printing Office, Washington, D.C.
2. *Ground Water, Its Development, Uses, and Conservation,* E. W. Bennison, Edward E. Johnson, Inc., St. Paul 4, Minnesota.
3. "Water Treatment for Urban Buildings," Dr. Sidney Sussman, Technical Director, and other papers by members of the staff of Water Service Laboratories, 615 West 131 Street, New York 27, New York.
4. "Water Quality and Treatment," 2nd edition, *Manual of the American Water Works Association,* 2 Park Avenue, New York 16, New York.

2

Water Systems

1. Piping, Tubing, and Fittings. The conveying of water through buildings to locations of use implies the design of a system of piping or tubing, efficient for its purpose, easily maintained, and interfering as little as possible with the interior architectural form. It may be assumed that, except in basements, in utility rooms, and at points of access to controls, the system will usually be concealed. Stud and joist construction provides space for concealment, but in fireproof buildings, vertical and horizontal spaces must often be provided.

The corrosive effects of water and the resistance of metals to corrosion are matters for the attention of chemists and metallurgists in many instances. In general, however, public or private treatment should be provided to correct corrosive qualities. Theoretically, when this is done, it is suitable to use the cheapest piping material—steel, yet prudence suggests that a better material be selected. Galvanized steel and wrought iron are better in use against rusting than plain steel which is often called black iron. In the nonferrous group, red brass and copper tubing are effective in corrosion resistance. Copper tubing is a very popular choice. It is less expensive than brass, assembles more easily, and is not subject to dezincification which is the attack by acids on the zinc in brass.

For ferrous pipes and "iron pipe size" brass, threaded connections are used. The external, tapered thread on the pipe is covered with pipe compound and makes up tight against the internal tapered thread of the coupling or other fitting. The solder-joint connection in copper depends upon capillary attraction which draws the solder into a cylinder of clearance between the mating surfaces of tube and fitting. This

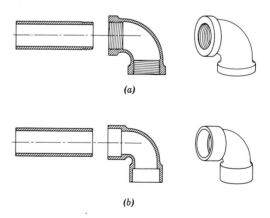

(a)

(b)

Fig. 2.1 Methods of connecting pipes and fittings, and tubes and fittings. (a) Threaded: For ferrous pipe and fittings and for "iron pipe size" (IPS) brass. (b) Soldered: For copper tubing and fittings.

Table 2.1 Characteristics of Pipe and Tubing

Kind of Pipe	Material or Manufacture	Connections	Qualities	Relative Cost	Notes
Steel	Butt welded to 2″ diam. seamless, large sizes	Threaded	Basic	Least expensive	Should be used only when water contains no impurities
Wrought iron	Butt welded to 2″ diam. seamless, large sizes	Threaded	More corrosion-resistant than steel	More expensive than steel	Identified by a red spiral stripe
Brass, red	85% copper 15% zinc	Threaded, "IPS," iron pipe size	Corrosion-resistant	More expensive than steel	Bulky because of the need for threading
Copper tube, type "K"	Seamless, hard or soft temper	Soldered fittings	Corrosion-resistant and easy to fabricate	Less expensive than brass	Thinner-walled than brass; Easy to put together and dismantle
Copper tube, type "L"	Seamless, thinner walls than type "K," hard or soft temper	Soldered fittings	Corrosion-resistant and easy to fabricate	Less expensive than brass	Thinner-walled than brass; easy to put together and dismantle
Nickel silver and chrome	Copper, nickel, and zinc, steel, and chromium	Threaded	Corrosion-resistant	More expensive than steel	Polished surface does not chip like nickel-plate
Galvanized steel	Zinc-coated steel	Threaded	Moderately corrosion-resistant	More expensive than steel	Suitable for mildly acid waters

occurs after polishing and fluxing the surfaces and placing the parts together in final position. They are then heated, and molten solder is applied to the circular opening where the fitting-edge surrounds the tube, with a small clearance. It is then drawn into the cylindrical connection by capillary action. Solders are tin-lead or tin-antimony alloys. This kind of joint permits the advantageous setting up of an entire tubing assembly without turning the parts (as in threaded installations), and before the soldering commences. For the same strength, copper tubing may have thinner walls because no threads need to be cut into it. Its smooth interior surface offers less friction to flowing water. While threaded- and solder-joint connections are the most common in small work, there are many other types. Ferrous pipes in the larger sizes are often welded or connected by bolted flanges.

2. Valves and Controls. A good system utilizes many valves. It is usually desirable to valve every riser, the branches that serve bathrooms or kitchens, and the runouts to individual fixtures. This facilitates repairs at any location with a minimum of shutdown within the system. Treatment equipment will have a valved by-pass (see Fig. 2.8). Pumps and other devices which may need repair should be disconnectable by unions (Fig. 2.2) after valves are closed.

The gate valve (Fig. 2.3a), with its retractable leaf which is machined to seal tightly against two sloping metal surfaces when closed, offers the least resistance to water flow when open. It is usually chosen for locations where it is left completely open most of the time. The compression-type globe valve (Fig. 2.3b) has for its usual purpose the closing or throttling of flow near a point of occasional use. Faucets are usually of the compression type, as are drain valves or hose connections. They are similar to the angle valve, (Fig. 2.3d). When it is necessary to prevent flow in a direction opposite to that which is planned, the introduction of a check valve (Fig. 2.3c) will accomplish this. The hinged leaf swings to permit flow in

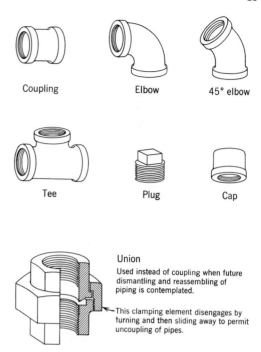

Coupling   Elbow   45° elbow

Tee   Plug   Cap

Union
Used instead of coupling when future dismantling and reassembling of piping is contemplated.

This clamping element disengages by turning and then sliding away to permit uncoupling of pipes.

Fig. 2.2 Examples of threaded pipe fittings. A few of the many fittings used in water piping. These and all common fittings are also available for solder-joint connecting and usually for transition from one system to the other.

the direction of the arrow but closes against attempted flow in the other direction.

3. Pipe Supports. If a piping system of conventional dimensions were to stand alone without a building to rest on, it would quickly collapse. Quite heavy because of its metallic nature and water content, it needs closely spaced supports (Fig. 2.4). Vertical runs of 1 in. piping should be supported at every story, but larger sizes may extend for two stories. Horizontal pipes should be supported at intervals of 10 ft. Closer spacing, 6 to 8 ft, is preferred for sizes $\frac{1}{2}$ in. and smaller. Horizontal copper tubing should always be supported at closer spacing than steel. Adequate positioning of horizontal runs is important to assure correct pitch and drainage. Hangers are adjustable for this purpose.

4. Planning for Efficiency and Easy Maintenance. (a) *Frost Protection.* In cold cli-

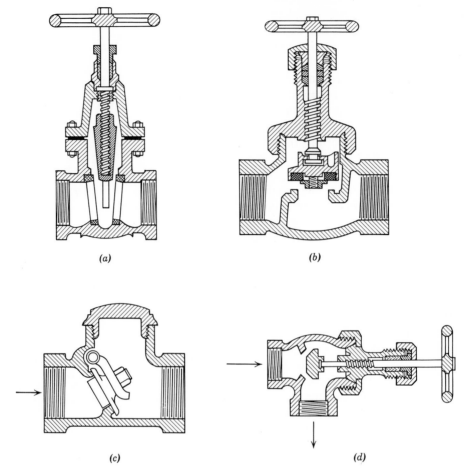

Fig. 2.3 Typical valves for water systems. (*a*) Gate valve. (*b*) Globe valve. (*c*) Check valve. (*d*) Angle valve.

mates water pipes in exterior walls or in unheated buildings can freeze and break. Pipes should be on the warm side of insulation. If a building is left without heat, all water pipes must be drained. The pipes must pitch to a low point where a drain faucet should be located. If, unavoidably, there are trapped low points in the system, these must be separately drainable or they must be provided with tees having removable plugs or nipple and cap to permit the trapped water to be blown out. The points at which the system is drained should be located above and near the collection points of drainage runoff lines leading to dry wells or sewers. Unheated buildings should not have water-carrying piping in their superstructures. Buildings which are occasionally used in winter, such as gun clubs, may have, at ground level, fixtures with long-spindled valves, the spindles reaching down to a position below the frost line where the water is stopped. When shutoff is at this point, there is a provision in the device to allow the water above to drain into the soil.

(*b*) *Shock and Water Expansion.* Water systems can be noisy. When faucets are shut off abruptly, or automatically when released, as in public buildings, the force exerted by the decelerated flowing water shakes and rattles the pipes. Lengths of vertical pipe about 2 ft long at the fixture

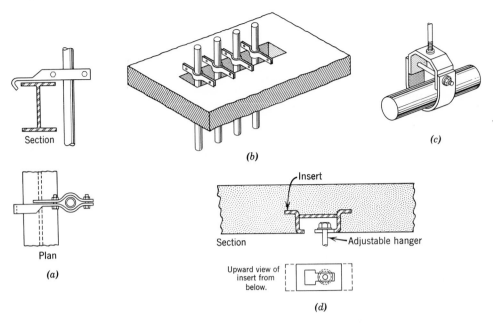

Fig. 2.4 Pipe supports. (*a*) Vertical riser supported at steel beam. (*b*) Vertical riser group supported at slot in concrete slab. (*c*) Horizontal pipe hung from slab above by adjustable-length clevis hanger. (*d*) Typical metal insert in soffit of concrete to receive hanger-rod.

branches (Fig. 2.5*a*) will usually solve this problem. They trap a certain amount of air which absorbs the impact of the water with some resilience. A somewhat better and a more controllable device is a "rechargeable air chamber" (Fig. 2.5*b*). By closing the valve and draining the water through the hose bibb while the petcock above is open

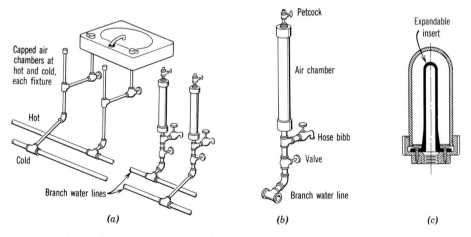

Fig. 2.5 Shock relief and expansion chambers. Air chambers to cushion the shock of water hammer when fixture faucets are shut off abruptly. They also permit hot water to expand instead of periodically forcing open the hot-water emergency pressure relief valve at the heater or tank. (*a*) Capped air chambers at each supply pipe of each fixture. (*b*) Rechargeable air-chambers on hot and cold branch water lines when used, the individual fixture chambers are omitted. (*c*) Special shock-absorber.

to admit air, the chamber may be refilled with air. Closing the petcock and hose bibb and opening the valve completes the service operation and reconnects the device with the water system. Rechargeable chambers are used on branch lines adjacent to groups of fixtures. Access for servicing them must be provided. When this method is chosen, the smaller pipe extensions (Fig. 2.5a) are usually omitted. Perhaps the best method is the use of a special shock absorber (Fig. 2.5c).

Air cushions also protect the relief valve against frequent operation with the resulting leakage of hot water, as the hot water periodically expands and contracts in closed systems.

(c) *Pipe Expansion.* The range of temperature from about 70 F, (normal indoor air temperature) to that of service hot water which often exceeds 160 F is an index of the expansion of pipes and water as their temperatures rise from shut-down status (70 F) to operating status (160 F). The longitudinal elongation of pipe, though negligibly small in houses, can be appreciable in a tall building. Two methods of allowing freedom for this longitudinal motion in long runs of expanding hot water piping are shown in Fig. 2.6. The use of these devices precludes the build-up of excessive stresses in the metal of the pipes and the tendency of the pipes to buckle laterally.

EXAMPLE 2.1. A 20-story zone in a tall building has a height of 280 ft. What will be

Table 2.2   Thermal Expansion of Pipe and Tubing

Elongation in inches per 100 ft of pipe or tube for various increases in temperature.

Increase in Temperature, Deg, F	Steel Pipe	Wrought Iron Pipe	Copper Tubing
20	.149	.156	.222
40	.299	.313	.444
60	.449	.470	.668
80	.601	.629	.893
100	.755	.791	1.119
120	.909	.952	1.346
140	1.066	1.115	1.575
160	1.224	1.281	1.805
180	1.384	1.447	2.035
200	1.545	1.616	2.268

the increase in length of a copper tube carrying "service hot water" (domestic hot water), when its temperature increases from 70 F to 160 F?

SOLUTION.

The difference in temperature is 90 F.

The coefficient of copper is .0000093 per inch per 1 F.

The expansion will be:

280 ft × 12 in. per ft × 90
        × .0000093 = 2.82 in.

Or (Reference to Table 2.2)

Elongation per 100 ft for 90 F increase
                                = 1.01 in.

2.8 × 1.01 = 2.82 in. Answer.

There are a number of ways of providing for this expansion; one is shown in Fig. 2.7. It consists of accepting the motion at 2 locations which would make the expansion in each case 1.41 in. Equidistant anchorage to fix the tubing is provided at the bottom, the tenth floor and the twentieth floor. The support of the vertical riser at floors other than those at which it is anchored could consist of clamps of the type illustrated in Fig. 2.4(a or b), supported on springs.

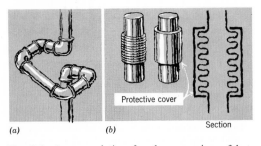

(a)   (b)   Section

Fig. 2.6 Accommodation for the expansion of hot-water piping. (a) Expansion joint of pipe and fittings. (b) Expansion joint, a manufactured product.

Protective cover

(*d*) *Condensation or "Sweating."* The moisture which is always present in air often condenses on the exterior surface of cold pipes. Dropping off the pipes, it creates an unpleasantly wet condition and disfigures finished surfaces. Ground water in some parts of the United States is 50 F and colder (see Fig. 1.2*a*). A pipe carrying such water might have a surface temperature of about 60 F. The psychrometric chart, (Fig. 16.6) indicates that at a summer air temperature of 85 F condensation will occur on this pipe when the relative humidity exceeds 40 percent. Because this condensation may occur anywhere within the building, all cold water piping and fittings should be covered. Glass fiber $\frac{1}{2}$ or 1 in. thick, or cork, rock wool, or hair felt $1\frac{1}{2}$ in. thick, are commonly chosen for this purpose. A tight vapor barrier on the exterior surface of the covering prevents the moisture-laden air from penetrating the insulation to reach the colder surface. The insulation provides another advantage of equal importance; it retards heat flow from the warmer air into the water thus preventing it from becoming disagreeably warm.

(*e*) *Heat Conservation.* Pipes carrying domestic hot water should be insulated to conserve the fuel used to heat the water and to assure a correct water temperature at the point of use. An efficient covering is a $\frac{1}{2}$ in. thick glass fiber. Fittings are troweled with 1 in. of asbestos, and the insulation of both pipe and fittings is protected by canvas jackets banded on. Parallel hot and cold water piping, even though insulated, should be separated by 6 in. or more to prevent heat interchange.

Small storage tanks and heaters are often manufactured with integral insulation. Uninsulated products should receive insulative covering after installation.

5. Upfeed Distribution. Water is usually received from city mains at about 50 psi. Private systems also adhere to this pressure as an approximate upper limit. Pressure diminishes at upper stories and after fric-

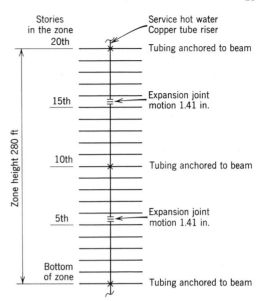

Fig. 2.7 Suggested scheme for locating points of anchorage and expansion for service hot-water tubing in a 20-story zone.

tional losses when water flows through pipes and fittings. Pressures of 5 to 8 psi are called for as a minimum for good service at lavatory faucets and tank-type water closets (see Table 2.6). Garden hoses require 30 psi which is usually available at their relatively low elevation. Fixtures in public buildings need pressures of up to 20 psi for automatic fixtures, including flushometers (flush valves). There is, of course, a limit of height to which 50 psi will lift water while overcoming friction and leaving 5 to 20 psi for the satisfactory operation of fixtures. Under static conditions of "no flow" and zero pressure at the top, 50 psi will sustain 50×2.3 (ft of head per psi) = 115 ft of water. This distance represents about 8 to 12 stories of conventional building height. Fixture pressure is needed and pressure will always be lost in pipe friction, even in large pipes and at moderate flow-rates. These practical considerations limit the height of most upfeed systems to about 6 stories maximum and 4 stories preferred.

Raising the outlet pressure above 50 psi

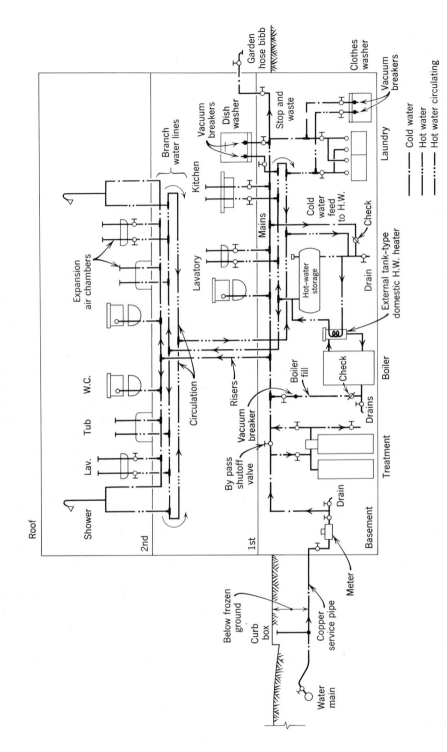

Fig. 2.8 Upfeed water distribution. Schematic section, the water services of a residence.

to gain more height is impractical for several reasons. Pressures in excess of 50 psi can cause splashing and wear to faucet seats and outlets at low elevation and near the source could be subjected to such pressures. If pneumatic tanks are used with high air pressures for tall lifts, the water absorbs much air, which is later released in the hot water part of the system, creating an undesirable condition. For buildings more than a few stories in height it is usual to pump water to elevated tanks for downfeed by gravity using pressure-reducing valves as needed. Direct pumping by variable speed upfeed pumps is gaining popularity.

Figure 2.8 is a 2-dimensional schematic routing diagram. In practice, concealed spaces must be found for all piping above the basement or outside of crawl spaces or utility rooms. For example, branch water lines can usually be accomodated within the joist depth by the use of headers as well as by a minimal and controlled use of notches and drilled holes. Risers generally fit easily within a stud wall, but it is often advantageous to allow a vertical plane of pipe space wider than the $3\frac{5}{8}$ in. stud size behind fixtures to accommodate air chambers, fixture runouts and branch water lines if these are run above the floor level, as is sometimes done. Although pipefitters can often be expected to make the best of conditions as found at the job, it is well for the architect to make a simple layout with explanatory isometric sketches and to discuss them with his consulting engineer, contractor, and plumber. Inspection and adaptability at the site are also highly essential. Unexpected developments including interferences by the work of other trades must be anticipated. When situations are faced promptly almost all difficulties can be solved, but neglect or the unwise delegation of space problems to others may leave serious scars on the architecture. While Fig. 2.8 is admittedly schematic and spread out for clarity, it can be seen that the system may require a bit of maneuvering to blend with the structure. It must not be

forgotten that a parallel and bulkier system of piping for drainage and venting serves the building (see Chap. 5) and must also be fitted in. Special study is needed for one story, slab-on-grade houses.

6. Downfeed Distribution. When pressures from city mains or from private pneumatic tanks are insufficient to maintain adequate fixture pressure at the top story under conditions of probable flow, water is pumped to wooden or steel elevated tanks for gravity downfeed. The lower part of the tank is often a reserve space to hold a supply of water for a fire hose system. In this case, only the water in the upper part is available for use as domestic (service) water. The amount stored must be enough to supplement what the pump will deliver during the several daily hours of high demand which occur in most buildings. The pump then continues, often for several hours, to replenish the house supply that had become partially depleted during the busy period. The suction tank is a buffer between the system and the street mains. It usually holds enough reserve to allow the pumps to make up the periodic depletion in the house tank. It refills automatically by gravity flow from the street main which, consequently, will not suffer as much drop in pressure as if it were connected directly to the suction side of the house pumps. Neighboring water users are protected from the adverse effects of sudden demands within adjacent large buildings.

House tanks and suction tanks are sometimes of steel plate and are divided vertically in half, each half having identical piping and controls. This permits cleaning out one half at a time during hours of low demand without shutting down the entire system. One full-capacity pump operates with an equal standby pump for alternate use. Since there is no suction lift below the pump or any fixture pressure at the top of the delivery leg (house tank supply), the head against which the pump works is the sum of the distance from the suction tank water level to the top of the house tank and

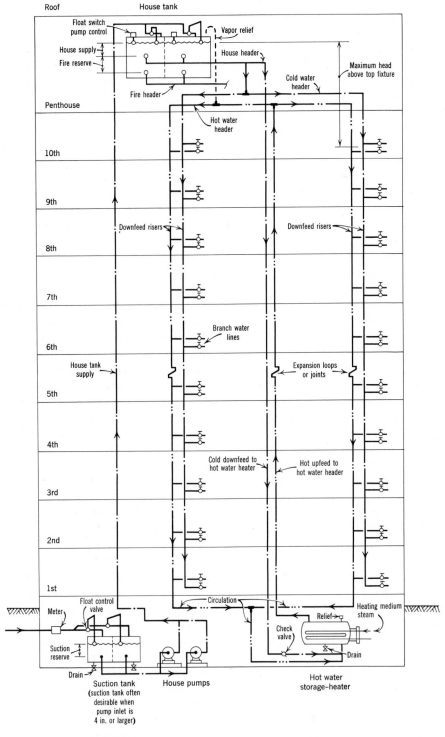

Fig. 2.9 Downfeed water distribution. Schematic section, part of the water services of a 10-story building.

the feet of head equivalent to the friction loss in tank supply pipe. For this kind of service the vertical piping is of the order of 3 or 4 in. in diameter for large buildings. Sizes are established by a formal engineering design (see Exs. 2.4 and 2.5).

The house supply is fed by a short pipe from the house header to the cold-water header which circles the top story and connects to many downfeed cold-water risers. For simplicity, Fig. 2.9 shows only two of them and also omits many valves and controls. Figure 2.10 is even more simplified. The hot water circuiting originates as cold water at the house tank header and takes quite a long route. Descending to the bottom of the hot-water heater, it rises to seek its own level at the hot-water header, becoming available there for hot water downfeed on demand. All this occurs as flow below the general pressurizing effect of the house tank. In effect, when there is a cold- and hot-water demand on a story near the top of the building, the cold water makes a short trip down to the faucet, while the hot water involves flow in three vertical pipes instead of one. The general scheme just described, with tank above and heater below is used in multiple form for very tall buildings. The zones, which generally do not exceed about 20 stories, are quite independent. Their only common service is the general suction tank. By this zoning method, problems of pipe expansion, excessive pipe sizes and of high pressures in lower stories are minimized. It is usual to have $2\frac{1}{2}$ stories or about 35 ft as the minimum pressure head above the top fixture served by any zone-tank. The static pressure created at the fixture is thus $35 \times .434 = 15$ psi. If, during flow, not too much pressure is lost in friction, flushometers may be possible at this level, though flush tanks, because of their lower fixture pressure demand, must often be accepted (see Example 2.6). Quite the opposite problem occurs at the bottom of the zones where excessive pressures must be valved down at the fixtures. In zone 1 of Fig. 2.10a, first floor fixtures are below a

head of $24\frac{1}{2}$ stories or about 149 psi of static pressure. It is obvious that pressure-reducing valves must be used, and that fixture control valves must be throttled. Taller zones would be difficult to handle.

7. Hot-Water Supply. Water expands and becomes lighter when heated above 39.2 F, as may be seen from Fig. 2.11. If heat is applied to the lower loop of a glass tube, both ends of which have been inserted in an inverted bottle containing water, the water will move from A to B and will rise through the tube BC into the bottle. It here becomes cooled and drops through the tube DA to A, is again heated, and rises in the tube BC, thus completing the circulation. Since the movement depends upon the difference in weight between the 2 columns of water, the velocity and consequent efficiency of the circulating system increase with the temperature of the water and the height of the circuit. Hot-water supply systems therefore usually consist of a heater with a storage tank, piping to carry the heated water to the farthest fixture, and a continuation of this piping to return the unused cooled water back to the heater. A constant circulation is thereby maintained, and hot water may be drawn at once from a fixture without first draining off through the faucet the cooled water which would be standing in the supply pipe if there were no return conduit for its escape. The chief retarding influence to the flow is friction; consequently, pipes must be smooth on the inside, reamed at cut ends, of ample size, and without sharp bends. Brass pipe or copper tubing should always be used throughout hot water systems.

This principle of constant circulation of hot water to make it promptly available in branch water lines may be examined in Fig. 2.8. Heated water from the tank rises to the hot-water main and the branch hot-water lines. At the ends of these horizontal pipes the slightly cooler water falls through the circulation piping to the bottom of the tank. Two other circulation processes can be found in Fig. 2.8 and all three operate re-

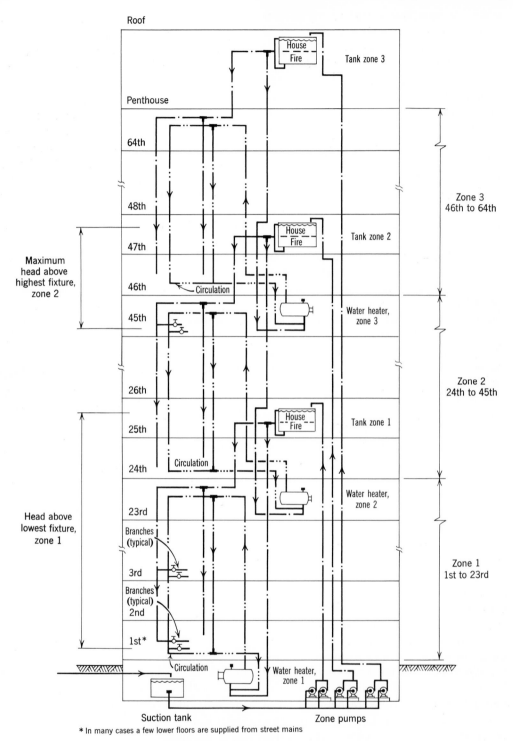

Fig. 2.10   (*a*) Downfeed water distribution; schematic section, part of the water services of a zoned building. Zone tanks include a fire reserve but standpipes are omitted from *this* drawing. For detail of steam-type domestic water heater, see Fig. 2.15*a*.

Fig. 2.10 (*b*) Pan Am Building, New York City. Emery Roth and Sons, Architects; Walter Gropius, Pietro Belluschi, Associated Architects. The distribution principles of the building in Fig. 2.10*a* can result in the "mechanical stories" as used in the Pan Am Building. Stories of this type may also contain air-conditioning compressors, water chillers, and blowers.

trate a similar system circulation but the source of heat is a steam-actuated storage heater instead of the external tank-type heater adjunct to a residential hot-water heating boiler as used in Fig. 2.8.

There are many buildings which do not have the advantage of height as do those in Figs. 2.8, 2.9, and 2.10. Low, long rambling buildings such as some large 1 story residences, schools, and factories lack sufficient height to set up good hot-water circulation. They also diminish the flow by friction in long pipe runs. In such cases the forced circulation scheme of Fig. 2.12 is good. Three independent aquastats, devices that create an electrical signal impulse when water temperature drops, control this very positive and efficient system. Aquastats A, B, and C respectively sense the temperatures of the water in the heater, the tank, and the end of the circulation return main. As needed, they turn on the oil burner, the tank circulating pump, and the system circulating pump. Fixtures remote from the tank are as close to hot water as the length of their hot-water runout pipes. Water is usually available at full temperature in 5 to 10 seconds. Trial aquastat settings in degrees F could be A 180, B 160, C 140.

For relatively small installations and

gardless of demand by the opening of faucets. In addition to the circulation which serves the fixtures. there is a second route of water motion from the top of the heating coil to the top of the tank and from the bottom of the tank to the bottom of the coil. The third and separate circulating process takes place when the boiler water circulates around the outside of the coil and then drops to be reheated by the boiler. Upon demand by the opening of any hot-water faucet, the pressure in the cold water-main opens the check valve below the tank and the cold water forces the hot water in the piping and the upper part of the tank toward the open faucet. Figures 2.9 and 2.10*a* illus-

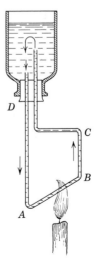

Fig. 2.11 Hot-water circulation.

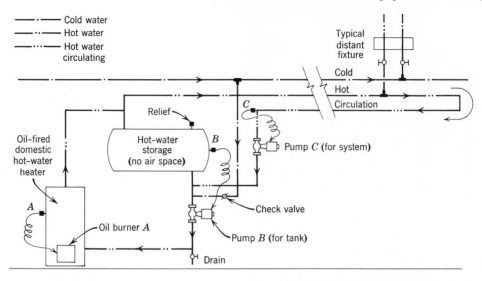

Fig. 2.12   Forced circulation of domestic hot-water especially needed in long, low buildings.

compact fixture grouping, the water may be heated directly and the storage tank omitted. This is done by a built-in or external tankless coil. Its length is great enough to effect a fast and thorough heat exchange between the boiler water and the domestic water. Unlike the short tank-type coil (Fig. 2.8) which operates at a slow recovery rate by the gravity circulation action of the water in it and in the tank, the tankless type operates under full flow whenever hot-water faucets are opened. Temperature blending valves are commonly employed to moderate the delivery temperature of the hot water (see alternate piping in Fig. 2.13). Temperature-pressure relief valves are essential.

The tankless heater, because it meets the full demand without utilizing some stored water, requires a large heat input rate.

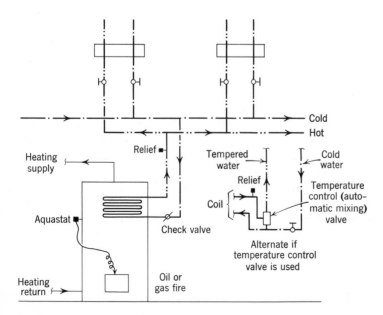

Fig. 2.13   Domestic hot water from a built-in tankless coil in a hot-water heating boiler.

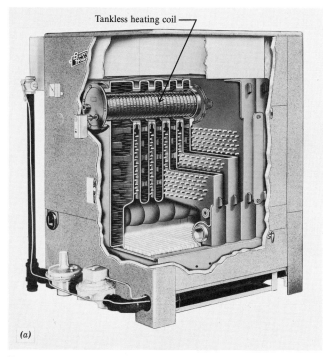

Tankless heating coil

(a)

Burnham

(b)

Taco

Fig. 2.14 Tankless heaters for domestic hot water: (*a*) submerged in boiler jacket-water; (*b*) external type to which jacket water is piped. In each case domestic water connections are shown at left with aquastat connection close by. Capacities 3 to 15 gpm at 100 F rise.

EXAMPLE 2.2. A tankless heater delivers 6 gpm at 100 F rise in temperature. How many Btuh are required?

SOLUTION.

Average weight of water: 8.33 lbs/gal

specific heat of water: 1 Btu/lb/1 F

Heat required: 6 gpm × 60 min. hr
    × 8.33 lb/gal × 1 Btuh/deg
        × 100 F = 300,000 Btuh

A large house (see Fig. 8.6) could have an hourly heat loss requiring a boiler that would deliver about 150,000 Btuh for heating only. During periods of operation a 6 gpm tankless heater delivering hot water while the house was being heated would approximately triple the demand on the boiler. Some heating systems turn off automatically when the domestic hot-water demand reduces the boiler water temperature. This favors the domestic water over the general heating. If, for instance, 200 gal of stored hot water would serve this house during its peak demand, a tank-type smaller coil could be used and it would fill the tank in 3 hrs. This would be at the rate of about 55,500 (Btuh) which would call for an increase in boiler size of only about one-third. When this joint demand is troublesome, independent domestic hot-water heaters are used. They can be electric, oil-fired, or gas-fired (Fig 2.15*b*). The largest demands are often met by the storage-tank heater (Fig. 2.15*a*), the use of which is shown in Figs. 2.9 and 2.10.

Because many fixtures have no hot-water supply, tests on actual buildings show that the consumption of hot water may be fairly assumed as about $\frac{1}{3}$ of the total water consumption. In hotels and apartments the total water is estimated at 120 gal per day (gpd) per person. The hot-water consumption would then be 40 gpd. For residences the daily hot-water demand is taken at 20 to 40 gal per person. For offices, factories, restaurants, and other buildings the estimates depend upon the activities. In order to specify the size of the hot-water storage tank and the load required of the heater, the

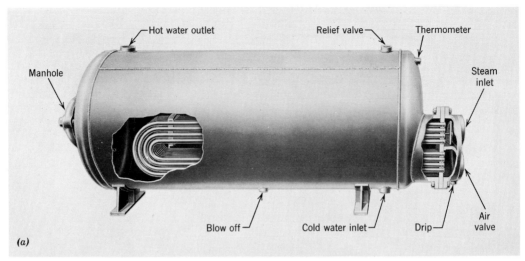

Hot water outlet   Relief valve   Thermometer

Manhole   Steam inlet

Blow off   Cold water inlet   Drip   Air valve

(a)

Patterson-Kelley

(b)

A. O. Smith

Fig. 2.15   Independent domestic hot-water heaters. *(a)* Storage-heater, steam coil submerged in tank (see Figs. 2.9 and 2.10), capacities 100 to 10,000 gph (gallons per hour), varying by length of coil, for 140 F (40–180) temperature rise. *(b)* Gas-fired heater, capacities 100 to 400 gph for 100 F temperature rise.

following data must be known: (1) daily total quantity of water to be heated, (2) maximum demand in any one hour, (3) duration of peak demand, and (4) storage and heating capacities in relation to day's use.

In hotels and apartments where the hot-water demand is fairly uniform throughout the day, a small storage tank and a large heater are appropriate. In factories and other buildings with peak loads confined to several hours, a large tank and small heater

Table 2.3 Hot-Water Demand per Person for Various Purposes

140° temperature, except restaurants at 180°

Type of Building	Hot Water Required	Maximum Hourly Demand in Relation to Day's Use	Duration of Peak Load (hours)	Storage Capacity in Relation to Day's Use	Heating Capacity in Relation to Day's Use
Residences, apartments, hotels	40 gal per person per day	$\frac{1}{7}$	4	$\frac{1}{5}$	$\frac{1}{7}$
Offices	2 gal per person per day	$\frac{1}{5}$	2	$\frac{1}{5}$	$\frac{1}{6}$
Factories	5 gal per person per day	$\frac{1}{3}$	1	$\frac{2}{5}$	$\frac{1}{8}$
Restaurants	1.8 gal per meal per day			$\frac{1}{10}$	$\frac{1}{10}$
Restaurants (three meals per day)		$\frac{1}{10}$	8	$\frac{1}{5}$	$\frac{1}{10}$
Restaurants (one meal per day)		$\frac{1}{5}$	2	$\frac{2}{5}$	$\frac{1}{6}$

Reprinted by permission of ASHRAE from the *Heating, Ventilating, Air Conditioning Guide*, 31st Edition.

are suitable. Between periods of peak demand the small heater can slowly replenish the supply of heated water in the tank.

The size of water-heating equipment may also be established from the number of fixtures. To obtain the probable maximum demand from Table 2.4, multiply the total number of gallons by the demand factor. The heater or coil should have a water-heating capacity equal to this probable maximum demand. The storage tank should have a capacity equal to the probable maxi-

Table 2.4 Hot-Water Demand per Fixture

Gallons of water per hour per fixture at 140 F

	Apartment House	Club	Hotel	Factory	Office Building	Residence	School
Private lavatory	2	2	2	2	2	2	2
Public lavatory	4	6	8	12	6		15
Bath tubs	20	20	20	30		20	
Dishwashers	15	50–150	50–200	20–100		15	20–100
Kitchen sink	10	20	20	20		10	10
Laundry trays	20	28	28			20	
Pantry sink	5	10	10			5	10
Showers	75	150	75	225		75	225
Service sink	20	20	30	20	15	15	20
Demand factor	0.30	0.30	0.25	0.40	0.30	0.30	0.40
Storage factor	1.25	0.90	0.80	1.00	2.00	0.70	1.00

Reprinted by permission of ASHRAE from the *Heating, Ventilating, Air Conditioning Guide*, 31st Edition.

mum demand multiplied by the storage factor.

EXAMPLE 2.3. Using Table 2.3, what size of heater and storage tank should be used in an apartment house to supply 250 persons?

SOLUTION. Daily requirement is $250 \times 40 = 10,000$ gal; maximum hourly demand is $10,000 \div 7 = 1430$ gal; water required for 4 hr duration of peak load is $4 \times 1430 = 5720$ gal. For a 1000 gal tank the net capacity is 750 gal. Water to be heated in 4 hr is $5720 - 750 = 4970$. The heater capacity per hour must be $4970 \div 4 = 1240$ gal.

If a 2500 gal tank were chosen the required heater capacity would be:

$$\frac{5720 - (2500 \times 0.75)}{4} = 960 \text{ gph}$$

The use of Table 2.4 may be illustrated by the following example:

EXAMPLE 2.4. What are the heater and tank sizes for a club building with the following fixtures?

SOLUTION.

20 private lavatories × 2	=	40 gph
15 public lavatories × 6	=	90
25 bath tubs × 20	=	500
9 showers × 150	=	1350
4 kitchen sinks × 20	=	80
2 pantry sinks × 10	=	20
Possible maximum demand	=	2080 gph
(Demand factor)		×0.3
Probable maximum demand	=	624 gph
Heater or coil capacity		624 gph
(Storage factor)		×0.9
Storage-tank capacity		561.6 gal

8. Design of Water-Supply Piping. (*a*) *General.* The design of the water supply for a building comprises first the determination of the total quantity required for the supply of plumbing, heating, air-conditioning, manufacturing, and fire-protection equipment. This question involves the satisfactory supply for a fixture of each kind and

Table 2.5   Consumption of Water per Capita per Day (Gallons)

Apartments and hotels	50–120
Office buildings	15–30
Residences, each occupant, including kitchen, bathroom, and laundry	30–80
Horse (winter, 4 to 8 gal; summer, 8 to 18 gal)	12
Cow	12
Hog	1
Sheep	1
Chickens, per 100	4
Lawn and garden sprinkling ($\frac{1}{2}$-in. hose), per hr	200
Lawn and garden sprinkling ($\frac{3}{4}$-in. hose), per hr	300
Lawn sprinkler, per hr	120

the number of fixtures assumed to be in use at the same time. This total having been calculated, the sizes of piping, tanks, and pumps must be decided to distribute the water to the various appliances in the proper quantities and under the desired pressures.

(*b*) *Water Consumption.* Table 2.5 presents generally accepted averages of water consumption for each occupant per day, which may vary according to circumstances.

In apartments, hotels, and office buildings, the requirements of laundries, kitchens, heating, refrigeration, air conditioning, and other equipment must be added to the personal consumption of the occupants.

Table 2.6 gives the rate of flow best suited to the common types of fixtures and the average pressure necessary to give this rate of flow.

(*c*) *Fixture Units.* The load in gpm required by each type of fixture is often computed in fixture units, each unit being equivalent to 7.5 gpm or 1 cu ft of water.

(*d*) *Probable Usage.* For residences, farms, and buildings with little plumbing, a maximum supply is advisable, because few fixtures are involved and all of them may be called into use simultaneously. An ample supply of water is a necessity; otherwise one fixture will rob another with most unsatisfactory results. For hotels, office

Table 2.6 Flow from Fixtures and Required Pressures

(A) Fixture	(B) Size Fixture Branch (in.)	(C) Flow Pressure (lb per sq in.)	(D) Flow (gal per min)
Lavatory	$\frac{3}{8}$	8	3.0
Self-closing faucet	$\frac{1}{2}$	12	2.5
Public sink, $\frac{3}{8}$ in.	$\frac{3}{8}$	10	4.5
Kitchen sink, $\frac{1}{2}$ in.	$\frac{1}{2}$	5	4.5
Bath tub	$\frac{1}{2}$	5	6.0
Laundry trays—1, 2, or 3	$\frac{1}{2}$	5	5.0
Shower bath	$\frac{1}{2}$	8	5.0
Water closet, flush tank	$\frac{3}{8}$	8	3.0
Water closet, flush valve	1	10–20	20–40
Urinal, flush valve	1	15	15.0
Garden hose, 50 ft and hose bibb	$\frac{1}{2}$	30	5.0

Reprinted by permission of ASHRAE from the *Heating, Ventilating, Air Conditioning Guide,* 31st Edition.

buildings, schools, and apartment houses, however, it is reasonable and customary to assume that not all the fixtures will be used simultaneously. With an installation of 2 fixtures it is quite possible that both may be in operation together, but with 200 fixtures it is unlikely that all will be called upon at once. Curves based upon tests and experience set forth the probable maximum demand in gpm corresponding to any total number of fixture units in a building. Certain installations may present special requirements for which demand loads must be determined to fit the needs.

This maximum demand covers the peak requirements at certain times of day, such

Table 2.7 Demand Load of Fixtures in Fixture Units

Fixture or Group	Public	Private	Supply Control
Water closet	10	6	Flush valve
Water closet	5	3	Flush tank
Lavatory	2	1	Faucet
Bath tub	4	2	Faucet
Shower head	4	2	Mixing valve
Kitchen sink	4	2	Faucet
Service sink	3		Faucet
Pedestal urinal	10		Flush valve
Stall or wall urinal	5		Flush valve
Stall or wall urinal	3		Flush tank
Bathroom group		8	Flush valve for closet
Bathroom group		6	Flush tank for closet
Separate shower		2	Mixing valve
Laundry trays (1–3)		3	Faucet
Combination fixture		3	Faucet

NOTE: For fixtures with both hot and cold supplies the units for separate demands are taken as three-quarters of the listed demand.
Reprinted by permission of ASHRAE from the *Heating, Ventilating, Air Conditioning Guide,* 31st Edition.

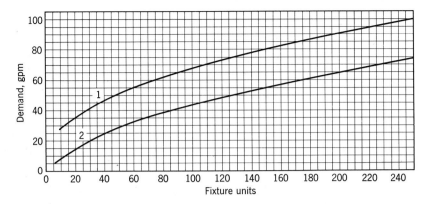

Fig. 2.16　Curves for demand load. No. 1 for system predominantly for flush valves. No. 2 for system predominantly for flush tanks. Reprinted by permission of ASHRAE from the *Heating, Ventilating, Air Conditioning Guide,* 31st edition.

as at 9 A.M. in hotels and office buildings and during the preparation of meals in apartments. Requirements, such as hose connections and air-conditioning equipment, which impose continuous demand during times of peak load should be estimated separately and added to the demand for fixtures used intermittently.

(*e*) **Friction.** Since the flow of water is greatly limited by the friction of the pipe surface, this factor has an important bearing upon the determination of pipe size. The usual equation for loss of head due to friction is

$$h_F = f\left(\frac{l}{d}\right) \times \frac{v^2}{2g}$$

in which l = length of pipe, d = diameter of pipe, v = velocity of water, and g = acceleration of gravity. From this equation it is seen that the friction losses depend upon the length and diameter of the pipe and the velocity of the water. Since the velocity = Q/A and therefore depends on the quantity of flow and the diameter of the pipe, tables or charts may be prepared giving the friction losses in head in psi per 100 ft of straight pipe for various diameters and flow rates of water. If a permissible friction loss in psi has first been calculated from the psi of available water pressure or head, then from these charts the proper size of pipe for a given flow of water may also be found.

The letter f in the above formula is a constant, depending upon the condition of the inner surface of the pipe, whether smooth or fairly rough. Copper, brass, and lead pipe, showing little roughness, are classed as smooth. Galvanized wrought iron and steel and cast-iron pipe after some years of service usually become fairly rough, and an allowance should therefore be made in their sizes.

Flow through water meters causes resistance by friction. Table 2.8 gives the maximum flow through disk meters of various sizes.

With the demand flow in gpm and the corresponding size of meter in inches, Figure 2.18 may be entered and the pressure loss in psi determined.

Table 2.8　Performance of Water Meters

Size (in.)	Normal Test Flow Limits (gal/min)	Size (in.)	Normal Test Flow Limits (gal/min)
$\frac{5}{8}$	1 to 20	2	8 to 160
$\frac{3}{4}$	2 to 34	3	16 to 315
1	3 to 53	4	28 to 500
$1\frac{1}{2}$	5 to 100	6	48 to 1000

Reprinted by permission of ASHRAE from the *Heating, Ventilating, Air Conditioning Guide,* 31st Edition.

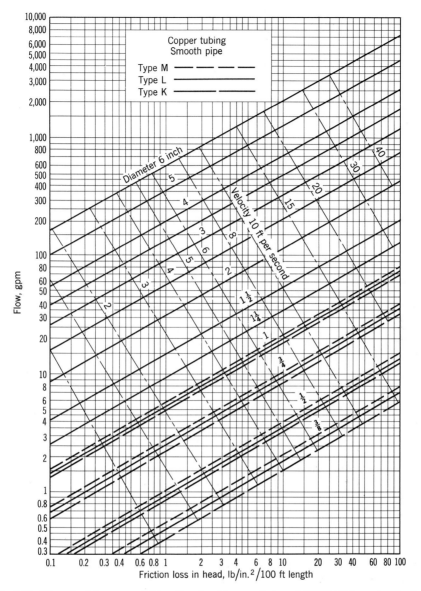

Fig. 2.17   Flow chart for copper tubing. Reprinted by permission of ASHRAE from the *Heating, Ventilating, Air Conditioning Guide*, 31st edition.

(*f*) *Water Pressure.* It was stated in Chapter 1 that the pressure head of water in psi equals 0.434 × *h*, the height in ft to which the water is elevated, and that *h* equals 2.3 × psi. Flush valves require 15-psi pressure, but 8 psi is considered sufficient for some other fixtures. It is sometimes impracticable to obtain a street main pressure or a tank elevation sufficient for a 15-psi pres-

sure at the highest fixture after allowing for pipe friction and gravity head. Consequently, flush tank fixtures are often used in the top story and flush valve fixtures on the floors below. The permissible pressure on fixtures is generally not over 50 psi. Higher pressures in mains should be limited in branches by pressure-reducing valves.

(*g*) *Pipe Sizes. Upfeed.* In the upfeed sys-

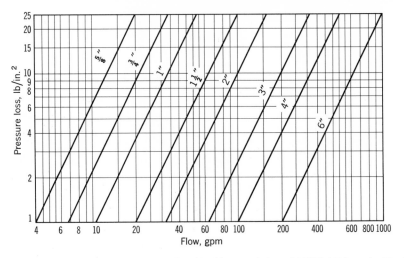

Fig. 2.18   Pressure losses in water meters. (Reprinted by permission of ASHRAE from the *Heating, Ventilating, Air Conditioning Guide,* 31st edition.)

tem the pressure required to overcome the gravity head in the vertical riser plus the pressure desired at the highest fixture is subtracted from the total pressure available from the street main or other supply. The remainder represents the pressure at hand to overcome friction losses from meter, piping, fittings, and valves. The total allowable friction loss in psi for piping, fittings, and valves is reduced to the allowable loss per 100 ft of pipe length. The quantity of water in gpm required in each section having been determined, the pipe size for each section is found by applying the allowable friction loss per 100 ft of equivalent length of pipe to the rate of flow as shown in Fig. 2.17.

The frictional losses caused by the valves and fittings may be changed into equivalent losses from straight runs of pipe, and these lengths added to the total run of pipe in

Table 2.9   Equivalent Lengths of Pipe in Feet for Loss in Fittings

Diam. (in.)	90° Ell	45° Ell	90° Tee	Straight Run of Tee	Gate Valve	Globe Valve	Angle Valve
$\frac{3}{8}$	1	0.6	1.5	0.3	0.2	8	4
$\frac{1}{2}$	2	1.2	3	0.6	0.4	15	8
$\frac{3}{4}$	2.5	1.5	4	0.8	0.5	20	12
1	3	1.8	5	0.9	0.6	25	15
$1\frac{1}{4}$	4	2.4	6	1.2	0.8	35	18
$1\frac{1}{2}$	5	3	7	1.5	1	45	22
2	7	4	10	2	1.3	55	28
$2\frac{1}{2}$	8	5	12	2.5	1.6	65	34
3	10	6	15	3	2	80	40
$3\frac{1}{2}$	12	7	18	3.6	2.4	100	50
4	14	8	21	4	2.7	125	55
5	17	10	25	5	3.3	140	70
6	20	12	30	6	4	165	80

Reprinted by permission of ASHRAE from the *Heating, Ventilating, Air Conditioning Guide,* 31st Edition.

determining the allowable friction loss per 100 ft, based on the total "equivalent" length.

EXAMPLE 2.5. In a dormitory building of 5 stories, the highest fixture is 45 ft above the service pipe. The pressure before the $1\frac{1}{2}$ in. meter is 45 psi. The measured (developed) length of copper tubing from the meter to the most remote, top floor fixture is 90 ft and the water, in reaching it, passes through 3 gate valves, 1 globe valve, 8 90° ells and 2 tees (straight run). On the ground floor there is a bathroom, a kitchen sink, and 2 laundry trays. On each of the upper floors there are two bathrooms. All water closets are of the flush-tank type. Find the proper size for the supply main.

SOLUTION. The number of fixture units is:

1 kitchen sink	$1 \times 2 =$	2
1 laundry tray set	$1 \times 3 =$	3
9 bathroom groups	$9 \times 8 =$	72
		77 Units
		(Table 2.7)

The probable flow (demand) in the main is 38 gpm (Fig. 2.16, curve 2)

The pressure loss in the meter will be	3.8 (Fig. 2.18)
The pressure lost in 45 ft height is $45 \times .434$	19.5
The minimum fixture pressure must be	8.0 (Table 2.6)
	31.3 psi (total)

The pressure loss that may be accepted in the tubing between the meter and the top, remote fixture is

45.0 available at entry	
−31.3 total (above)	
13.7 psi pressure loss in tubing due to friction	

It is necessary to establish the pressure loss per 100 ft of "total equivalent length" of tubing which is the developed length to the highest and farthest fixture plus the length equivalent to the resistance of the fittings.

Assume a $1\frac{1}{2}$ in. tubing to find equivalent length.

3 gate valves	$3 \times 1 =$	3
1 globe valve	$1 \times 45 =$	45
8 90° ells	$8 \times 5 =$	40
2 tees (straight run)	$2 \times 1.5 =$	3
		91 ft, equivalent length (Table 2.9)

Developed length	90
Equivalent length	91
Total equivalent length	181 ft

The pressure loss per 100 ft due to friction must be:

$$\frac{13.7 \times 100}{181} = 7.6 \text{ psi}/100 \text{ ft}$$

This pressure loss must be maintained at all points in the tubing if the pressure at the topmost remote fixture is to be not less than 8 psi. The tubing size at each location depends upon the probable flow at that location and the unit pressure loss just established. The probable flow at the main was found to be 38 gpm. In Fig. 2.17 a horizontal line at 38 gpm intersects a vertical line through 7.6 psi/100 ft at a point close to the sloping line indicating a $1\frac{1}{2}$ in. diameter tube. The main will be $1\frac{1}{2}$ in. in diameter. *Answer.*

Downfeed. Since this system is generally used with an elevated tank, the first requisite is to raise the tank sufficiently to give the desired pressures in the highest fixtures. The possible use of 8-psi fixtures on the upper stories and 15-psi fixtures below is explained in (f). When the building is zoned, each section is designed separately. The necessary pressures are built up by the gravity head in the risers.

The available pressures on the lower floors are usually computed on a floor-to-floor basis. The pressure required on any one floor is supplied by the net remaining pressure in the riser plus the gravity head in

Table 2.10 (Example 2.6)   Design of Downfeed Water Distribution

Floors	Fixture Units (Table 2.7)	Cumulative F.U.	Demand gpm (Fig. 2.16)	Pipe Length (ft)	Equivalent P.L. (ft)	Desired Pressure at Fixtures (psi)	Pressure Available for Fixtures and Friction (psi)	Pressure Available for Friction in Riser Interval (psi)	Pressure Drop due to Friction (psi per 100 ft)	Actual Pressure Riser (psi)	Pipe Size (in.) (Fig. 2.17)
B 6th	22	152	80	30	45	10	$27 \times 0.434 = 11.7$	$11.7 - 10 = 1.7$	$\dfrac{1.7 \times 100}{45} = 3.8$	10	$2\frac{1}{2}$
C 5th	22	130	74	11	16.5	10	$10 + (11 \times 0.434) = 14.77$ / 17 is needed in C–D / Use 10 drop/100 ft.	$\dfrac{10 \times 16.5}{100} = 1.65$ / $14.77 - 1.65 = 13.12$	Use = 10.0	13.12	2
D 4th	26	104	68	11	16.5	17	$13.12 + (11 \times 0.434) = 17.89$	$17.89 - 17 = 0.89$	$\dfrac{0.89 \times 100}{16.5} = 5.4$	17	2
E 3rd	26	78	62	11	16.5	17	$17 + (11 \times 0.434) = 21.77$	$21.77 - 17 = 4.77$	$\dfrac{4.77 \times 100}{16.5} = 28.9$	17	$1\frac{1}{2}$
F 2nd	26	52	52	11	16.5	17	$17 + (11 \times 0.434) = 21.77$	$21.77 - 17 = 4.77$	$\dfrac{4.77 \times 100}{16.5} = 28.9$	17	$1\frac{1}{2}$
G 1st	26	26	38	11	16.5	17	$17 + (11 \times 0.434) = 21.77$	$21.77 - 17 = 4.77$	$\dfrac{4.77 \times 100}{16.5} = 28.9$	17	$1\frac{1}{4}$

the downfeed interval between that floor and the floor above. It is often necessary to select riser sizes for the upper stories to produce fairly low pressure drop from friction which will permit the net pressure in the riser to develop quickly and contribute the required fixture pressure on the floor below. Then for each lower story the static pressure built up in that story by gravity is entirely devoted to overcoming the friction in that run of pipe.

EXAMPLE 2.6. An apartment house of 6 stories has 2 bathrooms and 2 kitchens and laundry combinations on each floor grouped around a downfeed riser. Floor to floor height, 11 ft. A gravity tank with 3-ft offset is 27 ft above the sixth floor fixtures. Flush tanks are used on the sixth and fifth floors, and flush valves on the remaining floors. Equivalent pipe length from tank to sixth floor, including valve and fittings, is 45 ft and from floor to floor is 16 ft, 6 in. Compute pipe sizes.

SOLUTION. (Table 2.10.) Adequate values should be added to the fixture pressures to overcome the friction in the fixture branches. In this example 2 psi is assumed, giving a total desired fixture and branch pressure of 10 psi on the fifth and sixth floors and 17 psi on the lower floors.

At the sixth floor the pressure is determined by the elevation of the tank, and, after deducting for fixture branches and friction, the actual pressure in the riser at the sixth-floor level is 10 psi. At the fifth floor this pressure is increased by the head developed in the 11-ft run from the sixth to the fifth floor and equals 14.77 psi. But more than 17 psi is desired at the fourth floor to provide for fixture branches and riser friction. An arbitrary value, say 10 psi, is therefore chosen as the friction loss per 100 ft, and the size of the riser from the sixth to the fifth floor is found from Fig. 2.17, using this value. The pressure loss from friction would then be $10 \times 16.5 \div 100 = 1.65$, and the net pressure in the riser at the fifth-floor level is $14.77 - 1.65 = 13.12$.

At the fourth floor the total head = 17.89 psi. Since 17 psi are needed at the fixture branches, 0.89 psi remain to overcome friction. $0.89 \times 100 \div 16.5 = 5.4$ psi per 100 ft. On each of the lower floors the net pressure in the riser will be 17 psi, which will be devoted to fixture branch pressure, and the static pressure increase, $11 \times 0.434 = 4.77$, in each riser interval will be used up in riser friction. The loss per 100 ft will then be $4.77 \times 100 \div 16.5 = 28.9$ psi.

References

1. *Plumbing Practice and Design,* Volumes I and II, Svend Plum, John Wiley and Sons, New York, New York.
2. *Standard Plumbing Details,* Louis J. Day, John Wiley and Sons, Inc., New York, New York.
3. *Design of Plumbing and Drainage Systems,* Louis Blendermann, The Industrial Press, New York 13, New York.
4. *Indirect Water Heaters, IBR Installation Guide Number 3,* The Institute of Boiler and Radiator Manufacturers, 608 Fifth Avenue, New York 20, New York.

3

Fire Protection

1. Planning. Among the many responsibilities placed upon the architect by society and more particularly by the state from which he receives his license to practice, is the protection against loss of life by fire. The preservation of the structure and its contents against fire damage or destruction, while secondary in importance, is, none the less, of serious concern to owners and others having a financial interest in property. The experience of municipal fire departments, volunteer fire companies and of the insurance companies who pay for loss of life and property is an invaluable aid to designers of new buildings. The National Fire Protection Association, of which the American Institute of Architects is one of the organization members, maintains a comprehensive and constantly improved set of standards for use in planning to reduce fire hazards and in designing equipment for fire fighting. The National Board of Fire Underwriters, an organization of insurance companies, is, in a sense, the agent of the Association and is always most cooperative in disseminating information about fire safety. Acceptance of their recommendations by the writers of building codes and by practicing architects has done much to reduce fire losses.

While the inclusion of fire-fighting equipment is always desirable and often mandatory, good practice begins with the design of the structure. This is necessarily affected by the permitted building density in the locality and by the flammability of the building and its expected contents. Some of the many items that must be considered are:

(*a*) Fire resistance of the selected structural type and material.

(*b*) Limitations of volumes within firesafe barriers in otherwise vulnerable buildings.

(*c*) Precautions against perforations of approved and required barriers.

(*d*) Exits.

(*e*) Protection against fires caused by defective electrical systems.

(*f*) Protection against fires caused by lightning.

(*g*) Detection and alarm systems.

(*h*) Standpipe and hose systems within and near buildings.

(*i*) Automatic sprinkler systems.

2. The Building. In countries where wood is plentiful, it is much used for houses because of its economy, though it is very vulnerable to fire. A relatively small and low frame residence, protected against regional conflagration by zoning requirements that call for a large plot and which specify minimum distances from property lines, is fairly safe for occupancy by a few people. In more congested areas, row houses, sometimes called garden apartments, provide units that are separated by unperforated thick masonry walls, though wood is often used between these fire barriers which should, to provide proper fire safety, be carried several feet above roof lines. This prevents a fire in one unit from spreading easily to the next. Small, one-story industrial buildings and other structures of a public nature are sometimes built by this method which is defined as "ordinary" construction and has as its main attribute the localization of fires. For larger and taller structures and those within established "fire limits" of high population density, incombustible materials are preferred. Of these, unprotected steel is subject to rapid collapse if attacked directly by fire or superheated air, and therefore is subject to limitations. When protected by fire resistant plaster or imbedded in masonry, it is available for unlimited use. Reinforced concrete and protected steel are the usual components of the most firesafe buildings.

Although the defining of building types and decisions concerning their selection for various occupancies, regional locations and "fire loading" (a measure of the flammability of contents) is not within the scope of this book, a brief general reference to this subject is made in Table 3.1. The designation "no limit" refers to fire safety only. It is obvious that use, esthetics, and zoning laws may limit the height and area of buildings for other reasons. When building types are limited in area, for reasons of fire safety, the size of the building is not necessarily fixed. In certain cases, multiples of this area are allowed, provided that fire walls and automatically closable fire doors separate the units. Fire companies have trouble fighting fires and preventing their spread when such "compartmenting" is not provided.

Tall buildings must, in general, be sealed by a fire closure at every story against the possible upward spread of fire, gases, and superheated air. Shafts must be enclosed in fire-resistive material. Doors of stair towers and elevators should be fireproof and self-closing. Perforations such as air-carrying ducts must be provided with a closable fire damper actuated by a fusible link (see Fig. 3.1). Multistory buildings must have full height exit stairways, fully enclosed by fire-resistive construction, located at the perimeter of the building. They provide protected egress by occupants and access by firemen to points of vantage close to possible local fires on upper stories. Standpipes and fire hoses are located in or near these

Table 3.1 *Limitations of Height and Area for Various Building Types as Determined by Their Resistance to Fire*

	Height, ft	Area of One-Story Building sq ft	Area of Building over One Story sq ft
Fire-resistive, Type A	No Limit	No Limit	No Limit
Fire-resistive, Type B	85	No Limit	No Limit
Protected, noncombustible	75	18,000	12,000
Heavy timber	65	12,000	8,000
Ordinary	45	9,000	6,000
Unprotected, noncombustible	35	9,000	6,000
Wood frame	35	6,000	4,000

Extracted from National Building Code, recommended by the National Board of Fire Underwriters.

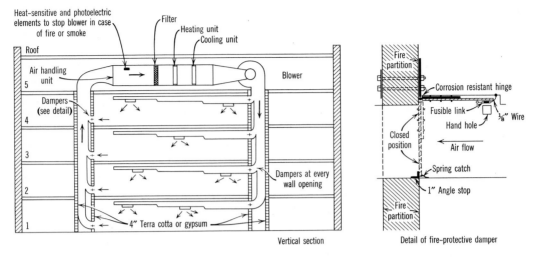

Fig. 3.1   Typical installation of air-conditioning system in building of fire-resistive, protected non-combustible or heavy timber construction. Adapted from information in NBFU No. 90A of The National Board of Fire Underwriters.

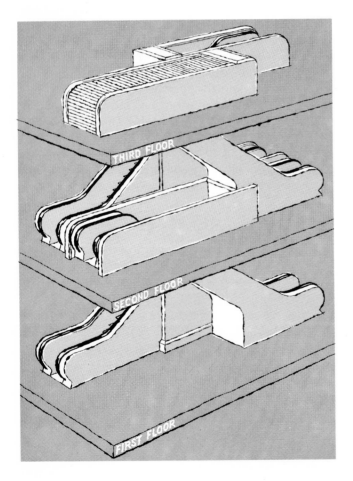

Fig. 3.2   Rolling-shutter method of wellway fire protection.

towers. The use of automatic sprinklers is becoming more common for safety and to reduce insurance rates. They are often mandatory by code or by insurance requirements for buildings of hazardous contents or low fire resistance.

It is usually inconvenient to enclose a moving stairway installation with masonry walls and fire doors in a manner similar to the wall-and-damper sealing of the air conditioning riser-ducts shown in Fig. 3.1. This may be omitted and an air passage between the stories allowed to exist during normal conditions. When a fire occurs, a motor-driven, fire resistant roller shutter closes on signal from a temperature-sensing element in the opening. Figure 3.2 shows 1 of the 2

openings between the second and third floors closed. The other opening at that level is equipped for similar protection, as are the 2 openings on the floor below. The closing of all would prevent any dangerous heat interchange between the floors. The blocking of egress through a moving stairway is desirable in any case if heat is rising through it. Furthermore, it is not an approved primary method of leaving a building. Occupants diverted by the closing shutters can leave by the legal fire stairways of which there are usually at least two.

An exception to the usual requirement of fixed or operable closure between stories is seen in Fig. 3 which solves the problem locally. In this sprinkler-vent method, a fire,

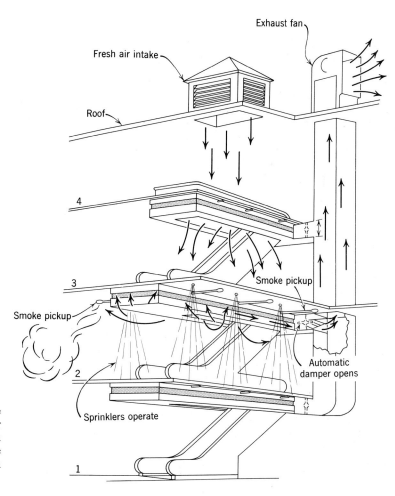

Fig. 3.3 Sprinkler-vent fire protection for escalator openings. An exception (with control) to the rule against perforations in floors.

for example at the second floor, will open a damper in the branch duct at the ceiling and also start the exhaust fan in the top of the vertical exhaust duct (which must be fire-protected). Dangerous gases and superheated air are drawn in through the sides of the smoke guard and pass through the branch duct that connects to it, and thence up the exhaust stack for disposal at the roof. To facilitate this process, replacement air is allowed to descend from open louvers at the fresh air intake directly above the openings in the floors. Concurrent with the start of the fan and the opening of the branch exhaust duct, sprinklers in the vicinity of the fire are triggered automatically in the usual way. They help to localize the fire. The principle of "venting out" the smoke and superheated air, so well illustrated by the sprinkler-vent method just described, is much approved by fire control executives. Ridding the building of these fatal gases increases the survival chances of both occupants and firemen and clears the atmosphere within the structure for fire fighting.

3. Electrical Planning. The fact that the National Electrical Code is sponsored and published by the National Fire Protection Association attests to the great hazard to life and property that is inherent in defec-

tive electrical systems. Compliance with the code and adherence to principles discussed in later chapters will do much to reduce this danger.

Failure to provide for adequate and easy expansion of electrical facilities, and for increase in service as electrical demands grow, can be very dangerous. It is possible to start with a legally correct and safe system, of a capacity just right for present demands, only to find that in a very short time inexpert extensions and overloadings have created a great fire hazard. Forward-looking designers will allow oversize service cables and feeders, and spare circuit breakers. It is well to plan branch circuits with few enough outlets that others may be added without overloading the existing conductors. The architect will do well to convince the building owner that an adequate electrical system will result in many economies when extensions are required, and also that it will help avoid the occasion for future illegalities and fire hazards.

4. Protection Against Lightning. Farm buildings, isolated buildings, and tall structures such as chimneys, steeples, peaked or gable roofs, television antennas, and flag poles are much in need of lightning protection to avoid damage and fire during electrical storms. Buildings of nonmetallic construction are most vulnerable. City buildings, especially those of steel frame or reinforced concrete construction appear to have less trouble. Lightning is one of the largest causes of fire and loss of life in farm buildings. In the case of these and all structures, lightning protection should be considered and the advice of experts sought in decisions about the need for installation and concerning the design of the system. Slim bronze points about 18 in. long are generally fixed at high points, and these, together with stout copper cables, form a cage around the building and extend down into the earth as grounds. The paths thus set up for the most direct transmission of the lightning charge to the ground are subject to a comprehensive set of rules and close

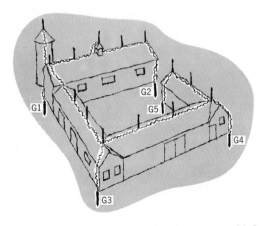

Fig. 3.4 Lightning protection on a barn group with 5 grounds (G1 thru G5). Conductors, much exaggerated, are actually inconspicuous.

inspection if the system is to have approval of the fire underwriters. This approval extends to the materials, which will carry labels of approval if they are in accord with published standards. An important part of any installation is the thorough grounding of all conductors to permanently moist earth. The grounds should extend well down into the earth (8 ft maximum) and point away from the building. Special importance is often accorded to buildings which house key personnel or irreplacable records, or if they fall into the category of historic prominence. An example is the White House in Washington, D.C., which has full lightning protection.

5. Standpipes and Hoses. Fire companies with their apparatus find difficulty in fighting fires from the street in structures more than 75 ft in height. Standpipes and hoses with a separate water reserve are extremely valuable in any building but become highly essential in tall buildings. Figure 3.5 shows such a system, which is intended for use both by building personnel until the fire engines arrive and thereafter by the trained staff of the fire department. It is not practical to store enough water for a protracted fire-fighting period and it is usually assumed that a half hour's supply will be more than enough to provide for the short period it takes the fire engines to arrive. This may be checked in a general way by reference to Figure 3.5. Under pressure of the tank a hose may discharge at about 100 gpm (less than the 200 gpm to be expected under fire engine pressure). If two hoses are used, their joint flow of 200 gpm will use up the 5,000 gal reserve in 25 min. When the system is used by the fire department, its pumps are attached to the street siamese to deliver water from street hydrants. The check valve closest to the siamese in use open and the check valves at the tank close to prevent the water from rising in the tank to no avail. After the engines are disconnected from the siamese, the water between the siamese and the adjacent check valve drains out through the ball drip so that it does not freeze.

The overhead tank is considered a most dependable source but it sometimes requires a height which is architecturally undesirable. In this case upfeed fire pumps operating automatically to deliver water to higher stories from lower suction reserve tanks may be used. Another alternate in this case is a pneumatic tank to deliver water by the power of the air which is compressed in the upper portion of the tank.

The water zones as shown in Fig. 2.10 are generally followed also in planning for fire protection. A fire standpipe zone will usually coincide with the service water zone.

6. Sprinklers. Automatic sprinkler systems consist of a horizontal pattern of pipes placed near the ceilings of industrial buildings, warehouses, stores, theaters, and other structures where the fire hazard may be particularly great. These pipes are provided with outlets and heads or valves so constructed that temperatures of 135 to 160 F will cause them to open automatically and emit a series of fine water sprays.

Sprinkler systems are (1) wet pipe, ordinarily with water constantly filling both the mains and the distributing pipes, and (2) dry pipe, generally confined to unheated buildings. There is no water in the distributing pipes except during a fire.

Operation of the wet-pipe system depends upon opening nozzles in the area affected by sensitive elements within the nozzles themselves. Remote valves, in the dry-pipe system, may be actuated by sensitive elements to admit water to sprinkler heads.

Spacing of sprinkler heads is governed by several factors: fire rating of the building, construction of the ceiling, spacing of joists, type of occupancy, and total area. For example, for open wood joist construction in a nonfireproof building, 1 head is required for every 80 sq ft of floor space for light and ordinary hazard, and 1 for every 70 sq ft for extra hazard rating. For fireproof construction 1 nozzle is required for every 196 sq ft of floor space for a light hazard rating, one for every 100 sq ft for ordinary, and 1 for every 90 sq ft for extra hazard ratings. Noz-

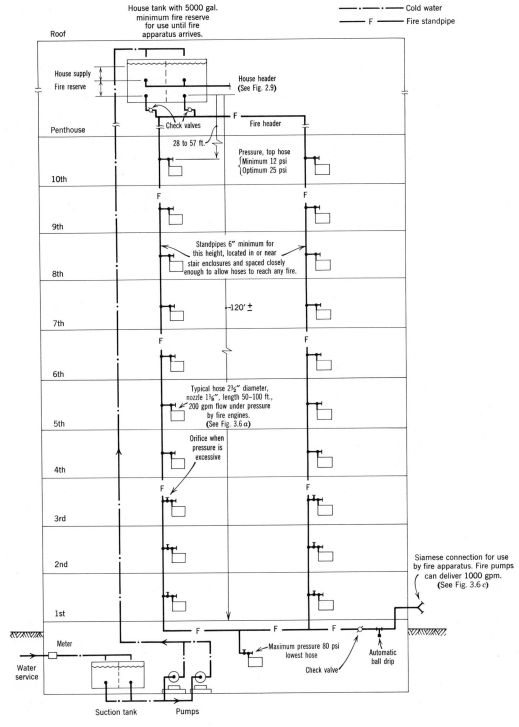

Fig. 3.5   Fire protection. Schematic section, part of a standpipe and hose system. Gravity tank downfeeds to hoses for use by building personnel. Fire department uses siamese connection.

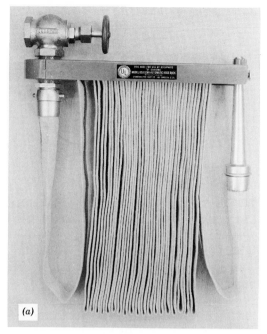

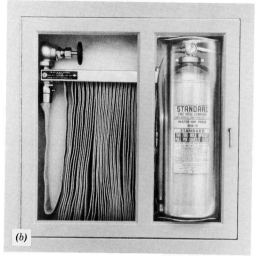

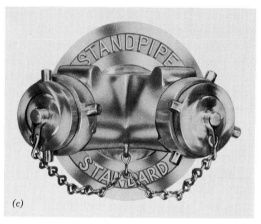

Fig. 3.6 Appurtenances for standpipe and hose system. (*a*) Standard hose rack. (*b*) Hose rack and fire extinguisher in cabinet with glass door. (*c*) Siamese connection for use of fire department pumping equipment to supply water to standpipe system. Sprinkler siamese similar but marked "sprinkler." Color codes sometimes differentiate the two. For principle of check valve see Fig. 2.3*c*.

zles are set about 8 to 12 ft apart on the supply pipes which, in turn, are spaced about 10 to 14 ft apart and are usually run at right angles to exposed beams or panels.

Special installation requirements for sprinkler systems include: (1) at least 1 fire department connection on each frontage; (2) a master alarm valve control for all water supplies other than fire department connections; (3) special fire walls between protected areas and unprotected areas; and (4) sloping waterproof floors with drains or scuppers to carry away waste water.

When gravity tanks are used with sprinkler systems they should reserve at least 5000 gal for this purpose and in any case enough to operate 25 percent of the sprinkler heads for 20 min. As in the case of standpipe and hose systems this gives the fire company a chance to arrive and take over.

A typical automatic sprinkler system is shown in Fig. 3.8. The building, a lithographing plant, is in the category of "ordinary hazard" (see Table 3.2). It is of noncombustible construction but not fireproof.

Table 3.2   *Examples of a Few Typical Classifications of Fire Hazard for Sprinkler Design*

Light Hazard	Ordinary Hazard	Extra Hazard
Apartments	Clothing Factories	Aircraft Hangars
Churches	Cotton and Woolen Mills	Chemical Works
Clubs	Dye and Print Works	Linoleum Manufacturing
Hospitals	Libraries, Stack Areas	Linseed Oil Mills
Hotels	Lithographing	Oil Refineries
Office Buildings	Sugar Refineries	Solvent Extracting
Schools	Tanneries	Varnish Works

The sprinkler design under the requirements of the National Fire Protection Association results in a nozzle spacing such that one nozzle (sprinkler head) takes care of 125 sq ft of floor area. This places it about midway between the extremes of the standards previously mentioned in this article. A building of "ordinary" construction with open wood joists and high hazard must have a nozzle for every 70 sq ft while the safer light hazard occupancy in a fireproof building allows 196 sq ft for each nozzle.

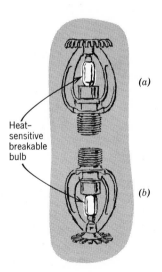

Heat-sensitive breakable bulb

Fig. 3.7 Sprinkler heads. These are of the quartzoid bulb type. The bulb is transparent and contains a colored liquid. At 136 F the bulb breaks and releases a water stream. (*a*) Upright. This type of sprinkler head is used above piping when piping is exposed. Safer against damage by workmen than the pendent type. (*b*) Pendent. This type of sprinkler head projects through a finished ceiling when piping is concealed. Heads can be plated, polished, or colored.

7. Alarm systems. An alarm gong mounted on the outside of the building (see Fig. 3.8) warns of a fire when water starts to flow through the alarm valve upon the actuating of a sprinkler head. This warning to the building personnel gives an opportunity to provide additional fire fighting arrangements to minimize loss and speed the termination of the fire so that the sprinklers may be turned off to prevent excess water damage to building contents after the fire is out. It is common for sprinkler alarms to be also connected to private regional supervisory offices which communicate promptly with municipal fire departments upon the receipt of a signal. Siamese connections permit fire engines to pump into the sprinkler system in a manner similar to that used for standpipe systems.

All public buildings and others of importance should be provided with a fire detection and alarm system, indicating in the custodian's office the location of the fire. (See Chapter 28.) Auxiliary electrical power sources such as batteries often supplement the utility company power which might be out during the beginning of a fire. Manual stations in private structures give the possibility of reporting a fire through a central agency similar to the operation of municipal fire alarm systems. Individual self-contained alarm horns operated by freon or other pressurized gas may be located in dangerous locations in private residences and other small buildings which may not be equipped with the preferred electrical detection system.

8. Designing for Fire Safety. When the architect and his client sit down to confer with an insurance underwriter and a fire captain they find that in most cases the latter two specialists hope that the proposed construction may conform to the following pattern:

(*a*) Structure of reinforced concrete with a 3 or 4 hr fire rating.

(*b*) No openings between stories unless fire-protected.

(*c*) Divisions on each story separated by fire walls and automatic fire doors.

(*d*) A good electrical system in full conformity with the National Electrical Code.

(*e*) All areas fully sprinklered.

(*f*) Standpipe and hose systems.

(*g*) Two sources of water for both systems and auxiliary possible use of siamese.

(*h*) Fire detection and alarm system with a connection to a central supervisory agency.

(*i*) Adequate protected and marked exits and fire towers giving access directly to the street.

It is obvious that some of these items may

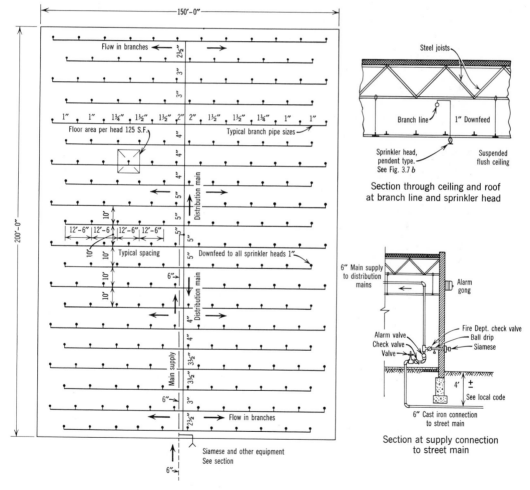

Fig. 3.8 Plan of sprinklered industrial building. Sprinklers (and standpipes) may use water from street mains when pressure suffices. Either system may use pneumatic or gravity tanks. When the latter is used to supply both sytems, an independent sprinkler reserve occupies the bottom, and the fire supply occupies the top. Auxiliary fire-engine feed by siamese should be provided in all cases.

Fig. 3.9 Signaling devices for private fire alarm systems. (*a*) Temperature sensing device for use in rooms and at locations of fire hazard. Electrical wiring transmits its signal to a central alarm station. (*b*) Manual alarm signals the location of a fire to a central alarm station. (*c*) Single station freon-operated horn which blows when temperatures in its vicinity are excessive.

be inconsistent with economy, architectural design, or use-pattern of the building, yet for fire safety they constitute a check list against which compromises can be considered. To qualify a building for fire insurance its final drawings must have the approval of an examining officer of the regional fire insurance rating bureau, whose findings also set insurance rates.

References

National Building Code.
NBFU No. 13 Standard for the Installation of Sprinkler Systems.

NBFU No. 14 Standard for the Installation of Standpipe and Hose Systems.
NBFU No. 71 Standard for the Installation, Maintenance and use of Central Station Protective Signalling Systems.
NBFU No. 72c Standard for the Installation, Maintenance and use of Remote Station Signalling Systems.
NBFU No. 80 Standard for the Installation of Fire Doors and Windows.
NBFU No. 90a Standard for the Installation of Air Conditioning and Ventilating Systems of other than Residence Type.

All of the above published by National Board of Fire Underwriters, 85 John Street, New York 38, New York.

Code for Protection against Lightning. National Fire Protection Association, 60 Batterymarch Street, Boston 10, Massachusetts.

4

Principles of

Sanitary Drainage

1. Drainage and Vent Piping. The human occupancy of buildings necessarily results in the accumulation of fluid waste and organic matter very susceptible to rapid decomposition. It is one of the functions of plumbing to dispose of these wastes as quickly as possible before the offensive and unwholesome products of decay can assail the senses or affect the health.

Pipes are consequently installed to conduct the wastes from the plumbing fixtures to the sewer. Gases of decomposition, however, are generated in these pipes or may penetrate into them from the public sewer. Hence it becomes necessary to form a bar against the passage of the gases into the fixtures and through them into the living quarters. To erect this bar or seal, an S-shaped pipe or one of similar bend, called a trap, is connected close to the fixture into the drain pipe. This trap catches and holds at each discharge a certain quantity of water through which the gases cannot force their way. It would obviously be very costly as well as wasteful of space to carry a separate pipe from each fixture to the sewer; therefore the individual pipes or branches from

the fixtures are connected at the several floor levels by a horizontal branch which leads into a main vertical pipe or stack which in turn joins into the main horizontal drain in the cellar. However, the sudden and often rapid discharges of water into a closed stack would cause a variety of air currents and air pressures throughout the piping system and would probably empty the water from the traps either by propulsion or by suction. The stacks must, therefore, be opened at their tops to the atmosphere, and sufficient fresh air must be supplied to the stacks and branches through vent pipes to balance the air pressures, dilute the gases, and reduce corrosion.

The stacks, drains, and branches must be of suitable size to convey their contents at velocities which prevent fouling and clogging, and the areas and lengths of the vents must be proportioned to the demands of the stacks, branches, and traps. Piping may be decreased in size and quantity by ingenious combinations and simplifications and by grouping fixtures in close proximity to the mains. Hygienic requirements must, however, always be maintained; hence the

49

science of plumbing is based upon hydraulics and pneumatics, and the efficient, sanitary, and economical design of pipe arrangements and sizes can result only from a thorough knowledge of the principles involved.

In most parts of the country, state and municipal regulations have been enacted in attempts to insure the installation of only such plumbing as may conform with the demands of hygiene and comfort. Architects must, therefore, lay out the drainage systems of their buildings in accordance with the local sanitary code in order to obtain the necessary permits to begin construction. These regulations have produced and insured vastly improved sanitary conditions, but they are not uniform and are often needlessly complicated and expensive. Constant progress is being made, however, toward simplicity and standardization founded upon scientific theory and the teachings of exact tests on full-size installations. The National Plumbing Code published by the American Society of Mechanical Engineers may be considered the latest scientific reference on the subject. With the cooperation of the Housing and Home Finance Agency and the U.S. Department of Commerce and with contributions from many recognized authorities, it summarizes the best current practices and has been adopted by more than 1300 cities. Its recommendations embrace many simplifications which lead to economy and efficiency in both large and small structures. Among these is the system of loop venting. Tests and experience have shown that this simple vent piping arrangement has much reduced the need for individual fixture vents. Local codes must be consulted however, because in some municipalities individual vents are still preferred.

2. The National Plumbing Code. Basic principles for the design of plumbing systems are set forth in this code. Among the many important objectives stated, a few have been selected for listing here. It will be noted that they include requirements about water supply which are necessary because plumbing includes this item (see definition of plumbing, Art. 4).

(*a*) All premises intended for human habitation, occupancy, or use shall be provided with a supply of pure and wholesome water, neither connected with unsafe water supplies nor subject to the hazards of backflow or backsiphonage.

(*b*) Plumbing fixtures, devices, and appurtenances shall be supplied with water in sufficient volume and at pressures adequate to enable them to function satisfactorily and without undue noise under all normal conditions of use.

(*c*) Every building having plumbing fixtures installed and intended for human habitation, occupancy, or use of premises abutting on a street, alley, or easement in which there is a public sewer shall have a connection with the sewer.

(*d*) Plumbing fixtures shall be made of smooth nonabsorbent material, shall be free from concealed fouling surfaces, and shall be located in ventilated enclosures.

(*e*) The drainage system shall be designed, constructed, and maintained so as to guard against fouling, deposit of solids, and clogging, and with adequate cleanouts so arranged that the pipes may be readily cleaned.

(*f*) The piping of the plumbing system shall be of durable material, free from defective workmanship and so designed and constructed as to give satisfactory service for its reasonable expected life.

(*g*) Each fixture directly connected to the drainage system shall be equipped with a water-seal trap.

(*h*) The drainage system shall be designed to provide an adequate circulation of air in all pipes with no danger of siphonage, aspiration, or forcing of trap seals under conditions of ordinary use.

(*i*) Each vent terminal shall extend to the outer air and be so installed as to minimize the possibilities of clogging and the return of foul air to the building.

(*j*) If water closets or other plumbing fixtures are installed in buildings where there is no sewer within a reasonable distance, suitable provision shall be made for disposing of the building sewage by some accepted method of sewage treatment and disposal.

(*k*) Sewage or other waste from a plumbing system which may be deleterious to surface or subsurface waters shall not be discharged into the ground or into any waterway unless it has first been rendered innocuous through subjection to some acceptable form of treatment.

3. Sanitary Drainage. Certain essential equipment is involved in all plumbing systems whether for a simple house or for a complicated institution. Figure 4.1 illustrates these constituent parts, which may be tabulated as follows:

House sewer	Soil and waste stacks
House drain	Fixture branches
House trap	Traps
Fresh-air inlet	Vents

"House" and "building" are interchangeable. See definition of building sewer, page 57.

The house sewer extends from the public sewer in the street or from the private sewage-disposal tank to the wall of the house and is entirely outside the building. Just inside or outside the foundation wall, a house trap may be connected into the horizontal main or house drain. The fresh-air inlet protects the house trap from loss of seal. The house drain and the vertical soil and waste stacks collect the sewage from the fixtures through their branches. The vent stacks receive the vent branches from the fixture traps and connect through to the open air. The traps are placed in the soil, and waste branches within or close to the fixtures.

Pipe of vitrified clay, steel, copper, brass, and wrought and cast iron should conform to the Standard Specification of the American Society of Testing Materials. Lead pipes are generally restricted in use to short

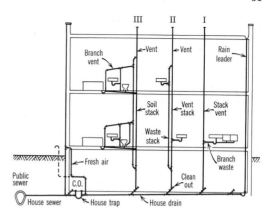

Fig. 4.1   Typical plumbing layout.

branches of soil and waste pipes, bends, traps, and leader roof connections.

(*a*) **_The House Sewer_** may be of copper (type K or L), glazed vitrified clay or of cast iron pipe, as shown in Fig. 4.2 (*a, b,* and *c*). When cast iron or clay pipes are being laid, the small or spigot end of a length of pipe is introduced into the hub end of the next length, and the joint is caulked. Vitrified clay pipe is less expensive than cast iron and copper but is not so strong. The joints of clay pipe are filled with hot bituminous compound or are caulked with oakum saturated in cement grout and filled with cement mortar, which is not always watertight and is likely to crack if the pipe settles. The joints of cast-iron pipe are made perfectly tight and at the same time slightly flexible by caulking with oakum and at least 1 in. of molten lead. Porous joints are undesirable because leaking sewage may be carried through the ground to contaminate wells and springs. Sewers are also often obstructed by the penetration of tree and shrubbery roots through the mortar joints of clay pipe, a condition seldom encountered with cast-iron pipe and lead joints. House sewers should have a grade of about $\frac{1}{8}$ in. or $\frac{1}{4}$ in. to the foot and should be not less than 6 in. in diameter if of vitrified clay or 4 in. if of cast iron or copper. For large buildings they should be of the same diameter as the house drain. For a distance of 5 ft beyond the wall the sewer should always be of metal.

Clay pipe is manufactured in standard laying lengths of 2 and 3 ft. The diameters vary from 4 to 36 in. Cast-iron pipe is produced in 5 and 10 ft laying lengths and in two weights—standard and extra heavy. Cast iron, sometimes coated with coal tar, pitch, or asphaltum, is preferable for underground pipes. The diameters range from 2 to 15 in.; copper comes in 12 to 20 ft lengths.

If the house sewer carries storm water as well as sewage it should be proportioned for both quantities.

(b) **The House Drain** is the horizontal main into which the vertical soil and waste stacks discharge. Copper or extra heavy cast iron pipe with lead joints is used; clay pipe should never be employed inside the building. It should have a slope of $\frac{1}{8}$ in. or $\frac{1}{4}$ in. per foot, and it connects directly into the house sewer. Primary horizontal branches or laterals lead from the base of a soil or waste stack to the house drain or to another primary branch. Secondary horizontal branches lead from fixtures to a stack. The location of the house drain depends upon the depth below grade of the public sewer, the contents of the drain in the majority of buildings being designed to flow by gravity into the sewer. The drain is most conveniently placed below the cellar floor with cleanouts set flush with the floor surface. If the depth of the sewer necessitates a higher position for the drain, it may be supported above the floor at every pipe-joint on masonry piers or on wall brackets, or be suspended from the first floor beams by metal hangers. House drains above ground

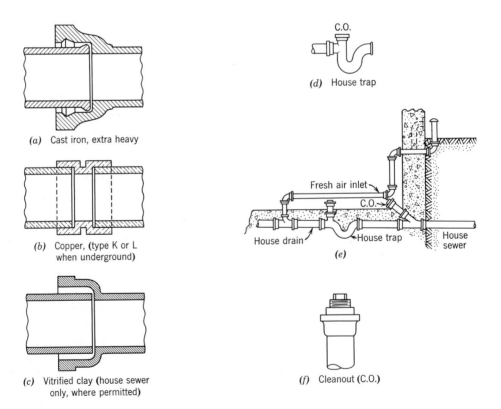

(a)   Cast iron, extra heavy

(b)   Copper, (type K or L when underground)

(c)   Vitrified clay (house sewer only, where permitted)

(d)   House trap

(e)

House drain   House trap   House sewer

Fresh air inlet

C.O.

(f)   Cleanout (C.O.)

Fig. 4.2   House drain and house sewer details.

may be of cast iron, copper, or of galvanized wrought iron and steel. In large buildings with deep basements some fixtures may be below the level of the sewer. The drain then discharges into the sewer and the low fixtures into a sump pit, their sewage being raised from the pit to the sewer by an electric pump or pneumatic ejector with an automatic float or probe control.

A cleanout consisting of a branch pipe projecting through the floor is connected into the drain just inside the cellar wall to permit clearing the house sewer of obstructions. Cleanouts are also placed at the end of the house drain beyond the last vertical stack and at intermediate points not more than 50 ft apart to render the entire horizontal run accessible for cleaning. It is also good practice to introduce a cleanout at the foot of each waste and soil stack. Cleanouts are made up of an elbow and a length of pipe into the hub of which is caulked a cast-iron ferrule threaded on the inside. When the cleanout is not in use the ferrule is closed with a threaded brass plug and nut, (Fig. 4.2f).

The house trap, when used, is connected into the house drain, usually inside the cellar wall just beyond the sewer cleanout. The fresh-air inlet is placed next on the building side of the house trap (Fig. 4.2e). No traps are placed at the foot of the stacks where they join the house drain.

House drains may be arranged to receive only the wastes from the plumbing fixtures, separate drains being installed with their own connections to the sewer to carry the rain water from the leaders. The latter method is advisable for buildings of more than moderate size. The house drains are then known as sanitary drains and the leader drains as storm-water drains.

Steam boiler exhaust, drip pipes, and blow-off pipes should not discharge into the house drain but should be led into a blow-off tank from which the water is conducted to the house sewer outside the building. In low-pressure steam systems the blow-off

tank may be omitted, and the pipes can discharge into the sewer.

(c) *House Traps* are required by some sanitary codes, their purpose being to furnish a water seal against the entrance of gases from the sewer into the piping system of the building. They are, however, considered unnecessary by the National Plumbing Code and other authorities, the argument being that they interfere with the flow of sewage and the air movements in the house drain and increase the possibility of back-pressure in the soil pipes. Gastight stacks which are open to the outside air and fixtures protected by properly vented individual traps provide a multitude of outlets for the ventilating of sewers in place of manholes near pedestrians in the streets. House traps are of the running type, set perfectly level and provided with a cleanout in one or both horns. They should be the full size of the house drain (Fig. 4.2d).

(d) *Fresh-Air Inlets* are intended to admit fresh air to the drainage system so that there will be a free circulation without compression throughout the house drain and stacks discharging above the roof. They are a necessary adjunct to a house trap but are often omitted when the house trap is left out. The outer end is furnished with a cowl or gooseneck when standing free and with a brass grille when embedded in the wall. The pipe should have a diameter equal to half the diam of the house drain with a minimum of 4 in. (Fig. 4.2e).

(e) *Soil and Waste Stacks* are generally made of extra heavy cast iron or copper, although brass, galvanized steel, and wrought iron are permitted in most codes. Galvanized steel is often considered more practical for the stacks of very tall buildings. They should rest solidly at the bottom on masonry piers or heavy iron posts and be supported at intervals at 10 ft in their height by stout wall hangers or brackets or on beams at each floor. The upper ends extend through the roof at the full diameter and (Fig. 4.3) have no caps or cowl. When

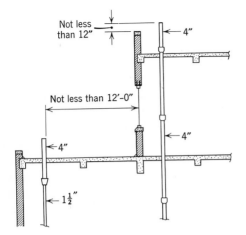

Fig. 4.3   Extension of stacks through roofs.

less than 4 in. in diameter the stacks should be increased to 4 in. at least 1 ft below the roof to prevent stoppage by snow or frost. The open tops of the pipes should rise at least 1 ft above wall copings and should be not less than 12 ft distant from shafts, windows, skylights, and ventilators. The stacks should be as straight as possible, free of sharp bends and turns. Connections with branches and house drain are made at angles greater than 45 degrees with the horizontal. No 90° ells are permitted except on those portions acting as vents above the highest fixture.

The circulation of air throughout the stacks and drain retards the decomposition of organic matter, bacteria being unable to function in the presence of free oxygen. It dilutes poisonous gases, delays pipe corrosion, and maintains balanced atmosphere pressures in the various parts of the system. A proper relation and connection between the stacks, drains, vents, and outside atmosphere are consequently as important as the disposal of the sewage.

For economy the sets of stacks should be as few as possible. The groupings of bathrooms, toilet, and other fixtures on the same and successive floors so that they may be served by a minimum number of stacks is, therefore, an important architectural con-

sideration and should be carefully studied in the planning of every building.

(*f*) *Fixture Branches* connect the fixtures with the stacks and may be of cast iron, brass, copper, or galvanized steel. Waste and soil branches are connected to the trap of each fixture and have a fall of $\frac{1}{8}$ to $\frac{1}{2}$ in. per foot. Branches serving water closets, urinals, and slop sinks are run if possible between the floor and the ceiling below; branches from other fixtures may be run in the floor or, when convenient, in the wall back of the fixtures. In general the length of a $1\frac{1}{4}$ in. horizontal branch measured from the vertical inlet of the trap to the vent opening should not be more than 5 ft. For branches larger than $1\frac{1}{4}$ in. the following lengths of branches are allowable with a $\frac{1}{4}$ in. slope: $1\frac{1}{2}$ in. branch, 6 ft; 2 in. branch, 8 ft; 3 in. branch, 12 ft. Long unvented branches are likely to have too little slope or to necessitate dangerous cutting of framing timbers. They permit deposits from small discharges or siphoning out of trap seals when the discharges are large, and they encourage corrosion by loss of air movement and concentration of gases. When the vent opening is below the dip of the trap, many municipal codes limit the distance from trap to vent to 2 ft.

(*g*) *Traps.*   The only separation between the unpleasant and dangerously unhealthy gases in a sanitary drainage system and the air breathed by room occupants is the water caught in the fixture trap after each discharge from a fixture. Sufficient water must flow, especially in water closets, so that this residual water is clean. Traps are of steel, cast iron, copper, or brass, except those in water closets and urinals which are of vitreous china cast integrally with the fixture. The deeper the seal, the more resistance there is to siphonage, but the greater the fouling area, therefore a minimum depth of 2 in. and a maximum of 4 in. with not more than 1 in. loss of seal are common standards. All traps should be self-cleaning, that is, capable of being completely flushed each time the trap operates so that no sediment will remain inside to decompose.

There are a few exceptions to a rule that each fixture should have its own trap. Common ones are the connecting of 2 laundry trays and a kitchen sink to a single trap or not more than 3 laundry trays or 3 lavatories on a single trap. In the case of the laundry trays and sink, the sink is equipped with the trap and is set nearest to the stack. The wastes from the laundry trays connect into the sink trap below the level of the water seal.

Traps are usually placed within 2 ft of the fixture and should be accessible for cleaning through a bottom opening which is otherwise closed by a brass plug. Overflow pipes from fixtures are connected into the inlet side of the trap. In long runs of horizontal pipe, so-called "running traps" are used only near the drains of floors, areas or yards and should be provided with handhole cleanouts.

When fixtures are very infrequently used, the water in traps can evaporate into the air, breaking the seal of the trap. In contemplating the possible frequency of use, this fact should be borne in mind by the designer. Evaporation to a dangerous degree rarely occurs except in the case of floor drains, where it becomes a real hazard. Trapped drains of this type, employed to carry away the water used in washing floors or drained from heating equipment, may often lose the water seal between infrequent operations. If they are connected to soil piping the results can be dangerous. Many authorities are reluctant to approve floor drains in soil systems, requiring instead that they be separately connected to a dry

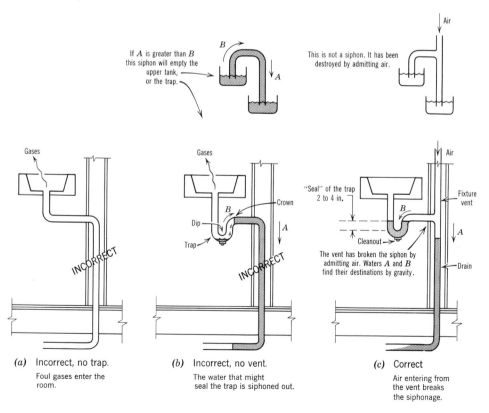

(a) Incorrect, no trap.
Foul gases enter the room.

(b) Incorrect, no vent.
The water that might seal the trap is siphoned out.

(c) Correct
Air entering from the vent breaks the siphonage.

Fig. 4.4   The function of a trap and one of the several functions of a vent (preventing siphonage).

well. In either case the use of a special hose bibb, affording a source of water directly above the drain, is a wise precaution. It can be used easily to refill the trap of the drain.

(*h*) *Vents.* For the admission of air and the discharging of gases, soil and waste stacks are extended through roofs and a system of air vents largely paralleling the drainage system is also provided. As in the case of the drainage stacks, the ventilating stacks also extend through the roof. The functions of venting are often misunder-

stood. It is true, of course, that one important purpose is to ventilate the system by allowing air from the fresh air inlet (or from the sewer if there is no house trap or fresh inlet) to rise through the system and carry away offensive gases. This affords some purification to the piping. However, several other purposes are served by the vent piping. The introduction of air near the fixture (and in the case of loop venting, at the branch soil line) breaks the possible siphonage of water out of the trap. Under other

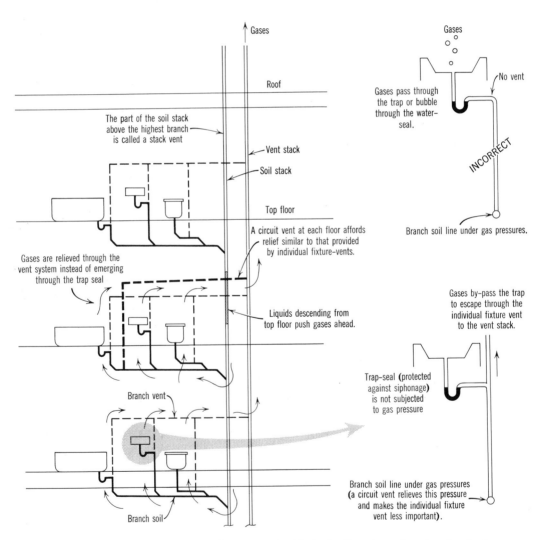

Fig. 4.5   Gas relief through vents. Gases pressurized by hydraulic action or by expansion due to putrefaction have a path of escape through the vent system and will not enter the rooms.

circumstances, namely when drainage fluids descend toward a fixture group through the soil stack, the foul gases would bubble through the trap-seals. The vent system provides a local escape for these gases. Comprehensive experiments have shown that loop venting which permits air and gases to pass in and out of the soil or waste branch instead of at each fixture, as in the case of continuous venting, is fully effective in preventing siphonage of trap-seals or their penetration by gases.

4. **Definitions.** Building codes and specifications have improved greatly in the use of simple direct statements and the gradual elimination of many strange terms that have grown up in each division of the mechanical services for buildings. Yet an agreement can be reached about the names to be applied to parts of the systems and to processes that occur within them. This type of uniformity does much to clarify instructions and to eliminate misunderstandings. The essence of the language of each division must be learned. The National Plumbing Code defines about 150 terms that are rather special to plumbing systems. The following is a partial list of these terms:*

Area Drain. An area drain is a receptacle designed to collect surface or rain water from an open area.

Backflow. Backflow is the flow of water or other liquids, mixtures, or substances into the distributing pipes of a potable supply of water from any source or sources other than its intended source. (See back-siphonage.)

Backflow Preventer. A backflow preventer is a device or means to prevent backflow into the potable water system.

Back-siphonage. Back-siphonage is the flowing back of used, contaminated, or polluted water from a plumbing fixture or vessel into a water-supply pipe due to a negative pressure in such pipe. (See back-flow.)

Branch Interval. A branch interval is a length of soil or waste stack corresponding in general to a story height, but there is

never less than 8 ft within which the horizontal branches from one floor or story of a building are connected to the stack.

Building Drain. The building (house) drain is that part of the lowest piping of a drainage system which receives the discharge from soil, waste, and other drainage pipes, inside the walls of the building and conveys it to the building (house) sewer beginning 3 ft outside the building wall.

Building Sewer. The building (house) sewer is that part of the horizontal piping of a drainage system which extends from the end of the building drain and which receives the discharge of the building drain and conveys it to a public sewer, private sewer, individual sewage-disposal system, or other point of disposal.

Building Storm Drain. A building (house) storm drain is a building drain used for conveying rain water, surface water, ground water, subsurface water, condensate, cooling water, or other similar discharge, to a building storm sewer or a combined building sewer, extending to a point not less than 3 ft outside the building wall.

Building Storm Sewer. A building (house) storm sewer is the extension from the building storm drain to the public storm sewer, combined sewer, or other point of disposal.

Building Trap. A building (house) trap is a device, fitting, or assembly of fittings installed in the building drain to prevent circulation of air between the drainage system of the building and the building sewer.

Circuit Vent. A circuit vent is a branch vent that serves two or more traps and extends from in front of the last fixture connection of a horizontal branch to the vent stack.

Combined Building Sewer. A combined building sewer receives storm water and sewage.

* Extracted from American Standard National Plumbing Code (ASA A40.8–1955), with the permission of the publisher, The American Society of Mechanical Engineers. United Engineering Center, 345 East 47th Street, N.Y. 17, N.Y.

Continuous Vent. A continuous vent is a vertical vent that is a continuation of the drain to which it connects.

Cross-Connection. A cross-connection is any physical connection or arrangement between two otherwise separate piping systems, one of which contains potable water and the other water of unknown or questionable safety, whereby water may flow from one system to the other, the direction of flow depending on the pressure differential between the two systems. (See *Backflow* and *Back-siphonage.*)

Developed Length. The developed length of a pipe is its length along the center line of the pipe and fittings.

Drain. A drain is any pipe which carries waste water or waterborne wastes in a building drainage system.

Drainage System. A drainage system (drainage piping) includes all the piping within public or private premises, which conveys sewage, rain water, or other liquid wastes to a legal point of disposal; but does not include the mains of a public sewer system or private or public sewage-treatment or disposal plant.

Fixture-Unit Flow Rate. Fixture-unit flow rate is the total discharge flow in gpm of a single fixture divided by 7.5, which provides the flow rate of that particular plumbing fixture as a unit of flow. Fixtures are rated as multiples of this unit of flow.

Flushometer Valve. A flushometer valve is a device which discharges a predetermined quantity of water to fixtures for flushing purposes and is actuated by direct water pressure.

Indirect Waste Pipe. An indirect waste pipe is a pipe that does not connect directly with the drainage system but conveys liquid wastes by discharging into a plumbing fixture or receptacle which is directly connected to the drainage system.

Industrial Wastes. Industrial wastes are liquid wastes resulting from the processes employed in industrial establishments and are free of fecal matter.

Interceptor. An interceptor is a device designed and installed so as to separate and retain deleterious, hazardous, or undesirable matter from normal wastes and permit normal sewage or liquid wastes to discharge into the disposal terminal by gravity.

Liquid Waste. Liquid waste is the discharge from any fixture, appliance, or appurtenance, in connection with a plumbing system which does not receive fecal matter.

Load Factor. Load factor is the percentage of the total connected fixture unit flow rate which is likely to occur at any point in the drainage system. It varies with the type of occupancy, the total flow unit above this point being considered, and with the probability factor of simultaneous use.

Loop Vent. A loop vent is the same as a circuit vent except that it loops back and connects with a stack vent instead of a vent stack.

Plumbing. Plumbing is the practice, materials, and fixtures used in the installation, maintenance, extension, and alteration of all piping, fixtures, appliances, and appurtenances in connection with any of the following: sanitary drainage or storm drainage facilities, the venting system, and the public or private water-supply systems, within or adjacent to any building, structure, or conveyance; also the practice and materials used in the installation, maintenance, extension, or alteration of storm-water, liquid-waste, or sewerage, and water-supply systems of any premises to their connection with any point of public disposal or other acceptable terminal.

Plumbing System. The plumbing system includes the water-supply and distribution pipes; plumbing fixtures and traps; soil, waste, and vent pipes; building drains and building sewers including their respective connections, devices, and appurtenances within the property lines of the premises, and water-treating or water-using equipment.

Potable Water. Potable water is water which is satisfactory for drinking, culinary, and domestic purposes, and meets the requirements of the Health Authority having jurisdiction.

Roof Drain. A roof drain is a drain installed to receive water collecting on the surface of a roof and to discharge it into the leader (downspout).

Roughing-In. Roughing-in is the installation of all parts of the plumbing system which can be completed prior to the installation of fixtures. This includes drainage, water-supply, and vent piping, and the necessary fixture supports.

Sanitary Sewer. A sanitary sewer is a pipe which carries sewage and excludes storm, surface, and ground water.

Septic Tank. A septic tank is a watertight receptacle which receives the discharge of a drainage system or part thereof, and is designed and constructed so as to separate solids from the liquid, digest organic matter through a period of detention, and allow the liquids to discharge into the soil outside of the tank through a system of open-joint or perforated piping, or a disposal pit.

Sewage. Sewage is any liquid waste containing animal or vegetable matter in suspension or solution, and may include liquids containing chemicals in solution.

Soil Pipe. A soil pipe is any pipe which conveys the discharge of water closets or fixtures having similar functions, with or without the discharge from other fixtures, to the building drain or building sewer.

Stack Vent. A stack vent (sometimes called a waste vent or soil vent) is the extension of a soil or waste stack above the highest horizontal drain connected to the stack.

Storm Sewer. A storm sewer is a sewer used for conveying rain water, surface water, condensate, cooling water, or similar liquid wastes.

Sump. A sump is a tank or pit which receives sewage or liquid waste, located below the normal grade of the gravity system and which must be emptied by mechanical means.

Trap. A trap is a fitting or device so designed and constructed as to provide, when properly vented, a liquid seal which will prevent the back passage of air without materially affecting the flow of sewage or waste water through it.

Trap Seal. The trap seal is the maximum vertical depth of liquid that a trap will retain, measured between the crown weir and the top of the dip of the trap.

Vacuum Breaker. See *Backflow Preventer.*

Vent Stack. A vent stack is a vertical vent pipe installed primarily for the purpose of providing circulation of air to and from any part of the drainage system.

Vent System. A vent system is a pipe or pipes installed to provide a flow of air to or from a drainage system or to provide a circulation of air within such system to protect trap seals from siphonage and back pressure.

5. Special Equipment. In addition to the basic network of drainage and vent piping and the protective traps, there are numerous special devices that are often required in plumbing systems. They include the following:

(*a*) Interceptors
(*b*) Sumps and Ejectors
(*c*) Backwater Valves
(*d*) Backflow Preventers
(*e*) Roof and Floor Drains

(*a*) *Interceptors.* Sanitary drainage installations ultimately discharge their waste matter into private or public sewage treatment plants that attempt to digest or cope with anything that may come through the pipes. Public plants are somewhat better equipped to handle this problem than private installations. Of course it is true that from any plumbing fixture to the end of the disposal process all parts of systems should be openable through cleanouts and other points of access to relieve clogging which will often occur in the piping as well as in the septic tank or public disposal plant. Since it is quite impossible to control hu-

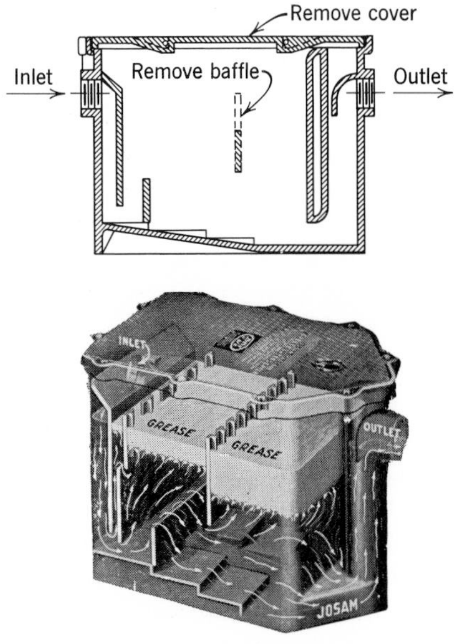

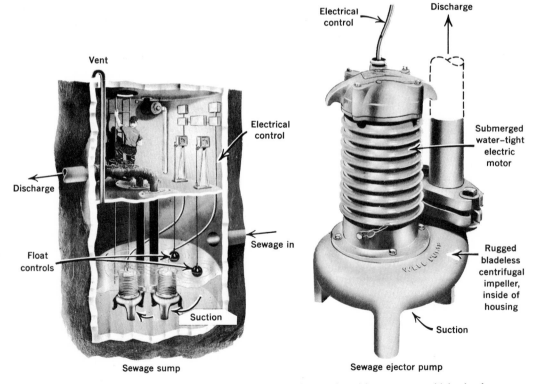

Fig. 4.6 A grease interceptor. The top cover of this model is flush with the kitchen floor and may be removed to allow the grease to be removed. Josam Manufacturing Company.

man judgment about what should and should not be introduced into the plumbing drains, trouble can usually be expected. This may be materially reduced by devices known as interceptors which catch foreign matter before it travels too far into the system. It is evident that the interceptors will require periodic servicing. Interceptors for as many as 25 different kinds of extraneous material are listed by some manufacturers. They include devices to catch hair, grease, plaster, lubricating oil, glass grindings, and troublesome unwanted material from many industrial processes.

One of the few interceptors that is sometimes needed in homes and more often in institutional kitchens is the grease interceptor.

By passing the waste from a kitchen sink through the circuitous path of this unit the grease floats to the top where it is trapped between baffles while the more fluid wastes

Fig. 4.7 Sump and ejector. Submersible type centrifugal pump for raising sewage to a higher level. This principle, shown here for an outdoor sub-grade installation may be used in basement applications within buildings. Venting must be carried to roof. (Weil Pump Company)

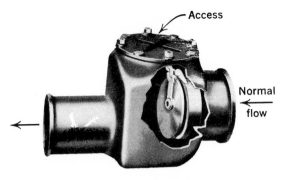

Access

Normal
flow

Fig. 4.8   Backwater valve.

pass through at a lower level. There are
rather special reasons for removing grease
because it congeals within piping and materially retards the sewage digestion process.

(b) *Sewage Sumps and Ejectors.* Whenever subsoil drainage, fixtures, or other
equipment are situated below the level of
public sewer, a sump pit or receptacle must
be installed, into which the drainage from
the low fixtures may flow by gravity and
from which the contents are then lifted up
into the house sewer. The outlet is connected to the house drain on the sewer side
of the house trap, (see Figure 5.9). A sepa-

rate trap, fresh-air inlet, and 3 in. ventilating pipe to the roof should be provided on
the inlet side of the sump. Sewage ejectors
may be motor-driven centrifugal pumps
(see Fig. 4.7) or they may be operated by
compressed air. The latter have no revolving parts within the receptacle. An air compressor is started when the float within the
sump reaches a certain level, and air at a
pressure of 2.3 psi for each foot of lift is
delivered into the space above the liquid.
The air pressure closes the inlet and opens
the outlet check valves, expelling the contents of the sump and elevating it to the
sewer.

(c) *Backwater Valves.* Occasionally, some
sewers are unable to cope with the drainage
load for short periods because of heavy
rains, tidewater conditions, or inadequate
pitch. In such cases the sewage could, unless
prevented, back up into the building and
overflow through low fixtures causing an
unsanitary condition. A backwater valve in
the branch that carries the discharge of the
low fixtures to the house drain can prevent
this by closing against this reverse flow
from the sewer. During this closure, hope-

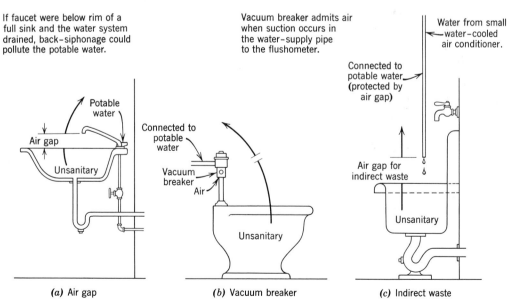

If faucet were below rim of a
full sink and the water system
drained, back–siphonage could
pollute the potable water.

Vacuum breaker admits air
when suction occurs in
the water–supply pipe
to the flushometer.

Water from small
water–cooled
air conditioner.

Connected to
potable water
(protected by
air gap)

Potable
water

Air gap

Unsanitary

Connected to
potable
water

Vacuum
breaker

Air

Air gap for
indirect waste

Unsanitary

Unsanitary

(a) Air gap

(b) Vacuum breaker

(c) Indirect waste

Fig. 4.9   Backflow preventers. Unsanitary fluid wastes cannot be siphoned into the potable water
piping.

Roof level

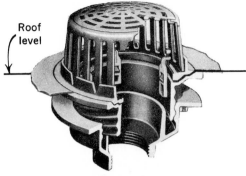

Roof drain

Floor level

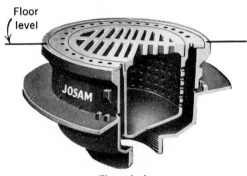

Floor drain

Fig. 4.10 Roof and floor drains. (Josam Manufacturing Company)

fully brief, trouble can develop within the building if there is much use of the fixtures whose drainage is cut off by the closing of the valve. Overflow could occur at low fixtures from too much pressure *within* the building. These valves are, for this reason, not standard equipment and their use indicates some defect in the sewer or in conditions external to the building. (Fig. 4.8)

(*d*) *Backflow Preventers.* Every plumbing fixture is supplied with pure water at one point and discharges contaminated fluids at another. The proximity of sewage to potable water at fixtures is inescapable. It is possible that sewage could accidentally be siphoned into a pipe carrying potable water. Consider a faucet improperly placed with its outlet below the rim of a fixture. If the fixture overflow is plugged and the fixture bowl full,

the faucet can easily project into the foul drainage water. If, in this circumstance, the water piping is drained while the faucet is open, contaminated water could be drawn by suction into the water piping.

In the case of water closets served by flushometers the water supply unavoidably enters the bowl below the rim. A vacuum breaker is placed in the flushometer. It closes with water pressure but opens to admit air if there is suction in the water pipe. This prevents siphonage in much the same way that a vent prevents trap siphonage.

(*e*) *Roof and Floor Drains.* Storm water removal systems and floor drains that usually lead into them are generally separate from sanitary drainage. It is none the less important to exclude foreign matter from the piping. Roof and floor drain fixtures, therefore have several functions. They must be flashed into the watertight roofing or to the similar material of the waterproofing that is frequently found in floors that are flooded with water. The connection from the fixture to the piping must be water tight as is always necessary in fixture-to-piping connections. Finally, it is necessary to provide a type of interception built into the drain fixture in the form of a screen or perforated basket to catch extraneous material that might clog the drain piping. These screens are removable for cleaning. Drains and their component parts are usually made of cast iron or bronze.

References

1. *American Standard National Plumbing Code, ASA A40.8-1955,* The American Society of Mechanical Engineers, United Engineering Center, 345 East 47th Street, New York 17, New York.
2. *Standard Plumbing Details,* Louis J. Day, John Wiley and Sons, 605 Third Avenue, New York 16, New York.
3. *Copper Drainage Tube,* Copper & Brass Research Association, 420 Lexington Avenue, New York 17, New York.
4. Cast Iron Soil Pipe and Fittings, The Cast Iron Soil Pipe Institute, 205 West Wacker Drive, Chicago 6, Illinois.

5

Plumbing Systems

1. Piping and Fittings. Changes in direction of drains and connections of stacks to drains and of branches to stacks should be made with easy bends in order that the flow of sewage is not restricted. The standard plumbing fittings are the T or 90° bend, the Y or 45° bend, the TY, the $\frac{1}{6}$, $\frac{1}{8}$, and $\frac{1}{16}$ bends, and the $\frac{1}{4}$ bend of large radius. T fittings should never be used with pipes carrying sewage but may be used with vent pipes. A change of direction of 90° is made with a Y fitting and a $\frac{1}{8}$ bend, by a TY having a wide sweep or by a $\frac{1}{4}$ bend with a radius at least 4 times the pipe diameter. A satisfactory fitting for 2 branches connecting to a stack at the same level is the crowfoot fitting. When the house drain is larger than the stack the connecting bend should be one size larger than the stack.

Pipes of different sizes are connected in the same line by means of reducer or increaser fittings tapered at 45° between the pipe openings.

The intersections of stacks and roof construction must be carefully flashed to render them watertight. Cast iron pipes are furnished with sheet copper aprons caulked into the hub and turned out on the roof 12 in. on all sides. Flashing on steel pipes is secured by a threaded ferrule which screws down over the pipe and the top of the flashing (Fig. 5.2).

The piping necessary to serve fixtures groups may be visualized as a "flag" form. The mast is the soil stack, the top of the flag is the vent branch, the bottom is the soil or

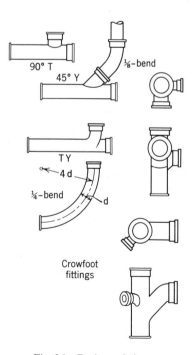

Fig. 5.1 Drainage fittings.

63

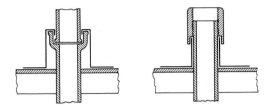

Fig. 5.2   Pipe flashing at roofs.

waste branch and the outer edge is the vertical pipe of the last fixture. In frame construction the flag usually fits into a 6 in. partition. Fixture branches project from the surface of the flag. There is considerable advantage in "back to back" planning of baths and kitchens which allows the piping assembly to pick up the drainage of fixtures on both sides of it.

In Fig. 5.3, because all of the fixtures are nearly on the same level it is unnecessary to have a separate vent stack standing beside the soil stack as in the case of multistory construction. In this illustration and in one-story construction generally, the upper part of the soil stack forms a vent, called a stack vent, to which the branch vents connect. A separate major vertical vent would be called a vent stack.

Fig. 5.3   Drainage and vent piping in a frame residence. This installation in copper "drainage waste and vent tubing" (DWV) serves 2 bathrooms at the upper level behind the 6 in. stud partition and a kitchen sink and laundry tray at the lower level this side of the partition. In the bathrooms the roughing serves, from left to right, a lavatory, water closet and bathtub and a lavatory, shower, and water closet. Bathtub and shower traps can usually be accommodated within the joist depth. The bend below the water closets, however, often leads to a horizontal branch exposed or furred-in below the joists. Some codes permit this branch from a water closet to be 6 to 10 ft long before joining a vent. The water piping is not yet in place. (Copper and Brass Research Association)

Fig. 5.4   An example of plumbing roughing for two lavatory rooms in a fireproof office building. A lavatory and water closet in each room are served by soil and waste branches below and vent branches above. Hot and cold water tubing with air chambers can be seen. The extensions of the water tubing above the 2 flushometer connections appear to connect into the horizontal vent branches but they do not. They are capped and merely touch the bottoms of the vent branches. Note that all soil and waste branches are above the structural slab. A fill of 5 or 6 in. will be necessary to cover the tubing. All vertical tubing will be within the masonry block used to enclose the cubicles. (Copper and Brass Research Association)

If the soil and vent branches do not fall in a single vertical plane as in Fig. 5.3, they usually comprise a series of planes that coincide with the partitions that may enclose several spaces or cubicles as shown in Fig. 5.4. Water piping occupies positions in the same planes.

In most cases the branch soil and waste piping perforates the floor and crosses below the slab to join the stack as seen in Fig. 5.5. Tubing has been developed, however, that sits above the structural slab, obviating the need for hung ceilings below. A lightweight concrete fill is cast to cover the tubing, raising the floor to 5 or 6 in. This can create a raised floor in the toilet room which is not good planning, so the higher floor level is usually carried throughout the floor of the entire story forming a convenient space into which to place electrical conduit at a time later than would have been required if it were placed in the structural slab. This affords some freedom in construction because conduits in the structural slab conflict with reinforcement and furthermore they must be planned and placed earlier.

Fig. 5.5 Vent and soil stacks (center) with copper waste and soil branches below the structural slab in a fireproof building. Horizontal branches join the stack at the 2 outstanding hubs of the double T-Y drainage fitting of the cast iron soil stack. Sheet metal sleeves in the slab create openings for the verticals. Duct opening is for the ventilation of the toilet room on this story. A hung ceiling will be necessary to conceal the branches and the trap. (Copper and Brass Research Association)

Multistory construction, especially in office buildings, needs to be free of random partitions that would interfere with flexibility in the periodic replanning of interior spaces and relocating the dividing partitions. The use of "cores" has become a solution to this problem. Risers of the various services are grouped in planes that coincide with fixed permanent partitions of block masonry. This island of fixed construction is at the central section of the building, releasing the perimital areas for access to daylight. A small hole in the floor for each pipe is often chosen in preference to a slot or shaft. It interferes less with the floor construction, (Fig. 5.6).

Offices often need a single lavatory or an executive's complete toilet room at locations away from the central core of the building. "Wet" columns with a full complement of plumbing pipes make this possible. If the pipes are to center on a column in a steel building, structural coordination must be sought early in the planning if the pipes are to clear the structural framing of the floor. (Fig. 5.7)

2. Flow in Pipes. Water entering a fixture is increased only slightly in bulk by the use of the fixture. The rate of flow out of a fixture is not much greater than the rate of flow into it. It has been seen above that the drainage piping route must be much straighter and more direct than that of water piping because solids are handled in addition to water. For the same reason the size of these pipes also must be considerably larger than those carrying almost the same volume of water to the fixture. Drainage

Fig. 5.6 Risers in a fireproof, multistory building. Pipes, tubes, conduits, and ducts virtually enclose toilet rooms and utility spaces. Ventilation ducts and a master, 5 in. copper hot-water riser are just left of center. Soil and vent stacks with hot and cold water supplies, all of copper, are seen to the right of this group. At the left in lighter tone is the galvanized steel feeder conduit and the distribution circuit-conduits, of the same metal, for a local electrical control panel box. Note that some pipes and tubes are supported at this floor by bolted clamps. After testing and before pipes are enclosed, covering will be completed. (Copper and Brass Research Association)

and soil piping is rated by fixture units in a manner similar to that used for water. One fixture unit represents a flow of about $7\frac{1}{2}$ gpm of wastes or sewage.

3. Pipe Sizes. After fixture units have been assigned to a system and to each of its parts, the sizes of pipe or tubing for drainage and venting may be selected from Tables 5.1, 5.2, 5.3, and 5.4, and other code standards which are based upon the experience of the flow of fluids and gases under actual conditions of operation. Vents are selected on the basis of the number of units of the fixtures that

they vent and must also conform to Sections 11.5.5, 12.21.2, 12.21.3, and 12.21.4 of the National Plumbing Code which are reprinted here.

In presenting Ex. 5.1 in this article, only the essence of the requirements of the National Plumbing Code (174 pages) can be given in this brief treatment. Most of the selection of pipe sizes is guided by Tables 5.1 through 5.4 or by the code sections which follow. Article numbers (11.5.5 etc.) are those of the National Plumbing Code.

11.5.5 *Minimum Size of Stack-Vent or Vent-Stack.* Any structure on which a building drain is installed shall have at least one stack-vent or vent-stack carried full size through the roof not less than 3 in. in diameter or the size of the building drain, whichever is the lesser.

12.21.2 *Size of Individual Vents.* The diameter of an individual vent shall be not less than $1\frac{1}{4}$ in. nor less than one-half the diameter of the drain to which it is connected.

12.21.3 *Size of Relief Vent.* The diameter of a relief vent shall be not less than one-half the diameter of the soil or waste branch to which it is connected.

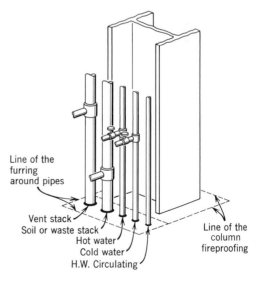

Line of the furring around pipes

Vent stack
Soil or waste stack
Hot water
Cold water
H.W. Circulating

Line of the column fireproofing

Fig. 5.7 Piping at a "wet" column. In large office buildings there are usually several of these, remote from the core, and out in the general office area.

Table 5.1   *Fixture Units per Fixture or Group*

Fixture Type	Fixture-Unit Value as Load Factors		Minimum Size of Trap Inches
1 bathroom group consisting of water closet, lavatory, and bathtub or shower stall	Tank water closet	6	
	Flush-valve water closet	8	
Bathtub* (with or without overhead shower)	2		$1\frac{1}{2}$
Bathtub*			
Bidet	3		2
Combination sink and tray	3	Nominal	$1\frac{1}{2}$
Combination sink and tray with food-disposal unit	4	Separate traps	$1\frac{1}{2}$
Dental unit or cuspidor	1		$1\frac{1}{4}$
Dental lavatory	1		$1\frac{1}{4}$
Drinking fountain	$\frac{1}{2}$		1
Dishwater, domestic	2		$1\frac{1}{2}$
Floor drains	1		2
Kitchen sink, domestic	2		$1\frac{1}{2}$
Kitchen sink, domestic with food waste grinder	3		$1\frac{1}{2}$
Lavatory†	1	Small P.O.‡	$1\frac{1}{4}$
Lavatory†	2	Large P.O.	$1\frac{1}{2}$
Lavatory, barber, beauty parlor	2		$1\frac{1}{2}$
Lavatory, surgeon's	2		$1\frac{1}{2}$
Laundry tray (1 or 2 compartments)	2		$1\frac{1}{2}$
Shower stall, domestic	2		2
Showers (group) per head	3		
Sinks			
Surgeon's	3		$1\frac{1}{2}$
Flushing rim (with valve)	8		3
Service (trap standard)	3		3
Service (P trap)	2		2
Pot, scullery, etc.	4		$1\frac{1}{2}$
Urinal, pedestal, syphon jet, blowout	8	Nominal	3
Urinal, wall lip	4		$1\frac{1}{2}$
Urinal stall, washout	4		2
Urinal trough (each 2-ft section)	2		$1\frac{1}{2}$
Wash sink (circular or multiple) each set of faucets	2	Nominal	$1\frac{1}{2}$
Water closet, tank-operated	4	Nominal	3
Water closet, valve-operated	8		3

* A shower head over a bathtub does not increase the fixture value.

† Lavatories with $1\frac{1}{4}$ or $1\frac{1}{2}$ in. trap have the same load value; larger P.O. plugs have greater flow rate.

‡ P.O. is an abbreviation for pullout, the size of the tailpiece of the fixture.

Extracted from American Standard National Plumbing Code (ASA A40.8–1955), with the permission of the publisher, The American Society of Mechanical Engineers, United Engineering Center 345 East 47th Street, N.Y. 17, N.Y.

12.21.4 *Size of Circuit or Loop Vent.* The diameter of a circuit or loop vent shall be not less than one-half the diameter of the horizontal soil or waste branch or the diameter of the vent stack, whichever is smaller.

4. A Typical Design

EXAMPLE 5.1. Select sizes for drainage and vent piping for the plumbing in an office building for which the fixtures are shown in Fig. 5.8.

SOLUTION. Individual fixture branches shall be not less than the size indicated in Table 5.1 for the minimum size of trap of each fixture. Fixture units are applied to each section of the piping and totaled for each branch and stack and for the building drain and the building sewer. An example of fixture unit summary and sizes of individual branches that connect into a typical branch of the men's toilet group on any floor is as follows:

Fixtures	Units per Fixture	Total Fixture Units	Diameter, Fixture Branch, Inches
1 service sink	3	3	3
3 lavatories	1	3	$1\frac{1}{2}$
3 urinals, washout	4	12	2
3 water closets, valve operated	8	24	3
		42 (Men's Toilet Branch)	

Reference to Table 5.2 indicates that a 3 in. horizontal fixture branch is inadequate for the above because it will handle only 40 fixture units and not more than 2 water closets. A 4 in. pipe is selected. Its capacity of 160 fixture units will be more than enough for the 42 applied to it. The same table shows that the soil stack can be 4 in. in diameter (it is run thus for its entire height). Its capacity of 500 fixture units per story is all right for the 78 that connect in at each T-Y connection. According to Table 5.3, the building drain and the building sewer at their pitch of $\frac{1}{4}$ in. in 1 ft should be 5 in. in diameter. Their capacity of 480 fixture units exceeds the $420\frac{1}{2}$ placed upon them. The circuit vent for the men's toilet group can be $2\frac{1}{2}$ in. in diameter (Table 5.4). In connection with a 4 in. soil stack, not more than 500 fixture units and a vent length of somewhat over 70 ft, it is closest to the $2\frac{1}{2}$ in. vertical column. The vent stack at 70 ft length and $420\frac{1}{2}$ fixture units could be $2\frac{1}{2}$ in., but section 11.5.5 quoted in this article supersedes this and requires 3 in. This is increased to 4 in. as it passes through the roof. Checking with Table 5.5 it is found

that the 4 in. horizontal branch permits 8 water closets and 60 fixture units for a single circuit vent. Since the men's toilet has only 3 water closets and only 42 fixture units, 1 circuit vent is satisfactory. If the allowed values were exceeded but not doubled it would be necessary to have one circuit vent after 8 water closets or 60 fixture units away from the soil stack and then to provide another circuit vent in the usual place just ahead of the last fixture. In the lower stories of tall buildings it is customary to provide a vertical relief vent in the soil branch just before it joins the soil stack, and to connect it to the circuit vent above just before it joins the vent stack. This affords direct relief of gases compressed by descending fluids.

5. Continuous Venting. (Fig. 5.9). A number of cities have codes that require that every fixture be vented separately. The effects of such a regulation are shown in Fig. 5.9 which is an alternate solution to Example 5.1, using continuous venting instead of circuit venting. Some plumbing experts believe that continuous venting, by its multitude of air passages, relieves, at lower stories, the air pressures that develop from downward fluid flow in very tall buildings.

It will be noticed that Fig. 5.9 also includes a building trap and a fresh air inlet for the building drain. There are many arguments for and against the use of these parts. Those in favor of them feel that it is good for the piping in each building to be separately ventilated by fresh air rather than by sewer gases which may sometimes, by their acid reaction, cause corrosion in the piping. Those who are against them claim that it is more sanitary and less odorous to vent public sewers through the roofs of a multitude of buildings rather than have the odors rise through manholes in the street.

6. Plumbing Fixtures. All the advantages of a well-designed plumbing system would be nullified if the fixtures absorbed liquid wastes or possessed either open or concealed roughened areas and projections to catch and hold foul matter. Plumbing fixtures of every kind must, therefore, be

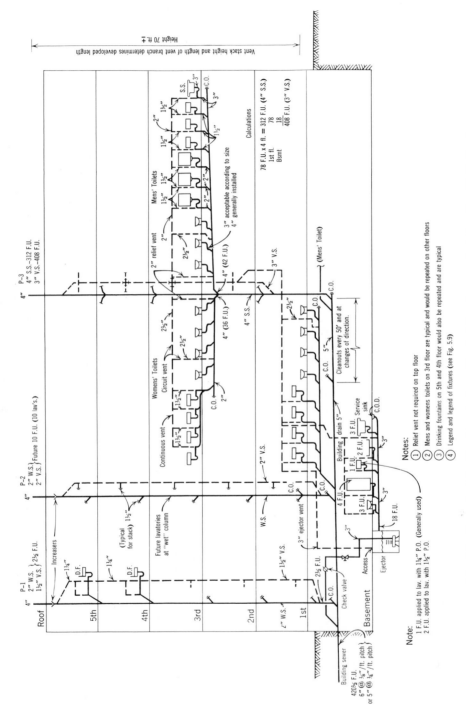

Fig. 5.8 (Example 5.1) Plumbing section, office building, in general conformity with National Plumbing Code. Circuit vents serve branch soil lines. House trap and fresh air inlet are omitted from building drain.

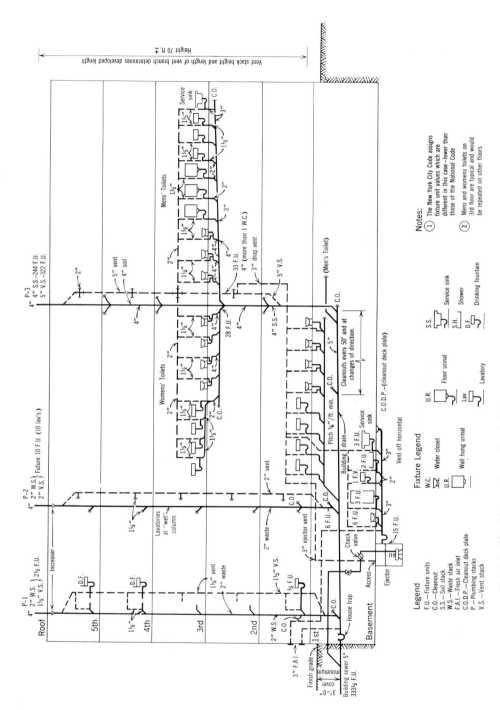

Fig. 5.9 Plumbing section, office building, continuous venting (individual fixture vents) and the use of house trap and fresh air inlet in the house drain. This design is in general conformity with the Code of New York City and the Codes of numerous other large cities.

71

Table 5.2   *Horizontal Soil and Waste Fixture Branches and Stacks*

Maximum Number of Fixture Units that May be Connected to:

Diameter of Pipe (Inches)	Any Horizontal* Fixture Branch	One Stack of 3 Stories in Height or 3 Intervals	More Than 3 Stories in Height	
			Total for Stack	Total at 1 Story or Branch Interval
$1\frac{1}{4}$	1	2	2	1
$1\frac{1}{2}$	3	4	8	2
2	6	10	24	6
$2\frac{1}{2}$	12	20	42	9
3	20†	30‡	60‡	16†
4	160	240	500	90
5	360	540	1,100	200
6	620	960	1,900	350
8	1,400	2,200	3,600	600
10	2,500	3,800	5,600	1,000
12	3,900	6,000	8,400	1,500
15	7,000	—	—	—

*Does not include branches of the building drain.
†Not over 2 water closets.
‡Not over 6 water closets.
Extracted from American Standard National Plumbing Code (ASA A40.8–1955), with the permission of the publisher, The American Society of Mechanical Engineers, 345 East 47th Street, N.Y. 17, N.Y.

made of dense, impervious material with smooth surfaces exposed as far as possible to view. They should be set free from enclosures to give circulation of air and access for cleaning and should be well lighted by either natural or artificial means. Since plumbing fixtures are both the terminals of the water supply and the beginnings of

Table 5.3   *Building Drains and Sewers*

*Maximum Number of Fixture Units That May Be Connected to Any Portion**
of the Building Drain or the Building Sewer

Diameter of Pipe (Inches)	Fall per Foot			
	$\frac{1}{16}$ *Inch*	$\frac{1}{8}$ *Inch*	$\frac{1}{4}$ *Inch*	$\frac{1}{2}$ *Inch*
2			21	26
$2\frac{1}{2}$			24	31
3		20†	27†	36†
4		180	216	250
5		390	480	575
6		700	840	1,000
8	1,400	1,600	1,920	2,300
10	1,500	2,900	3,500	4,200
12	3,900	4,600	5,600	6,700
15	7,000	8,300	10,000	12,000

*Includes branches of the building drain
†Not over 2 water closets.
Extracted from American Standard National Plumbing Code (ASA A40.8–1955), with the permission of the publisher, The American Society of Mechanical Engineers, 345 East 47th Street, N.Y. 17, N.Y.

Table 5.4 *Size and Length of Vents*

Size of Soil or Waste Stack (Inches)	Fixture Units Connected	Diameter of Vent Required (Inches)								
		1¼	1½	2	2½	3	4	5	6	8
		Maximum Length of Vent (Feet)								
1¼	2	30								
1½	8	50	150							
1½	10	30	100							
2	12	30	75	200						
2	20	26	50	150						
2½	42	..	30	100	300					
3	10	..	30	100	200	600				
3	30	..	...	60	200	500				
3	60	..	...	50	80	400				
4	100	..	...	35	100	260	1000			
4	200	..	...	30	90	250	900			
4	500	..	...	20	70	180	700			
5	200	..	...	...	35	80	350	1000		
5	500	..	...	...	30	70	300	900		
5	1100	..	...	...	20	50	200	700		
6	350	..	...	...	25	50	200	400	1300	
6	620	..	...	...	15	30	125	300	1100	
6	960	..	...	...	...	24	100	250	1000	
6	1900	..	...	...	...	20	70	200	700	
8	600	..	...	...	...	...	50	150	500	1300
8	1400	..	...	...	...	...	40	100	400	1200
8	2200	..	...	...	...	...	30	80	350	1100
8	3600	..	...	...	...	...	25	60	250	800
10	1000	..	...	...	...	...	....	75	125	1000
10	2500	..	...	...	...	...	....	50	100	500
10	3800	..	...	...	...	...	....	30	80	350
10	5600	..	...	...	...	...	....	25	60	250

Extracted from American Standard National Plumbing Code (ASA A40.8–1955), with the permission of the publisher, The American Society of Mechanical Engineers, 345 East 47th Street, N.Y. 17, N.Y.

the sewage systems they control to a large extent both the quantity of water which must be furnished and the amount of sewage which must be cared for by stacks, drains, sewers, ejectors, and pumps. Economy and efficiency, then, require a careful study of the number and disposition of the fixtures, their selection, and the standardization of their design. They should always be chosen from samples in the show rooms, not from catalogues. (See Figs. 5.11 and 5.12.)

Fixtures may be divided into classes according to their use as follows:

(a) Water closets
(b) Urinals
(c) Lavatories
(d) Bath tubs
(e) Shower sinks
(f) Kitchen sinks
(g) Pantry sinks
(h) Laundray trays
(i) Slop (Service) sinks

(a) **Water Closets** should be made of solid vetrified china not subject to crazing of the glaze, with the trap cast integrally with the bowl and rim. The passage through the trap to the outlet is at least 2½ in. and often 3 in. in diameter. The portion of the bowl containing water should be wide and comparatively shallow and the portion not

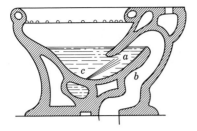

Fig. 5.10   Siphon-jet water closet.

covered by water reduced to a minimum. The flow of water or flush should be vigorous with a strong scouring action and expelling force. In the flush-tank closet the water is supplied from a 4 to 7 gal tank placed somewhat above the bowl; in the flushometer closet the water enters the bowl directly from the supply piping. The flush-valve equipment is somewhat less expensive than that of the flush tank but necessitates a branch water connection of $1\frac{1}{4}$ in., a flush tank requiring only a $\frac{1}{2}$ in. branch. Flush valves are consequently seldom used in residences and small buildings but more often in large buildings equipped with a house tank. Closets are 14 to 15 in. high, 14 in. wide, and project 24 to 30 in. from the wall.

The most effective type of water closet is the siphon-jet, as illustrated in Fig. 5.10, consisting of a bowl encircled at the top with a hollow rolled flushing rim. Water enters the rim and flows down the sides of the bowl through a series of small outlets in the rim, scouring the inner surface of the fixture. The trap has the shape of a siphon, (*a*) being the short leg and (*b*) the long leg. The water from the flushing rim fills the bowl until it flows through the trap and siphonic action begins, assisted in quick and vigorous operation by the water jet at (*c*). The siphonic action draws the contents of the bowl and some foul air through the trap and cleans the fixture without undue noise. The bowl is then refilled by the afterwash from the tank. The supply to the tank is controlled by a float which closes a valve on the inlet pipe when the tank is full. The

opening of the outlet valve admits water to the flushing pipe connecting the tank with the bowl, thereby starting siphonic action in the tank and a vigorous discharge into the fixture. The flush pipe's diameter should be at least $1\frac{1}{4}$ in.

(*b*) *Urinals* should likewise be made of vitreous china in one piece without joints, and all exposed surfaces should be thoroughly flushed. There are three types of urinals, the wall type, the stall, and the pedestal. The wall type is hung to the wall and is generally unsanitary. The stall type stands on the floor and is $3\frac{1}{2}$ ft high. When completely washed by each flush it represents a most satisfactory and sanitary fixture.

The pedestal type is also satisfactory and sanitary and consists of a bowl 14 in. wide by 25 in. deep, standing 20 to 21 in. high upon a vitreous china pedestal.

(*c*) *Lavatories* may be of vitreous china or enameled iron, the latter being often employed because it is less costly and is sufficiently durable for the usage ordinarily received. They may be hung on the wall by special hangers, supported on the floor by an enameled pedestal, or rest on one or two metal or enamel front legs and be braced to the wall at the back.

Lavatories stand 30 to 32 in. high and are 18 by 20 in; 20 by 24 in; or 22 by 36 in. for the hung and legged types and 20 by 24 in. or 22 by 27 in. for the pedestal type.

(*d*) *Bath Tubs* are generally made of enameled cast iron since their usage is not severe and their size is too great for the firing of earthenware. Built-in tubs rest on the floor and are built into the wall at the back and at one or both ends. They are consequently very sanitary. Bath tubs are 30 and 36 in. wide and from 4 to 6 ft long, the 5 and $5\frac{1}{2}$ ft lengths being generally preferred.

(*e*) *Shower Baths* consist of an overhead spray nozzle which discharges water down upon the bather in a fine rain, the nozzle or shower head being made of chrome or nickel-plated brass and perforated with

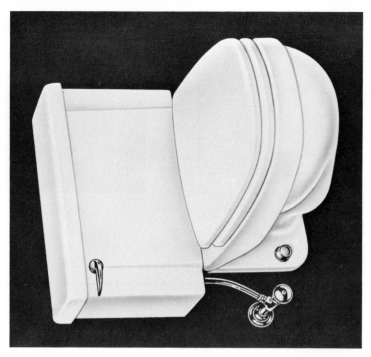

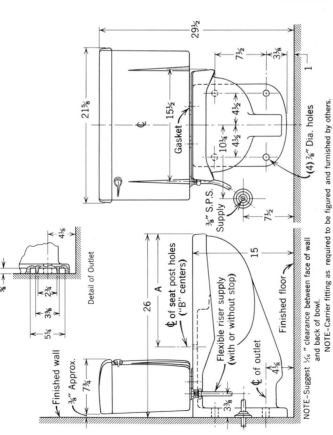

Fig. 5.11 Manufacturer's roughing dimensions and an illustration of a wall hung, tank-type water closet using the principle of the siphon jet shown in Fig. 5.10. (American Standard)

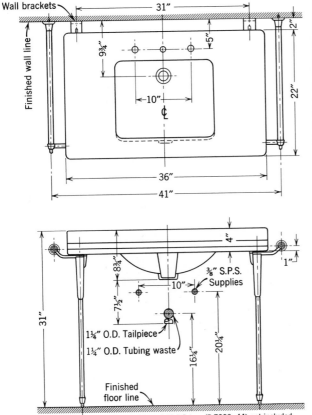

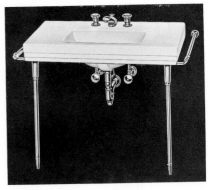

Fig. 5.12   Manufacturer's roughing dimensions and an illustration of a vitreous china lavatory. (American Standard)

NOTE: ⅜″ supply pipes (R 2604) and 1¼″ P trap (R 7000-44) not included in lavatory combination and must be ordered seperately.

PLUMBER NOTE—Provide suitable reinforcement for all wall supports. These roughing measurements may vary 1¼″ (plus or minus) and are for this job only.

fine holes. The shower heads may be placed over a bath tub or over special watertight, 36 by 36 by $3\frac{3}{4}$ in., porcelain enamel receptors set flush with the floor and connected to the draining system. The position of the bather is surrounded by a curtain or glass to confine the water to the tub or the receptor. Showers are also placed in stalls with marble, tile, cement, or slate walls and floor.

(*f*) **Kitchen Sinks** are sometimes made of enameled cast iron which is now so perfected that the enamel withstands ordinary hard usage and the action of fruit and vegetable acids. However, the enamel may be chipped by an unusually severe blow. Sinks of Monel metal, $\frac{1}{3}$ copper and $\frac{2}{3}$ nickel, and of chrome-nickel stainless steel are also available. The bowls are drawn from one piece of sheet metal, and the backs, drainboards, and aprons are welded to the bowl with invisible joints. The sizes of sinks run from 16 in. sq. to 25 in. wide by 74 in. long.

Table 5.5   Limits for Circuit and Loop Venting

(1) Diameter of Horizontal Branch (in.)	(2) Water Closets and Pedestal Urinals (Number)	(3) Fixture Units for Fixtures other than Those in Column 2 (Number)
2	None	6
3	2	20
4	8	60
5	16	120
6	24	180

Table 5.6 Size of Vertical Leaders

Size of Leader or Conductor* (Inches)	Maximum Projected Roof Area (Square Feet)
2	720
$2\frac{1}{2}$	1300
3	2200
4	4600
5	8650
6	13500
8	29000

* The equivalent diameter of square or rectangular leader may be taken as the diameter of that circle which may be inscribed within the cross-sectional area of the leader. Extracted from American Standard National Plumbing Code (ASA A40.8–1955), with the permission of the publisher, The American Society of Mechanical Engineers, 345 East 47th Street, N.Y. 17, N.Y.

Table 5.7 Size of Horizontal Storm Drains

Diameter of Drain	Maximum Projected Roof Area for Drains of Various Slopes		
Inches	$\frac{1}{8}$-in. Slope	$\frac{1}{4}$-in. Slope	$\frac{1}{2}$-in. Slope
	sq ft	sq ft	sq ft
3	822	1160	1644
4	1880	2650	3760
5	3340	4720	6680
6	5350	7550	10700
8	11500	16300	23000
10	20700	29200	41400
12	33300	47000	66600
15	59500	84000	119000

Extracted from American Standard National Plumbing Code (ASA A40.8–1955), with the permission of the publisher, The American Society of Mechanical Engineers, 345 East 47th Street, N.Y. 17, N.Y.

(g) *Pantry Sinks* are similar in type to kitchen sinks and are made of the same materials but are of smaller dimensions. Electric dishwashing machines are sometimes combined with sinks, being placed on one side of the bowl.

(h) *Laundry Trays* are made of enameled cast-iron, vitreous earthenware, alberene or soapstone, and slate. Slate and alberene are open to the objection that the several slabs must be joined together and the joints are likely to catch grease and dirt. Vitreous earthenware is expensive; enameled cast iron appears to be the most practical material. The usual sizes measure from 23 to 27 in. sq. and 14 in. deep for each tray. They are often in combinations, 2 or 3 trays being set side by side, and are also joined with the kitchen sink.

(i) *Service Sinks* may be made of enameled cast iron when used in residences where they are not exposed to very hard usage, but for office buildings, hotels, and hospitals the material should be vitreous china. They range in size from 18 by 22 in.

Table 5.8 Size of Semicircular Gutters

Diameter of Gutter*	Maximum Projected Roof Area for Gutters of Various Slopes			
Inches	$\frac{1}{16}$-in. Slope	$\frac{1}{8}$-in. Slope	$\frac{1}{4}$-in. Slope	$\frac{1}{2}$-in. Slope
	Square Feet	Square Feet	Square Feet	Square Feet
3	170	240	340	480
4	360	510	720	1020
5	625	880	1250	1770
6	960	1360	1920	2770
7	1380	1950	2760	3900
8	1990	2800	3980	5600
10	3600	5100	7200	10000

* Gutters other than semicircular may be used provided they have an equivalent cross-sectional area. Extracted from American Standard National Plumbing Code (ASA A40.8–1955), with the permission of the publisher, The American Society of Mechanical Engineers, 345 East 47th Street, N.Y. 17, N.Y.

Table 5.9 Minimum Facilities

Type of Building or Occupancy	Water Closets		Urinals	Lavatories		Bathtubs or Showers	Drinking Fountains*
Dwelling or apt. house†	1 for each dwelling or apartment unit		—	1 for each apartment or dwelling unit		1 for each apartment or dwelling unit	
Schools:							
Elementary	1 per 100		1 per 35 males	1 per 60 persons			1 per 75 persons
Secondary	1 per 100		1 per 30 males	1 per 100 persons			1 per 75 persons
	Male *Female*						
	1 per 100 1 per 35						
	1 per 100 1 per 45						
Office or Public buildings	*No. of Persons* / *No. of Fixtures*		Wherever urinals are provided for men, one water closet less than the number specified may be provided for each urinal installed except that the number of water closets in such cases shall not be reduced to less than $\frac{2}{3}$ of the minimum specified.	*No. of Persons* / *No. of Fixtures*			1 per 75 persons
	1–15 — 1			1–15 — 1			
	16–35 — 2			16–35 — 2			
	36–55 — 3			36–60 — 3			
	56–80 — 4			61–90 — 4			
	81–110 — 5			91–125 — 5			
	111–150 — 6			1 fixture for each 45 additional persons			
	1 fixture for each 40 additional persons						
Manufacturing, Warehouses, workshops, loft buildings, foundries and similar establishments	*No. of Persons*		Same substitution as above	1–1000 persons, 1 fixture for each 10 persons.		1 shower for each 15 persons exposed to excessive heat or to skin contamination with poisonous, infectious, or irritating material	1 per 75 persons
	1–9			Over 100, 1 for each 15 persons			
	10–24						
	25–49						
	50–74						
	75–100						
	1 fixture for each additional 30 employees						

78

Type of building	Water closets	Urinals	Lavatories	Bathtubs or showers	Drinking fountains
Dormitories‡	Male: 1 for each 10 persons Female: 1 for each 8 persons Over 10 persons, add 1 fixture for each 25 additional males and 1 for each 20 additional females	1 for each 25 men Over 150 persons, add 1 fixture for each additional 50 men	1 for each 12 persons. (Separate dental lavatories should be provided in community toilet rooms. Ratio of dental lavatories for each 50 persons is recommended.) Add 1 lavatory for each 20 males, 1 for each 15 females.	1 for each 8 persons. In the case of women's dormitories, additional bathtubs should be installed at the ratio of 1 for each 30 females. Over 150 persons, add 1 fixture for each 20 persons.	1 per 75 persons
Theatres, auditoriums	*No. of Persons* — *No. of Fixtures* M F 1–100 1 1 101–200 2 2 201–400 3 3 Over 400, add 1 fixture for each additional 500 males and 1 for each 300 females.	*No. of Persons* — *No. of Fixtures* (Male) 1–200 1 201–400 2 401–600 3 Over 600; 1 for each additional 500 males	*No. of Persons* 1–200 201–400 401–750 Over 750, 1 for each additional 500 persons		1 per 100 persons

* Drinking fountains shall not be installed in toilet rooms.

† Laundry trays—one single compartment tray for each dwelling unit or 2 compartment trays for each 10 apartments. Kitchen sinks—1 for each dwelling or apartment unit.

‡ Laundry trays, 1 for each 50 persons. Slop sinks, 1 for each 100 persons.

Extracted from American Standard National Plumbing Code (ASA A40.8–1955), with the permission of the publisher, The American Society of Mechanical Engineers, 345 East 47th Street, N.Y. 17, N.Y.

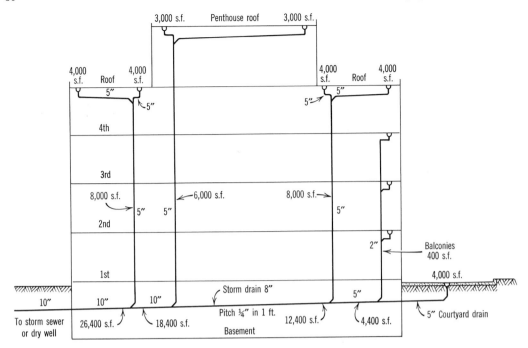

Fig. 5.13 Separate storm drainage. Areas drained and corresponding sizes of vertical leaders and horizontal drains from Tables 5.6 and 5.7.

to 20 by 24 in; are 14 in. high, and are set 26 to 28 in. above the floor.

7. Storm Drainage. If the rainwater that collects on roofs were not led away through a piping system, it would overflow and cause leaks in walls, annoy people, undermine foundations, and erode the soil. It is necessary to drain all flat and sloping roofs and all balconies and courtyards. Every effort is made to keep the storm drainage separate from the sanitary drainage. Combining them increases the bulk of the fluids and complicates the purification problem in municipal and private sewage treatment installations. Storm water is generally led off to rivers or disposed of in dry wells on one's own property. Each owner of a building has an obligation to prevent heavy runoff of water onto an adjacent property. Occasionally combined sanitary and storm sewers exist. Within the building the systems should be kept separate and preferably join at the building drain below the last plumbing fixture. In these combined

systems, all storm piping must be trapped, but traps are not needed in separate storm drainage systems.

In small systems (see Fig. 4.1), when a rain leader is occasionally introduced into the sanitary system if permitted, it is trapped and its effect evaluated on the basis of 3.9 sq ft of roof area counting as 1 fixture unit. Tables 5.6, 5.7, and 5.8 are based upon an average of 4 in. of rainfall per hr. In a few locations the rainfall can be almost twice this and in others much less. For extreme cases, an adjustment will have to be made.

8. Planning. Buildings must be planned with sufficient plumbing fixtures for the expected population. Records may be found that will afford units such as sq ft of building area per person for various kinds of occupancy. These and conferences with the owner can establish probable occupancy. Based upon this, the minimum number of fixtures may be selected from Table 5.9. It should be borne in mind that often more fixtures are needed than appear as minimum requirements.

9. Testing. Drainage piping is tested by filling it with water after plugging all openings. With not less than 10 ft of head above any joint, it must be shown that there are no leaks. There is also an air test which consists of maintaining not less than 5 psi for a period of 15 min. without loss of pressure through leaks. Water-supply piping must be tested to a pressure not less than the expected working pressure.

References

1. *American Standard National Plumbing Code, ASA A40.8–1955*, The American Society of Mechanical Engineers, 345 East 47th Street, New York 17, New York.
2. *Domestic Engineering Catalog Directory*, Domestic Engineering Company, 1801 Prairie Avenue, Chicago 16, Illinois.

6

Sewage Disposal

1. Effects of Population Growth. In Chapter 5 the proximity of potable water at the water connection of a plumbing fixture and the polluted water leaving the fixture was discussed. Preserving the purity of the water at the faucet by means of devices such as air gaps and vacuum breakers is a relatively simple matter. The situation at the other ends of these circuits, namely the sources of water supply (wells, rivers, lakes) and their possible contamination by sewage disposal presents a greater problem. It is one of increasing complexity.

Looking back at the facilities of dispersed living at the beginning of this century, one finds an easy and safe separation of water sources and sewage disposal. Open, dug wells on high ground were usually safe from the contaminating effects of the open pit privy some distance away and at a lower level. Garbage was fed to the animals or placed in compost piles for garden fertilization.

In 1900 the dangers to health brought about by close urban living affected only about one third of the population, (see Fig. 6.1a). By 1960 three quarters of the national population resided in urban communities. The preservation of the purity of water sources was then recognized as a matter of national concern, and the purification of sewage by treatment was found to be increasingly necessary to protect health and to avoid possible contamination of water supplies.

Between 1920 and 1960 the industrial waste problem increased greatly. Industrial production tripled in volume during that period and increased greatly in chemical complexity, (See Fig. 6.1b). Indiscriminate discharge of fluid industrial wastes into natural watercourses had reached startling proportions when correction of this abuse began.

The combined pollution effect of sewage and industrial wastes on the purity of water was brought to national attention by the President of the United States in his Message to Congress of February 23, 1961, when he said, "Pollution of our country's rivers and streams has, as a result of our rapid population and industrial growth and change, reached alarming proportions." Far-seeing legislators and technical experts have been conscious of the problem for many years and have laid the groundwork for its solution. The Federal Water Pollution Control Act (Law 845) of 1948 pledged federal support to those who would aid in improving the situation. The year 1928 saw the formation of the Water Pollution Control Federation. Other organizations are

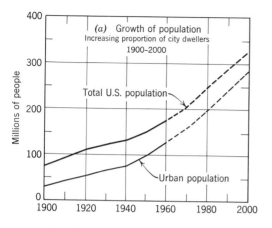

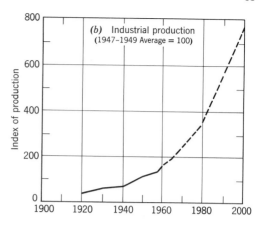

Fig. 6.1 Population increase and industrial growth in the United States during the 20th century. (Reprinted from "Clean Water, A Report to the Nation," the National Technical Task Committee on Industrial Wastes.)

at work, including the National Water Institute, and the National Technical Task Committee on Industrial Wastes.

Naturally, with these movements afoot, the control of sewage treatment as well as water conservation and protection has passed into the hands of large governmental and public organizations. Private septic tanks are generally not permitted when public sewers are available and the less efficient cesspool is fast disappearing. In many communities, general sewage problems and those of industrial wastes are solved by joint treatment plants (See Fig. 6.2). In spite of all this, the population growth is so great that municipal sewage collection and treatment systems cannot keep pace with it. Currently more than half a million private, relatively small, disposal systems are built annually where sewers do not yet exist. It is good practice to locate them on the side of the building that faces the future location of the sewer that will eventually replace them.

Early in the century, most large cities began the design and construction of sewage treatment works and now treat a large part of urban sewage. New York City, for instance, treats about 60 percent of its sewage, the balance finding its way to private disposal or to the surrounding water-ways. The New York City water supply comes, of course, from relatively pure upstate lakes, but for cities that use river water (with treatment) as potable supplies, the danger of dumping sewage close to the location of the water source is obvious. Many cities still face decades of effort before the problem is fully solved.

2. Municipal Sewage Treatment. An example of large-volume public sewage treatment is the Ward's Island Sewage Treatment Works in New York City (See Fig. 6.3). Handling over two hundred million gallons per day, it serves large parts of two city boroughs, Manhattan and the Bronx. Along the shorelines, "intercepting" sewers were built to head off the multitude of street sewers previously emptying into the waters surrounding the city. They lead the sewage through deep under-river tunnels to the island plant.

Only two tenths of 1 percent of sewage is solid material. Sewage, therefore, represents the rate of daily water supply with only a small amount of impure solid material that pollutes the whole. This is a clear reason for separate handling of storm water for dispersal to the ground or to waterways rather than permitting it to swell the volume of sewage requiring treatment.

Ward's Island uses the activated sludge

Table 6.1 A Partial List of Industries and a Tabulation of Techniques and Methods Being Applied in Industrial Water Quality Management Programs for Clean Water

• Indicates Use

Industries*	Pre-Treatment					Waste Treatment — Physical						Waste Treatment — Chemical					Waste Treatment — Biological					Special	Effluent Disposal						
	Waste Reduction	Water Reuse	Process Changes	By-Products	Other	Strainer-Comminution	Sedimentation	Flotation	Filtration	Heat Transfer	Other	Coagulation	Oxidation-Reduction	Chemical Reaction	pH Adjustment	Other	Biological Filtration	Aeration-Activated Sludge	Oxidation Ponds	Digestion	Other	Special	Dilution	Impoundment-Lagoons	Irrigation	Underground	Evaporation	Combustion	Other
Atomic	•	•	•		•		•		•	•	•	•	•	•	•	•	•	•				•	•	•		•	•	•	•
Automotive	•	•	•		•	•	•	•	•	•	•	•	•	•	•	•						•	•	•			•	•	
Beet Sugar	•		•	•	•	•	•	•	•			•						•					•	•	•		•		
Cane Sugar	•		•	•	•	•	•	•	•			•						•	•				•	•	•		•		
Canning	•	•	•	•	•	•	•	•	•			•			•		•	•	•	•		•	•	•	•		•		
Chemical Manufacturing	•	•	•	•	•		•		•	•	•	•	•	•	•	•	•	•	•	•	•	•	•	•	•	•	•	•	•
Coal	•		•		•							•	•	•	•								•	•					•
Coke	•	•	•		•					•	•	•	•	•	•	•	•	•					•	•			•	•	•
Corn	•		•		•	•	•	•	•		•						•		•	•	•		•	•					•

* The above are a few of the many industries that treat their industrial wastes to make water "clean" before returning it to nature. Extracted from "Clean Water, A Report to the Nation," the National Technical Task Committee on Industrial Wastes.

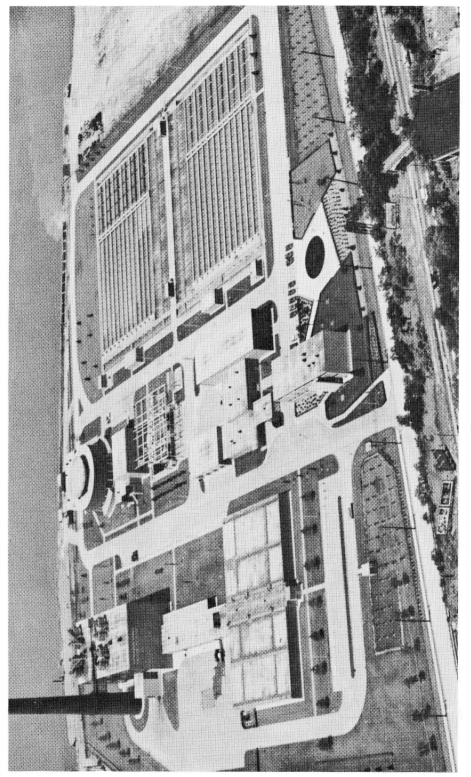

Fig. 6.2 Pittsburgh treatment plant. 68 communities and over 100 manufacturers jointly solve their waste disposal problems with this treatment plant. It is a part of a $100 million program in Allegheny County, Pennsylvania, designed to handle a flow of 150 million gallons of waste water daily. The joint disposal of wastes from communities and industry is becoming a national trend. (Reprinted from "Clean Water, A Report to the Nation," The National Technical Task Committee on Industrial Wastes.)

85

Fig. 6.3 Sewage treatment works, Ward's Island, New York City. Activated sludge process. *A* Manhattan grit chamber. *B* Manhattan ewage tunnel. *C* Bronx sewage tunnel. *D* Laboratory and Administration. *E* Power plant. *F* Pump and blower building. *G* Preliminary setling chambers. *H* Aeration chambers. *I* Final settling chambers. *J* Sludge storage building. *K* and *L* Pure water discharge. *M* Dock for sludge boats.

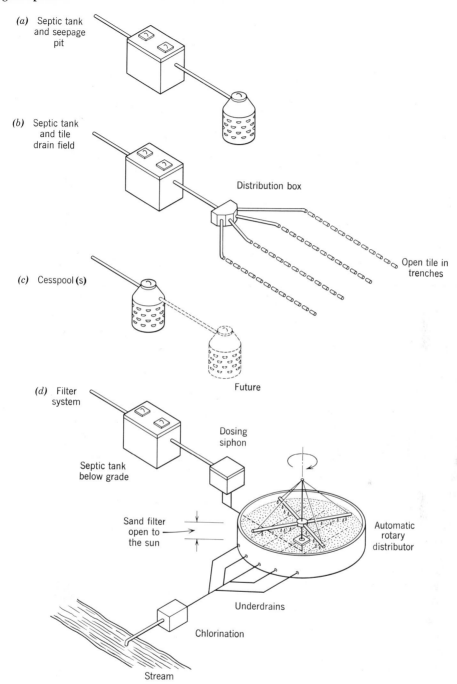

(a) Septic tank and seepage pit

(b) Septic tank and tile drain field

Distribution box

Open tile in trenches

(c) Cesspool (s)

Future

(d) Filter system

Dosing siphon

Septic tank below grade

Sand filter open to the sun

Automatic rotary distributor

Underdrains

Chlorination

Stream

Fig. 6.4 Private sewage disposal systems.

process, one of the more efficient of treatment methods. Grit settles out at chambers in Manhattan and the Bronx. Together with other intercepted solids such as pieces of wood it is trucked to outlying marshy districts where it is dumped as "garbage fill" along with garbage from other sources. Other heavy solids drop during an hour's pause of the sewage in the preliminary settling tanks. The remaining highly polluted fluid flows through the aeration tanks for a 3-hour trip in the presence of a biologically active culture. As a result of bacterial action, accelerated by air pumped in along the way, digestion takes place and the fluid can be made 95 percent pure before it is discharged at two points to the river. The resulting floc, digested and much purified, is collected in the final settling tanks. Then, together with the solids from the preliminary settling tanks, it is pumped to barges and shipped to a distant point at sea where it is discharged and dropped to the ocean floor.

3. Private Sewage Disposal Systems. When connection to a city sewer is not feasible, consideration should be given to the creation by administrative authority of a community sewer and a regional sewer treatment plant to serve it. The third possibility is an individual private sewage disposal system for a single house or building. Its type and size will depend upon the number of people served, the permeability of the soil, the elevation of the groundwater level (water table), the size of the lot and the proximity of wells which might be vulnerable to

pollution by the products of the disposal system. The installation should be designed to handle all sanitary drainage, including laundry wastes. Roof and area drainage should be disposed of separately in dry wells.

Reference to Table 6.2 indicates that if there is a shallow well on the property, its suction line could be a source of danger because any leak or opening in this pipe could be a path through which particles of sewage could be drawn into the drinking water system. It is often difficult to fit a disposal system on a small lot and the necessary requirements of spacing established in Table 6.2 increase this difficulty. A disposal field or seepage pit must be 100 ft from a well or its suction line and a cesspool, if permitted, must keep a greater distance (150 ft) from these elements of the potable water system. The use of city water from a pressure pipe reduces the distances, but other factors may increase them. For instance, if a seepage pit is impractical because low permeability of the soil and a tile disposal field is required, its greater area may crowd the lot. This is further complicated by the fact that drain fields should not be located below driveways or

Table 6.2   Location of Components of Sewage-Disposal System

			Distance (in ft)				
Type of System	Well or Suction Line	Water Supply Line Pressure	Stream	Dwelling	Property Line	Disposal Field	Seepage Pits
Building sewer	50	10	....	....	....	....	....
Septic tank	50	....	....	....	....	....	....
Distribution box	50	....	....	....	....	....	....
Disposal field*	100	....	25	10	10	....	....
Seepage pit	100	....	50	20	10	20	20
Dry well	50	....	....	....	....	....	....
Cesspool†	150	....	50	20	15	15	15

*This separation may be reduced to 50 ft when the well is provided with an outside watertight casing to a depth of 50 ft or more.

†Not recommended as a substitute for a septic tank. To be used only when approved by the Administrative Authority.

Extracted from American Standard National Plumbing Code (ASA A40.8–1955), with the permission of the publisher, The American Society of Mechanical Engineers, 345 East 47th Street, N.Y. 17, N.Y.

Table 6.3   Minimum Capacities for Septic Tanks Serving an Individual Dwelling

Number of Bedrooms	Nominal Liquid Capacity of Tank	Maximum Number of Persons Served	Recommended Inside Dimensions							
			Length		Width		Liquid Depth		Total Depth	
	Gallons	Persons	ft	in.	ft	in.	ft	in.	ft	in.
2 or less	500	4	6	0	3	0	4	0	5	0
3	600	6	7	0	3	0	4	0	5	0
4	750	8	7	6	3	6	4	0	5	0
5	900	10	8	6	3	6	4	6	5	6
6	1,100	12	8	6	4	0	4	6	5	6
7	1,300	14	10	0	4	0	4	6	5	6
8	1,500	16	10	0	4	6	4	6	5	6

NOTE: Liquid capacity is based on number of bedrooms in dwelling. Total volume in cubic feet includes air space above liquid level.

Extracted from American Standard National Plumbing Code (ASA A40.8–1955), with the permission of the publisher, The American Society of Mechanical Engineers, 345 East 47th Street, N.Y. 17, N.Y.

areas of heavy planting. Roots often find their way into the tiles, clogging them.

It is fortunate when soil of high absorptive value is encountered together with a low water table. The septic tank then may discharge its effluent (partially purified fluids) to one or more seepage pits (see Figs. 6.4*a* and 6.5). The pits are compact in area but not very shallow and they must not perforate the water table lest they discharge harmful bacteria directly to the ground water.

Least desirable and seldom permitted is the cesspool. This is identical in construction to the seepage pit, but sewage is emptied directly into it without the benefit of digestive purification in the septic tank. The soil adjacent to its openings quickly becomes contaminated and the apertures of the masonry and of the earth become clogged. Secondary cesspools are often added later, in which case the first one takes on part of the character of a septic tank but without its tightness which assures sanitation.

Occasionally, in rural locations near streams the ground is too marshy to allow tile drains and the filter method is used. The septic tank effluent is filtered through sand open to the purifying effects of the sun. A siphon dosing chamber discharges the effluent in large doses and it turns the automatic rotary as in drops on to the sand. Below the filter bed, underdrains collect the filtered and additionally purified effluent and lead it to a chlorinator before it is run off or pumped into the stream. Since it does not depend upon final dispersal to the ground, this system is also appropriate when very impervious clay is encountered. Health authorities exercise strict supervision over this kind of process which connects directly with natural waterways.

4. The Septic Tank and Seepage Pit. Private sewage treatment is necessarily very different from municipal or community arrangements. There is no possibility of settling out heavy, putrescent solids and disposing of them at sea. Aeration of the effluent in the open air is also impractical. Except for the filter system, which is not used in congested locations, the cycle must be completed below ground and within the property, with only infrequent removal of digested sludge from the septic tank. The septic tank holds approximately one day's yield of sewage. Tees prevent floating solids from passing through the tank. The

*Table 6.4   Requirements for Seepage—
Pit Design*

Soil Structure:	Effective Absorption Area Required per Bedroom* (Square Feet)
Coarse sand and gravel	20
Fine sand	30
Sandy loam or sand clay	50
Clay with considerable sand and gravel	80
Clay with small amount of sand and gravel	160

* In calculating absorption wall area of pit, gross diameter of pit excavation shall be used.

Extracted from American Standard National Plumbing Code (ASA A40.8–1955), with the permission of the publisher, The American Society of Mechanical Engineers, 345 East 47th Street, N.Y. 17, N.Y.

activity of anaerobic (active without air) bacteria digests the solids to a compact sludge. So small is the volume of this sludge that it needs to be pumped out only after several years. The liquid effluent, about 70 percent purified, then passes to the soil of the seepage pit where other bacteria below the vegetation complete the process. Very little solid matter passes to the seepage pit. The digestion is entirely biological. Chemicals would only retard the septic tank process. Chemicals, of course, are used in the final stage of the filter system where the residual bacteria must be destroyed before they reach the stream.

EXAMPLE 6.1 (Fig. 6.5). Design a septic tank and seepage pit system for a suburban residence under the following conditions.

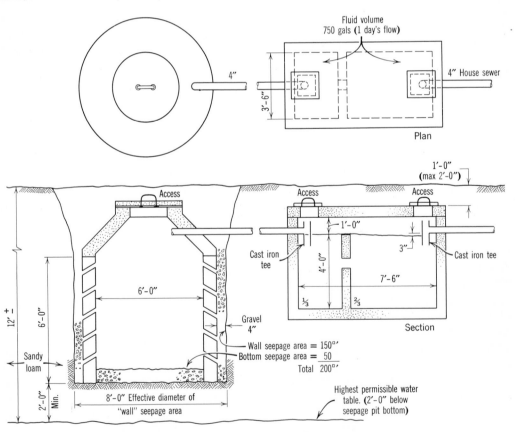

Fig. 6.5   (Example 6.1)   Plan and section of septic tank and seepage pit for 4-bedroom house. Pit is suitable when the earth is absorbent and the water table low (below pit-bottom).

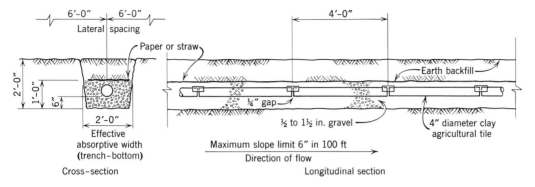

Fig. 6.6 (Example 6.2) Typical details, tile drain for drain field.

Bedrooms 4
Occupants 8
Soil structure—sandy loam
Water table depth—minus 12 ft

SOLUTION. From Table 6.3 a septic tank of 750 gallons liquid capacity is chosen and the dimensions established. In accordance with recommendations of the National Plumbing Code the primary chamber is two-thirds of the total tank volume. The seepage pit (a bucket-shaped depression in the earth), is "lined" with porous masonry. Table 6.4 calls for the seepage pit area to be 50 sq ft for each bedroom. Eight feet of effective earth diameter and 6 ft of depth provides the required 200 sq ft since this is the combined area of the cylindrical wall and the circular bottom. Access is provided to all fluid chambers.

5. Tile Drain Field. In some regions, especially near the coastline and major bodies of water, the water table is quite high. Example 6.1 (Fig. 6.5) indicates that when the water table is closer than 12 ft to the surface, it becomes difficult to fit seepage pits into the relatively thin layer of available dry earth above the water table. In this case a tile drain field solves the problem. Before designing it, tests are made to determine how long it takes for water in a test pit at the proposed level of the disposal field to drop 1 in. Table 6.5 lists the effective absorption area per bedroom required for various degrees of earth permeability as

measured by the test. For certain non-absorptive soils, even if seepage pit depth were available, if is necessary to make the choice of a tile drain disposal field because the number and size of seepage pits would be too great. Some sanitarians are of the opinion that for fall-rates of more than 6 min per in. of fall in test pits, tile drain fields are more appropriate and economical than seepage pits. Drains of square-edge agricultural tile, 4 in. or more in diam and

Table 6.5 Absorption Areas for Individual Residences

Time Required for Water to Fall 1 Inch (Minutes)	Effective Absorption Area Required in Bottom of Disposal Trenches (Square Feet per Bedroom)
2 or less	50
3	60
4	70
5	80
10	100
15	130
30	180
60	240
Over 60	*

* Special design.
NOTE: A minimum of 150 sq ft should be provided for each dwelling unit.
Extracted from American Standard National Plumbing Code (ASA A40.8–1955), with the permission of the publisher, The American Society of Mechanical Engineers, 345 East 47th Street, N.Y. 17, N.Y.

Table 6.6   Minimum Standards for Disposal Field Construction

Disposal-Field Construction	Minimum Standard
Lines per field, minimum number	2
Individual lines, maximum length	100 ft
Trench bottom, minimum width	18 in.
Field tile, minimum diameter	4 in.
Field-tile lines, maximum slope	6 in. in 100 ft
Field trenches, minimum separation	6 ft
Effective absorption area, minimum per dwelling unit*	

* See Table 6.5.

Extracted from American Standard National Plumbing Code (ASA A40.8–1955), with the permission of the publisher, The American Society of Mechanical Engineers, 345 East 47th Street, N.Y. 17, N.Y.

laid in shallow trenches are covered with gravel. The ends of the tiles do not meet, being separated by a $\frac{1}{4}$ in. opening. The effluent runs out of these spaces and stands in the interstices of the gravel until it seeps into the earth. In effect the gravel provides spaces that act as a dry well to receive the fluids and accomodate them until they slowly sink into the ground.

EXAMPLE 6.2 (Figs. 6.6 and 6.7).   Design a tile drain disposal field for the house described in Ex. 6.1—but with a less pervious soil. For this purpose assume that the tests show a time of 10 min for a 1-in. fall.

SOLUTION. Table 6.5 calls for a trench-bottom area of 100 (sq ft) per bedroom. For 4 bedrooms the total area must be 400 (sq ft).

If 2 ft wide trenches are used as shown in Fig. 6.6, there are (Table 6.7) 2 (sq ft) per foot of length of trench. The total trench length needs to be 200 ft. Table 6.6 forbids lengths greater than 100 ft. Four 50-ft lengths are chosen for this system and they are spaced 6 ft on centers. Other design choices, including 4 in. diameter tiles, con-

form to the requirements of Table 6.6. The possible position of the house on a lot is shown in Fig. 6.7.

In large septic tank systems using tile drain fields it is sometimes desirable to use a dosing chamber and siphon (Fig. 6.8). This arrangement delivers a large volume of effluent at one time when a certain level is reached in the siphon chamber. Not considered necessary for individual (small) disposal systems by the National Plumbing Code, their use is common when there are extensive lengths of tile drains. When not used, the small constant trickle taxes the earth around the nearby tiles because it seldom reaches the distant ones. Constant wetting consolidates this nearby earth to greater compactness. This and the deposit of small particles which finally accumulate here make the soil less absorptive. A large dose of fluid utilizes the distant tiles more effectively.

6. Materials and Products. It is safest to carry a tight cast iron house sewer to the septic tank and to use cast iron pipe between the tank and the distribution boxes. Vitrified clay tile is satisfactory for the lines that emerge from the distribution boxes and, of course, it is open-jointed in the trenches. Septic tanks, distribution boxes,

Table 6.7   Size and Spacing for Disposal Fields

Width of Trench at Bottom	Recommended Depth of Trench	Spacing Tile Lines*	Effective Absorption Area per Lineal Foot of Trench
Inches	Inches	Feet	Square Feet
18	18 to 30	6.0	1.5
24	18 to 30	6.0	2.0
30	18 to 36	7.6	2.5
36	24 to 36	9.0	3.0

* A greater spacing is desirable where available area permits.

Extracted from American Standard National Plumbing Code (ASA A40.8–1955), with the permission of the publisher, The American Society of Mechanical Engineers, 345 East 47th Street, N.Y. 17, N.Y.

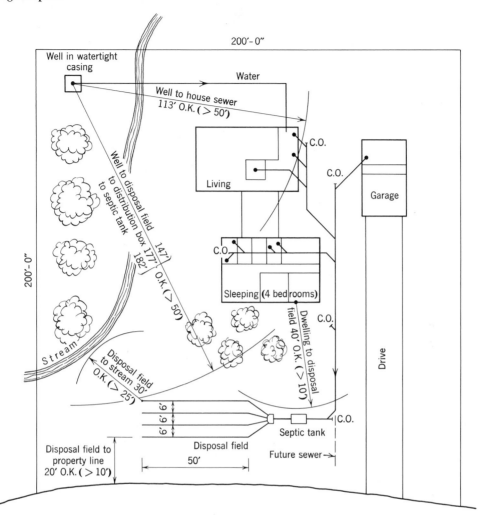

Fig. 6.7 (Example 6.2) Disposal field, stream, well, house sewer, and septic tank fit on a lot with clearances to satisfy the requirements of Table 6.2. Consult also the local health authorities.

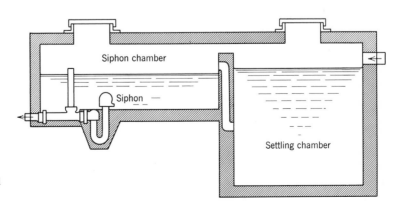

Fig. 6.8 Two-chambered septic tank with siphon.

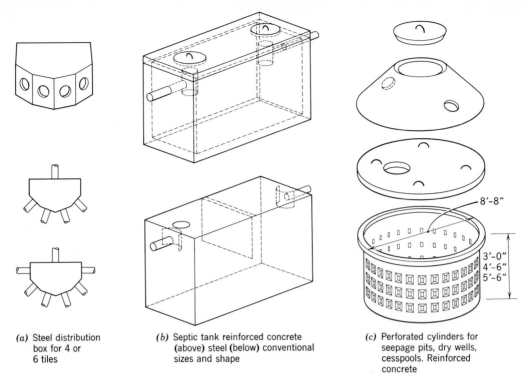

(a) Steel distribution box for 4 or 6 tiles

(b) Septic tank reinforced concrete (above) steel (below) conventional sizes and shape

(c) Perforated cylinders for seepage pits, dry wells, cesspools. Reinforced concrete

Fig. 6.9 Prefabricated elements for sewage disposal and storm drainage.

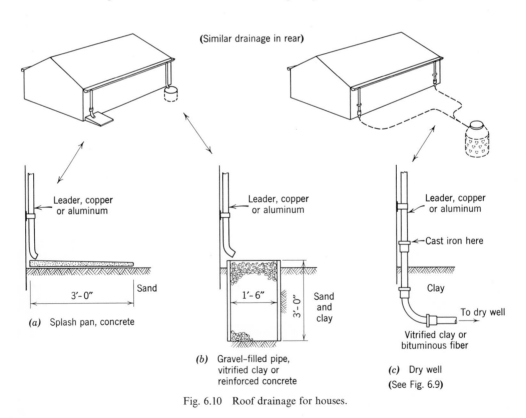

(Similar drainage in rear)

Leader, copper or aluminum

Leader, copper or aluminum

Leader, copper or aluminum

Cast iron here

Sand

3'-0"

1'-6"

3'-0"

Sand and clay

Clay

To dry well

Vitrified clay or bituminous fiber

(a) Splash pan, concrete

(b) Gravel-filled pipe, vitrified clay or reinforced concrete

(c) Dry well (See Fig. 6.9)

Fig. 6.10 Roof drainage for houses.

and seepage elements can be of varied construction. The trend over the years has shown progress from rubble stone to concrete block to cast-in-place reinforced concrete and, more recently, to prefabricated units of steel and of precast reinforced concrete. The steel is of heavy gauge and well coated with bituminous compounds. The reinforced concrete is of the best quality, cast under controlled factory conditions and often of special concrete that tests to 4000 or 5000 psi at 28 days (see Fig. 6.9).

7. Storm Drainage Disposal. Large buildings, air fields, and other level areas that unavoidably collect large quantities of rainwater should drain to storm sewers that discharge into watercourses or into large dry wells. Every effort must be made to avoid allowing this water to swell the volume of sanitary drainage. In the cases of houses, separate handling of rainwater is also essential. It is delivered to the ground with varying degrees of ease depending on the absorptive value of the soil.

In sandy soils the water may be run off several feet from the building with some assurance that it will sink into the ground without causing erosion of the topsoil.

Denser ground may require a short section of wide masonry pipe filled with gravel. This provides space in which the water may stand while slowly finding its way into the soil. For nearly impervious clay, large dry wells entirely below the ground are the best selection (see Fig. 6.10).

References

1. *Publication No. 526, Manual of Septic Tank Practice,* Public Health Service, Superintendent of Documents, Washington, D.C.
2. *Water, a Matter of Survival, and Pollution, a Matter of Health,* The National Water Institute, 420 Lexington Avenue, New York 17, New York.
3. *Journal,* Water Pollution Control Federation, 4435 Wisconsin Avenue, N.W., Washington 16, D.C.
4. *Paper 1715, Design Details for Individual Sewage Disposal Systems,* Harrison A. Martin, M.ASCE, Proceedings of the American Society of Civil Engineers.
5. Literature of the National Technical Task Committee on Industrial Wastes, Mr. L. F. Warrick, Secretary, U.S. Public Health Service, 3rd and C Streets, S.W., Washington 25, D.C.
6. *Sewage Treatment Plant Design,* American Society of Civil Engineers, 345 East 47 Street, New York 17, New York.
7. *Operation of Wastewater Treatment Plants,* Water Pollution Control Federation, 4435 Wisconsin Avenue, Washington 16, D.C.

7

Environmental

Comfort

1. Human Comfort and Efficiency. People live more happily and work more efficiently in a comfortable indoor climate. In the case of larger buildings the architect retains a consulting engineer whose special knowledge and experience has resulted in standards of comfort that are well recognized. For smaller buildings and houses, the services of the engineer are not always available. In these cases the heating contractor has recourse to the same educational literature available to the architect and engineer, much of it written with his interest especially in mind. Many research centers and associations have contributed to this effort in the dissemination of information for better living. They include:

University of Illinois Engineering Experiment Station
National Warm Air Heating and Air Conditioning Association
Better Heating Cooling Council
Environmental Laboratory, Kansas State University
Institute of Boiler and Radiator Manufacturers

It is well for the architect, engineer, client, and heating contractor to be mutually aware of the conditions to be controlled before ducts, boilers, radiators and fans are chosen and installed.

In past decades it was often considered satisfactory to raise the room air temperature in winter and to reduce it with some accompanying humidity reduction in summer. Gradually the control of other factors has merited recognition and a philosophy of "climate control" has begun to emerge. Regulation of the following items may be considered essential to the comfort of humans:

(a) Temperature of the surrounding air
(b) Temperature of the surrounding surfaces
(c) The relative humidity of the air
(d) Motion of the air
(e) Odors
(f) Dust

The first four of these have a specific effect on the heat loss rate of the human body. They can accelerate or retard it to create a general feeling of coolness or warmth.

2. Metabolism. The human body uses food

as a fuel to maintain a body temperature of about 98.6 F. In summer or winter, a person usually occupies conditioned space in which the temperatures are lower than this. Heat, which always flows to objects of lower temperature, leaves the body and flows to its surroundings. The body loses heat in three ways, convection, radiation, and evaporation. Except in the case of radiation, these losses are accelerated by air motion. For indoor conditions in either summer or winter the body experiences a "controlled cooling" and can be made to feel comfortable or uncomfortable by the regulation of the several items.

A person in a room in winter, surrounded by 70 F air, warms the particles of air that are in contact with his warmer body. These rise by convection and are replaced by other, cooler particles. A fan blowing these cooler particles of air toward him at a faster rate will make him feel cooler. If he sits in a telephone booth where even normal convection is retarded, he will feel warmer. His comfort, based on the item of convection will depend upon the air temperature chosen and the effect of air currents within the room.

The body loses heat by interchange of radiant energy which relates to the difference between the skin temperature and the Mean Radiant Temperature (MRT) of the surfaces that the body "faces." Figure 7.2 shows an approximate MRT of 59 F for poor construction and 64 F for good construction. The differentials, skin to room MRT are 26 and 21 respectively. A person will feel warmer in the room of better construction with a higher MRT and a lower temperature differential between the body and its surrounding surfaces. Air motion does not affect this.

In a room under normal conditions, human beings perspire. The body which is largely fluid by nature will give off moisture to dry air at a fast rate and to moist air at a slower rate. In order to vaporize its moisture, the body must use heat to "boil" the moisture so that it will pass into the air. If

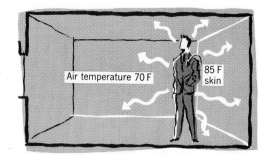

Fig. 7.1   Heat loss by convection.

the relative humidity (RH) in the room air is high, a person will feel warmer because he is not using body heat to vaporize body moisture. Conversely, if the room RH is lowered he will feel cooler. Under either of these circumstances fast air motion will make one feel cooler than otherwise because air which the body has partially humidified will blow away to be replaced with drier air ready to absorb more perspiration with a corresponding loss of heat from the body.

For any specific degree of activity the

Fig. 7.2   Heat loss by radiant energy to surrounding surfaces.

Surface	Approximate surface temperatures, room uninsulated and single glazed, Deg. F	Approximate surface temperatures, room insulated and double glazed, Deg. F
(a)	58	67
(b)	58	67
(c) (interior)	70	70
(d)	62	68
(e)	22	47
	glass, single	glass, double
Mean radiant temperature (weighted by areas)	59 (approximate)	64 (approximate)
Differential	85 − 59 = 26 F	85 − 64 = 21 F

Fig. 7.3   Heat loss by evaporation: 5% RH, body loses much heat by evaporation to this dry air; 35% RH, heat loss retarded by greater humidity; 50% RH, heat loss further retarded but window condensation becomes a problem.

body generates and loses heat at a fairly constant rate. By accelerating or retarding this cooling process the body can be made to *feel* cool or warm. In summer air conditioning, the body heat loss is speeded up, resulting in cooler temperatures of the body surfaces. This may be done by maintaining:

Low air temperatures
Low surfaces temperatures (radiant cooling)
Relatively dry air
Reasonably active air motion

During winter "heating" which, to the body, is still cooling but to a different degree, the body heat loss rate can be retarded and the

body surface temperatures increased to make a person feel warm. This may be done by maintaining:

High air temperature
High surface temperatures (radiant heating)
Relatively moist air (limited by condensation on windows)
Slow air motion

It should be noted that air temperature is only one of the four controls of human comfort and it is not always the most effective. Frequently it is easiest and cheapest to control air temperature only, but it does not always result in the greatest comfort.

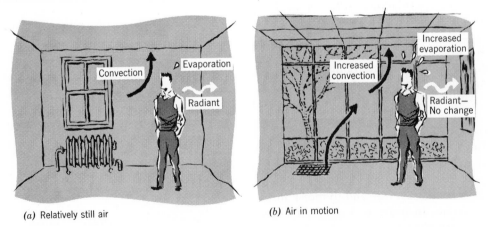

(a) Relatively still air   (b) Air in motion

Fig. 7.4   Air motion. It speeds the physical heat loss by convection and evaporation. Radiant loss is not affected.

Heat generated, Btuh	400	400	400	400	400 (curve 1)
Heat lost by:					
Radiation and convection	350	300	200	100	0 (curve 2)
Evaporation	50	100	200	300	400 (curve 3)
Total, Btuh	400	400	400	400	400 Total
					(curve 1)

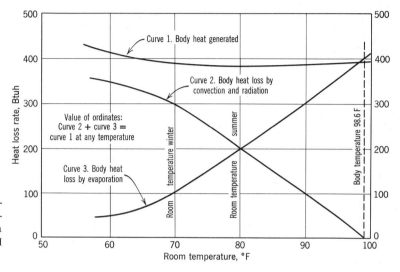

Fig. 7.5 Heat generated and lost (approximate) by a person at rest (RH fixed at 45%).

Methods for controlling air temperature and the other three items are to be found in other chapters of this book. It is not always necessary or convenient to use all four methods, but they are all available for comfort-control if desired. In these times when relative humidity can be accurately controlled, a radiantly cool or warm panel introduced into the environment or the air temperature raised or lowered speedily and at will, it becomes necessary to appraise the importance of each of these items to human comfort in summer or winter.

3. Relative Value of the Several Heat Loss Controls. A human being *at rest* generates and loses about 400 Btuh and this rate is fairly constant regardless of the surrounding conditions, but the relative amount of heat lost hourly by each of the foregoing methods varies, depending on the variation of the surrounding air and surface temperatures, the latter being affected, in general by the trend of air temperature. Curve 1 in Fig. 7.5 indicates a fairly constant rate of heat generation at various temperatures from 60 through 100 F. Curves 2 and 3 show by their ordinates the amounts lost by convection and radiation in one case and by evaporation in the other. At 60 F and less, almost all is lost by radiation and convection. This is quite understandable when it is considered that the pores close up at low temperatures, preventing the process of perspiring. Conversely, when the air and surrounding temperatures are at the blood temperature of 98.6, no heat can be lost to the surrounding air and surfaces because there is no temperature differential. At the same time, because the body *must* dispose of the 400 Btu, it is all lost by the process of evaporation because no other method is possible at this temperature. Since one pound of body fluid is evaporated for about each 1000 Btu expended, it is usual in summer to lose weight by evaporation. See Fig. 7.10, which indicates the much increased bodily heat production and loss under heavy exercise. At 1300 Btuh loss (instead of 400) one would lose more than a pound of body fluids per hour, at temperatures approaching those of the body.

Considering the generally normal indoor temperature of 70 F in winter and 80 F in summer, several interesting conclusions can be made. At 70 F, the body heat loss by convection and radiation is three times that of the evaporative loss. Not shown, but it is nevertheless important that, of the 300 Btuh loss by both convection and radiation, 200 is by radiation. This means that the control of the mean radiant temperature (MRT), as a determinant of the radiant environment is the most important regulative process in winter. It accounts for the comfort and popularity of radiant heating. At 80 F the loss by evaporation (200 Btuh) is as much as the combined effect of the convective and radiant items. Conclusion: Humidity regulation is the most important item in summer. And so one finds that humidity regulation is not the strongest tool in winter comfort and should merely be chosen high enough for health and low enough to avoid condensation during cold weather. Conversely, radiant regulation in summer is not the most important item. Furthermore it can result in condensation on radiantly cool panels unless separate dehumidification is arranged.

4. Conditions for Equal Comfort. By varying the several conditions treated in the foregoing article it is possible to provide proper comfort for any task. Equal comfort may be arranged in many different ways. It has been found that many industrial processes taking place in the new so-called "white rooms" are far more demanding than the requirements for human comfort.

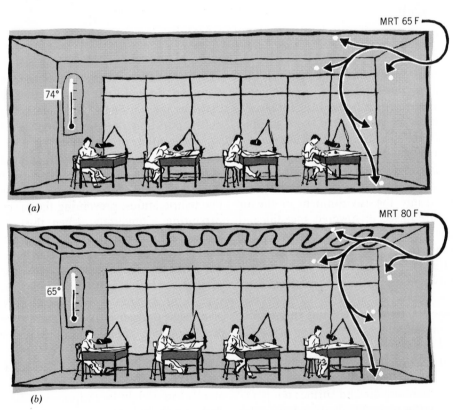

Fig. 7.6 Winter heating, equal comfort. (a) High air temperature, low MRT (mean radiant temperature). (b) Low air temperature, high MRT. Relative humidity and air motion the same for (a) and (b).

Fig. 7.7 Summer conditioning, equal comfort. (*a*) Low temperature, high humidity. (*b*) High temperature, low humidity. Air motion and MRT the same for (*a*) and (*b*).

Temperatures and relative humidity have to be kept within limits so narrow that they present an exercise in precision that does not often occur in planning for comfort heating or conditioning. The experience of engineers in the design of many industrial applications has contributed much to the excellence of control of environment for human occupancy.

With regard to air temperature, relative humidity and air motion, experiments by various laboratories upon a number of subjects at rest have shown that there are definite relationships between the proportions of heat, humidity, and air movement producing comfort. Different proportions yielding the same sensation of warmth have been tabulated, and a comfort chart (Fig. 7.8) has been constructed which presents for summer and winter the various proportions of air temperature and humidity at

fixed air motion found comfortable by 97 or 98 percent of the subjects tested. An arbitrary index called effective temperature (ET) has been introduced, serving as a scale for use with the comfort chart, indicating in a single value the amount of effective warmth experienced under the various combinations. It is divided into degrees of temperature whose numerical values are fixed by the temperatures of saturated air inducing identical sensations of warmth as the effective temperature combinations. The chart shows that a maximum number of subjects were comfortable at effective temperatures of 71 F in summer and at 68 F in winter. These effective temperatures may be produced by a dry-bulb temperature of 76.5 F and a relative humidity of 50 percent in summer, and by a dry-bulb temperature of 74 F and a relative humidity of 30 percent in winter. From the chart it may be seen

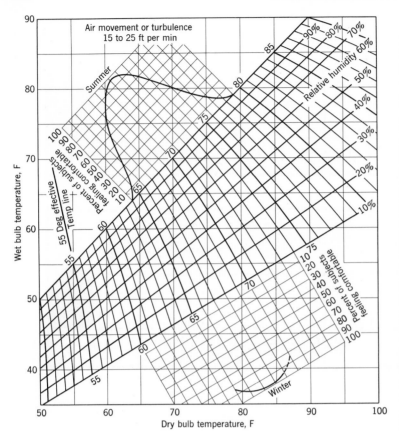

Fig. 7.8 ASHRAE comfort chart for still air.* Reprinted by permission from *ASHRAE Guide and Data Book*. 1961.

*Note. Both summer and winter comfort zones apply to inhabitants of the United States only. Application of winter comfort line is further limited to rooms heated by central station systems of the convection type. The line does not apply to rooms heated by radiant methods. Application of summer comfort line is limited to homes, offices, and the like, where the occupants become fully adapted to the artificial air conditions. The line does not apply to theaters, department stores, and the like where the exposure is less than 3 hours. The optimum summer comfort line shown pertains to Pittsburgh and to other cities in the northern portion of the United States and Southern Canada, and at elevations not in excess of 1000 ft above sea level. An increase of one degree ET should be made approximately per 5° reduction in north latitude.
† Dotted portion of winter comfort line was extrapolated beyond test data.

that the same ET may be produced by many other combinations of dry-bulb temperatures and relative humidities. The air movement is 15 to 25 fpm.

In large office buildings, inspections of thermostat settings, adjusted either by the occupants or by obliging building superintendents, show an average 75° setting for both summer and winter to be the most desired by the occupants. With this setting the humidity control varied from 50 percent in summer to 30 percent in winter.

5. Condensation Control. Although the presence of a reasonable amount of moisture is desirable in winter to prevent furniture shrinkage and to promote comfort of the passages of the nose and throat, its condensation on glass is an inconvenience. Figure 7.9 shows that condensation will occur at 15 percent RH when single glass separates indoor air at 70 F from outdoor air at

0 F. There are methods of circumventing this. The conventional one of placing a convector below the window solves the problem by warming the glass. Lest intermittent heat permit moisture to form between heating cycles, it is well to supply water to the convector at a mild temperature so that it will operate nearly continuously to provide a constant updraft that will warm the glass above the temperature at which moisture will form. Defrosting (or fog removal) may be accomplished by warm air from a forced air heating system bathing the glass. The air can rise from a floor register or a heating cabinet below the sill. It may even be blown down from a ceiling opening or be directed at the window from a register on an interior wall.

In many systems of summer and winter air conditioning, accurate control of relative humidity is possible and the goals of

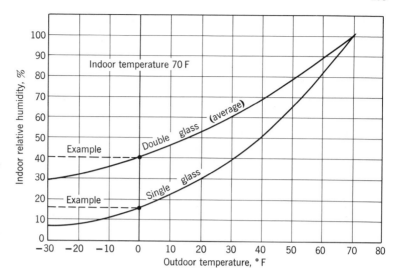

Fig. 7.9 Condensation of glass (indoor temperature 70 F). Example: at 0 F outdoors, relative humidities above 15 will cause condensation on single glass. Double glass will permit about 40% RH.

Table 7.1 may be achieved. When this is not the case, it is now quite usual to provide fans to remove moisture at its source. In modern, tight houses, if this is not done the relative humidity will frequently exceed the desired levels. Exhaust fans are now standard in bathrooms and kitchens. Exhaust fans at laundries are much to be desired, and it is approved practice that items such as clothes dryers be vented directly to outdoors. A gauge to indicate relative humidity is an item of very small expense and there should be one or several in each house. Fans may then be operated manually to reduce humidities to proper standards. It is not always possible to maintain the values suggested by Fig. 7.9 and, because of the usual action by which the glass is warmed, compromises are possible. Table 7.1 sets some values which will be found practical for most houses.

The accumulation of moisture which fans must relieve is shown in Table 7.2. A secondary benefit of humidity reduction is that it presents less of a burden to the vapor barrier (see Chapter 8). It is sometimes difficult to achieve a perfect vapor barrier to contain house moisture within the occupied sections of the structure. When water vapor escapes to structural spaces it condenses and sometimes freezes. In addition to a good vapor barrier and provisions for ventilating out the vapor that may escape to concealed spaces, the reduction of vapor pressure within the house is a contribution to the solution of this problem.

6. Indoor Climate. Much reference has been made to common indoor winter temperatures of 70 and 74 F. In many countries other than the United States, these temperatures are considered quite high. Human beings can become acclimated to lower temperatures and indeed some think that they are more healthful. Quite apart from this matter of personal choice, it has been shown

Table 7.1 Suggested Practical Upper Limits for Relative Humidity in Houses at 70 F in Winter at Various Outdoor Temperatures

Outside Air Temperature, Deg. F	Maximum Indoor Relative Humidity Percent
Below −20	15
−20 to −10	20
−10 to Zero	25
Zero to +10	35
Above +10	40

Engineering Experiment Station, University of Minnesota.

Table 7.2   Moisture Production for Various Domestic Operations

Operation			Pounds of Moisture
Floor mopping (8′ × 10′ kitchen, 0.03 psf)			2.40
Clothes drying indoors			26.40
Clothes washing			4.33
Cooking	From food	From gas	
Breakfast	0.34 plus	0.56 equals	0.90
Lunch	0.51 plus	0.66 equals	1.17
Dinner	1.17 plus	1.52 equals	2.69
Dishwashing			
Breakfast			0.20
Lunch			0.15
Dinner			0.65
Bathing			
Shower			0.50
Tub			0.12
Human contribution, family of four		per hr	0.46
Gas refrigeration		per hr	0.12
House plants, each		per hr	0.04
Humidifier, when used		per hr	2.00

From *Research in Home Humidity Control,* by S. C. Hite and J. L. Bray, Purdue University Engineering Experiment Station Bulletin Research Series No. 106, p 24.

that many conditions besides air temperature can be employed to promote comfort. There is, however, a general relationship between the kind of activity taking place within a space and the air temperature to be maintained for comfort. Heavy exercise in a gymnasium entails a bodily heat loss rate of about four times as much as would occur in the case of a hospital patient.

Table 7.3 shows temperatures of air that

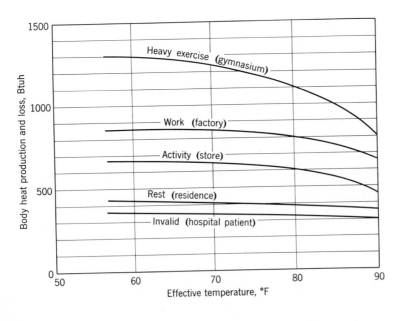

Fig. 7.10   Effect of activity on body heat production and loss.

Table 7.3   Recommended Indoor Air Temperatures for Varying Degrees of Activity, Heating Season

Activity		Btuh Generated per Person	Recommended Indoor Air Temperature F
Heavy exercise	Gymnasium	1300	55
Work	Factory	850	60
Activity	Store	650	65
Rest	Residence	400	70
Hospital patient	Operating Room	300	75 (varies)

could be suitable for varied pursuits. It can be assumed that adjustments would also be made in the relative humidity and the temperature of surrounding surfaces.

In summer the human body becomes "acclimated" to the conditions of outdoor heat and humidity. If a person in such a condition were then subjected to the usual indoor winter conditions, the environment would prove to be too cold. It is sufficient to provide in summer a slightly better situation than would exist in unconditioned space. It is possible to overdo the cooling and dehumidifying; this must be avoided. The period of expected occupancy is also important. For occupancy of 2 or 3 hours, less cooling is preferred. Otherwise the shock of change into the cooled space and again into the warm surroundings would be too great. When it is expected that a full day is to be spent in the conditioned space, a cooler environment may be utilized, because there will be time to get used to it.

In any environment, "differentials" in summer are usually considered instead of absolutes. Thus a differential of 15 F below an outside design temperature of 90 F would result in a selection of an inside temperature of 75 F.

7. Impact of Outdoor Conditions. In planning for indoor comfort, one selects the conditions to be maintained in winter and in summer. Chapters 8 and 9 deal with the outdoor conditions to be expected in various climates and the methods of calculating the heat and moisture to be supplied or removed from the building in order to maintain the indoor conditions as chosen. This is the method by which the sizes of the central plant and of the room or zone units are established and the cost of the fuel or other energy source computed. However, it is not quite as simple as this. If heating and cooling elements are placed incorrectly, the *average* of indoor conditions may still be as planned; but there can be a breakthrough

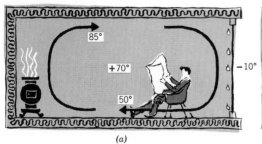
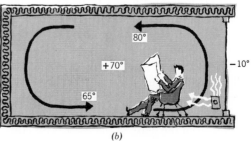

(a)   *(b)*

Fig. 7.11 Dealing with outdoor conditions. Convection is inevitable. It can work for you or against you. The temperatures are approximate. (*a*) The stove is not merely in the wrong place. It *accelerates* the "down-slip" of cold air from the glass. (*b*) The convector strip moves air up to warm the glass and provides local radiant warmth.

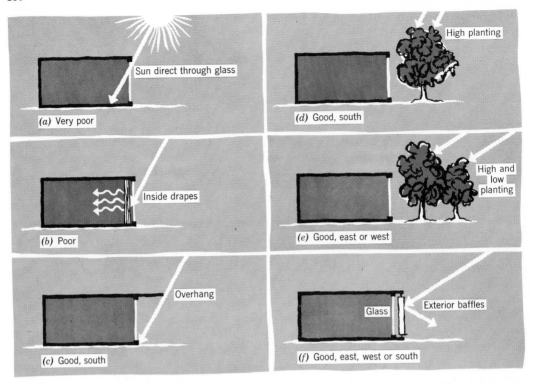

Fig. 7.12   (a through f) Indoor comfort in summer. Sun on shaded and unshaded glass.

of outdoor effects that will make for uncomfortable local spots within some rooms.

Consider a fully exposed room with 5 of its 6 enclosing surfaces heavily insulated and the sixth side a wall of single glass (see Fig. 7.11). The location of the heat source is a vital matter in regard to comfort. An interior position could be disastrous (see Fig. 7.11a). The convector strip below the glass would be the correct solution. The updraft that it creates needs to be reasonably continuous and this is the reason for modulation of water temperature. In mild weather the water is reduced in temperature so that the convector will coast along continuously at low output, but definitely assuring the upflow of some warm air. If this were not done, distinct reversal would occur, spilling cold air from the glass to the floor. This condition is often encountered in office buildings. The glass wall is the only path of heat loss because the other 5 sides of any room at the perimeter have no heat loss when they are contiguous with adjacent interior space.

In the matter of heat gain, which is the basis for the design of air conditioning, it is equally essential to protect the space so that there will be no breakthrough of heat concentration that cannot easily be handled by the air conditioning system.

Even if sufficient cooling is provided to handle the heavy load of direct sun effect through glass, the concentrations of heat make for uncomfortable portions of the room. See Fig. 7.12.

8. Stability and Control of Indoor Climate. The special conditions described in the previous article are only two of the many difficulties that can occur to throw an interior climate control system off balance. Dead spots can develop where temperature is too high or too low or where humidity concentrations can build up. These are best solved by air movement. In air systems, whether for heating only or for summer and winter

Fig. 7.12 (g) Example of sun control by motor-operated louvers which reduce solar gain by 25% in the Ala Moana office building in Honolulu, Hawaii. (Architect, John Graham of Seattle, Wash.)

air conditioning, the paths of air should be studied very carefully so that no sluggish spots develop. It is a three-dimensional study and when the air flows it should pass through, or at least induce movement in, every part of the space. Registers and diffusers are usually directional and have a "throw" which aids in this matter. Vitiated air can be exhausted from locations identified as dead spots and in general the use of fans and moving air is becoming more and more common.

Automatic controls that regulate temperature and other conditions have long been used. There is a change, however, in the general thinking concerning them. Several developments have been strengthened in the last decade. One is to study more

carefully the need for zoning in regard to sun and shade, orientation, wind, occupancy, and similar related subjects. Another is to place the controls near the affected area so that occupants may regulate their immediate environment. To aid in the latter process, systems have been developed that respond well to this need. They include the high velocity dual duct system and the fan-coil cabinet so widely used in schools.

9. Odors. For normal occupancy, other than special industrial processes, odors arise from smoking, the human body, and similar sources. These odors cling to draperies, upholstery, and even to smoother materials. The use of fresh outdoor air introduced into the space is the usual method of reducing these odors to a condition in which the air

Table 7.4   Minimum Outdoor Air Requirements to Remove Objectionable Body Odors Under Laboratory Conditions

Type of Occupants	Air Space per Person Cu Ft	Outdoor Air Supply CFM per Person
HEATING SEASON WITH OR WITHOUT RECIRCULATION. AIR NOT CONDITIONED.		
	100	25
	200	16
Sedentary adults of average socio-economic status	300	12
	500	7
Laborers	200	23
	100	29
Grade school children of average socio-economic status	200	21
	300	17
	500	11
Grade school children of lower socio-economic status	200	38
Children attending private grade schools	100	22
HEATING SEASON. AIR HUMIDIFIED BY MEANS OF CENTRIFUGAL HUMIDIFIER. WATER ATOMIZATION RATE 8 TO 10 gph. TOTAL AIR CIRCULATION 30 cfm PER PERSON.		
Sedentary adults	200	12
SUMMER SEASON. AIR COOLED AND DEHUMIDIFIED BY MEANS OF A SPRAY DEHUMIDIFIER. SPRAY WATER CHANGED DAILY. TOTAL AIR CIRCULATION 30 cfm PER PERSON.		
Sedentary adults	200	<4

Reprinted by permission from *ASHRAE Guide and Data Book*, 1961.

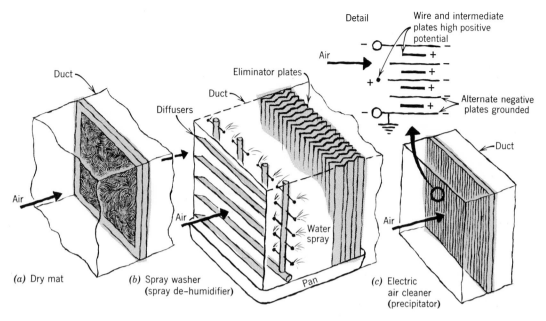

Fig. 7.13 Air filtration devices.

will be considered pleasant. A number of factors are involved. If the space is relatively large for its occupancy, the number of cfm of fresh air used per person can be less. The cfm of fresh air also depends upon the people who occupy the space since there would obviously be a difference between odors caused by laborers, elementary school children, and sedentary adults. The rates will be found in Table 7.4. For grade school children of lower socio-economic status in non-air-conditioned space 38 cfm per person are required if the air space per person is not more than 200 cu ft. In contrast, if air conditioning is provided in a system where occupancy is by sedentary adults, less than 4 cfm per person is satisfactory for the same air space per person. This also presupposes the use of a spray dehumidifier. This is similar in principle to the spray washer shown in Fig. 7.13b. Its thorough action in washing out dust also freshens the air. Though the air leaving the spray is saturated, it is considered a *de*humidifier because, if the water is chilled, the absolute humidity (humidity ratio) of the air leaving the washer is less than that of the air entering. See Chap. 16.

10. Dust. In systems using air to warm or cool occupied space, cleanliness can be assured by the use of filters. Dry filters may be of felt, cloth, wire screens, or cellulose. Some are disposable. All must be kept clean during use, otherwise unwanted resistance is placed on the fan and rates of air delivery are cut down. The electric dust precipitator, Fig. 7.13c, is especially suited to the removal of very fine dust. In large systems the periodic washing down of the plates by water is automatic. In an air-conditioning system utilizing a spray washer, the dust is dealt with by the sprays, which also serve functions related to the regulation of humidity.

Convection systems using convectors and radiators often carry dust upward in air currents resulting in streaky walls. By using water of lower temperature and selecting convectors that discharge the warm air toward the room instead of directly up the wall, this may be minimized.

References

1. *ASHRAE Guide and Data Book,* American Society of Heating, Refrigeration and Air-Conditioning Engineers, 1961, Chap 8, "Physiological Principles."

8

Heat Loss

1. Thermal Value of Walls and Roofs. For economy of fuel consumption, walls, and roofs, and sometimes floors—if there is outdoor space below—must be resistant to the rapid transmission of heat. Slow passage of heat also results in warmer, more comfortable inside surface temperatures. In modern practice, 2 to 4 in. of insulation is considered minimal and should not be omitted except for very special reasons. Vapor barriers are needed to prevent room moisture from penetrating outward to colder parts of roofs and walls where it condenses or freezes. Tight construction retains warm air and resists the entry of cold air during windy times. Finally, the proportion of glass to insulated opaque walls and roofs should be studied if fuel economy and human comfort are to be achieved.

2. Importance of Heat Conservation. One of the requirements for the comfort of people occupying indoor spaces during cold weather is a constant temperature of room air considerably higher than that of the outdoor air. Heat supplied to the room for this purpose is constantly dissipated by transmission losses through the surfaces of the enclosure. It is lost also by the escape of warm air through minute openings, such as the cracks between window sash and frames. The air is forced out by cold outdoor air infiltrating through similar openings on the opposite (windward) side of the room. Loss of warm air may occur also when controlled ventilation operates to change the air in the room at established rates. Since fuel must be purchased to offset these losses, a careful study of infiltration, ventilation, and transmission rates is part of every architectural design.

Among the criteria for the selection of exterior construction, thermal transmission is one of considerable importance because every square foot of material carries a permanent upkeep cost for fuel over the years. The index for comparison is the U-coefficient of transmission. The method of establishing this value for selected walls is developed in the following articles. For the purpose of interpreting the relative merits of the walls shown in Fig. 8.1—the U-coefficient is defined here as the number of British thermal units per hour (Btuh) that pass through 1 sq ft of wall, floor, or roof under actual conditions at the building when the difference between the inside and outside air temperature is 1 F under a steady rate of heat flow.

A few examples of walls are illustrated in Fig. 8.1. Undue consideration for fuel savings *only* might suggest the elimination of all glass and the use instead of insulated

110

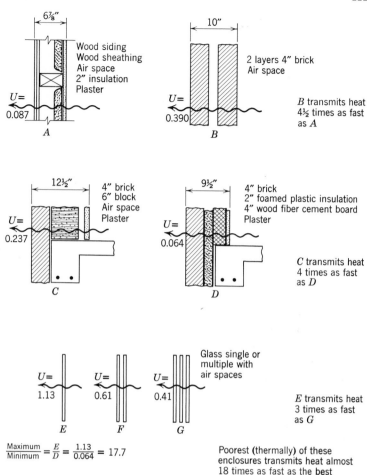

Fig. 8.1 Approximate comparison by U-coefficients of the heat transmitting rates of some opaque and transparent enclosing walls.

$$\frac{\text{Maximum}}{\text{Minimum}} = \frac{E}{D} = \frac{1.13}{0.064} = 17.7$$

walls such as *A* or *D*, which have minimum heat losses. Although this might be an unsound decision, it is nevertheless urged that, in the case of opaque walls, insulation be freely used. Its cost is quickly repaid by fuel savings. The economic advantage of double and triple glazing may not be quite as promising, but it should be considered. The proportion of glass to opaque materials must obviously be judged by many qualities in addition to those relating to heat. It should be pointed out, however, that while glass is quick to lose heat under critical conditions, including the absence of sunshine, it is most receptive, when correctly oriented, to the passage of solar energy into the building during sunny hours. This may largely offset

the excessive fuel use which occurs during cold and dark hours. Structures enclosed largely in glass must have big heating plants assuring a high rate of heating when it is required, yet, if properly designed, need not be extravagant in over-all fuel consumption.

3. Nature of Heat Flow. Beginning with the combustion of fuel in boilers or furnaces, heat flows by various methods to warm the occupied spaces and thence to outdoors by transmission through exterior room surfaces or by the loss or expulsion of warmed air through openings in the building. The analysis and evaluation of the transmission through combinations of building materials leads to the finding that the rate of heat flow is related to the passage

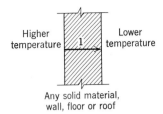

Any solid material,
wall, floor or roof

A single solid material illustrates the transfer of heat from the warmer to the cooler particles by conduction (1).

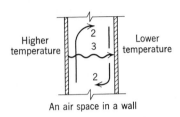

An air space in a wall

As air is warmed by the warmer side of the air space it rises. As it falls down along the cooler side it transfers heat to this surface (2). Radiant energy (3) is transferred from the warmer to the cooler surface. The rate depends upon the relative temperature of the surfaces and upon their emissive and absorptive qualities. Direction is always from the warmer to the cooler surface.

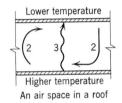

An air space in a roof

The convective action (2) in the air space of a roof is similar to that in a wall although the height through which the air rises and falls is usually less. The radiant transfer is up in this case because its direction is always to the cooler surface.

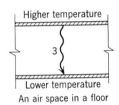

An air space in a floor

When the higher temperature is at the top of a horizontal air space the warm air is trapped at the top and, being less dense than the cooler air at the bottom, will not flow down to transfer its heat to the cooler surface. This results in little flow by convection. The radiant transfer in this case is down because that is the direction from the warmer surface to the cooler.

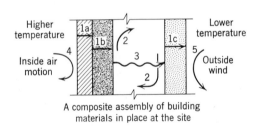

A composite assembly of building
materials in place at the site

This example of a wall in place illustrates the several methods by which heat is lost through a composite assembly of materials. Conduction at varying rates in different materials is accounted for in 1a, 1b, 1c. Convection currents (2) and radiation (3) carry the heat across the air space.

Heat is conducted from the room air by warm air currents that strike the inside wall. Heat is conducted away from the exterior surface of the wall by the action of the wind.

Fig. 8.2   Nature of heat flow through materials, air spaces and assembled structures.

Conduction 1	Inside surface conductance 4
Convection 2	Outside surface conductance 5
Radiation 3	

of heat through these assembled materials by conduction, convection, radiation, or combinations of them.

It is evident that a reduction in the rate of heat loss can be achieved by the use of insulating materials having slow conduc- tion rates, the interposition of one or several air spaces and the reduction of radiant transfer by the use of reflective linings in air spaces. Greater thicknesses of the selected solid materials helps, but there can be little control of the internal convection or the inside and outside surface conductance losses.

4. Heat Flow through Homogeneous Solids.
Conductivity (unit conductance), is designated as k and defined as the number of Btuh that flow through one square foot of material one inch thick when the temperature drop through the material under conditions of steady heat flow is one degree Fahrenheit. Conductivity is established by tests and is the basic rating for a material. When conductance C is referred to, in a homogeneous material, it is for a thickness other than one inch. The other conditions remain the same.

Figure 8.3 compares the conductivities of a dense and a light material. It also shows the method of computing the thermal resistance, R, of one inch of material. R is the reciprocal of the conductivity. This is $1/k$ and is stated as the number of hours needed for 1 Btu to flow through the material. For thicknesses other than 1 in., the conductance C decreases (k/x) with the increase in thickness. The resistance, R, increases directly (x/k) with the increase in thickness. In each case x stands for the thickness of the material in inches.

5. Air Spaces.
Reference to Table 8.1 shows that air has a basic conductance value of .17. This is for a theoretical condition where there is no convection or radiation. In general, air spaces transmit more heat than this because of the effects of the latter two items. While convection depends solely on the position of the air space in the structure, radiant transfer may be reduced by the use of a bright, polished lining which will emit

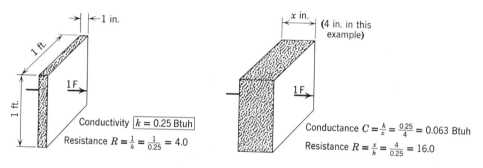

Glass Fiber Insulation Board

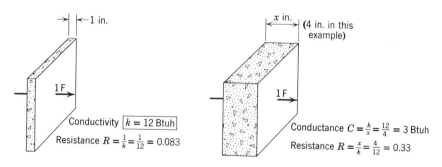

Sand and Gravel Concrete

Fig. 8.3 Example of conductivities (k) for 1 in. thickness, conductances (C) for any thickness (4 in. in this example) and resistances (R) for glass fiber, a material of low conductivity, and concrete, a material of high conductivity.

Note: Standard unit of area 1 s.f. Standard unit temperature differential 1 F.

Table 8.1   *Conductivity (k) and Resistance (R) Values for Some Common Building Materials*

All Values for 1 Inch Thickness of Material

Material	Conductivity* (k) Btuh for 1 sq ft 1 in. Thick 1 F Differential	Resistance* (R) or (1/k) Btuh for 1 sq ft 1 in. Thick 1 F Differential
Air	.17	6.00
Metals		
Aluminum	1416.00	.00071 (Negligible)
Copper	2640.00	.00038 (Negligible)
Steel	312.00	.00321 (Negligible)
Glass	Range 3.60	.28
	to 7.32	.14
Building Board Materials		
Asbestos cement	4.00	.25
Plywood	.80	1.25
Wood fiber board	.42	2.38
Wood fiber, hardboard	1.40	.72
Insulating Materials		
Cotton fiber	.26	3.85
Mineral wool fiber	.27	3.71
Wood fiber	.25	4.00
Cellular glass	.40	2.50
Foamed plastic	.29	3.46
Wood fiber cement board	.55	1.82
Masonry Materials		
Cement mortar	5.00	.20
Concrete, lightweight aggregates		
Density 120 lbs per cu ft	5.20	.19
Density 20 lbs per cu ft	.70	1.43
Concrete, sand, and gravel or stone	12.00	.08
Stucco	5.00	.20
Brick, common	5.00	.20
Brick, face	9.00	.11
Sandstone or limestone	12.50	.08
Plastering Materials		
Cement plaster, sand aggregate	5.00	.20
Gypsum plaster		
Sand aggregate	5.60	.18
Vermiculite or perlite aggregate	1.60	.63
Woods		
Maple, oak, and similar hardwoods	1.10	.91
Fir, pine, and similar softwoods	.80	1.25

*These conductivities and resistances are based upon a "steady state" of heat flow during which the temperatures on the surfaces of the 1 in. thick material are different by 1 F. (Extracted by permission from *ASHRAE Guide and Data Book, 1961,* The American Society of Heating, Refrigerating, and Air Conditioning Engineers.)

(or receive) only a small portion of the radiant energy transferred by the rough surfaces of common building materials. It is sufficient to use this kind of material (such as bright aluminum foil) on one of the surfaces only. The improvement by its use on both sides of the air space is negligible.

Thicknesses of the air spaces in conventional construction commonly range between $\frac{3}{4}$ and 4 in. With the exception of floors, discussed below, the dimension of the air space makes little difference because the greatest transfer is by convection and radiation. In such a situation the use of additional inches of air does not help. It is interesting to observe that an air space in a floor where heat loss is downward improves when the air space dimension is increased. Figure 8.1 indicates that in this case there is only radiant transfer because air currents

are not set up. Using 4 in. of air and a low-emissivity liner, a low transmission rate (a) of .11 is achieved which beats the basic figure of .17 mentioned above, for 1 in. thickness of still air, permitting conduction only with little accompanying radiation or convection.

6. Effects of Air Motion. When a wall or roof is in place to enclose a room under conditions resulting in heat loss from the space, the gentle motion of the nominally "still" air within the room and the more active motion of the wind outside of the room both act to increase the rate of heat loss. The room air is, of course, higher in temperature than the inside surface of the room. The convection currents within the room cause the warmer air particles to collide with the cooler surface. The resulting surface conductance, called f_i (i for

Table 8.2   Conductances (a) and Resistances (R) of a Plane Air Space

Position of Air Space	Air Space Thickness Inches	Conductance (a) Btuh/sq ft/1 F		Resistance (R = 1/a)	
		Value of Emissivity (E)		Value of Emissivity (E)	
		.05	.82	.05	.82
Vertical					
Heat flow horizontal as through a wall.	$\frac{3}{4}$ to 4	.38	1.08	2.64	.92
Horizontal					
Heat flow up as through a roof.	$\frac{3}{4}$ to 4	.54	1.24	1.84	.80
Horizontal					
Heat flow down as through a floor.	$\frac{3}{4}$	.28	.98	3.57	1.02
	$1\frac{1}{2}$	.18	.87	5.56	1.15
	4	.11	.81	9.01	1.23

For nature of heat flow across air spaces, refer to Fig. 8.2.

If the surfaces of the air space are common building materials such as wood, masonry, or plaster, use an emissivity of .82. If one or both surfaces are bright aluminum foil, aluminum sheet, or aluminum-coated paper, polished, use an emissivity of .05.

Emissivity E of a material is the fraction of the energy that will be transmitted across an air space by radiant energy when both surfaces are black. It is a measure of the heat emitting (or absorbing) qualities of the surface. Thus shiny surfaces will transfer about .05 as much as a black-body condition and common building materials about .82 as much. (Extracted by permission from *ASHRAE Guide and DataBook, 1961,* The American Society of Heating, Refrigerating, and Air Conditioning Engineers.)

Table 8.3 Surface Conductances for Indoor Air (f_i) and for Outdoor Air (f_o) and Their Corresponding Resistances, R

Indoor Air

Position of Surface	Direction of Heat Flow	Conductance f_i Btuh/sq ft/1 F	Resistance $R = 1/f_i$
Vertical (a wall)	Horizontal	1.46	.68
Horizontal (a roof)	Upward	1.63	.61
Horizontal (a floor)	Downward	1.08	.92

Outdoor Air 15 mph wind (average)

Position of Surface	Direction of Heat Flow	Conductance f_o Btuh/sq ft/1 F	Resistance $R = 1/f_o$
Any	Any	6.00	.17

(Extracted by permission from *ASHRAE Guide and Data Book, 1961,* The American Society of Heating, Refrigerating, and Air Conditioning Engineers.)

interior), is least on the floor and increases slightly for the walls and ceiling. The outdoor air temperature is less than that of the outside surface of the structure. When the wind blows these cooler air particles against this warmer exterior surface, the heat loss rate is increased. This conductance factor is called f_o (*o* for outside). The factors are for the number of Btuh passing through 1 sq ft of surface for 1 F difference in temperature. Thickness is not involved.

7. Transmission Through Building Units. It is only coincidental when building materials or products are produced in exactly 1 in. thickness. Determining the conductance factor C of *homogeneous* materials not 1 in. thick was treated in Art. 4 and Fig. 8.3. For instance, the conductance C value for a 4 in. thick wall of face brick is $k/x = 9/4 = 2.24$ Btuh for 1 sq ft when 1 F temperature difference exists. A $\frac{1}{2}$ in. layer of gypsum plaster with sand aggregate and a k value (for 1 in.) of 5.60 would have a conductance of $5.60/.50 = 11.20$ Btuh. In each instance the resistance is the reciprocal of the conductance.

Table 8.4 presents conductances and re-

sistances for some building materials of standard type and thicknesses. In calculating the over-all U-factor of total transmission through a construction in place, the use of Table 8.4 will eliminate the need in many cases of starting with the basic k value and adjusting it for thickness.

There are many special building products which are not listed in Table 8.4. Manufacturers will quote the C and R values of their products. These values may be used in establishing U-coefficients. Examples of the calculations for C and R_T are given in Fig. 8.4. They do not include the effects of surface conductances because the uses of these panels are not known. It will be noted, however, that the position of panels containing air spaces may affect slightly the quoted values for C and R_T. For completeness of presentation, the examples in Fig. 8.4 begin with the k values but whenever convenient, the resistance values may be read directly from the tables and then added to find the total resistance.

8. Over-all Coefficients of Heat Transmission. The rate of heat flow through a roof, wall or floor is known as the over-all trans-

Table 8.4 Conductances (C) and Resistances (R) of Some Building and Insulating Materials and Products

Conductances are expressed as Btuh/sq ft/1 F temperature difference. They are for the thickness listed.

Material	Description	Thickness, Inches	Conductance C for Thickness Listed	Resistance R = 1/C for Thickness Listed
Building Boards, Panels Sheathing	Asbestos—cement board	$\frac{1}{8}$	33.00	.03
	Gypsum or plaster board	$\frac{3}{8}$	3.10	.32
	Gypsum or plaster board	$\frac{1}{2}$	2.25	.45
	Plywood	$\frac{1}{4}$	3.20	.31
	Plywood	$\frac{1}{2}$	1.60	.63
	Plywood	$\frac{3}{4}$	1.07	.94
	Sheathing, impregnated	$\frac{1}{2}$	.76	1.32
	Wood fiber, hardboard type	$\frac{1}{4}$	5.60	.18
Building Paper	Vapor—permeable felt		16.70	.06
	Vapor—seal, 2 layers of mopped 15 lb felt		8.35	.12
	Vapor—seal, plastic film			Negligible
Flooring Materials	Carpet and fibrous pad		.48	2.08
	Terrazzo	1	12.50	.08
	Tile—asphalt, linoleum, vinyl, rubber		20.00	.05
	Wood subfloor	$\frac{25}{32}$	1.02	.98
	Wood—hardwood finish	$\frac{3}{4}$	1.47	.68
Insulating Materials	Wood fiberboard acoustical tile	$\frac{1}{2}$	.84	1.19
	Wood fiberboard acoustical tile	$\frac{3}{4}$	.56	1.78
	Insulating roof deck	2	.18	5.56
	Insulating roof deck	3	.12	8.33
Masonry Units	Clay tile, hollow 1 cell deep	4	.90	1.11
	Clay tile, hollow 2 cells deep	8	.54	1.85
	Clay tile, hollow 3 cells deep	12	.40	2.50
	Concrete blocks, sand and gravel aggregate, hollow	4	1.40	.71
	Concrete blocks, sand and gravel aggregate, hollow	8	.90	1.11
	Concrete blocks, sand and gravel aggregate, hollow	12	.78	1.28
	Concrete blocks, lightweight aggregate, hollow	4	.67	1.50
	Concrete blocks, lightweight aggregate, hollow	8	.50	2.00
	Concrete blocks, lightweight aggregate, hollow	12	.44	2.27
	Gypsum partition tile, 4 cell	3	.74	1.35
	Gypsum partition tile, 3 cell	4	.60	1.67
Plastering Materials	Cement plaster, sand aggregate	$\frac{1}{2}$	10.00	.10
	Cement plaster, sand aggregate	$\frac{3}{4}$	6.60	.15
	Cement plaster, sand aggregate	$\frac{1}{2}$	11.10	.09
	Gypsum plaster, sand aggregate, on metal lath	$\frac{3}{4}$	7.70	.13
Roofing	Shingles, asbestos—cement		4.76	.21
	Shingles, wood, double, 16 in., 12 in. exposure		.84	1.12
	Siding, wood, drop	1	1.27	.79
	Built-up roofing	$\frac{3}{8}$	3.00	.33

(Extracted by permission from *ASHRAE Guide and Data Book, 1961,* The American Society of Heating, Refrigerating, and Air Conditioning Engineers.)

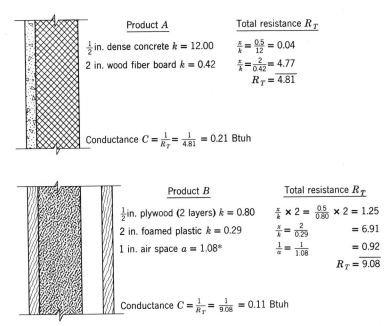

	Product A	Total resistance R_T
	$\frac{1}{2}$ in. dense concrete $k = 12.00$	$\frac{x}{k} = \frac{0.5}{12} = 0.04$
	2 in. wood fiber board $k = 0.42$	$\frac{x}{k} = \frac{2}{0.42} = 4.77$
		$R_T = \overline{4.81}$

Conductance $C = \frac{1}{R_T} = \frac{1}{4.81} = 0.21$ Btuh

	Product B	Total resistance R_T
	$\frac{1}{2}$ in. plywood (2 layers) $k = 0.80$	$\frac{x}{k} \times 2 = \frac{0.5}{0.80} \times 2 = 1.25$
	2 in. foamed plastic $k = 0.29$	$\frac{x}{k} = \frac{2}{0.29} = 6.91$
	1 in. air space $a = 1.08*$	$\frac{1}{a} = \frac{1}{1.08} = 0.92$
		$R_T = \overline{9.08}$

Conductance $C = \frac{1}{R_T} = \frac{1}{9.08} = 0.11$ Btuh

Fig. 8.4 Method of computing resistance and conductance of manufactured composite building products.

* This factor applies when the panel is used as a *wall* and the air space has no reflective lining.

mission coefficient U. This and other coefficients that affect it are defined as follows, for conditions of steady-state flow of heat:

$U = Over$-all $Coefficient$ of $Heat$ $Transmission$. The Btuh flowing from air to air through 1 sq ft of roof, wall, floor, or other building component in place in the structure under actual conditions for a difference of 1 F in temperature between the air on the inside and the air on the outside. It can apply to a combination of materials or to a single material such as glass.

$k = Conductivity$. The Btuh rate of heat flow through 1 sq ft of a homogeneous material 1 in. thick for a 1 F difference in temperature between its 2 surfaces.

$C = Conductance$. The Btuh rate of heat flow through 1 sq ft of a homogeneous material or a combination of materials for 1 F difference in temperature between the exteriors surfaces, for the thickness of construction stated, not necessarily per inch of thickness.

$a = Air$-$space$ $conductance$. The Btuh rate of heat flow through 1 sq ft of area for 1 F difference in temperature between the bounding surfaces. It is affected by position and by the emissivity E of the surfaces.

$f = Film$ or $Surface$ $Conductance$ $Coefficient$. The rate of heat flow in Btuh through 1 sq ft of surface due to the motion of air against the surface, for 1 F difference in temperature. f_i is the symbol for the inside film coefficient and f_o the symbol for the outside film coefficient. These coefficients reflect the speed at which the air strikes the surface.

$E = Emissivity$. The effective thermal emission (or absorption) of the surfaces bounding an air space.

$R = Thermal$ $Resistance$. Its value is obtained from the reciprocal of heat transfer as expressed by such coefficients as U, C, f, or a. It may be expressed as hrs/Btu for the standard sq ft of surface and 1 F temperature difference. For example, a wall with a U-coefficient of .25 would have a thermal resistance R of 1/.25 = 4.0.

The U value in Tables 8.5, 8.6, and 8.7, modified for insulation as indicated in Table 8.8, may be used directly in heat loss calculations. These values are developed from basic data that appear in Tables 8.1, 8.2, 8.3, and 8.4. The U values of other constructions may also be calculated from these tables. Space limitations permit only a few of the most common U values to be listed here. The designer who is continuously engaged in heat-loss problems and who deals with unusual structures is referred to the *Guide and Data Book* of the American Society of Heating, Refrigerating, and Air Conditioning Engineers, from which much of this information has been adapted.

In computing U values it is evident that component heat transmissions are not additive. The value of the over-all coefficient is always less than that of any of its parts. Greater thickness, more parts, insulation, and air spaces all serve to lower the over-all coefficient of transmission. To arrive at this coefficient it is necessary to add the resistances of the various elements, including film coefficients. This results in a total resistance R_T which may be expressed in total hours for the passage of 1 Btu through

Table 8.5 Coefficients of Transmission (U) for Exterior Walls*
Btuh/1 sq ft/1 F air to air for a wall in place.

Frame Walls	Interior Finishes on Frame		
In each case, studs with exterior finish of bevel wood siding, wood shingles, or $\frac{3}{4}$ in. wood panels. Sheathing and interior finishes as indicated.	$\frac{3}{8}$ in. gypsum lath and $\frac{1}{2}$ in. plaster	Metal lath and $\frac{3}{4}$ in. plaster	$\frac{3}{4}$ in. wood panels
Sheathing type			
$\frac{5}{16}$ in. plywood	.29	.31	.25
$\frac{25}{32}$ insulating board	.19	.21	.18
	Interior Finishes on Masonry Furring (air space)		
Masonry Walls			
Common brick	$\frac{3}{8}$ in. gypsum lath and $\frac{1}{2}$ in. plaster	Metal lath and $\frac{3}{4}$ in. plaster	None
thickness			
8 in.	.26	.28	.41
12 in.	.22	.23	.31
16 in.	.18	.19	.25
Limestone			
thickness			
8 in.	.35	.39	.67
12 in.	.31	.34	.55
16 in.	.28	.31	.47
4 in. common brick and hollow concrete block of lightweight aggregate			
with 8 in. block	.21	.22	.29
with 12 in. block	.20	.21	.28
Cavity wall, 4 in. face brick, cavity (ar space) and 4 in. common brick	.23	.24	.33

* Uninsulated. For adjustments to *U* values due to insulation, see Table 8.8. (Extracted by permission from *ASHRAE Guide and Data Book, 1961,* The American Society of Heating, Refrigerating, and Air Conditioning Engineers.)

Table 8.6   Coefficients of Transmission (U) for Roofs with Built-up Roofing *
Btuh/sq ft/1 F air to air for a roof in place.

	Interior Finishes Below Joists Suspended Ceiling (air space)		
	$\frac{3}{8}$ in. gypsum lath and $\frac{1}{2}$ in. plaster	*Metal lath and $\frac{3}{4}$ in. plaster*	*None*
Wood Roofs			
Thickness of wood			
1 in.	.30	.33	.48
3 in.	.18	.19	.23
	Interior Finishes Below Beams Suspended Ceiling (air space)		
Masonry Roofs			
Concrete slab	*$\frac{3}{8}$ in. gypsum lath and $\frac{1}{2}$ in. plaster*	*Metal lath and $\frac{3}{4}$ in. plaster*	*None*
(Gravel aggregate)			
Slab thickness			
4 in.	.37	.41	.70
6 in.	.35	.39	.63
8 in.	.33	.37	.57
Concrete slab			
(Lightweight aggregate, corrugated metal form left in place)			
Slab thickness			
2 in.	.22	.23	.30
3 in.	.18	.18	.23
4 in.	.15	.15	.18
Gypsum slab			
($\frac{1}{2}$ in. gypsum board form left in place)			
Slab thickness			
2 in.	.25	.27	.45
3 in.	.22	.23	.45
4 in.	.19	.20	.45
Metal Roofs			
Flat metal roof deck	.42	.48	.90

* Uninsulated. For adjustments to *U* values due to insulation, see Table 8.8. (Extracted by permission from *ASHRAE Guide and Data Book, 1961,* The American Society of Heating, Refrigerating, and Air Conditioning Engineers.)

Table 8.7 Coefficients of Transmission (U) for Interior Partitions, Floors and Ceilings*
Btuh/1 sq ft/1 F air to air for a partition, floor or ceiling in place.

	Interior Finishes		
	$\frac{3}{8}$ in. gypsum lath and $\frac{1}{2}$ in. plaster	Metal lath and $\frac{3}{4}$ in. plaster	None
Partitions			
Frame			
Studs with specified finish on both sides	.32	.39	
Hollow concrete block			
Lightweight aggregate			
Block thickness			
3 in.			.38
4 in.			.35
8 in.			.30
Hollow gypsum tile			
Tile thickness			
3 in.			.37
4 in.			.33
Metal lath and plaster			
Solid partition 2 in. thick			.58

	Interior Finishes Below Joists or Beams Suspended Ceiling—(air space)		
	$\frac{3}{8}$ in. gypsum lath and $\frac{1}{2}$ in. plaster	Metal lath and $\frac{3}{4}$ in. plaster	None
Floor—Ceiling Construction†			
Frame (wood joists)			
Wood subfloor $\frac{25}{32}$ in., felt and hardwood $\frac{3}{4}$ in.	.24	.26	.61
Concrete (gravel aggregate)			
Floor tile or linoleum			
Slab thickness 4 in.	.34	.38	.60

Resistances for still air on both sides of each construction are reflected in the coefficients.

* Uninsulated. For adjustments to *U* values due to insulation, see Table 8.8.
† These coefficients are for heat flow upwards. For downward flow they would be less, especially when air spaces are involved. (Extracted by permission from *ASHRAE Guide and Data Book, 1961,* The American Society of Heating, Refrigerating, and Air Conditioning Engineers.)

the construction. The reciprocal of this total resistance, stated as Btuh, is the overall U coefficient of transmission. An example will illustrate this.

EXAMPLE 8.1. Table 8.5 lists a coefficient of .22 for an exterior wall of 4 in. common brick, 8 in. hollow concrete block of lightweight aggregate, furring which creates an air space and $\frac{3}{4}$ in. cement plaster on metal lath. This U value was calculated as follows:

nesses are sometimes used. A calculation to verify the value of .064 as taken from Table 8.8 would be as follows:

EXAMPLE 8.2.

Resistance of uninsulated wall	4.67
Resistance of 3 in. of insulation 3/.27	11.10
Revised R_T	15.77 Btuh

EXAMPLE 8.1

Item	Resistance Values Taken From Table No.		Resistance
Outside surface film coefficient (15 mph)	8.3		.17
4 in. of common brick	8.1	4 in. $\times$ .20	.80
8 in. hollow concrete block, lightweight aggregate	8.4		2.00
Air space bounded by common materials (not reflective)	8.2		.92
$\frac{3}{4}$ in. cement plaster on metal lath	8.4		.10
Inside surface film coefficient (still air)*	8.3		.68
Total Resistance, air-to-air, R_T			4.67

* In the case of interior partitions, floors, and ceilings (Table 8.7), film coefficients for still air are used on both sides.

SOLUTION.
U = 1/R = 1/4.67 =
.215 Btuh (.22 in Table 8.5).

It is satisfactory to express U values to two digits following the decimal point, though in insulated constructions one more is usually shown.

Note that the value arrived at compares favorably with that of .237 (.24) for Wall "C" of Fig. 8.1, (p. 111) which transmits heat slightly faster because the block is 6 in. instead of 8 in.

The U value of the wall in this example could be much reduced by adding insulation. If it is assumed that 3 in. of glass fiber or foamed plastic be added, Table 8.8 indicates a reduction from .22 to a U value of .064. This insulation would reduce the heat loss rate of the wall by 70 percent. It is assumed that the air space is retained. About 4 in. of insulation is often considered an economic maximum though greater thick-

Revised U value for insulated wall U = $1/R_T$ = 1/15.77 = .064 Btuh.

The present availability of water-resistive rigid fibrous insulations should encourage the insulation of masonry walls. This may become as common as the use of mineral wool batts in stud and joist space in frame construction. It is unfortunate that the thickness of masonry walls must usually be increased to accommodate the insulation.

9. Glass, Windows and Doors. Glass, of course transmits heat more rapidly than almost any other material except perhaps a single sheet of metal. Except for the use of multiple surfaces with air spaces there is little that can be done to reduce this rate. The orientation and placing of glass can do much to admit solar energy during sunny hours, but since heat losses are calculated for critical, dark hours the standard U coefficients of Table 8.9 must be used. (Doors are also included in this table.)

10. Heat Loss from Basements, Crawl

Spaces, and Attics. In a later article the method of calculating the total hourly heat loss from buildings is developed. The part of this that relates to transmission losses makes use of the U coefficients discussed. In the surfaces of basements below grade, there is no outside surface film coefficient in the usual sense because there is no wind to carry the heat away. Thus the resistance of the basement enclosing surface in contact with the ground is great. Moreover the earth temperatures rise after an appreciable operating time, further reducing the heat transmitted. For these reasons the loss through basement surfaces below ground is *not* computed by multiplying a U coefficient by the area and a tem-

perature difference. It has been found that the loss from these surfaces has frequently been overestimated. An approximation of this small loss is expressed directly in the Btuh/sq ft of wall and floor area. The loss rate is related to the ground water temperature and is listed in Table 8.10.

In the absence of evidence about the temperature of ground water, a value of 2 Btuh/sq ft is acceptable for the floor and value of 4 for the walls below grade. For walls, windows, and other construction above grade in the basement, the heat loss rate is calculated in the same way as for other spaces above the ground.

Unheated crawl spaces are often ventilated with outdoor air in winter. Usually,

Table 8.8 *Coefficients of Transmission (U) Resulting from Addition of Insulation to the Constructions in Tables 8.5, 8.6, and 8.7*

Value of U Without Insulation	Inches of Fibrous Insulation (k value = .27), Added to Uninsulated Construction						
	$\frac{1}{2}$	1	2	3	4	5	6
.70	.304	.194	.113	.080	.061	.051	.042
.60	.284	.186	.110	.078	.061	.052	.042
.45	.246	.168	.104	.075	.059	.048	.041
.40	.230	.161	.101	.074	.058	.048	.041
.35	.212	.152	.097	.072	.057	.047	.040
.30	.192	.142	.093	.069	.057	.046	.039
.28	.184	.138	.091	.068	.054	.045	.039
.26	.175	.133	.089	.066	.054	.045	.038
.24	.166	.127	.087	.065	.053	.044	.038
.22	.156	.121	.084	.064	.052	.044	.038
.20	.145	.115	.081	.062	.051	.043	.037
.18	.134	.108	.078	.060	.049	.042	.036
.16	.123	.100	.074	.057	.048	.040	.035
.14	.111	.092	.069	.054	.046	.039	.034
.12	.098	.083	.064	.051	.043	.037	.033
.10	.085	.073	.058	.047	.040	.035	.031
.08	.070	.062	.050	.041	.037	.032	.029

EXAMPLE: If an uninsulated construction has a U value of .35, the addition of 2 in. of insulation will result in a new U value of .097.

U values for uninsulated and insulated constructions are the Btuh flowing through 1 sq ft of surface under actual conditions at the site for 1 F temperature difference inside air to outside air.

If, in adding insulation, an air space is filled, it will be necessary to further adjust the U value for the loss of the resistance of an air space. (Extracted by permission from *ASHRAE Guide and Data Book, 1961*, The American Society of Heating, Refrigerating, and Air Conditioning Engineers.)

Table 8.9 Coefficients of Transmission (U) for Glass, Windows, and Doors

Btuh/1 sq ft/1 F air to air for material in place.

Vertical Glass Sheets

	One	Two			Three		
Number of sheets ⟶	One	Two			Three		
Air space, inches ⟶	None	$\frac{1}{4}$	$\frac{1}{2}$	1*	$\frac{1}{4}$	$\frac{1}{2}$	1*
Outdoor exposure	1.13	.61	.55	.53	.41	.36	.34
Indoor exposure (partition)	.75	.50	.46	.45	.38	.33	.32

Horizontal Glass Sheets

(Heat flow upward)

Outdoor exposure	1.40	.70	.66	.63
Indoor exposure (partition)	.96	.59	.56	.56

Windows

Modification factors for glass set in windows. Multiply the above sheet value by these factors.

	Single glass	Double glass	Windows with storm sash
Wood sash	.90	.95	.90
Steel sash	1.00	1.20	1.00
Aluminum	1.10	1.30	1.10

Doors, Solid Wood

Thickness, inches	Exposed door	With glass storm door
$1\frac{1}{4}$	.55	.34
$1\frac{3}{4}$	.48	.31
3	.31	.23

* For spaces 1 in. or *more*.

For storm sash use values for 2 vertical sheets 1 in. apart, but apply storm sash modification factors.

Plastic skylights are evaluated the same as horizontal glass. (Extracted by permission from *ASHRAE Guide and Data Book, 1961*, The American Society of Heating, Refrigerating, and Air Conditioning Engineers.)

the floor above is heavily insulated and air tight. Instead of calculating a loss from the crawl space to outdoors, it is often preferred to evaluate the loss from the room to the crawl space. For this purpose it is safest to assign the outdoor temperature to the crawl space. When crawl space vents are closed and the space heated to house temperature, there is no loss through the room floor and the heat loss from the crawl space is computed as though it were a basement.

The attic appears infrequently in modern architectural design. The loss of heat from top floor rooms to unused attics, or from rooms (including finished attic rooms) to unused attic parts such as at peaks and at eaves outside of knee walls poses a special problem. Nonclosable louvers are quite generally used in such attics or attic parts to permit the circulation of outdoor air, even in winter, on the outside of the vapor barrier and insulation which enclose the

Table 8.10 Heat Loss Rates through Basement Floors and Walls below Grade

Ground Water Temperature	Basement Floor Loss	Basement Wall Loss
Deg. F	Btuh/sq ft	Btuh/sq ft
40	3.0	6.0
50	2.0*	4.0*
60	1.0	2.0

* Average values for general use. (Extracted by permission from *ASHRAE Guide and Data Book, 1961*, The American Society of Heating, Refrigerating, and Air Conditioning Engineers.)

room. This circulation is good for many reasons. In winter, one of the reasons is to allow the air to carry away moisture that may escape from the room to the attic through the vapor barrier. If not removed, such moisture condenses and sometimes freezes on the inside of exterior surfaces causing structural deterioration.

It is apparent, however, that if outdoor air is thus introduced within the construction, the usual over-all U-coefficient which includes the effect of the exterior surface has no meaning. A calculation is usually made of a U-coefficient from the room to the attic air. This may well involve assuming still air conditions in the attic as well as in the room. In using this U-coefficient it is often assumed that the temperature of the attic space is half way between the temperature of the room and that of outdoors. Ventilation methods vary greatly. When large louvers are used it may be safer to assume outdoor wind velocity on the attic side and, in using the coefficient, assume the attic temperature to be the same as that of outdoors.

11. Heat Losses at Edges of Slabs. Unlike basement floors which have a steady, slow rate of heat loss set by a reasonably constant temperature of adjacent earth or ground water, concrete slabs at or near grade have losses which are affected by the proximity of their edges to the outdoor air. To prevent cold floors it is essential to provide 2 in. thick, rigid, moisture-resistant insulation 2 ft wide. Table 8.11 gives the losses per foot of edge for various outdoor design temperatures, assuming heated conditions indoors. Since unheated slabs are seldom satisfactorily comfortable, even with insulation, heat is usually introduced within the slab. Warm air in ducts or warm water in radiant pipes are often at 100 F or more. This increases the heat loss and demands

Table 8.11   Edge-Losses. Heat Loss Rates, Btuh Per Foot of Slab-Edge (House Perimeter) for Insulated Slabs at or near Grade

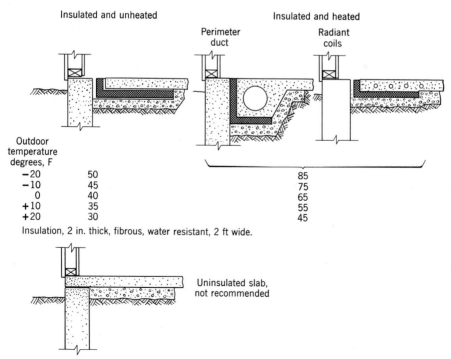

Outdoor temperature degrees, F	Insulated and unheated	Insulated and heated
−20	50	85
−10	45	75
0	40	65
+10	35	55
+20	30	45

Insulation, 2 in. thick, fibrous, water resistant, 2 ft wide.

Uninsulated slab, not recommended

more fuel but it assures warmer floors. Values in Table 8.11 differ from U-coefficients in that they are not quoted for a 1 F difference in temperature but for conditions as existing between a normally heated room (usually 70 to 75 F) and commonly encountered outdoor design conditions. Thus in New York City where 0 F is the usual outdoor design temperature, 100 ft of insulated but unheated slab edge would lose 100 × 40 = 4000 Btuh.

12. Infiltration and Ventilation. Winter winds blow cold outdoor air into indoor spaces through cracks around windows and doors on the windward side of the house. After this air has been warmed by heating units near these locations, the warmed air leaves through similar cracks on the leeward side where there is usually a reduced air pressure on the outside, creating a suction. This process is costly because fuel is required for the warming operation. Losses due to infiltration are part of the heat loss calculations. Weatherstripping reduces the rate of air infiltration. It is customary to expect manufacturers of windows and of sliding-door-and-frame combinations to state the infiltration rates of their products at various wind velocities. These are expressed as the cubic feet of air infiltrating per hour through 1 linear ft of crack between sash and frame or door and frame.

Houses are somewhat tighter than they were in former years. This is good, yet there are reasons why excessive tightness should not be sought. Moisture produced by cooking, bathing, and laundering, and trapped in a tight house will condense on cold exterior glass. Lack of fresh air will finally result in unpleasant house odors. The exhausting of air by fans in kitchens and baths and at laundry dryers helps to solve problems of odor concentrations. The air ejected from the house must be replaced. If the house has very tight doors and windows, air is sometimes unexpectedly drawn down through the flues of fireplaces and heating boilers, disturbing their combustion processes and causing the introduction of dangerous carbon monoxide into the rooms. In large buildings, outdoor air for ventilation is delivered to the rooms at carefully planned rates to reduce odors and to replace the air exhausted by fans from congested or odorous areas. In this case a slight indoor pressure reduces the accidental infiltration that would normally occur at the cracks of exterior openings. The air for ventilation must be warmed before it is admitted, a measure somewhat impractical in houses, except in those using forced warm air heating systems.

There are two methods of establishing the amount of air that will enter a room by infiltration in an hour. Both of these are detailed in Table 8.12. The more accurate method, the crack method, uses the rate of air infiltration through one foot of crack between sash and frame or between door and frame. These values are established by experience and tests. They vary with the velocity of the wind. Since no more than two exterior walls of a room can face the wind, it is suggested that in rooms with three exposures, the openings in the two adjacent walls having the most openings be used. The air change method is only an approximation, but it is often satisfactory. It is assumed that the air in the room changes $\frac{1}{2}$ to 2 times per hour depending upon the number of walls that have openings. In a room with openings on one side the air may be expected to change once per hour. Each hour a roomful of air must be heated from outside temperature to that of the room. In very large buildings it is sometimes customary in calculating the heat loss for the entire building, to deduct one half of the sum of the infiltration losses from all of the rooms. This is based upon the belief that air will enter the openings on the windward side only which represents about half of the exterior faces of the building. It is usually not done for houses or small buildings, where the total loss is assumed to be the sum of all the room losses including in each case the infiltration in the room.

It is, of course, not expected that the two

Table 8.12 Infiltration

Crack Method

Cu ft of air per hr entering between sash (or door) and frame per ft of crack	Wind Velocity, MPH		
Double-Hung Wood Windows	10	20	30
Non-weatherstripped	21	59	104
Weatherstripped	13	36	63
Double-Hung Metal Windows			
Non-weatherstripped	47	104	170
Weatherstripped	19	46	76
Rolled Steel Sash (not weatherstripped)			
Industrial, pivoted	108	244	372
Residential, casement	18	47	74
Wood Doors			
Non-weatherstripped	69	154	249
Weatherstripped	19	51	92

NOTE: These values may be reduced by $\frac{1}{3}$ when storm sash or doors are added to weatherstripped sash or doors and by $\frac{1}{2}$ when added to non-weatherstripped sash or doors.

Air Change (Approximate) Method		Air Changes Taking Place Per Hour
Kind of Room		
No windows or exterior doors		$\frac{1}{2}$
Windows or exterior doors on	1 Side	1
	2 Sides	$1\frac{1}{2}$
	3 Sides	2
Entrance halls		2

(Extracted by permission from *ASHRAE Guide and Data Book, 1961,* The American Society of Heating, Refrigerating, and Air Conditioning Engineers.)

methods will yield comparable results. An example of calculations by both methods could be based on a room 10 × 15 ft by 8 ft high with three 3 × 5 ft high weatherstripped double-hung wood windows on one wall subjected to a 20 mph wind.

EXAMPLE 8.3. By the crack method, the solution would be as follows: The length of crack in one window would be the sum of the lengths of contact between sash and frame and between upper and lower sash. This is twice the height plus three times the width, or 19 ft. Table 8.12 shows the infiltration to be 36 cu ft/hr per ft. Since there are 3 windows, the total hourly air flow would be 3 × 19 × 36 = 2050 cu ft/hr. For

the air change method the wind velocity has no significance because the air change is based upon an average value. The volume of the room 10 × 15 × 8 = 1200 cu ft. Table 8.12 states that, for rooms with openings on one side only, one air change per hour should be assumed. The air change would therefore be 1200 cu ft/hr.

Differences even larger than this and in either direction may be expected. For this reason, the crack method is recommended when the work is important and conditions are known.

After the rate of flow of outdoor air in cu ft/hr into the room is found by either method the calculation for heat loss is simple. The heat required to raise 1 lb of air 1 F is .24 Btu. This is the specific heat value for air. The density of air may be assumed to be represented by an average value of .075 lbs per cu ft. If, for example, the infiltration rate is 2050 cu ft/hr and the outdoor and indoor temperatures are 0 and 70 F, the hourly heat lost in warming this air to room temperature is: 2050 × .075 × .24 × 70 = 2580. The product of the density and the specific heat is .075 × .24 = .018. The expression usually given for the heat lost by infiltration is

$$\text{cu ft/hr} \times .018 \times \Delta t = \text{Btuh} \quad (1)$$

where Δt is the difference in temperature between indoor and outdoor air.

13. Indoor and Outdoor Temperatures. In the design for a controlled environment, temperature is only one of many items to be considered. Chapter 7 deals with the various conditions involved in the total design. Since hourly heat loss rates from buildings with known U-values depend upon the temperature differential between inside and outside air, some thought must be given to the selection of appropriate temperatures. From Table 7.3, it appears that indoor temperatures may range from 55 to 75 F for varied occupancy requirements. The range of outdoor design temperatures in the United States extends from plus 40 in southern Florida to minus 50 in Montana, as shown in Fig. 8.5. This map has been included to facilitate a general grasp of winter conditions throughout the United States. More detailed data may be found in Table 9.1.

If one considers the example of a heated residence, the indoor temperature of which is often 70 F, the design differential in Florida will be 30 and in Montana 120. It is reasonable to expect that the heating system in the Montana residence should have four times the output capacity of that in the Florida residence. The comparative

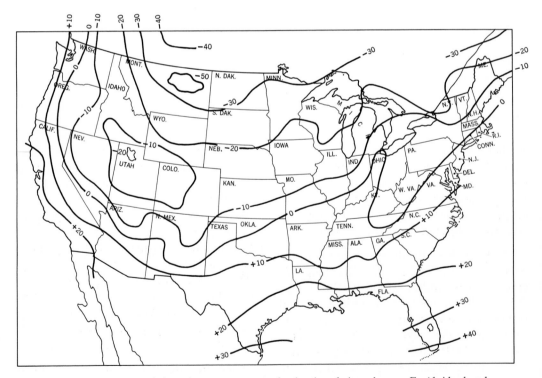

Fig. 8.5 Recommended outdoor temperatures for heating design, degrees F. Abridged and adapted from a comprehensive diagram of the Guide of the American Society of Heating and Air Conditioning Engineers, 34th edition. For specific cities, see Table 9.

Table 8.13   (Example 8.4)   Values for Use in Calculations of Hourly Heat Loss of House in Figure 8.6

Design Conditions

  Indoor temperature 70 F   Outdoor temperature zero (Fig. 8.5)   Wind velocity 20 mph

U Coefficients

Building Surface	*Materials*	*U Coefficient*	*From Table No.*
Walls, lower story	8 in. brick, 1 in. rigid insulation air space, metal lath, $\frac{3}{4}$ in. plaster	.138	8.5 & 8.8
Walls, upper story	$\frac{3}{4}$ in. wood, $\frac{5}{16}$ in. plywood, studs, 2 in. insulation, metal lath, $\frac{3}{4}$ in. plaster	.094	8.5 & 8.8
Roof over living, dining, entry, lounge	build-up roofing, 2 in. insulation, 3 in. wood	.086	8.6 & 8.8
Roof, elsewhere	built-up roofing, 1 in. wood, joists, 4 in. insulation, metal lath, $\frac{3}{4}$ in. plaster	.057	8.6 & 8.8
Wood doors	$1\frac{3}{4}$ in. thick	.48	8.9
Fixed glass	double, $\frac{1}{4}$ in. space	$.61 \times .95 = .58$	8.9
Glass in wood sash	single	$1.13 \times .90 = 1.02$	8.9

Walls Below Grade

4 Btuh per sq ft of wall			8.10

Basement Floors

2 Btuh per sq ft of floor			8.10

Edge Loss, Slab on Grade with Radiant Coils

65 Btuh per linear ft of edge (at zero outdoor temperature)			8.11

Infiltration Rates

Weatherstripped wood casement and awning windows (assumed to be the same as for double-hung)		36 cu ft/hr/ft	8.12
Weatherstripped wood doors		51 cu ft/hr/ft	8.12

yearly fuel use is additionally related to the number of the degrees days in the two locations.

It should be understood that the temperatures given in Fig. 8.5 are not the lowest ever recorded in each locality. These will often be several degrees lower. The recommended outdoor temperature for heating design represents the concensus of many heating designers about the correct temperature assumption for a satisfactory system. To make the system much larger to cope with an infrequent critical day is usually unnecessary. For instance, in Boston,

Massachusetts, where the design temperature is zero, the temperature has been found to drop to minus 8 once in 40 years and to minus 2 once in 20 years. If, on these few days, the house temperature cannot be kept above 62 or 68 F, the slight discomfort will have to be tolerated.

14. Heat Losses from Buildings. The hourly rate of heat loss from a building when the indoor temperature is maintained during critically cold outdoor temperatures is the basis for the selection of a proper central heating unit. The net or minimum rating of the boiler or furnace must match or exceed

Fig. 8.6a (Example 8.4) House at Sands Point, Long Island, New York. View looking west. (Olindo Grossi, Architect)

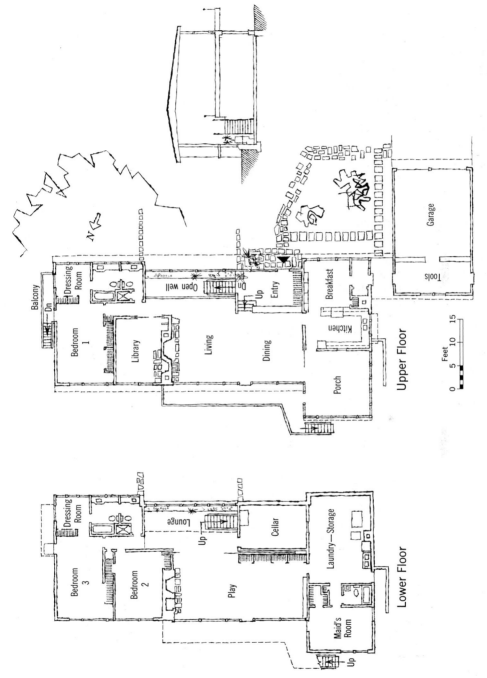

Fig. 8.6b (Example 8.4) Floor plans from which calculations in Table 8.14 were made.

131

Table 8.14   (Example 8.4)   Hourly Heat Loss Calculations for the House in Figure 8.6

Space	Item	Area, Volume or Length*		U Coefficient or Other Unit		Temperature Difference, Inside to Outside		Heat Loss Btuh
Upper Floor								
Living	Wall	70	×	.094	×	70		460
Dining	Glass, double	288	×	.58	×	70		11,700
	Door	21	×	.48	×	70		710
	Roof	600	×	.086	×	70		3,600
	Infiltration	3,600 cu ft/hr	×	.018	×	70		4,500
								20,970
Library	Wall	52	×	.094	×	70		340
	Glass, double	35	×	.58	×	70		1,400
	Glass, single	15	×	1.02	×	70		1,070
	Roof	205	×	.057	×	70		820
	Infiltration	760 cu ft/hr	×	.018	×	70		960
								4,590
Bedroom	Wall	200	×	.094	×	70		1,320
No. 1	Door	21	×	.48	×	70		710
	Glass, double	35	×	.58	×	70		1,420
	Glass, single	25	×	1.02	×	70		1,780
	Roof	300	×	.057	×	70		1,190
	Infiltration	2,260 cu ft/hr	×	.018	×	70		2,850
								9,270
Dressing	Wall	125	×	.094	×	70		820
room and	Door	21	×	.48	×	70		710
baths	Glass, double	60	×	.58	×	70		2,450
	Glass, single	50	×	1.02	×	70		3,570
	Roof	230	×	.057	×	70		920
	Infiltration	3,640 cu ft/hr	×	.018	×	70		4,600
								13,070
Kitchen	Wall	283	×	.094	×	70		1,870
Breakfast	Door	42	×	.48	×	70		1,420
	Glass, double	65	×	.58	×	70		2,630
	Glass, single	55	×	1.02	×	70		3,930
	Roof	390	×	.057	×	70		1,540
	Infiltration	4,600 cu ft/hr	×	.018	×	70		5,800
								17,190
Lower Floor								
Playroom	Wall	31	×	.138	×	70		300
	Door	21	×	.48	×	70		710
	Glass, double	217	×	.58	×	70		8,800
	Slab edge	34 l.f.	×	65 Btu/ft				2,200
	Infiltration	1,000 cu ft/hr	×	.018	×	70		1,260
								13,270

* Unless otherwise indicated, the numbers in this column are areas in square feet.

Table 8.14 (Continued)

Space	Item	Area, Volume or Length*		U Coefficient or Other Unit		Temperature Difference, Inside to Outside	Heat Loss Btuh
Lower Floor, continued							
Bedroom No. 2	Wall	46	×	.138	×	70	450
	Glass, double	35	×	.58	×	70	1,420
	Glass, single	15	×	1.02	×	70	1,070
	Slab edge	12 l.f.	×	65 Btu/ft			780
	Infiltration	760 cu ft/hr	×	.018	×	70	960
							4,680
Bedroom No. 3	Wall	189	×	.138	×	70	1,820
	Door	21	×	.48	×	70	710
	Glass, double	35	×	.58	×	70	1,420
	Glass, single	35	×	1.02	×	70	2,500
	Slab edge	36 l.f.	×	65 Btu/ft			2,350
	Infiltration	2,080 cu ft/hr	×	.018	×	70	2,630
							11,430
Dressing room and baths	Wall	149	×	.138	×	70	1,440
	Door	21	×	.48	×	70	710
	Glass, double	50	×	.58	×	70	2,030
	Glass, single	55	×	1.02	×	70	3,910
	Slab edge	36 l.f.	×	65 Btu/ft			2,350
	Infiltration	3,200 cu ft/hr	×	.018	×	70	4,030
							14,470
Cellar	Wall below grade	144	×	4 Btu/sq ft			576
	Cellar floor	182	×	2 Btu/sq ft			364
							940
Laundry, storage (and heater) room	Wall below grade	304	×	4 Btu/sq ft			1,216
	Cellar floor	362	×	2 Btu/sq ft			724
	Door	21	×	.48	×	70	700
	Infiltration	1,000	×	.018	×	70	1,260
							3,900
Maid's room, bath and closet	Wall	179	×	.138	×	70	1,730
	Door	21	×	.48	×	70	710
	Glass, double	15	×	.58	×	70	610
	Glass, single	30	×	1.02	×	70	2,150
	Roof (porch is above)	256	×	.057	×	70	1,020
	Slab edge	32 l.f.	×	65 Btu/ft			2,080
	Infiltration	2,200 cu ft/hr	×	.018	×	70	2,770
							11,070

Table 8.14 (Continued)

Space	Item	Area, Volume or Length*		U Coefficient or Other Unit		Temperature Difference, Inside to Outside	Heat Loss Btuh
Two-Story Space							
Entry, lounge, and well	Wall	63	×	.094	×	70	420
	Door	21	×	.48	×	70	710
	Glass, double	238	×	.58	×	70	9,650
	Glass, single	120	×	1.02	×	70	8,570
	Roof	504	×	.086	×	70	3,040
	Slab edge	24 l.f.	×	65 Btu/ft			1,560
	Infiltration	8,850 cu ft/hr	×	.018	×	70	11,150
							35,100

Summary

Space	Heat Loss, Btuh
Upper Floor	
Living-dining	20,970
Library	4,590
Bedroom No. 1	9,270
Dressing room and baths	13,070
Kitchen-breakfast	17,190
	65,090
Lower Floor	
Playroom	13,270
Bedroom No. 2	4,680
Bedroom No. 3	11,430
Dressing room and baths	14,470
Cellar	940
Laundry-storage	3,900
Maid's room and bath	11,070
	58,760
Two-Story Space	
Entry, well, and lounge	35,090
	35,090
Total	158,940

slightly the heat loss rate of the building. The convectors, radiators, and air registers, depending on the kind of system used, must be of proper size in each space to make up for the heat loss in that space. Spaces are sometimes grouped to give the heat loss in a selected "zone" of control with its own separate circulator pump, motorized valve, fan, or even a separate heating unit.

EXAMPLE 8.4. An example of typical heat loss calculation summaries is given in Tables 8.13 and 8.14, which relate to the house pictured in Fig. 8.6. In practice they are somewhat more detailed than this, including computations of the areas of all surfaces. For brevity in this example, adjacent small rooms are grouped. When selecting the heating units for these rooms, the heat losses must be calculated separately. The large loss due to infiltration at the open well is due to the 21-hinged, awning-type sash. The floor of the lower story is on the ground and is warmed by radiant coils. It is correct to assume edge losses in rooms such as the playroom which is level with the ground. For the cellar and the laundry-storage space, separate below-grade floor losses (Table 8.10) in Btu/sq ft are used because these floors are a story below grade.

15. Condensation and Vapor Barriers. The air in houses has, at all times, a humidity content. During cold weather when windows and doors are closed, the humidity may be reduced by exhaust fans in kitchens and baths or it may be increased by humidifying devices. The latter process was important when houses were draughty, permitting a large infiltration of dry outdoor air, always very low in absolute moisture content, to replace the indoor air which had picked up humidity from the processes of bathing, cooking, and laundering. Under normal circumstances and without mechanical humidification, the relative humidity in modern, tight houses is usually about 35 percent at 70 F, which is quite moist enough for comfort and health. Indeed, if it were very much greater, there might be considerable difficulty caused by conden-

sation on the cold surfaces of rooms, especially on glass. Reference to the psychrometric chart, Fig. 16.6, will show that air at 70 F and 35 percent RH has a dew point of 41°. The moisture in this air will condense on surfaces that are at or below this temperature. The dew point is found by carrying a horizontal (constant moisture content) line to the left from the intersection of the 70° vertical line and 35 percent RH to the saturation curve. Conversely, if the inside surface temperatures are known, the corresponding relative humidities that can be "tolerated" may be found. The temperatures of single glass, double glass, and an upper-story wall in the house in Fig. 8.6 are 21, 42, and 65.5 F respectively under conditions of steady-state flow from indoor air at 70 F to outdoor air at zero. The relative humidities that could be tolerated without condensation would be, respectively, 15, 36, and 85 percent. It is evident that condensation might be expected on the single glass but not on the double glass or the surface of the wall. Placing the heating elements below the glass improves this situation because the glass is warmed.

The calculation of the surface temperatures or a temperature at any point within the construction is based upon a simple relationship.

$$\text{Temperature drop from room air to the selected point} = \text{Temperature difference, room to outdoors} \times \frac{\text{Resistance from room air to the point}}{\text{Total resistance}}$$

Applied to the three cases, the calculations are as follows:

Material	Temperature Drop Deg F*	Inside Surface Temperature Deg F	Relative Humidity in Room, Upper Limit Percent
Glass, single	$70 \times \frac{.69}{.98} = 49$	$70 - 49 = 21$	15
Glass double	$70 \times \frac{.68}{1.72} = 28$	$70 - 28 = 42$	36
Wall, upper story	$70 \times \frac{.68}{10.60} = 4.5$	$70 - 4.5 = 65.5$	85

* In each case the resistance, room air to surface (.69), is that of the inside surface film.

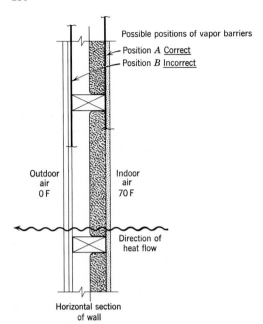

Possible positions of vapor barriers

— Position A <u>Correct</u>

— Position B <u>Incorrect</u>

Outdoor air 0 F

Indoor air 70 F

Direction of heat flow

Horizontal section of wall

Resistances (upper story wall, Fig. 8.2)

		Resistance, Room air to point A .78	Resistance, Room air to point B 8.95
Inside air film	.68		
$\frac{3}{4}$ in. plaster on metal lath	.10		
Insulation (2 in.)	7.25		
Air space	.92		
$\frac{5}{16}$ in. plywood sheathing	.31		
$\frac{3}{4}$ in. wood siding	1.07		
Outside air film	.17		
	10.50	Total resistance	

Vapor Barriers	Temperature Drop, Room to Barrier Position	Temperature at Barrier	Relative Humidity* in Room, Upper Limit
Position A Correct	$70 - \frac{.78}{10.50} = 5.2$	$70 - 5.2 = 64.8$	82%
Position B Incorrect	$70 - \frac{8.95}{10.50} = 59.5$	$70 - 59.5 = 10.5$	8%

Fig. 8.7   Vapor barriers, correct and incorrect.   * From Psychrometric Chart, Fig. 16.6.

Walls and ceilings, even those with apparently tight surfaces such as finished plaster, are pervious to moisture laden air which escapes to colder parts of the construction and there the moisture condenses. This causes dampness, rot, discoloration of finishes, and peeling of exterior paint. When the temperatures are below freezing the condensed moisture becomes ice—which accumulates. Later this melts in large quantities, making the condition noticeably worse. The room with its air and moisture should therefore be contained in a "plastic bag" to prevent the moisture from penetrating to locations colder than the dew point temperature of the room air-moisture mixture. Each construction requires special study. Figure 8.7 indicates correct position A and incorrect position B for a vapor barrier. The barrier may be a film of plastic or other impervious material, well joined, and continuous behind all surfaces of the room.

References

1. *Guide and Data Book 1961*, American Society of Heating, Refrigerating, and Air Conditioning Engineers, 234 Fifth Avenue, New York 1, New York.
2. *The Weather Conditioned House*, Groff Conklin, Reinhold Publishing Corporation, 430 Park Avenue, New York 22, New York.
3. *Design of Insulated Buildings for Various Climates*, Tyler Steward Rogers, F. W. Dodge Corporation, 119 West 40 Street, New York, New York.

Heat Gain

1. Nature of Residential Heat Gain. Because of the rather complex nature of heat gain calculations, discussion of them will be limited largely to their application in houses. For an example (Art. 5), a residence is chosen. If one were to compare the detailed accounting of the hourly heat gain of a residence, an office building, a specialized industrial building, and an auditorium, great differences would be apparent in the sources of the heat. Comparison of a house and an auditorium presents a good example of this. A small house might easily have a cooling load of about 60,000 Btuh. This consists largely of transmission through walls, roof, and glass. If 4 people were in residence, their contribution as part of the 60,000 Btuh would be only $4 \times 400 = 1600$ Btuh. The heat of cooking is largely eliminated by exhaust fans, and lighting imposes a negligible burden. In contrast, an auditorium for 800 people deep within the interior of a building would gain $800 \times 400 = 320,000$ Btuh from occupants, a large gain from lights when they are turned on, and negligible gain from the sun or transmission, the effects of which are absorbed by rooms adjacent to the perimeter. There is little similarity in these 2 examples. Another variation in the pattern of residential and other cooling problems is the relation of the sensible and latent cooling loads. The sensible (increase in air temperature) is built up by general heat flow. The latent load is the heat that must be withdrawn in order to condense the moisture and maintain a reasonable relative humidity. Here again, the auditorium with its moisture-producing crowd and with much fresh air needed for ventilation, but also carrying moisture, would present a greater latent heat problem than a house. On the other hand, houses, within their own category show a similar pattern, one to the other, in which the major items of the cooling load bear some resemblance. All of this suggests that there could be a separate and perhaps a simpler method of calculating heat gains in houses. There is such a method and it is the basis for most of the discussions in this chapter.

The standard reference for heat flow in general is the *Guide and Data Book* of the American Society of Heating, Refrigerating, and Air Conditioning Engineers (ASHRAE). This was used with some adaptation and simplification for heat *loss* calculations in Chapter 8 of this text. The ASHRAE chapters on heat gain are extremely complete and well presented. They form an authentic background for the most resourceful designers and for any expected contingency. Space precludes their use in this book, but, in their place, a recently developed approach, that of the Industry Heat Gain Joint Study Group, which is simpler, but based upon ASHRAE principles, will be used. It is especially intended for residences.

2. Comparison with Heat Loss. The general assumptions and methods of calculating the hourly rate of heat entering a building in the summer are different in almost every respect from those relating to heat loss in winter. The differences occur in transmission through roofs, walls, and glass surfaces and in the heat contributed by people, lighting, bathing, and cooking. As a background against which to discuss the summer problem, brief references to heat *loss* calculations will be helpful. For winter heat loss studies, inside and outside *dry bulb* temperatures are selected. Dry bulb is the actual outside air temperature. For an explanation of *wet bulb* temperature, see Chapter 16. The difference between the selected inside and outside temperatures is a measure of the thermal *pressure* that exists. The U-coefficient of heat transfer is the other factor involved. The product of the temperature difference and the U-coefficient represents the rate of Btuh that pass out of the building through one sq ft of roof, wall or window. Assume a temperature difference of 80 F (inside 70, outside −10). This difference could exist at night or during a sunny day. The night situation would be thermally in accord with the calculations. The intense radiant solar effect of the sun materially reduces this rate during sunny hours. It is correct to say that heat loss transmission calculations are made for night conditions when no relief from the sun is possible. Conversely, heat gain is computed for the sunny hours. There is, however, another variation. If the inside summer temperature is to be 75 F (standard for this chapter) and the outside temperature is to be 90 F, the numerical difference of 15 F is not necessarily the one to be used. The effective difference includes also

the extra thermal pressure effect of the sun. It is called the *equivalent* temperature difference and is identified not only with the sun effect, but also with the kind of construction, with special regard to insulative value, mass, and thermal time lag. A list of common differences is given in Table 9.4. Refer to the equivalent differences in the first vertical column of this table which represents a 90° to 75° actual dry bulb difference. Most of the differences exceed 15° and the highest is 43° which is for roofs. The product of the U-coefficient of transmission and the equivalent temperature difference gives the Btuh/sq ft that pass into the building through the roof, wall, or other construction. It is called the *Heat Transfer Multiplier* (HTM). A number of common ones are summarized in Table 9.2. It is only necessary to multiply the area of a roof, for instance, by its HTM to find the average hourly rate of heat flowing in through the roof during a 24 hr or long-time period.

Some more detailed tables (the ASHRAE method referred to later in this chapter) list HTM's and equivalent temperature differences for various hours of the day. Those in Table 9.2 are the hourly averages for daily operation which is correct for the purposes of Example 9.1 because it is based on 24 hr operation, a standard assumption for the "Joint Study Group" method which is used in Example 9.1.

Through glass the heat gain is large and related to the compass point. One must use its orientation to find the HTM. It is the sum of the absorbed solar energy and the transmission due to the air-to-air temperature difference. See Table 9.3.

Under winter conditions, no credit is taken for the contribution of people who emit about 400 Btuh each when at rest. The reason is that rooms must often be kept up to temperature at times when they are unoccupied. Similarly, no credit is taken for lights, cooking, and other heat contributing processes. The cooling load, however, must be based on the assumption that every potential heat source is operating at once.

There is little difference between summer and winter computations for infiltration. This item, or its counterpart, controlled ventilation, carries a thermal rate-value which is based upon the rate of air flow and the air-to-air temperature difference. Whether air enters through cracks or is mechanically passed through the ventilated space, the sensible heat gain is expressed by the statement.

$$\text{cfm} \times 60 \text{ min/hr} \times \text{air density}$$
$$\times \text{ air specific heat}$$
$$\times \text{ temperature difference} = \text{Btuh} \quad (9.1)$$

3. Standardized Calculation Methods. Always very attractive are approximate or rule-of-thumb methods of arriving at sizes for air conditioners. Cooling load, however, is not usually a suitable subject for such short cuts. Serious errors can develop. Yet simplification of established methods is, to some extent, possible. Particularly in the case of houses it has often been attempted. During recent years the use of air conditioning for residences has increased so greatly that many calculation routines have appeared. Such was their multiplicity and their divergence in results that responsible organizations in the industry felt impelled to act. Discrepancies of as much as 100 percent in the proposed size for some unitary conditioners hastened this decision.

Recently, three prominent associations serving the field of heating and air conditioning joined to form the Industry Heat Gain Joint Study Group to write a correct and simple procedure for calculating heat gains in residences. The participants were the National Warm Air Heating and Air Conditioning Association, the Institute of Boiler and Radiator Manufacturers, and the Air Conditioning and Refrigeration Institute. These organizations have released their report based upon sound principles of heat flow and humidity. Its use presupposes certain limiting conditions which must be observed if results are to be valid. The reference booklet, used in this chapter for the solution of Example 9.1 is *Manual J, Load Calculation,* of the National Warm Air Heating and Air Conditioning Association. It was written under the direction of Herbert T. Gilkey, Director of Technical Services of the Association, and is based upon research and the methods of the *ASHRAE Guide and Data Book.*

Some of the problems that had to be solved related to walls, roofs, glass, infiltration, occupancy, equipment, portions of house to be air conditioned, and period of day during which apparatus would run. Some of the variations to be clarified were; orientation of surfaces, time of day, inside and outside design temperatures, daily temperature range, desired indoor temperature "swing" light and dark exterior surfaces, latent heat (moisture) gain. In stating the objectives, comparison was made to the classic methods of the *ASHRAE Guide and Data Book.*

The three principal limiting conditions on the use of the Joint Study Group method are:

(*a*) That the entire house be air conditioned. If, for instance, a west wing only were conditioned, it might call for operation only in the afternoon. The equipment would need to be oversized for fast pickup at that time, before and after which it would cycle infrequently—permitting warm spots and humidity concentrations to develop.

(*b*) The system is planned for cooling over a 24 hr period. This provides radiantly cool surfaces that help to assure comfort during critically warm times in the several sections of the house when the air temperature might rise slightly.

(*c*) That the unit shall not be oversized. Actually, a slightly undersized plant is preferred. This provides reasonably continuous operation which results in uniform conditions throughout the space. Interior surfaces become cool to help occupants "coast by" periods in which the indoor air temperature might rise a few degrees above the design temperature.

Problems relating to elements in the calculation of residential heat gain, subject to the three limiting conditions just discussed, are resolved as follows:

(*a*) **Design Temperatures.** An inside design temperature of 75 F is considered satisfactory for residences. Outside temperatures vary from 90 to 110 F and the value to be used at any geographic location may be found in Table 9.1. As in the case of outdoor temperatures for heating, they are not the most extreme recorded temperatures, but they are high enough to be the basis for satisfactory conditioning designs.

(*b*) **Outside Daily Temperature Range** (see Fig. 9.1 and Table 9.1). In some of the western dry areas of the country the outside temperatures may drop at night as much as 30 F below the design temperatures. This is considered a high daily temperature range. In coastal regions and near the Mississippi and the Gulf of Mexico the stabilizing effects of large bodies of water keep night temperatures from dropping more than about 15 F, a low daily temperature range. For any specific outside design temperature, the heat gain is further affected by the daily temperature range (high, medium, or low). Low ranges result in greater heat gains. This may be seen in the variation in Heat Temperature Multipliers in Table 9.2.

(*c*) **Walls.** Dark colored walls absorb more heat than light ones. Because wall colors can be changed and heat gain through walls is relatively less than through roofs and glass, no distinction is made in consideration of wall color. Orientation, of course, makes a difference in the heat flow. West walls transmit more heat than north walls. Because of the stipulation that 24 hr operation is expected, the gain through walls of any specific construction is averaged, regardless of orientation, over a period of 24 hrs or the hours during which there is a significant heat gain. The hourly rate thus established can be used as an average value in the calculations.

(*d*) **Roofs.** Since roofs admit more heat than walls because they face the sun, and are less likely to change in color than walls which may sometimes be repainted, a distinction is made between light and dark roof surfaces. The latter are recognized for greater heat transmission. Like walls, however, the Heat Transfer Multipliers (HTM's) of roofs, expressed in Btuh/sq ft, represent an average over the hours of appreciable heat gain. This is different than ASHRAE listings which quote values for roofs (and walls) at various hours of the day.

(*e*) **Glass.** Table 9.3 shows the great variation in gain caused by orientation, glass type and shading. The item of Cooling Load due to Transmitted and Absorbed Solar Energy varies from a minimum of 7 Btuh/ sq ft for north or shaded heat-absorbing double glass to 11 times this value (77 Btuh/ sq ft) for east and west, single, unshaded glass. As in the case of walls or roofs, the rates are averages. One must use the sum of the two items in this table in accord with the note below it.

(*f*) **Infiltration.** This is not a large item in summer because of the light winds. The committee felt justified in assuming $\frac{1}{2}$ air change per hour which is the basis for values in D of Table 9.2. If mechanical ventilation is employed, line E is used instead.

(*g*) **Occupants.** Residences, unlike structures of dense occupancy where sensible and latent gain from people in varying stages of activity is a large item, gain relatively little heat from normally small family groups. *Manual J* suggests making allowance for 2 persons per bedroom and recommends that their combined effect be added at the living space. The *sensible* effect of people is added to the other sensible loads previously discussed. A value of 300 Btuh/person is used. When on line 21 of Table 9.6, 30 percent is added for latent effect, the value per person is raised to 390 which is the approximate total amount (sensible plus latent) for a person at rest.

(*h*) **Equipment.** This load could be a large one. For instance, an 8000 watt electric range at full capacity could add 8000 × 3.41

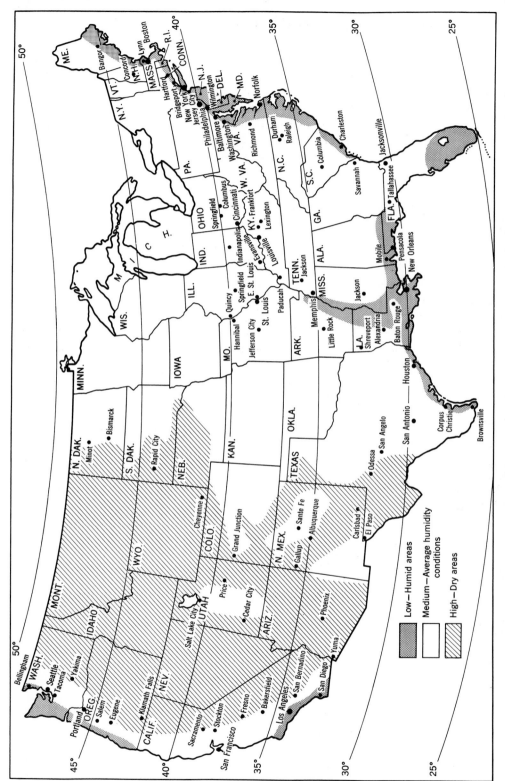

Fig. 9.1 Summer daily temperature range (United States). (From "Load Calculation for Residential Winter and Summer Air Conditioning.")

141

Table 9.1　Outside Design Conditions for United States

State and City	Winter DB	Summer DB	Daily Range	Summer WB	Latitude Deg.	State and City	Winter DB	Summer DB	Daily Range	Summer WB	Latitude Deg.
ALABAMA						**CONNECTICUT**					
Anniston	10	95	M	78	35	Bridgeport	0	85	L	75	40
Birmingham	10	95	M	78	35	Hartford	0	90	M	75	40
Gadsden	10	95	M	78	35	New Haven	0	85	M	75	40
Mobile	20	90	L	80	30	New London	5	85	L	75	40
Montgomery	20	95	M	78	30	Norwalk	0	85	L	75	40
Tuscaloosa	10	95	M	78	35	Torrington	0	90	M	75	40
ALASKA						Waterbury	0	90	L	75	40
Anchorage	−24	—	M	—	60	**DELAWARE**					
Barrow	−48	—	—	—	70	Dover	10	90	M	78	40
Bethel	−43	—	—	—	60	Milford	10	90	M	78	40
Cordova	−13	—	—	—	60	Wilmington	5	90	M	78	40
Fairbanks	−57	—	M	—	65						
Juneau	−5	—	—	—	60	**DIST. OF COLUMBIA**					
Ketchikan	4	—	—	—	55	Washington	10	90	M	78	40
Kodiak	4	—	—	—	55						
Kotzebue	−46	—	—	—	65	**FLORIDA**					
Nome	−36	—	—	—	60	Apalachicola	25	95	L	80	30
Seward	−4	—	—	—	60	Fort Myers	40	95	M	78	25
Sitka	2	—	—	—	60	Gainesville	30	95	M	78	30
ARIZONA						Jacksonville	30	95	M	78	30
Bisbee	30	100	H	72	30	Key West	55	100	L	78	25
Flagstaff	−5	85	H	61	35	Miami	45	90	L	79	25
Globe	30	105	H	76	35	Orlando	35	90	M	78	30
Nogales	30	105	H	72	30	Pensacola	25	95	L	78	30
Phoenix	35	105	H	76	35	Tallahassee	25	95	M	78	30
Tucson	30	100	H	72	30	Tampa	35	95	M	78	30
Winslow	−5	95	H	65	35						
Yuma	40	110	H	78	35	**GEORGIA**					
ARKANSAS						Athens	10	95	M	76	35
Bentonville	0	95	M	76	35	Atlanta	10	95	M	76	35
Fort Smith	5	95	M	76	35	Augusta	20	100	M	76	35
Hot Springs	10	95	M	78	35	Brunswick	25	95	L	78	30
Little Rock	10	95	M	78	35	Columbus	20	100	M	76	35
Pine Bluff	10	95	M	78	35	Macon	20	95	M	78	35
Texarkana	10	100	M	78	35	Rome	10	95	M	76	35
CALIFORNIA						Savannah	25	95	M	78	30
Bakersfield	30	105	H	70	35	Way Cross	25	95	M	78	30
El Centro	35	110	H	78	35						
Eureka	30	90	M	65	40	**IDAHO**					
Fresno	30	105	H	74	35	Boise	−10	95	H	65	45
Long Beach	35	90	M	70	35	Idaho Falls	−15	90	H	65	45
Los Angeles	40	90	L	70	35	Lewiston	−10	95	H	65	45
Montague	15	95	M	70	40	Pocatello	−15	90	H	65	45
Needles	25	115	H	—	35	Twin Falls	−15	95	H	65	40
Oakland	30	80	M	65	40						
Pasadena	40	95	M	70	35	**ILLINOIS**					
Red Bluff	15	100	H	70	40	Aurora	−10	95	M	75	40
Sacramento	30	100	H	72	40	Bloomington	−10	95	M	76	40
San Bernardino	30	105	H	72	35	Cairo	0	100	M	78	35
San Diego	45	80	L	68	35	Champaign	−10	95	M	77	40
San Francisco	35	80	M	65	40	Chicago	−10	95	M	75	40
San Jose	40	90	M	70	35	Danville	−10	95	M	77	40
COLORADO						Decatur	−10	95	M	77	40
Boulder	−15	95	M	64	40	Elgin	−15	95	M	78	40
Colorado Springs	−10	95	H	65	40	Joliet	−10	95	M	76	40
Denver	−10	95	H	64	40	Moline	−10	95	M	76	40
Durango	−5	95	H	65	35	Peoria	−15	95	M	76	40
Fort Collins	−15	95	M	65	40	Rockford	−15	95	M	78	40
Grand Junction	−5	95	H	65	40	Rock Island	−10	95	M	76	40
Leadville	−10	95	M	64	40	Springfield	−10	95	M	77	40
Pueblo	−15	95	H	65	40	Urbana	−10	95	M	77	40

Table 9.1 (Continued)

State and City	Winter DB	Summer DB	Daily Range	Summer WB	Latitude Deg.	State and City	Winter DB	Summer DB	Daily Range	Summer WB	Latitude Deg.
INDIANA						**MARYLAND**					
Elkhart	−10	95	M	75	40	Annapolis	10	90	M	78	40
Evansville	−5	95	M	78	40	Baltimore	10	90	M	78	40
Fort Wayne	−5	95	M	75	40	Cambridge	10	90	L	78	40
Indianapolis	−10	95	M	76	40	Cumberland	0	90	M	75	40
Lafayette	−10	95	M	76	40	Frederick	5	90	M	78	40
South Bend	−10	95	M	75	40	Frostburg	−5	90	M	75	40
Terre Haute	−5	95	M	78	40	Salisbury	10	90	M	78	40
IOWA						**MASSACHUSETTS**					
Burlington	−10	95	M	78	40	Amherst	−5	90	M	75	40
Cedar Rapids	−15	95	M	78	40	Boston	0	85	M	74	40
Charles City	−20	95	M	75	45	Fall River	0	85	L	75	40
Clinton	−15	95	M	78	40	Fitchburg	−5	90	M	75	45
Council Bluffs	−15	100	M	78	40	Framingham	−5	85	L	75	40
Davenport	−10	95	M	78	40	Lawrence	−5	85	L	74	40
Des Moines	−15	95	M	78	40	Lowell	−5	85	L	74	45
Dubuque	−15	95	M	78	40	Nantucket	0	85	L	75	40
Fort Dodge	−15	95	M	78	40	New Bedford	0	85	L	75	40
Keokuk	−15	95	M	78	40	Pittsfield	−10	90	M	75	40
Marshalltown	−15	95	M	78	40	Plymouth	0	85	L	75	40
Sioux City	−15	95	M	78	40	Springfield	−5	90	M	75	40
Waterloo	−15	95	M	78	40	Worcester	−5	90	M	75	40
KANSAS						**MICHIGAN**					
Atchison	−10	100	M	76	40	Alpena	−10	90	M	75	45
Concordia	−10	95	M	78	40	Ann Arbor	−5	90	M	75	40
Dodge City	−10	95	H	78	40	Big Rapids	−5	90	M	75	45
Iola	−5	100	M	75	40	Cadillac	−10	90	M	75	45
Leavenworth	−10	100	M	76	40	Calumet	−20	80	M	73	45
Salina	−10	100	M	78	40	Detroit	−5	90	M	75	40
Topeka	−10	100	M	78	40	Escanaba	−20	85	M	74	45
Wichita	−5	100	M	75	40	Flint	−10	90	M	75	45
						Grand Haven	−5	90	M	75	45
						Grand Rapids	−5	90	M	74	45
KENTUCKY						Houghton	−20	80	M	73	45
Bowling Green	0	95	M	78	35	Kalamazoo	−5	90	M	75	40
Frankfort	0	95	M	78	40	Lansing	−10	90	M	75	45
Hopkinsville	0	95	M	78	35	Ludington	−5	90	M	75	45
Lexington	0	95	M	78	40	Marquette	−15	80	M	73	45
Louisville	0	95	M	78	40	Muskegon	−5	90	M	74	45
Owensboro	0	95	M	78	40	Port Huron	−10	90	M	75	45
Shelbyville	0	95	M	78	40	Saginaw	−10	90	M	75	45
						Sault Ste. Marie	−20	80	M	71	45
LOUISIANA											
Alexandria	20	95	L	78	30	**MINNESOTA**					
Baton Rouge	20	95	M	80	30	Alexandria	−25	85	M	74	45
New Orleans	25	95	L	80	30	Duluth	−25	80	M	71	45
Shreveport	15	95	M	78	35	Minneapolis	−25	90	M	76	45
						Moorhead	−30	95	M	75	45
						St. Cloud	−25	90	M	76	45
MAINE						St. Paul	−25	90	M	75	45
Augusta	−15	85	L	73	45						
Bangor	−20	85	L	73	45						
Bar Harbor	−10	85	L	73	45	**MISSISSIPPI**					
Belfast	−10	85	L	73	45	Biloxi	25	90	L	80	30
Eastport	−10	85	L	70	45	Columbus	10	95	M	78	35
Lewiston	−10	85	L	73	45	Corinth	5	95	M	78	35
Millinocket	−15	85	M	73	45	Hattiesburg	20	95	M	80	30
Orono	−20	85	M	70	45	Jackson	15	95	M	78	30
Portland	−10	85	M	73	45	Meridian	15	95	M	79	30
Presque Isle	−20	85	L	73	45	Natchez	15	95	L	78	30
Rumford	−15	85	L	73	45	Vicksburg	15	95	L	78	30

Table 9.1 (Continued)

State and City	Winter DB	Summer DB	Daily Range	Summer WB	Latitude Deg.	State and City	Winter DB	Summer DB	Daily Range	Summer WB	Latitude Deg.
MISSOURI						**NEW MEXICO**					
Columbia	−10	100	M	78	40	Albuquerque	10	95	M	65	35
Hannibal	−10	95	M	77	40	El Morro	0	85	H	65	35
Kansas City	−10	100	M	76	40	Raton	−5	95	H	65	35
Kirksville	−10	95	M	78	40	Roswell	5	100	H	71	35
St. Joseph	−10	100	M	76	40	Santa Fe	5	90	M	65	35
St. Louis	−5	95	M	78	40	Tucumcari	5	95	H	70	35
Springfield	−5	100	M	77	40						
						NEW YORK					
MONTANA						Albany	−10	90	M	74	45
Anaconda	−30	85	H	59	45	Auburn	−10	90	M	74	45
Billings	−30	90	H	66	45	Binghamton	−5	90	M	72	40
Butte	−30	85	H	59	45	Buffalo	−5	85	M	73	45
Great Falls	−40	90	H	63	50	Canton	−20	85	M	73	45
Havre	−40	95	M	70	50	Cortland	−10	90	M	74	45
Helena	−40	90	H	63	45	Elmira	−5	90	M	73	40
Kalispell	−30	90	H	63	50	Glens Falls	−15	90	M	73	45
Miles City	−35	95	H	69	45	Ithaca	−5	90	M	73	40
Missoula	−30	90	H	63	45	Jamestown	−5	90	M	74	40
						Lake Placid	−15	90	M	73	45
NEBRASKA						New York	5	90	M	76	40
Grand Island	−15	100	H	75	40	Niagara Falls	−5	85	M	73	45
Hastings	−15	100	M	75	40	Ogdensburg	−20	85	M	73	45
Lincoln	−15	95	M	78	40	Oneonta	−10	90	M	73	45
Norfolk	−15	95	M	78	40	Oswego	−5	90	M	74	45
North Platte	−15	100	H	73	40	Port Jervis	0	90	L	75	40
Omaha	−15	100	M	78	40	Rochester	−5	90	M	74	45
Valentine	−20	95	M	78	45	Schenectady	−10	90	M	74	45
York	−15	95	M	78	40	Syracuse	−10	90	M	74	45
						Watertown	−15	85	M	73	45
NEVADA						**NORTH CAROLINA**					
Elko	−10	95	H	63	40	Asheville	5	90	M	75	35
Las Vegas	10	110	H	71	35	Charlotte	15	95	M	78	35
Reno	5	95	H	65	40	Greensboro	10	90	M	76	35
Tonopah	5	90	M	63	40	Hatteras	20	90	L	80	35
Winnemucca	−10	95	H	65	40	New Bern	20	95	L	78	35
						Raleigh	15	95	M	78	35
NEW HAMPSHIRE						Salisbury	10	90	M	78	35
Berlin	−15	85	H	73	45	Wilmington	20	90	M	81	35
Claremont	−15	85	M	73	45	Winston-Salem	10	90	M	76	35
Concord	−10	85	H	73	45						
Franklin	−15	85	M	73	45	**NORTH DAKOTA**					
Hanover	−15	85	M	73	45	Bismarck	−30	95	H	73	45
Keene	−10	85	L	73	45	Devils Lake	−30	90	M	70	50
Manchester	−10	85	M	74	45	Dickinson	−30	95	H	70	45
Nashua	−10	85	L	74	45	Fargo	−30	95	H	75	45
Portsmouth	−5	85	L	74	45	Grand Forks	−30	90	M	72	50
						Jamestown	−30	95	M	73	45
NEW JERSEY						Minot	−35	90	M	71	50
Asbury Park	5	90	L	78	40	Pembina	−35	90	M	73	50
Atlantic City	10	90	L	78	40	Williston	−35	90	M	73	50
Bayonne	0	90	L	75	40						
Belvidere	0	90	M	75	40	**OHIO**					
Bloomfield	0	90	L	75	40	Akron	−5	90	M	75	40
Bridgeton	5	90	L	78	40	Cincinnati	−5	95	M	78	40
Camden	5	90	L	78	40	Cleveland	−5	90	M	75	40
East Orange	0	90	L	75	40	Columbus	−5	90	M	76	40
Elizabeth	0	90	L	75	40	Dayton	−5	90	M	76	40
Jersey City	0	90	L	75	40	Lima	−5	90	M	75	40
Newark	0	90	M	76	40	Marion	−5	90	M	75	40
New Brunswick	5	90	L	75	40	Sandusky	−5	90	M	75	40
Paterson	0	90	L	75	40	Toledo	−5	90	M	75	40
Phillipsburg	0	90	M	75	40	Warren	−5	90	M	75	40
Trenton	0	90	L	78	40	Youngstown	−5	90	M	75	40

Table 9.1 (Continued)

State and City	Winter DB	Summer DB	Daily Range	Summer WB	Latitude Deg.	State and City	Winter DB	Summer DB	Daily Range	Summer WB	Latitude Deg.
OKLAHOMA						**TEXAS**					
Ardmore	5	100	M	78	35	Abilene	5	95	M	74	30
Bartlesville	−5	100	M	77	35	Amarillo	0	95	H	72	35
Guthrie	0	100	M	77	35	Austin	15	100	M	78	30
Muskogee	0	95	M	79	35	Brownsville	30	95	M	80	25
Oklahoma City	0	100	M	77	35	Corpus Christi	25	95	M	80	30
Tulsa	0	100	M	77	35	Dallas	10	100	M	78	35
Waynoka	−5	105	M	75	35	Del Rio	20	100	H	78	30
						El Paso	20	100	M	69	30
OREGON						Fort Worth	10	100	M	78	35
Arlington	5	95	M	68	45	Galveston	25	95	L	80	30
Baker	−15	90	M	66	45	Houston	20	95	M	80	30
Eugene	15	90	H	68	45	Palestine	10	100	M	78	30
Medford	20	95	H	68	40	Port Arthur	20	95	M	80	30
Pendleton	−10	90	H	66	45	San Antonio	20	100	M	78	30
Portland	10	85	M	68	45	Waco	10	100	M	78	30
Roseburg	20	90	H	66	45						
Salem	15	90	H	68	45	**UTAH**					
Wamic	0	90	H	66	45	Logan	−10	95	H	65	40
						Milford	−5	95	H	66	40
PENNSYLVANIA						Ogden	−5	90	H	65	40
Altoona	−5	90	M	75	40	Salt Lake City	0	95	H	65	40
Bethlehem	0	90	M	75	40						
Coatesville	5	90	M	75	40	**VERMONT**					
Erie	−5	85	M	74	40	Bennington	−10	90	M	73	45
Harrisburg	5	90	M	75	40	Burlington	−15	90	M	73	45
New Castle	−5	90	M	75	40	Montpelier	−20	90	M	73	45
Oil City	−5	90	M	75	40	Newport	−20	85	M	73	45
Philadelphia	5	90	M	78	40	Northfield	−20	90	M	73	45
Pittsburgh	−5	90	M	75	40	Rutland	−15	90	M	73	45
Reading	5	90	M	75	40						
Scranton	0	90	M	75	40	**VIRGINIA**					
Warren	−5	90	M	75	40	Cape Henry	15	90	L	78	35
Williamsport	−5	90	M	74	40	Charlottesville	10	90	M	78	40
York	5	90	M	75	40	Danville	10	90	M	78	35
						Lynchburg	10	90	M	76	35
RHODE ISLAND						Norfolk	15	90	L	78	35
Block Island	5	85	L	75	40	Petersburg	10	90	M	78	35
Bristol	0	90	L	75	40	Richmond	10	90	M	78	40
Kingston	0	85	L	75	40	Roanoke	5	90	M	76	35
Pawtucket	0	90	M	75	40	Wytheville	5	90	M	76	35
Providence	0	90	M	75	40						
						WASHINGTON					
SOUTH CAROLINA						Aberdeen	20	85	L	64	45
Charleston	20	90	L	80	35	Bellingham	10	80	L	65	50
Columbia	20	95	M	78	35	Everett	15	80	L	65	50
Florence	20	95	M	79	35	North Head	20	80	L	65	50
Greenville	10	95	M	75	35	Olympia	15	80	M	64	45
Spartanburg	10	95	M	78	35	Seattle	15	80	M	65	50
						Spokane	−15	80	H	65	50
SOUTH DAKOTA						Tacoma	15	80	M	64	45
Aberdeen	−25	95	M	75	45	Tatoosh Island	20	80	L	65	50
Huron	−20	100	H	75	45	Walla Walla	−10	90	H	65	45
Pierre	−20	95	M	73	45	Wenatchee	−10	90	M	65	50
Rapid City	−20	95	H	70	45	Yakima	−5	90	H	67	45
Sioux Falls	−20	95	H	75	45						
Watertown	−25	95	M	73	45	**WEST VIRGINIA**					
						Bluefield	0	95	M	75	35
TENNESSEE						Charleston	0	90	M	75	40
Chattanooga	10	95	M	76	35	Elkins	−5	90	M	73	40
Jackson	5	95	M	78	35	Fairmont	0	90	M	75	40
Johnson City	0	95	M	78	35	Huntington	0	90	M	76	40
Knoxville	5	95	M	75	35	Martinsburg	0	90	M	75	40
Memphis	5	95	M	78	35	Parkersburg	0	90	M	75	40
Nashville	5	95	M	78	35	Wheeling	−5	90	M	75	40

Table 9.1 *(Continued)*

State and City	Winter DB	Summer DB	Daily Range	Summer WB	Latitude Deg.	State and City	Winter DB	Summer DB	Daily Range	Summer WB	Latitude Deg.
WISCONSIN						**WYOMING**					
Ashland	−25	80	M	71	45	Casper	−25	90	H	62	45
Beloit	−15	95	M	78	45	Cheyenne	−20	90	H	62	40
Eau Claire	−20	90	M	75	45	Lander	−30	90	H	65	45
Green Bay	−20	90	M	73	45	Sheridan	−30	90	H	65	45
La Crosse	−20	95	M	75	45	Yellowstone Park	−35	85	H	62	45
Madison	−20	90	M	75	45						
Milwaukee	−15	90	M	75	45						
Oshkosh	−20	90	M	75	45						
Sheboygan	−20	90	M	75	45						

Reprinted from Load Calculation for Residential Winter and Summer Air Conditioning, Manual J of National Warm Air Heating and Air Conditioning Association. (Information on Hawaii not yet recorded.)

Btuh/watt = 27,280 Btuh. But for the reason that modern kitchens have effective exhaust ventilation and that design-level comfort conditions are not expected in kitchens during meal preparation, only 1200 (Btuh) are added at the kitchen.

(*i*) *Latent Heat.* Line 20 of Table 9.6 is the sum of the *sensible* heat gains. If heat were removed from the space at this rate, the indoor design temperature could be maintained. Humidity, however, would increase unless additional heat were extracted from this moisture to condense it and maintain a comfortable relative humidity. The sources of moisture are cooking, bathing, infiltra-

tion of moist warm outdoor air, and the moisture vaporized from human bodies. Experience has shown that in houses the latent heat rate to condense this moisture is about 30 percent of the sensible heat rate which affects the air temperature. Therefore, in Table 9.6, line 21, *total* heat gains appear which are 1.3 times those in line 20.

(*j*) *Indoor Temperature Swing.* *Manual J* recommends slightly undersizing the cooling unit, so that in the short period following the day's maximum outdoor temperature the indoor temperature may be expected to rise 3 to 6 F (see Fig. 9.2) and that accordingly the thermostat be set down 3 F to accommodate half of this swing. Table 9.5 gives multipliers for use in sizing equipment. Since Table 9.5 lists multipliers that purport to *reduce* the calculated maximum heat gain in the house to a value that can be used for selecting slightly undersized equipment, an explanation needs to be made of the fact that some of the multipliers exceed 1.0. This table does double duty. The Air Conditioning and Refrigeration Institute (ARI) capacity ratings of equipment are for conditions of 80 F indoors and 95 F outdoors. On the basis of indoor temperature, only *larger* equipment must be selected because the standard indoor temperature of the *Manual J* method is 75 F. For outdoor temperatures above 95 F still larger units would

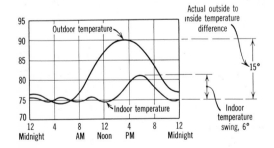

Fig. 9.2 Temperature variations. This "swing" is above a thermostat setting of 75°. *Manual J* suggests setting the thermostat at 73° to "center" the swing around the inside design temperature. This condition is for an outside design temperature of 90°. On critically warm days a thermostat setting of 72° is preferred. The actual temperature will, in this case, not exceed 78°.

be necessary since ARI ratings refer to cooling outdoor air at 95 F. In some cases the increase that is indicated for these reasons exceeds the reduction called for by the intention to undersize. In these cases the multiplier may exceed unity. Equipment selected after the use of these multipliers, even those exceeding 1.0, will be undersized and will produce a swing.

4. Planning for Minimum Residential Heat Gain. To minimize heat gain, the design really begins with the selection of the site, consideration of desirable orientations and views, and decisions concerning the location of glass and the relative areas of glass and the more heat-resistant insulated construction. Unlike heat loss, the reduction of which is directly accomplished by insulation, double glazing, and the like, heat gain is a more complex thing which is likely to influence the architectural design.

Direct sunshine through glass is especially to be avoided, yet compromises are always faced in the interest of esthetics. The Azzarone Residence of Ex. 9.1 has some east and west glass behind which the sun is intercepted by interior blinds. Consideration of views will often dictate the acceptance of conditions which do not offer the most economical thermal results. When sun is so admitted it is well to blanket the sunny wall with a direct, fan-like air delivery from floor registers which was done in this residence.

Figure 9.3 evaluates the morning, noon, and afternoon thermal bombardment by the sun, reaching a maximum at noon of 290 Btuh/sq ft. A single pane of glass normal to the sun's rays would admit nearly all of this fierce heat which exceeds the amount delivered by a sq ft of cast iron radiation in a steam heating system (240 Btuh/sq ft). Reference to Table 9.3, which is averaged for a day's performance, still shows east and west glass to admit an average of 60 and 70 Btuh/sq ft. The architect, in forming his design, will search for the smaller numbers in this table and in Table 9.2 where it is found that common walls and roofs admit

heat at a rate varying between about 2 and 20 Btuh/sq ft. These tables are, in a sense, the thermal market in which he can shop for constructions that will be advantageous if they are otherwise admissable in his general design. The assistance of the engineer at this stage can be helpful. It may be to the ultimate advantage of the owner to authorize preliminary heat gain calculations for several possible schemes.

Idealistic objectives may be listed as follows. The quoted numbers are approximate.

(*a*) Double glazing, which reduces the heat transmission through single shaded glass by about 50 percent at critical hours and 20 percent on the daily average. See Table 9.3.

(*b*) No sun on any glass.

(*c*) Full insulation in all construction, especially roofs.

(*d*) Use of thick masonry walls whose thermal time lag often delays full transmission by as much as 12 hrs.

(*e*) Shading of every possible surface of the house by deciduous trees whose leafless winter condition will advantageously admit sun.

(*f*) Outside baffles, shades or blinds which reduce gain by 70 percent at critical hours as compared to interior devices whose value is only about 10 to 30 percent.

(*g*) Effective ventilation of attics or spaces between double roofs. Insulation should be in the ceiling or lower surface.

(*h*) Windows weatherstripped and closed. Controlled ventilation by admission of outdoor air, tempered in the conditioner and added to the recirculated air, pressurizes the house slightly and retards random warm infiltration from outdoors.

5. Typical Heat Gain Calculations

EXAMPLE 9.1 Calculate the total hourly heat gain, sensible plus latent, for the Azzarone Residence (Figs. 9.4 and 9.5) on the basis of the design conditions and construction summarized in the lower part of Table 9.6.

Table 9.2 Heat Transfer Multiplier

Daily Temperature Range	Low		Medium				High				Coefficient of Thermal Conductivity
Outside Design Temperature, F	90	95	90	95	100	105	95	100	105	110	U
A. WALLS AND DOORS											
No. 1 Frame and veneer-on-frame											
(a) No insulation	6.0	7.2	4.8	6.0	7.5	8.7	4.8	6.0	7.5	8.7	0.26
(b) Less than 1-in. insulation, or 1 reflective air space	4.3	5.1	3.5	4.5	5.4	6.3	3.5	4.5	5.4	6.3	0.19
(c) 1- to 2-in. insulation, or 2 reflective air spaces	2.9	3.6	2.4	3.1	3.7	4.4	2.4	3.1	3.7	4.4	0.13
(d) More than 2-in. insulation, or 3 reflective air spaces	1.8	2.2	1.5	1.9	2.3	2.7	1.5	1.9	2.3	2.7	0.08
No. 2 Masonry walls, 8-in. block or brick											
(a) Plastered or plain	7.2	9.7	5.4	7.9	10.4	12.5	5.4	7.9	10.4	12.5	0.48
(b) Furred, no insulation	4.6	6.0	3.4	4.9	6.3	7.9	3.4	4.9	6.3	7.9	0.30
(c) Furred, with less than 1-in. insulation, or 1 reflective air space	3.1	4.1	2.3	3.3	4.3	5.4	2.3	3.3	4.3	5.4	0.20
(d) Furred, with 1- to 2-in. insulation, or 2 reflective air spaces	2.1	2.8	1.6	2.3	3.0	3.7	1.6	2.3	3.0	3.7	0.14
(e) Furred, with more than 2-in. insulation or 3 reflective air spaces	1.4	1.8	1.0	1.5	1.9	2.4	1.0	1.5	1.9	2.4	0.09
No. 3 Partitions											
(a) Frame, finished 1 side only, no insulation	8.5	11.4	6.0	9.1	12.0	15.0	6.0	9.1	12.0	15.0	0.60
(b) Frame, finished both sides, no insulation	4.8	6.6	3.4	5.1	6.9	8.5	3.4	5.1	6.9	8.5	0.34
(c) Frame, finished both sides, more than 1-in. insulation, or 2 reflective air spaces	2.0	2.7	1.4	2.1	2.8	3.5	1.4	2.1	2.8	3.5	0.14
(d) Masonry, plastered one side, no insulation	2.6	4.4	1.2	3.0	4.7	6.6	1.2	3.0	4.7	6.6	0.35
No. 4 Wood doors. (Consider glass area of doors as a window)	11.4	14.0	9.4	12.0	14.0	17.0	9.4	12.0	14.0	17.0	0.50

* Heat Transfer Multiplier for cooling equals the "U" value times the Equivalent Temperature Difference. For Outside Design Temperatures not listed use nearest Design Temperature and for constructions not listed here, obtain Equivalent Temperature Difference from Table 9.4 and "U" value.

† Thermal conductivity of roof-ceiling combination, from Guide (Multiply by Equivalent Temperature Differential to obtain Heat Gain Factor).

‡ Thermal conductivity of ceiling only, calculated.

From *Load Calculation for Residential Winter and Summer Air Conditioning, Manual J* of National Warm Air Heating and Air Conditioning Association.

B. CEILINGS AND ROOFS

No. 1 Ceilings under naturally vented attic or vented flat roof

Description											U†	U‡
(a) Uninsulated (attic must be vented for cooling) —dark	10.0	11.0	9.1	10.0	11.4	12.5	9.1	10.0	11.4	12.5	0.23	0.44
—light	8.2	9.1	7.2	8.2	9.4	10.4	7.2	8.2	9.4	10.4		
(b) Less than 2-in. insulation, or 1 reflective air space —dark	4.3	4.8	3.9	4.4	4.9	5.4	3.9	4.4	4.9	5.4	0.10	0.13
—light	3.5	4.1	3.1	3.6	4.1	4.6	3.1	3.6	4.1	4.6		
(c) 2- to 4-in. insulation, or 2 reflective air spaces —dark	2.6	2.9	2.3	2.6	2.9	3.2	2.3	2.6	2.9	3.2	0.06	0.075
—light	2.1	2.4	1.9	2.2	2.5	2.8	1.9	2.2	2.5	2.8		
(d) More than 4-in. insulation, or 3 or more reflective air spaces —dark	1.8	1.9	1.6	1.8	2.0	2.2	1.6	1.8	2.0	2.2	0.04	0.045
—light	1.4	1.6	1.2	1.4	1.6	1.8	1.2	1.4	1.6	1.8		

No. 2 Built-up roof, no ceiling

Description											U†	U‡
(a) Uninsulated —dark	17.0	19.0	16.0	18.0	20.0	22.0	16.0	18.0	20.0	22.0	0.40	
—light	14.2	16.4	12.5	14.0	16.0	18.0	12.5	14.0	16.0	18.0		
(b) 2-in. roof insulation —dark	8.5	9.7	7.9	8.7	9.7	11.0	7.9	8.7	9.7	11.0	0.20	
—light	6.9	7.9	6.3	7.2	8.2	9.1	6.3	7.2	8.2	9.1		
(c) 3-in. roof insulation —dark	6.0	6.6	5.4	6.3	6.9	7.5	5.4	6.3	6.9	7.5	0.14	
—light	4.9	5.6	4.3	5.1	5.6	6.3	4.3	5.1	5.6	6.3		

Description											U†	U‡
No. 3 Ceilings under unconditioned rooms	2.7	3.6	1.9	2.9	3.8	4.8	1.9	2.9	3.8	4.8	0.19	

C. FLOORS

Description											U†	U‡
No. 1 Over unconditioned rooms	3.4	4.6	2.4	3.6	4.8	6.0	2.4	3.6	4.8	6.0	0.24	
No. 2 Over basement, enclosed crawl space, or concrete slab on ground	0	0	0	0	0	0	0	0	0	0		
No. 3 Over open space	4.8	6.6	3.4	5.1	6.9	8.5	3.4	5.1	6.9	8.5	0.34	

D. INFILTRATION, BTUH PER SQ FT OF GROSS EXPOSED WALL AREA

1.1	1.5	1.1	1.5	1.9	2.2	1.6	1.9	2.2	2.6	

E. MECHANICAL VENTILATION, BTUH PER CFM

16.0	22.0	16.0	22.0	27.0	32.0	22.0	27.0	32.0	38.0	

Table 9.3 Glass Heat Transfer Multiplier

Cooling Load Due to Transmitted and Absorbed Solar Energy

Direction Window Faces	Regular Single-Glass	Regular Double-Glass	Heat-Absorbing Double-Glass
NO AWNINGS OR INSIDE SHADING			
N. (or shaded)	19	17	10
N.E. and N.W.	52	44	25
E. and W.	77	66	40
S.E. and S.W.	66	57	33
S.	36	31	19
DRAPERIES OR VENETIAN BLINDS			
N. or (shaded)	11	10	7
N.E. and N.W.	28	25	18
E. and W.	44	40	28
S.E. and S.W.	36	33	22
S.	19	18	13
ROLLER SHADES HALF-DRAWN			
N. (or shaded)	14	13	8
N.E. and N.W.	36	36	22
E. and W.	57	52	33
S.E. and S.W.	48	44	28
S.	25	25	16
AWNINGS			
N. (or shaded)	16	11	8
N.E. and N.W.	17	12	9
E. and W.	18	12	10
S.E. and S.W.	17	12	9
S.	16	11	9

Cooling Load Due to Air-to-Air Temperature Difference

Outdoor Design Temperaure	90	95	100	105	110
Single glass	8	12	16	19	25
Double glass	4	7	9	11	13

NOTE: The Heat Transfer Multiplier for glass is obtained by adding the appropriate factor for transmitted and absorbed solar energy and the factor for air-to-air temperature difference. These factors are expressed in Btuh per sq ft—30° and 40° north latitude.

From *Load Calculation for Residential Winter and Summer Air Conditioning, Manual J* of National Warm Air Heating and Air Conditioning Association.

Table 9.4 Equivalent Temperature Differences

Design Temperature, F	90		95			100			105		110
Daily Temperature Range*	L	M	L	M	H	L	M	H	M	H	H
A. WALLS AND DOORS											
1. Frame and veneer-on-frame	22.6	18.6	27.6	23.6	18.6	32.6	28.6	23.6	33.6	28.6	33.6
2. Masonry walls, 8-in. block or brick	15.3	11.3	20.3	16.3	11.3	25.3	21.3	16.3	26.3	21.3	26.3
3. Partitions, a, b, c, frame;	14.0	10.0	19.0	15.0	10.0	24.0	20.0	15.0	25.0	20.0	25.0
d, masonry	7.5	3.5	12.5	8.5	3.5	17.5	13.5	8.5	18.5	13.5	18.5
4. Wood doors	22.6	18.6	27.6	23.6	18.6	32.6	28.6	23.6	33.6	28.6	33.6
B. CEILINGS AND ROOFS											
1. Ceilings under naturally vented attic											
or vented flat roof —dark	43.0	39.0	48.0	44.0	39.0	53.0	49.0	44.0	54.0	49.0	54.0
—light	35.0	31.0	40.0	36.0	31.0	45.0	41.0	36.0	46.0	41.0	46.0
2. Built-up roof, no ceiling —dark	43.0	39.0	48.0	44.0	39.0	53.0	49.0	44.0	54.0	49.0	54.0
—light	35.0	31.0	40.0	36.0	31.0	45.0	41.0	36.0	46.0	41.0	46.0
3. Ceilings under unconditioned rooms	14.0	10.0	19.0	15.0	10.0	24.0	20.0	15.0	25.0	20.0	25.0
C. FLOORS											
1. Over unconditioned rooms	14.0	10.0	19.0	15.0	10.0	24.0	20.0	15.0	25.0	20.0	25.0
2. Over basement, enclosed crawl space, or concrete slab on ground	0	0	0	0	0	0	0	0	0	0	0
3. Over open crawl space	14.0	10.0	19.0	15.0	10.0	24.0	20.0	15.0	25.0	20.0	25.0

*Daily Temperature Range

L (Low) Calculation Value: 12
    Applicable Range: less than 15 F
M (Medium) Calculation Value: 20
    Applicable Range: 15 to 25 F
H (High) Calculation Value: 30
    Applicable Range: more than 25 F

From *Load Calculation for Residential Winter and Summer Air Conditioning, Manual J* of National Warm Air Heating and Air Conditioning Association.

Table 9.5 Capacity Multiplier for Selection of Air-Cooled and Evaporatively-Cooled Air Conditioning Units

(Based upon the calculated heat gain and the Standard ARI equipment capacity rating.)

Outside Design Conditions		Desired Indoor Temperature Swing, Degrees		
Temperature, F	Daily Range	6	4½	3
90	M	0.69	0.83	0.97
	L	0.71	0.84	0.98
95	H	0.74	0.88	1.02
	M	0.75	0.89	1.03
	L	0.77	0.90	1.04
100	H	0.81	0.95	1.08
	M	0.82	0.96	1.09
105	H	0.86	1.01	1.16
	M	0.87	1.02	1.17
110	H	0.92	1.07	1.22

This table to be used according to the relationship: (Calculated Heat Gain) × (Capacity Multiplier) = (Equipment Standard ARI Capacity Rating).
From *Load Calculation for Residential Winter and Summer Air Conditioning, Manual J* of National Warm Air Heating and Air Conditioning Association.

Areas are calculated for walls, roof, and for the floor above the covered outdoor sitting area as well as for glass (double and single; shaded and unshaded; blinds and no blinds). The Heat Transfer Multipliers are entered next. They are based upon a 75 F indoor temperature. The relative HTM values for the various elements of enclosing construction and some of the glass walls make an interesting study. Arranged in order of their transmitting values, they are as follows:

Item	HTM (Btuh)
Floor, concrete, 4 in. + insulation	1.6
Walls, studs, insulated	2.9
Walls, brick or stone	4.6
Roof, concrete, 2 in. insulation	6.9
Doors	11.4
Glass, double, north, blinds	14.0
Glass, double, east or west, blinds	44.0
Glass, single, east or west, no blinds	85.0

The products of areas and HTM's are entered and totaled for each room. Infiltration is computed as positive ventilation because outside air is drawn in through the conditioners to pressurize the house and minimize random infiltration. This air must be cooled. Using formula 9.1, it is possible to check the sensible heat HTM of 16 (Btuh) for each 1 cfm which was selected from Table 9.2. The temperature difference, air to air, is 15 F.

The formula

$$\text{cfm} \times 60 \text{ min/hr} \times \text{air density} \times \text{air specific heat} \times \text{temp. difference} = \text{Btuh}$$

Substituting

$$1 \times 60 \times .075 \times .24 \times 15 = 16 \text{ Btuh/cfm}$$

The total cfm of outdoor air delivered to the house (340) is apportioned to the rooms in ratio to the room volumes. The products of these and the HTM 16 expresses the room sensible heat gains due to ventilation. (Line 18, Table 9.6.)

The 300 Btuh *sensible* gain per person is multiplied by 8 (2 people per bedroom, including the 2 future bedrooms downstairs) for an entry of 2400 in line 19. This item is charged to the living space since occupants are likely to be there during the critically warm hours of the day. The standard 1200 Btuh sensible heat gain in the kitchen is also entered.

To add an amount that represents the latent (moisture) heat gain, each room's

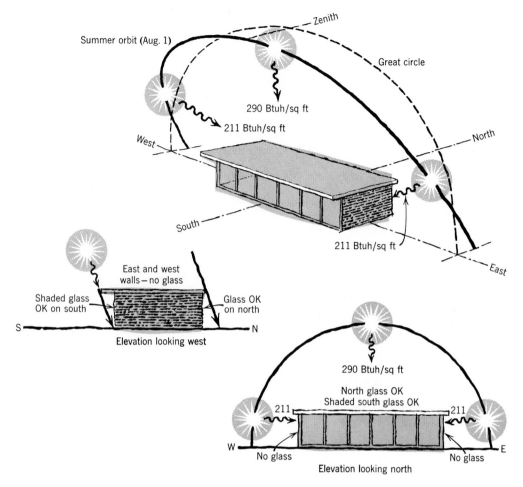

Fig. 9.3 Protection against heat gain. Shielding the interior from the radiant effect of the sun by insulated construction or heavy masonry is the first step. Glass is not a good choice within this orbit. When used it should be in full shade of trees or outside baffles. Values are approximate and for conditions on August 1st at 40° north latitude.

sensible heat gain is multiplied by 1.3 to produce the values in line 21.

For a swing of about 6 F, use multiplier .71 from Table 9.5. It is for a 90 F outside temperature and a *low* daily temperature range. The latter is chosen from Fig. 9.2 where Long Island is shown in the low category. This is a rather special condition because Long Island is surrounded by water. Almost all other locations in New York State (see Table 9.1) are classified in the *medium* daily temperature range.

95,800 × .71 = 68,000 Btuh at ARI

Standard Rating Conditions. Select a 6-ton unit. A ton of refrigeration, based upon old standards is the rate of heat flow that would melt a ton of ice in 24 hours. This establishes a rate of 12,000 Btuh.

12,000 × 6 = 72,000 Btuh. This is close to the 68,000 that would cause approximately a 6 F swing. The swing will actually be a little less than 6 F. Ratings are now usually expressed in Btuh in preference to the term, *tonnage*.

When a cooling unit is chosen, i.e., the 72,000 Btuh unit just discussed, the cir-

Fig. 9.4 (Example 9.1) West facade, Azzarone residence, Lattingtown, Long Island, N.Y. View looking northeast from garage wall. (Bentel and Bentel, Architects)

culation rate of the air must relate to the cooling capacity of the unit to assure proper heat transfer performance between coils and air. In Table 9.6, therefore, the totals in line 21 are adjusted (downward, in this case in the ratio of $\frac{72,000}{95,800} = .75$. In the design of the air conditioning system, the adjusted values and their total in line 22 will form the basis for the computation of air rates to the several spaces.

Planning for a small heat gain is evident in the west elevation (Fig. 9.4) so vulnerable to the sun. The dining room and the entire lower story are protected from the western sun by masonry walls. Deciduous trees (this is a winter photograph) develop foliage that shades the kitchen and the master bedroom in the summer. No credit was taken for this extra shade. This is conservative because some of the trees could die. Beyond the bridge entrance two 36,000 Btuh air-cooled air conditioners project through the lower story stone wall at the location of the utility room. The projecting ends draw in air to cool the compressors and condense the refrigerant, after which this heated air is ejected laterally below the upper-story overhang.

6. General Heat Gain Problems. The foregoing articles of this chapter have applied to a problem that is rather special—the cooling load for a residence. This specialty was chosen because residential heat gains are

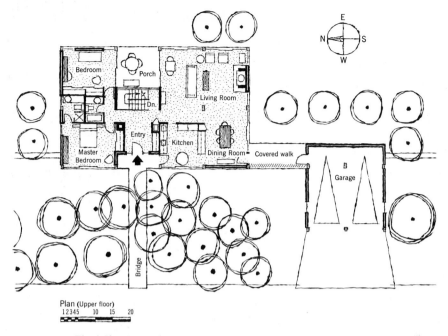

Fig. 9.5*b* (Example 9.1) Plan of upper floor, Azzarone residence.

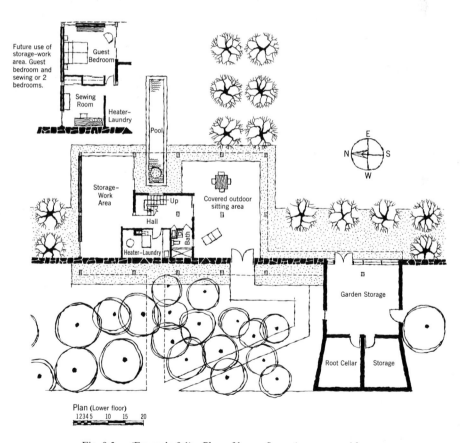

Fig. 9.5*a* (Example 9.1) Plan of lower floor, Azzarone residence.

155

Table 9.6 (Example 9.1) Heat Gain Calculation, Azzarone Residence, Using Method of Manual J, National Warm Air Heating and Air Conditioning Association

Worksheet—Heat Loss* and Heat Gain Calculations

			Const. No.	HTM	Area or Length	Btuh	Area or Length	Btuh	Area or Length	Btuh	Area or Length	Btuh
1	Name of room				*Entire House*		¹ *Liv-Din-Kit*		² *Entry*		³ *Master B.R.*	
2	Room size, ft						26 × 34		12 × 18		13 × 16	
3	Running ft, exposed wall											
4	Ceiling height, ft						8 +		8		8 +	
5*	Room compass direction						E, S, W, N		E, W		W, N	
Type of Exposure												
14	Glass and Doors	Single W		85			48	4080				
		Double W		44			84	3700	21	924	105	4620
		Single N		27			20	540				
		Double N		14			70	980			21	294
		Single E		85			48	4080				
		Double E		44			168	7400	84	3700		
		Single S		44								
		Double S		22			140	3080				
		Doors		11.4			21	240	21	240		
15	Net exposed walls and partitions	a		4.6			140	640	42	192	70	322
		b		2.9								
		c										
		d										
16	Warm ceilings			6.9			890	6100	216	1490	218	1510
17	Warm floors			1.6			890	1420				
18	Infiltration (ventilation)			16	340 cfm		126 cfm	2020	31 cfm	496	30 cfm	480
19	People/appliances				8 People/1 Kit.		{ 2400 { 1200					
20	Sensible Btu gain							37,880		7,042		7,226
21	Total Btu gain (add 30%)			1.3	95,800		49,300		9,200		9,400	
22	Btuh for air quantities			.75	72,000		37,100		6,900		7,100	

(Column labeled "See Manual J, NWAHACA" runs vertically alongside the Const. No. column.)

* This form, J-1, *Manual J,* NWAHACA, was originated for heat loss and gain calculations. Used here for heat gain only, it is abridged by omitting lines 6 thru 13 which pertain to heat *loss.*

Assumed Design Conditions

Location—Long Island, New York
Outside design temperature—90 F, dry bulb; 76 F, wet bulb
Inside design temperature—75 F
Daily temperature range—Low
Line 18—Ventilation at the rate of one air change per hour
Swing 6 deg. F (Table 9.5) 95,800 × .71 = 68,000 Btuh
Use unit with capacity of 72,000 Btuh

4 Baths		*5 Bedroom*		*6 Lower Hall*		*7 Future Toilet*		*8 Storage- Work-Heater*		9		10	
8 × 16		13 × 16		11 × 17		7 × 8		Irregular					
8+		8+		9		9		9					
N		E, N		E, S		S, W		E, S, W, N					
Area or Length	*Btuh*	*Area or Length*	*Btuh*	*Area or Length*	*Btuh*	*Area or Length*	*Btuh*	*Area or Length*	*Btuh*	*Area or Length*	*Btuh*	*Area or Length*	*Btuh*
								23	620				
21	294							40	560				
		24	2030										
		42	1840	36 × 14 Shaded	505			54	2376				
		20	880										
		70	1540	27 × 14 Shaded	380	23 × 14 Shaded	308	81 × 14 Shaded	1130				
				21	240								
35	161	147	675	117	540	63	290	456	2100				
				36	104	54	156						
128	885	218	1510										
17 cfm	272	30 cfm	480	27 cfm	430	8 cfm	128	71 cfm	1140				
	1,612		8,955		2,199		882		7,926				
	2,100		11,600		2,800		1,100		10,300				
	1,500		8,800		2,100		800		7,700				

Construction

Walls—Masonry, cavity brick. Use A-2(*b*) Table 9.2. Stud, 2 in. insulation. Use A-1(*c*) Table 9.2.
Roofs—4 in. concrete, 2 in. insulation. Light color, closest HTM is B-1(*b*) Table 9.2.
Glass—General, double, with interior blinds. Upper curved segments, single, no blinds.
Floors (above terrace)—4 in. concrete, 4 in. insulation. Use C-3 Table 9.2, but adjust to 1.6 (4.8/3) because of U-value less than .11 instead of 3.4.

calculable by the simplified method recently developed by the joint efforts of several prominent associations. Based upon 24 hour operation and several other limiting requirements, the cooling load for a residence is by no means typical of the diverse problems in heat gain that would be encountered by the average busy architect or consulting engineer.

It has been seen that the major components of the cooling load are:

(a) Transmission through walls and roof
(b) Transmission through glass
(c) Occupants
(d) Infiltration or ventilation
(e) Appliances

For items c, d and e there can be a moisture gain in addition to a sensible heat gain. When computations are undertaken for a wide variety of buildings such as theaters, department stores, sports arenas, and offices, each with a different configuration, occupancy and specific hours of use, great differences in the magnitude and importance of the above 5 items may be expected and the ratio of sensible to total heat will also vary considerably. Two factors become quickly apparent. Data, far more detailed than that for a residence are needed and the rates of gain must relate, not to 24 hrs but to the specific hours of expected use.

The valuable reference material of the ASHRAE *Guide and Data Book* is available to those whose investigations must be resourceful. A *few* tables have been chosen from the *Guide* to help here in presenting the general nature of these studies. They illustrate:

Table No.   Subject

(a) 9.7   Design Room Conditions (for *outdoor* conditions, Table 9.1 of this chapter is applicable)
(b) 9.8   Outdoor air requirements (Ventilation)
(c) 9.9   Temperature Differentials, Roofs
(d) 9.10   Heat Gain from Occupants
(e) 9.11   Heat Gain from Appliances (partial list)

In Chapter 7, a few standards of minimum ventilation rates were quoted. For spaces of special occupancy such as meeting rooms, board rooms, and cocktail bars, special high rates of ventilation are necessary (see Table 9.8). Cooling and dehumidifying this warm and moist outdoor air can be an expensive item. The use of Tables 9.1 and 9.7 is valuable in finding the heat to be removed.

Transmission rates for walls, roofs, floors, and glass at various hours under varying conditions make a very large compilation of data. Selected for consideration is Table 9.9

Table 9.7 Design Room Conditions Usually Specified for Summer Average Peak Load in Comfort Air Conditioning*

Type of Installation	Dry-Bulb Temp.	Wet-Bulb Temp.†	Relative Humidity Percent	Grains Per Lb†	Effective Temp.‡
Ample capacity	78	65	50	72.7	72.2
Practical application	80	67	51	78.5	74.0
Occupancy—15 to 40 min	82	68	49	80.0	75.3

* Values in Table 9.7 are for *peak load* conditions. It is general practice to operate a system at approximately 75 F and 50 percent relative humidity at other than peak load.
† Psychrometric data for standard barometric pressure.
‡ Air movement 15 to 25 fpm.
(Reprinted by permission from *ASHRAE Guide and Data Book, 1961,* The American Society of Heating, Refrigerating, and Air Conditioning Engineers.)

*Table 9.8 Outdoor Air Requirements**

| Application | Smoking | Cfm per Person† | | Cfm per Sq† Ft of Floor |
		Recommended	Minimum‡	Minimum‡
Apartment				
Average	Some	20	10	. . . .
DeLuxe	Some	20	10	. . . .
Banking space	Occasional	10	$7\frac{1}{2}$	. . . .
Barber shops	Considerable	15	10	. . . .
Beauty parlors	Occasional	10	$7\frac{1}{2}$	. . . .
Brokers' board rooms	Very heavy	50	20	. . . .
Cocktail bars		40	25	. . . .
Corridors (supply or exhaust)		. . .	. . .	0.25
Department stores	None	$7\frac{1}{2}$	5	0.05
Directors' rooms	Extreme	50	30	. . . .
Drug stores‖	Considerable	10	$7\frac{1}{2}$	. . . .
Factories§, ¶	None	10	$7\frac{1}{2}$	0.10
Five and Ten Cent stores	None	$7\frac{1}{2}$	5	. . . .
Funeral parlors	None	10	$7\frac{1}{2}$	. . . .
Garages§		. . .	. . .	1.0
Hospitals				
Operating rooms¶, **	None	. . .	. . .	2.0
Private rooms	None	30	25	0.33
Wards	None	20	10	. . . .
Hotel rooms	Heavy	30	25	0.33
Kitchens				
Restaurant		. . .	. . .	4.0
Residence		. . .	. . .	2.0
Laboratories‖	Some	20	15	. . . .
Meeting rooms	Very heavy	50	30	1.25
Offices				
General	Some	15	10	. . . .
Private	None	25	15	0.25
Private	Considerable	30	25	0.25
Restaurants				
Cafeteria‖	Considerable	12	10	. . . .
Dining room‖	Considerable	15	12	. . . .
Schoolrooms§	None	. . .	. . .	. . . .
Shop, retail	None	10	$7\frac{1}{2}$	. . . .
Theater§	None	$7\frac{1}{2}$	5	. . . .
Theater	Some	15	10	. . . .
Toilets§ (exhaust)		. . .	. . .	2.0

* Taken from present-day practice.
† This is contaminant-free air.
‡ When minimum is used, take the larger of the two.
§ See local codes which may govern.
‖ May be governed by exhaust.
¶ May be governed by special sources of contamination or local codes.
** All outside air recommended to overcome explosion hazard of anesthetics.
(Reprinted by permission from *ASHRAE Guide and Data Book, 1961,* The American Society of Heating, Refrigerating, and Air Conditioning Engineers.)

Table 9.9   Total Equivalent Temperature Differentials for Calculating Heat Gain Through Sunlit and Shaded Roofs

Description of Roof Construction*	Sun Time								
	A.M.			P.M.					
	8	10	12	2	4	6	8	10	12
Light Construction Roofs—Exposed to Sun									
1″ Wood† or 1″ Wood† + 1″ or 2″ insulation	12	38	54	62	50	26	10	4	0
Medium Construction Roofs—Exposed to Sun									
2″ Concrete or 2″ Concrete + 1″ or 2″ insulation or 2″ Wood†	6	30	48	58	50	32	14	6	2
2″ Gypsum or 2″ Gypsum + 1″ insulation 1″ Wood† or 2″ Wood† or } + 4″ rock wool 2″ Concrete or } in furred ceiling 2″ Gypsum	0	20	40	52	54	42	20	10	6
4″ Concrete or 4″ Concrete with 2″ insulation	0	20	38	50	52	40	22	12	6
Heavy Construction Roofs—Exposed to Sun									
6″ Concrete	4	6	24	38	46	44	32	18	12
6″ Concrete + 2″ insulation	6	6	20	34	42	44	34	20	14
Roofs Covered with Water—Exposed to Sun									
Light construction roof with 1″ water	0	4	16	22	18	14	10	2	0
Heavy construction roof with 1″ water	−2	−2	−4	10	14	16	14	10	6
Any roof with 6″ water	−2	0	0	6	10	10	8	4	0
Roofs with Roof Sprays—Exposed to Sun									
Light construction	0	4	12	18	16	14	10	2	0
Heavy construction	−2	−2	2	8	12	14	12	10	6
Roofs in Shade									
Light construction	−4	0	6	12	14	12	8	2	0
Medium construction	−4	−2	2	8	12	12	10	6	2
Heavy construction	−2	−2	0	4	8	10	10	8	4

*Includes $\frac{3}{8}$ in. felt roofing with or without slag. May also be used for shingle roof.

† Nominal thickness of the wood.

NOTES

Explanation: $\left\{ \begin{array}{l} \text{Total heat transmission from solar} \\ \text{radiation and temperature difference} \\ \text{between outdoor and room air. Btuh/} \\ \text{sq ft of roof area} \end{array} \right\} = \left\{ \begin{array}{l} \text{Equivalent temperature} \\ \text{differential from above} \\ \text{table} \end{array} \right\} \times \left\{ \begin{array}{l} \text{Heat transmission} \\ \text{coefficient for sum-} \\ \text{mer. Btuh/sq ft F} \end{array} \right\}$

1. *Source.* Calculated by Mackey and Wright method and adjusted after studying ASHRAE original test data. Estimated for about August 1 in 40° north latitude. For typical design day where the maximum outdoor temperature is 95 F and minimum temperature at night is approximately 75 F (daily range of temperature, 20 F) mean 24 hr temperature 84 F for a room temperature of 80 F. All roofs have been assumed a dark color which absorbs 90 percent of solar radiation, and reflects only 10 percent.

2. *Application.* These values may be used for all normal air conditioning estimates; usually without correction, in latitude 0° to 50° north or south when the load is calculated for the hottest weather. Note 5 explains how to adjust the temperature differential for other room and outdoor temperatures.

3. *Peaked Roofs.* If the roof is peaked and the heat gain is primarily due to solar radiation, use for the area of the roof, the area projected on a horizontal plane.

4. *Attics.* If the ceiling is insulated and if a fan is used in the attic for positive ventilation, the total temperature differential for a roof exposed to the sun may be decreased 25 percent.

5. *Corrections. For temperature difference when outdoor maximum design temperature minus room is different from 15°.* If the outdoor design temperature minus room temperature is different from the base of 15°, correct as follows: When the difference is greater (or less) than 15° add the excess to (or subtract the deficiency from) the above differentials.

For outdoor daily range of temperature other than 20°. If the daily range of temperature is less than 20°, add 1° for every 2° lower daily range; if the daily range is greater than 20°, subtract 1° for every 2° higher daily range. For example, the daily range in Miami, Florida, is 12° or 8° less than 20°, therefore, the correction is +4° at all hours of the day.

(Reprinted by permission from *ASHRAE Guide and Data Book, 1961,* The American Society of Heating, Refrigerating, and Air Conditioning Engineers.)

160

Table 9.10   Rates of Heat Gain from Occupants of Conditioned Spaces*

Degree of Activity	Typical Application	Total Heat Adults, Male Btuh	Total Heat Adjusted† Btuh	Sensible Heat Btuh	Latent Heat Btuh
Seated at rest	Theater—Matinee	390	330	180	150
	Theater—Evening	390	350	195	155
Seated, very light work	Offices, hotels, apartments	450	400	195	205
Moderately active office work	Offices, hotels, apartments	475	450	200	250
Standing, light work; or walking slowly	Department store, retail store, dime store	550	450	200	250
Walking; seated Standing; walking slowly	Drugstore, bank	550	500	200	300
Sedentary work	Restaurant‡	490	550	220	330
Light bench work	Factory	800	750	220	530
Moderate dancing	Dance hall	900	850	245	605
Walking 3 mph; moderately heavy work	Factory	1000	1000	300	700
Bowling§ Heavy work	Bowling alley Factory	1500	1450	465	985

* NOTE: Tabulated values are based on 80 F room dry-bulb temperature. For 78 F room dry bulb, the total heat remains the same, but the sensible heat values should be increased by approximately 10 percent, and the latent heat values decreased accordingly.

† *Adjusted total heat gain* is based on normal percentage of men, women, and children for the application listed, with the postulate that the gain from an adult female is 85 percent of that for an adult male, and that the gain from a child is 75 percent of that for an adult male.

‡ Adjusted total heat value for *sedentary work, restaurant*, includes 60 Btuh for food per individual (30 Btu sensible and 30 Btu latent).

§ For *bowling*, figure one person per alley actually bowling, and all others as sitting (400 Btuh) or standing (550 Btuh).

(Reprinted by permission from *ASHRAE Guide and Data Book, 1961*, The American Society of Heating, Refrigerating, and Air Conditioning Engineers.)

Table 9.11 Rate of Heat Gain From Appliances WITHOUT HOODS

Appliance	Capacity	Over-all Dimensions (Less Legs and Handles; Last Dimension is Height) Inches	Control A—Automatic M—Manual	Miscellaneous Data	Manufacturer's Rating Watts	Btuh	Maintaining Rate Btuh	Recommended Rate of Heat Gain Btuh		
								Sensible	Latent	Total
Restaurant Electrical Appliances										
Coffee brewer and warmer	½ gal		M	Brewer 660 w	600	2000	306	900	220	1120
			M	Warmer 90 w	90	300		230	60	290
Coffee brewer unit with tank	½ gal	20 × 30 × 26		2000 w water heater, 2960 w brewer	4960	17000		4800	1200	6000
Coffee urn	3 gal	12 × 23 × 21	A	Nickel plated	4500	15000	2600	2200	1500	3700
	5 gal	18 (Diam.) × 37	A	Nickel plated	5000	17000	3600	3400	2300	5700
Doughnut machine		22 × 22 × 57	A	Exhaust system	4700	16000		5000	0	5000
Egg boiler	2 cups	10 × 13 × 25	M		1100	3750		1200	800	2000
Food warmer, with plate warmer, per sq ft of top surface			A	Insulated, separate heat unit for each pot; plate warmer in base	400	1350	500	350	350	700
Food warmer, alone, per sq ft of top surface			A		300	1000	400	200	350	550
Fry kettle	11½ lb fat	12 (Diam.) × 14	A		2600	8900	1100	1600	2400	4000
Fry kettle	25 lb fat	16 × 18 × 12	A		7000	24000	2000	3800	5700	9500
Griddle, frying		18 × 18 × 8	A	Area 12 × 14 in.	2350	8000	2800	3100	1700	4800
Griddle, frying		24 × 20 × 10	A	Area 18 × 14 in.	4000	13500	5000	5300	2900	8200
Grill, meat		14 × 14 × 10	A	Area 23 × 18 in.	3000	10250	1900	3900	2100	6000
Grill, sandwich		13 × 14 × 10	A	Area 10 × 12 in.	1650	5600	1900	2700	700	3400
Roll warmer		23 × 23 × 29	A	Area 12 × 12 in.; Three drawers	1000	3400	900	2400	300	2700
Toaster, continuous	360 slices/hr	15 × 15 × 28	A	2 slices wide	2200	7500	5000	5100	1300	6400
Toaster, continuous	720 slices/hr	20 × 15 × 28	A	4 slices wide	3000	10250	6000	6100	2600	8700
Toaster, pop-up	216 slices/hr	12 × 11 × 9	A	4 slices	2450	8400	2000	4900	900	5800
Waffle iron	20 waffles/hr	12 × 13 × 10	A	7 in. diam. waffle	750	2500	600	1100	750	1850

(Extracted by permission from *ASHRAE Guide and Data Book, 1961*, The American Society of Heating, Refrigerating, and Air Conditioning Engineers.)

for roofs. The second item, 1 in. wood roof with 1 or 2 in. insulation shows a maximum temperature differential of 62 F at 2 P.M. and a minimum of 4 F at 10 P.M. It is evident that for short term conditioning it is important to know the hours of use. Glass is even more variant. The temperature differentials of Table 9.9 for the various hours of the day and night are averaged for the roof values of Table 9.4.

The rates of heat gain from occupants was shown as total heat gain in approximate schematic form for various degrees of activity in Fig. 7.10. They are tabulated with greater precision in Table 9.10. Note that with increasing activity the latent gain begins to exceed the sensible gain.

The ASHRAE Guide and Data Book includes several pages of heat gain values from apparatus. A small section of these is reproduced here in Table 9.11.

Tables 9.7 through 9.11 may prove of value as reference material, but it should be understood that they are only a small part of a large framework of information to which the reader is referred if his problems in heat gain are of some magnitude and pertain to buildings other than residences.

References

1. *Load Calculation, Manual J,* National Warm Air Heating and Air Conditioning Association, 640 Engineers Building, Cleveland 14, Ohio.
2. *Guide and Data Book,* American Society of Heating, Refrigerating and Air Conditioning Engineers, 345 East 47 Street, New York 17, New York.
3. *Solar Control and Shading Devices,* Olgyay and Olgyay, Princeton University Press, Princeton, New Jersey.

10

Principles of Heating

1. Fuels and Combustion. Human beings have used a great variety of fuel to heat their places of shelter. Direct use of natural growth such as wood and peat have given way in busy and congested civilizations to the *fossil* fuels—coal, gas, and oil. In some instances these sources of energy are used to generate electricity which, in turn, is used for heating. Water power utilized by hydroelectric plants can also supply electricity for heating. An interesting source of heat in office buildings is the heat given off by the new high-intensity lighting which is usually turned on during all office hours. It can furnish a large portion of the heating demand, permitting a corresponding reduction in the output of the heating system. In summer it adds a burden to the air conditioning system unless, as is sometimes done, it is exhausted from the building by direct ventilation of the luminaires. Heat can be withdrawn from the air, the ground, or from ground water by the heat pump which, supplied with some electrical energy, can pump this heat into buildings. Perhaps the most recently employed source of heat is a product of nuclear fission. By heat exchange, the reactor coolant can transfer its heat to high temperature water under pressure, or it can produce steam. A number of such plants are in operation serving entire communities in the United States, England, and on the continent.

Proximity to the source of supply is still a strong factor in the choice of a fuel in spite of the development of pipe lines for gas and oil which often cross many states. Thus a city adjacent to coal mines would make use of coal though its high cost of labor in handling and firing might preclude its use in more distant locations. Similarly electric heating is quite universal in the vicinity of the electric plant of the Tennessee Valley Authority despite the fact that in many other areas it would cost 2 or 3 times as much as other fuels. If, as is usual, economy is a consideration, a careful cost-comparison of the common fuels, coal, gas, oil, and electricity should be made at each geographic location. If cost were not a consideration, it is likely that most people would select fuel in this order:

(1) Electricity
(2) Gas
(3) Oil
(4) Coal

Electricity offers easy thermostatic control in each room. It is almost instantaneous in response and, since there need be no combustion on the premises, assures a measure of fire safety if the electrical system is carefully installed in accordance with prescribed regulations and good practice. Gas eliminates fuel storage problems, and both gas and oil involve no labor for handling as coal does. Electricity is the cleanest, but with good combustion there should be little difference in the cleanliness of the other three, though coal dust rising from that fuel prior to burning may be unpleasant.

EXAMPLE 10.1. Calculate the rates of burning the several fuels (or the rate of using electricity) to make up the hourly heat loss, under design conditions, of the residence in Fig. 8.6. Its maximum hourly heat loss is 158,940 Btuh. For fuel values refer to the data in Table 10.1.

SOLUTION. If coal were used, the statement would be:

lbs/hr × Btu/lb heat value
$$\times \text{ efficiency} = \text{Btuh heat loss}$$

Transposing—

$$\text{lbs/hr} = \frac{\text{Btuh heat loss}}{\text{Btu/lb} \times \text{efficiency}}$$

(other efficiency statements are similar)

Applying values to this and to statements for the other fuels, the rates are:

Coal $\dfrac{158,940}{14,600 \times .75} = 14.5 \text{ lbs/hr}$

Oil $\dfrac{158,940}{139,000 \times .80} = 1.43 \text{ gals/hr}$

Gas $\dfrac{158,940}{1052 \times .80} = 189 \text{ cu ft/hr}$

Electricity $\dfrac{158,940}{3.41 \times 1.00}$

$$= 46,500 \text{ watts (46.5 kilowatts)}$$

The foregoing results are based upon the assumption that the boiler and its piping are enclosed within the useful volume of the house as is most usual. If they were in cold basements, or if the ducts or pipes ran

Table 10.1 Approximate Heat Values of the Three Fossil Fuels and the Thermal Equivalent of Electricity. Approximate Efficiencies of Burner-Boiler and of Electrical Heating

Fuel	Heat Value	Efficiency, Percent
Anthracite coal	14,600 Btu/lb	75
No. 2 oil	139,000 Btu/gal	80
Natural gas	1,052 Btu/cu ft	80
Electricity	1 watt = 3.41 Btuh	100

through unheated space, more fuel would be used and the efficiency would be less. The rates established set the values by which the fuel-burning apparatus is selected. For instance, if oil were used, a nozzle which would inject oil at the rate of about $1\frac{1}{2}$ gals/hr might be tried.

These rates are for design (extreme) conditions and are not typical of the lower average rate of operation throughout the winter. Annual fuel costs bear a direct relationship to the number of degree days in the locality. A degree day is defined as a unit based upon temperature difference and time used in estimating fuel consumption and specifying a nominal heating load of a building in winter. For any one day when the mean temperature is less than 65 F, there will be as many degree days as there are Fahrenheit degrees difference in the mean temperature for the day and 65 F.

As fuels burn to produce heat they require oxygen to support the combustion. Since oxygen is only about $\frac{1}{5}$ of the volume of air, reasonably large rates of air flow are required. The air should be drawn in from outdoors at a position close to the fuel burner or led to this location by a duct. For residences and other small buildings a louver about twice the cross sectional area of the flue should prove satisfactory. It should be arranged to remain open at all times. If an attempt is made to draw this air from the general space of the house, modern tight construction may retard the effort. If the air rate *is* sufficient by the use of this scheme, it is likely to result in undesirable acceleration of cold infiltration flowing in to replace the air that is used.

The most important combustible element in the chemical makeup of fuels is carbon. It may be burned well or poorly. When burned poorly it can cause great economic losses and sooty operation. For success, much depends upon the proper selection of well designed boilers, furnaces and burners. This, however, is only part of the story. Adjustments of primary and secondary air rates of flow and of draft (flow of air and gases through the boiler) are important responsibilities of the engineer and the heating contractor. Carbon may burn to carbon monoxide (CO) or more completely to carbon dioxide (CO_2) with greater heat production. Flue gases should be analyzed and the percentage of carbon dioxide measured. The best economy and the cleanest and most efficient combustion occurs when the CO_2 content of the flue gases most nearly approaches the values in Table 10.2 for Maximum Theoretical or Ultimate Percent CO_2. The architect should require that these tests be made with the adjustments necessary to effect acceptable performance.

The storage space to be allowed for coal or oil depends upon the proximity of the supplier and the space available at the building. In the case of oil, when more than 275 gallons are stored, it is common practice to use an outside tank buried in the ground. It is often set on a concrete slab and strapped down to the slab. This prevents the tank from sinking when full or rising in flotation bouyancy that might be caused by adjacent ground water when the tank is empty. The tank, usually of steel, receives two coats of asphalt emulsion to inhibit rust. Tubing for the gauge and for the supply and circulating lines are of copper and the fill and vent lines are of wrought iron with swing joints to accommodate possible slight settlement of the tank. Oil deliveries are often made on the basis of the degree days elapsed since the last fill-up of the tank. Thus the customer is relieved of the chore

Table 10.2   *Approximate Maximum Theoretical CO_2 Values, and CO_2 Values for Various Fuels with Different Percentages of Excess Air*

Type of Fuel	Maximum Theoretical or Ultimate Percent CO_2	Percent CO_2 at Given Excess Air Values		
		20%	40%	60%
Coke	21.0	17.5	15.0	13.0
Anthracite	20.2	16.8	14.4	12.6
Bituminous coal	18.2	15.1	12.9	11.3
No. 1 and 2 fuel oil	15.0	12.3	10.5	9.1
No. 6 fuel oil	16.5	13.6	11.6	10.1
Natural gas	12.1	9.9	8.4	7.3
Carbureted water gas	17.2	14.2	12.1	10.6
Coke oven gas	11.2	9.2	7.8	6.8
Mixed gas (natural and carbureted water gas)	15.3	12.5	10.5	9.1
Propane gas (commercial)	13.9	11.4	9.6	8.4
Butane gas (commercial)	14.1	11.6	9.8	8.5

Reprinted by permission from the *ASHRAE Guide and Data Book,1961,* American Society of Heating, Refrigerating and Air Conditioning Engineers.

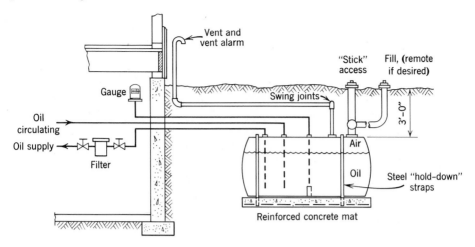

Fig. 10.1   Details, fuel oil storage tank.

of checking the gauge and ordering periodically.

2. Fuels and Burners. Coal with its derivative coke, is the most commonly used *solid* fuel. It was formed by the partial decomposition of enormous masses of vegetable matter in prehistoric times under tremendous heat and pressure without free access of air. Coal is found in all stages of this change, from peat through lignite and bituminous to anthracite coal. The chief constituents are carbon, hydrogen, and oxygen, and carbon being partly combined with the hydrogen and oxygen forming hydrocarbons, and partly uncombined as fixed carbon. The hydrocarbons are volatile and escape as gases upon the application of heat. Coals are classified as anthracite or bituminous according to the relative proportions of fixed carbon and volatile matter.

The noncombustible constituents are the ash and moisture. The ash varies from 3 to 30 percent of the total weight and moisture from 0.75 to 25 percent. An excessive amount of ash and moisture reduces the calorific value of the coal and retards rapid combustion.

Anthracite coal is dense, hard, and clean. It ignites slowly but burns freely with great radiant heat when started. It has a short flame and burns uniformly and with practically no smoke, cakes very little, and requires a minimum of attention between firings.

Two types of mechanical stoker are most commonly used with heating boilers and furnaces, the underfeed and the overfeed. In the first type (Fig. 10.2), coal is fed from a hopper by means of a conveyor screw to the under side of the fire. The screw and a blower are operated by an electric motor. As the coal approaches the fire the volatile gases are given off, begin to burn, and are forced up through the fire by the blower. Air in proper quantity is also introduced to the fire through small pipes called tuyeres. The speed of the screw and the volume of air may be controlled by thermostat, steam pressure, hot water and furnace temperatures, or time period. Plungers or rams with reciprocating motion are sometimes used instead of conveyor screws to feed the coal to the retort, and automatic ash removal and discharge into ash cans are possible additions to the equipment. The overfeed type consists of an elevated coal magazine from which the fuel feeds down by gravity to a sloping grate.

Mechanical stokers can handle the smaller and cheaper sizes of coal, require

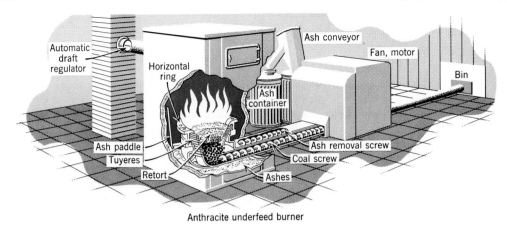

Anthracite underfeed burner

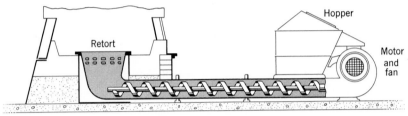

Variation of underfeed burner feeding
from hopper instead of bin.

Fig. 10.2   Automatic firing of anthracite coal by means of an underfeed stoker. (Adapted from University of Illinois Bulletin, Index Number G 3.5.)

attention only at long intervals, produce excellent uniform firing, and in many cases offer definite economy in heating costs.

Oil has gained greatly in popularity in recent years owing to increased facility of procurement and transportation, capability of complete automatic control, and small required storage space. Fuel oil is the residue after gasoline, kerosene, and naphtha have been distilled off from crude petroleum. It is manufactured in various grades, the lighter and more refined types having a low flash point or temperature from 110 to 165 F at which their vapor will ignite in a flash. The fire point or temperature at which an oil burns with a steady flame is about 20° above its flash point. The heavier low-grade oils are more viscous, begin to burn at higher temperatures, and in some cases must be preheated before being introduced to the burner. Lighter oils, Nos. 1 and 2, consequently, are better adapted for intermittent, automatically controlled heating systems and the heavier oils for large, continuously fired power plants. The lighter oils are, however, more expensive, and for this reason burners for domestic service have been developed to make use of oils much heavier than heretofore considered possible. The heavier more viscous oils, Nos. 5 and 6, are used in larger installations such as hotels, office buildings, and stores where economy rather than convenience is important. The burners are adapted to the low-grade oils.

To burn properly, oil must be changed from a liquid to a vapor. The conversion is accelerated by atomization or breaking the liquid up into tiny globules. This atomization is effected in domestic burners by centrifugal force produced by a rotating cup or by forcing the oil under pressure through a nozzle. In both methods air is blown into the burner for perfecting the atomization and combustion, ignition being produced by an electric arc. A motor, fan, and pump with electrical connection form part of the equipment. Combustion takes place in the lowest part of the boiler, corresponding to the ash pit in a coal burner, which is lined with fire brick or other refractory to protect the metal sides from contact with the flame and to assist the combustion of the oil.

Gas fuel consists of natural gas found in the earth in petroleum regions, manufactured gas made from coal and oil, and propane, commonly called "tank gas." Natural gas, originally restricted to use in the localities where it was found, has almost completely replaced manufactured gas by means of a vast network of gas pipelines covering the country. Its composition is largely methane (CH_4), combined with small amounts of the higher hydrocarbons, which brings its heating value to about 1050 BTU/cu ft. Propane is available in all areas not served by piped gas. Gas fuel is usually competitive in price with the other fossil fuels.

A wide variety of heating boilers and furnaces are available for all types of heating systems. The American Gas Association has testing laboratories to maintain the high standard of structural and efficiency standards which have been adopted by the gas industry. Every item of approved equipment contains protective devices designed to provide safe operation. In recent years, new forms of gas heating equipment have been perfected for commercial and industrial buildings, such as overhead infrared units for spot or over-all heating—even outdoor heating—and direct fired makeup air heaters operating at high efficiency.

Many natural gas companies offer gas service on an interruptible basis to large users, thus competing with the lowest priced fuels. These utilities provide detailed assistance in the utilization of gaseous fuels.

3. Boilers, Furnaces, and Chimneys. Cast iron and steel are the metals most commonly used for boilers and furnaces in the range of sizes appropriate for residences. For boilers the cast iron is molded in sections which are made hollow to contain water. Steel plates are welded together into assemblies that frequently use steel water tubes or fire tubes. In furnaces, cast iron or steel is usually the barrier between the fire chamber and the space through which air passes to be warmed. In large boilers for

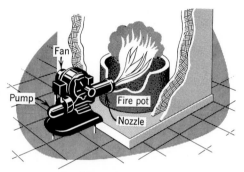

(a) Pressure-type oil burner

(b) American standard oil burner. Firing rate .65 to 1.10 gallons of oil per hour.

Fig. 10.3 (a) Pressure (gun) type of oil burner. (Adapted from University of Illinois Bulletin, Index Number G 3.5.) (b) A manufacturer's product.

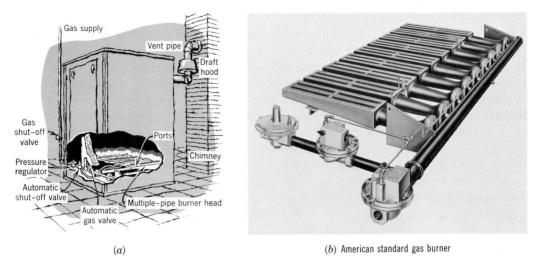

Gas supply

Vent pipe

Draft
hood

Gas
shut-off
valve

Ports

Pressure
regulator

Chimney

Automatic
shut-off valve

Multiple-pipe burner head

Automatic
gas valve

(*a*)

(*b*) American standard gas burner

Fig. 10.4   Application and detail of gas burners. (*a*) is adapted from University of Illinois Bulletin, Index Number G 3.5.

Fig. 10.5   Steel boiler for steam heating (note gauge glass on left side to indicate water level). Hopper-type stoker feed for coal firing. (*Pacific*)

commercial and industrial use, steel is often preferred. The Institute of Boiler and Radiator Manufacturers sets standards by which cast iron boilers may be rated for output and for many other important qualities. Similar control by the Steel Boiler Institute applies to most steel boilers. The American Gas Association has certain requirements for products that it approves. It is well to be sure by identifying marks on the products that they have the approval of these governing organizations.

Old standards for the quotation of output often used "sq ft of cast iron steam radiation." Each sq ft of radiator surface has an hourly heat emission of 240 Btuh. Thus a boiler that could carry 1000 sq ft of radiation would have an output of 240,000 Btuh. Recent practice is to state the output directly in Btuh. The *net* rating of the boiler should be about the same as the calculated critical hourly heat loss of the house. Hot water and steam heating boilers may be safely used if somewhat oversize, but warm air furnaces should match the house demands rather closely.

Fig. 10.6   Oil-fired cast iron sectional boiler for hot-water heating. Heater-coil for domestic hot water at upper right. (*American Standard*)

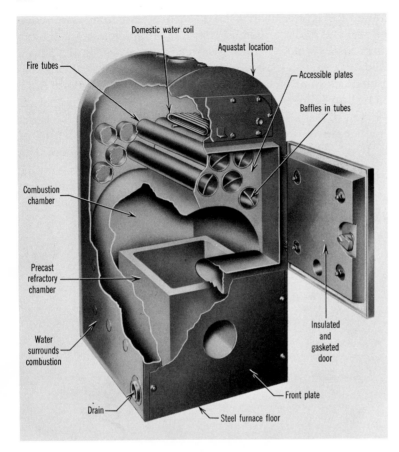

Fig. 10.7 Steel boiler with horizontal fire tubes. Adapted for oil-firing and suitable for steam or hot-water heating. It may be adapted to other fuels. (*Federal*)

Fig. 10.8 Compact package-type oil-fired boiler for hot-water heating. Front closure at right covers controls, circulator, and gun-type burner. (*Federal*)

One may pick up a boiler catalog and find 3 items for a given boiler:

(1) Gross output including pickup and piping, Btuh
(2) Gross output including piping, Btuh
(3) Rating, *net,* Btuh

For a gas-fired warm air furnace, 3 items also appear:

(1) Input Btuh
(2) Bonnet, Btuh
(3) Register, *net,* Btuh

In both series, the interest is in the *net* rating which should match the hourly heat loss of the house. Except in unusual circumstances, it is the problem of the designer of the heating boiler or furnace and the rating association to decide how much extra margin to leave. Now conditions have changed. Aquastats operate intermittently to actuate the boiler, keeping it warm to obviate the long *pickup* that was necessary from a cold start. Pipes seldom run in cold basements or in uninsulated walls. In any case the *net* rating is the one that is of interest to the designer of the heating *system*. Allowance should always be made, however, for coils that heat domestic hot water. Tank-type coils add a small additional burden, but tankless (continuous) heating coils call for a large increase in boiler size. See Ex. 2.2, p. 27.

Most boilers can be used interchangeably for hot water heating or for steam heating, though the latter is decreasing in popularity in residential applications. Boilers are provided with tapped openings for the various devices needed for hot water or steam.

It is important that chimneys with their high temperature flue gasses be safely isolated from combustible construction to

Fig. 10.9 Gas-fired cast iron sectional boiler for hot-water heating. Circulating pump is seen at left below gas equipment. (*Weil-McLain*)

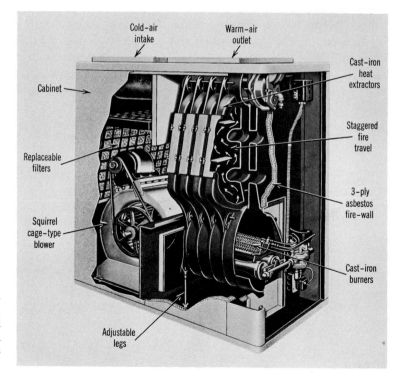

Fig. 10.10 Gas-fired furnace for warm-air heating. Fan blows cold air around cast-iron enclosure within which gas-fired element is located. (*Thatcher*)

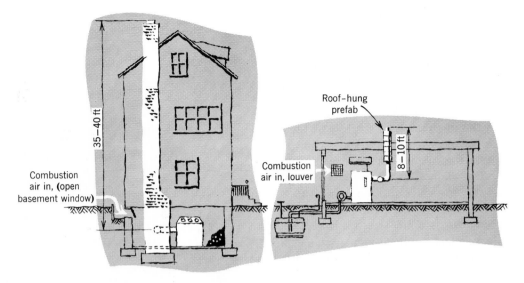

Fig. 10.11   Controlled draft in burners has eliminated the need for 40 ft chimneys. Check with your engineer about minimum height.

prevent the possibility of fire. Conventional standards call for a terra cotta flue lining surrounded by 8 in. of brick with 2 additional in. of space between the brick and any wood. The space is usually filled with incombustible rockwool. The size of flue will be dictated by the specification for the boiler or furnace selected for use. Its height (see Fig. 10.11) has been traditionally 35-40 ft. The function of providing a draft, for

which chimney height was an important consideration, is no longer as necessary as it previously was—because fans are used now. For example, oil is injected under pressure accompanied by air and forced in by a fan. Often a draft adjuster in the breeching that carries the flue gases to the chimney is arranged to open slightly to *reduce* the normal stack draft. If increased draft should ever be required, an induced draft fan that

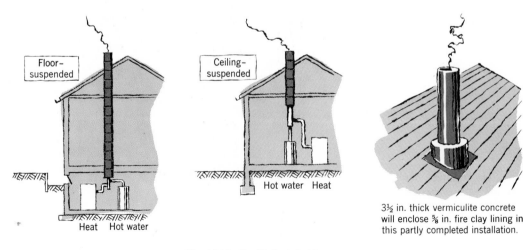

Fig. 10.12   Prefabricated chimneys.

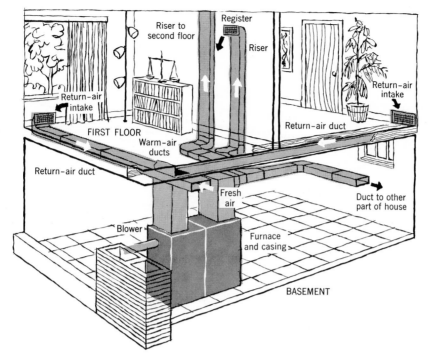

Fig. 10.13   Forced warm-air system. (Adapted from Circular Series, Index No. G 3.1, Small Homes Council, University of Illinois.)

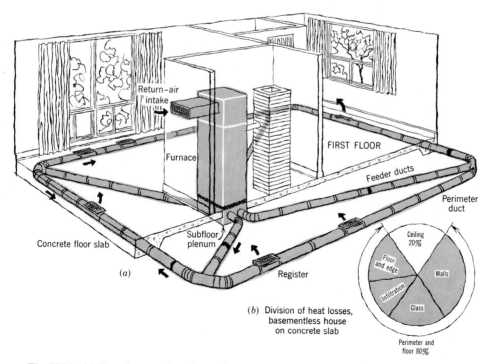

Fig. 10.14   (a) Forced warm-air perimeter loop system, employing downflow furnace. (Adapted from Circular Series Index No. G 3.1, Small Homes Council, University of Illinois.) (b) Predominance of *perimital* heat losses.

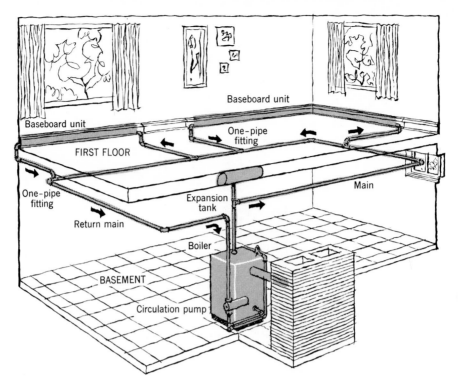

Fig. 10.15 Forced hot-water system using the one-pipe principle with special one-pipe fittings to divert water to the baseboard units. (Adapted from Circular Series, Index No. G 3.1, Small Homes Council, University of Illinois.)

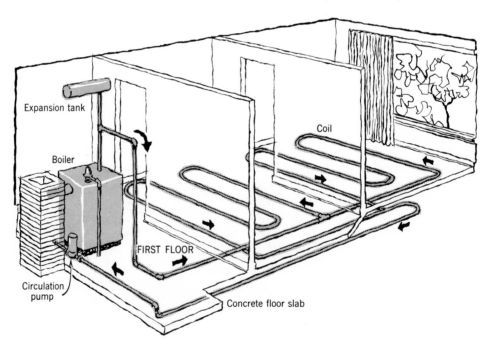

Fig. 10.16 Forced-hot-water, floor-type radiant heating showing 2 coils. (Adapted from Circular Series, Index No. G 3.1, Small Homes Council, University of Illinois.)

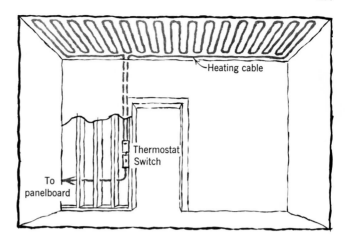

Fig. 10.17 Electric radiant heating. Cables fastened to gypsum lath ready to be imbedded in plaster or ceiling.

puts a suction on the flue side of the fire is usually chosen instead of greater stack height. Draft hoods above gas burners prevent downdraft from blowing out the flames.

Prefabricated chimneys are replacing with increasing frequency the bulkier and heavier field-built masonry. They offer a number of advantages and may be easily supported on normal structure.

4. Heat Distribution. Common methods of distributing heat throughout a house are by the forced circulation of warm air or hot water. Electrical heating by coils imbedded in plaster ceilings or concrete floors or by resistance units set into walls is increasing where utility rates are favorable.

The choice of a method depends very much on the kind of house to be heated. A house with a basement, several stories, many interior partitions, and relatively little glass lends itself ideally to the method of formed warm air heating shown in Fig. 10.13. An example of a design is given in Ex. 11.1. The warm air is forced through ducts in interior partitions and is blown across at the glass through high wall registers above the heads of the occupants. It should have sufficient velocity and "throw" to reach and warm the glass and exterior wall. As the air cools, it is picked up by the suction side of the system below the glass or near exterior doors.

When a house has considerable glass, it is well to reverse this process and deliver warm air up across the glass and collect the return air at locations where people are not likely to be, as the cool air might cause them discomfort. If the delivered air is well distributed to blanket cold areas, the location and number of returns is not a matter of serious concern, especially in houses of open planning, and provided that closed doors do not shut off the circulation.

People should not live on cold concrete slabs that rest on the ground. By using a counterflow air furnace, or a downfeed duct from a conventional furnace, air can be delivered to a sub-slab plenum and thence through radial ducts to a perimeter duct with registers below glass. The floor is warmed by the passage of air, which is later fanned out across the glass. The heat loss "pie" in Fig. 10.14 indicates that about 80 percent of the loss in this kind of room is at the floor and perimeter. This system is well arranged to warm the locations of greatest loss. This is a prime objective in all heating systems.

When hot water is used, the elements that heat the rooms may be baseboard convectors or cast iron baseboard, convector cabinets below windows, or in some cases cast iron radiators, now considerably less popular than the other devices.

In hydronic (piped) systems it is no less important to warm concrete floor slabs on grade than with air systems. Radiant coils accomplish this, (see Fig. 10.16). An example of their use is given in the Sands Point residence, shown in Figs. 13.9 and 13.10. The floor coils may be omitted if the floor provides a raised wood surface with an air space below and a radiant ceiling, which, by its position, warms this wood floor. This is illustrated in the Olindo Grossi Residence, Fig. 13.5.

Electricity can be another form of radiant heating. Prefabricated coils of special wire, complete with leads, may be imbedded in the plaster of the ceiling or the concrete of the floor. In common use in several parts of the United States, its wider application awaits a further reduction of utility company power rates.

Reference

1. Robert Henderson Emerick, *Heating Handbook,* McGraw-Hill Book Co., New York.

11

Warm Air Heating

1. Characteristics. Almost all heating systems make use of *some* moving warm air. The popular fin-tube convector depends on gravity *convection* to move the air which has been warmed in passing over the fins that attach to the hot-water carrying pipe. A heating method in which air motion is at a minimum is the ceiling radiant panel. Air that is warmed by this panel remains in contact with the ceiling because it cannot drop unless it cools. The ceiling, of course, does its job of heating in an effective manner, but largely by the principle of the transfer of radiant energy. Piped (hydronic) systems are compact and quiet but often require separate, small supplementary ventilating facilities—exhaust fans and similar equipment. Forced warm-air systems, combine ventilation and filtration as inherent items. Proper selection and location of registers and return grills can assure a moderate but effective air motion which distributes the heat evenly, precluding drafts, but clearing out locations where static or stagnant air might accumulate. The qualities of the various methods of heating must be appraised before a system is selected. Very often the choice will be influenced by the nature of the architecture and the conformation of the house. The clear-cut demarcations between what were formerly considered standard systems—steam, water, and air—are fast disappearing, and *combinations* are often encountered. Thus a convector strip may supplement an air system, or a local ventilating duct system utilizing tempered air may find its place in a "wet" installation. In large buildings these combinations are very common but, due to economy, houses generally still use one method or the other.

Forced warm-air heating, which employs blowers, does not depend primarily on convection as the older gravity systems did. It was formerly most desirable to deliver the warm air at baseboard registers so that it would rise to warm the room. Cool air was collected at the foot of stairs, below windows and near exterior doors. The advent of power has changed all this. Warm air is delivered at locations of greatest heat loss and in a direction that least disturbs the occupants. After this air has moderated in temperature and velocity, it is drawn across the space to return-air grills preferably in the same room and usually located high on the wall so that stagnant warm air is drawn away for re-processing. When return grills are located more remotely, doors should be undercut at the bottom by 1 in., or grills provided at transom locations over doors. Contrary to some erroneous but persisting opinions, it is not usually necessary to make any change in the method of handling cooled air if summer central air conditioning is also part of the general air system. It can be circulated by the same ducts, registers, and grills, though often these elements must be larger. If year-round air conditioning is contemplated, sizes should be calculated for both summer and winter operation and the larger equipment chosen. This was done in the case of the Azzarone Residence, discussed in part later in this chapter.

In planning warm-air systems, good balance is achieved if the heating furnace is located reasonably close to the center of the house. After the system is designed a furnace must be selected. It should be capable of burning fuel at a rate suitable to make up the hourly heat loss in the house. The rate of air delivery must be correct to transmit this heat to the house at the air temperature *rise* that is planned. Finally, the motor and blower must be powerful enough to overcome the friction of air against metal in both the supply and return duct system and the friction of air flowing through the furnace, filters, registers, and grills. Minor adjustments can be made at the furnace to adapt to the demands of the system and the house.

2. Furnace, Ducts, Dampers, Registers, and Controls. (*a*) *Furnace.* Figure 11.1 represents a typical furnace which embraces within its housing, the fan (blower), motor, filters, oil burner, and heat-transfer surfaces. A humidifier can be added to this assembly. Arrows indicate the direction of the air. In passing through the fan or blower the air enters at the end of the cylinder opposite the pulley and is forced into the warming chamber by a cylindrical impeller unit.

(*b*) *Ducts.* These are constructed of sheet metal or glass fiber—either round or rectangular. For carrying the return air back to the furnace, spaces between studs or joists may be enclosed, the air flowing in contact with the wood. This method is not permitted in supply ducts where hotter air is handled. When used as return ducts the enclosed spaces must be made very tight to prevent air leakage. Ductwork will conduct noise

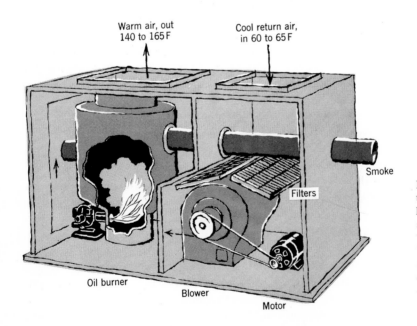

Warm air, out
140 to 165 F

Cool return air,
in 60 to 65 F

Smoke

Filters

Oil burner

Blower

Motor

Fig. 11.1 Principle of the mechanical warm-air heating furnace. Other styles have the elements "in-line" and replace the U-path flow of air with straight line flow, vertically upward, horizontal or vertically downward (counterflow).

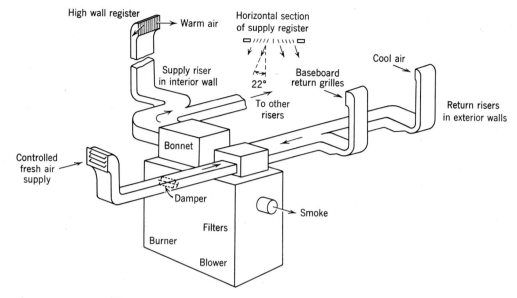

Fig. 11.2   Schematic duct-system for mechanical warm-air heating.

unless the following suggestions are followed:

Do not place the fan too close to a return grille.

Select quiet motors and cushioned mountings.

Do not permit connection or contact of conduits or water piping with the fan housing.

Use canvas-asbestos connection between bonnet and ductwork.

(c) *Dampers.* These will be necessary to balance the system and adjust it to the desires of the occupants. Splitter dampers are used where branch ducts leave the larger trunk ducts. Each riser can have its flow controlled by an adjustable damper in the basement at the foot of the riser. Labels should indicate the rooms served. Some codes require dampers of fire-resistant material actuated by fusible links in order to prevent the possible spread of fire through a duct system.

(d) *Registers.* Supply registers should be equipped with dampers and should have their vanes arranged to disperse the air and to reduce its velocity as soon as possible after entering the room. A common method is to provide vanes which divert the air half to the right and half to the left, independently of whether the register location is high or low. When a supply register is in the corner of a room it is best practice for the fans to deflect all the air in one direction, away from the corner. Return grilles are of the slotted type in walls and of the grid type in floors. All registers and grilles should be made tight at the duct connection.

(e) *Controls.* The burner is started and stopped by a thermostat which is placed in or near the living room at a thermally stable location that is protected from cold drafts, direct sunlight, and the warming effects of nearby warm air registers. A cut-in temperature of between 80 and 95 F is selected for the fan switch in the furnace bonnet. After the burner starts, the fan switch turns on the blower when the furnace air reaches the selected cut-in temperature. Burner and blower then continue to run while heat is needed. When the burner turns off, the blower continues to run until the temperature in the furnace drops to a level a little below the cut-in temperature of the fan switch. If, during operation, the temperature unexpectedly exceeds 200 F, a high limit switch turns off the burner in the interest of comfort and safety. As in all automatically fired heating units, a stack temperature control in the breeching (smoke pipe) turns off the fire if ignition fails.

3. Design. For a relatively small house with a basement and one or two stories, whose hourly heat loss does not exceed about 120,000 Btuh, a simple design procedure for ducts may be used. Other limiting conditions on its use require that no register be more than 55 ft horizontally along the duct from the warm air plenum and that the furnace-blower combination shall not have a temperature rise of more than 100 F and shall have a static pressure of .20 in. of water to overcome pressure losses in the distribution system. Distances A plus B in the manometer tubes of water in Fig. 11.3 must not be less than .20 in.

The design method, originated by the National Warm Air Heating and Air Conditioning Association and used for Example 11.1, utilizes tables reprinted here by permission of the American Society of Heating,

Refrigerating, and Air Conditioning Engineers. A more complete discussion of this design method will be found in Manual 7 of the NWAHACA, and for systems having heat losses in excess of 120,000 Btuh, reference is made to *Manual 9* of the association.

EXAMPLE 11.1. Design a mechanical warm air heating system for the house shown in Fig. 11.4*a*. Tables 11.1 and 11.2 are the work sheets for this problem. Reference is made to Tables 11.3 and 11.4 and Fig. 11.5*a* and *b* for design data. The suggested steps and procedure in this design are as follows:

(*a*) *Heat Losses.* These are computed according to the principles in Chapter 8 and are recorded for each space to be heated.

(*b*) *General Arrangement.* Locate on the plans of the floors and basement all supply and return ducts and leaders. Indicate the method of combining them into trunk ducts. Consult Fig. 11.5 and indicate on the plans the code letter of each typical fitting as dictated by architectural considerations. In this problem all the return ducts and leaders are of metal, but joist space could be used for economy and compactness. Spaces having large heat losses should be served by two or more ducts in order to avoid excessive sizes. Decisions are made whether ductwork shall be insulated and where supply registers and return grills are to be located. These are noted on the work sheets. In this problem ductwork is insulated. All supply grills are placed by choice at a high wall position where there will be no direct draught on occupants. Also, as indicated in Table 11.2, baseboard return intakes are used except in the lower hall where two floor-type intakes are chosen. The fresh air is drawn in at position U, which is a wall-type intake on the outside of the basement wall. Generally the supply ducts are placed in the warmer interior walls, and the returns in exterior walls. An exhaust fan disposes of the kitchen air which is balanced by the amount of the intake of fresh air. There

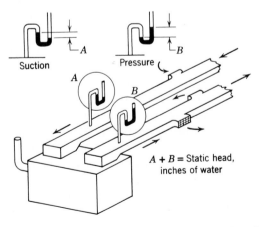

Fig. 11.3   The static head is the pressure in inches of water available to overcome friction in the entire system.

is no return in the bath or upper hall, these spaces being served by the two intakes *R* and *O* in the lower hall. The direct return of air from bathrooms or kitchens is not recommended.

(*c*) *Horizontal Leaders.* The capacity of a duct system is affected by the horizontal distance of air travel, that is, the horizontal length of the supply and return leaders in feet from bonnet to vertical stack. Include horizontal sections of any crossover at the second floor if such exist. In this example there is no additional crossover length in any leader. These horizontal distances are entered in the work sheets for supply and return ducts, Tables 11.1 and 11.2, column 4.

(*d*) *Resistance and Equivalent Length of Fittings.* The kinds of fittings chosen are already marked on the plans. Each offers resistance equal to a certain number of feet of straight duct. Add up the equivalent resistance of the fittings in each run, and enter this in column 5 of the work sheets. The resistance of the bonnet is included in each run, but no resistance is assumed where the main air stream passes an elbow to another riser. An example of the computation of an equivalent length, that for supply duct *A* follows (refer to Fig. 11.5)

Plenum (at bonnet)	Type 1b	10 feet
Trunk duct take-off	Type 3i	15
Trunk elbow	Type 2b	10
Stack angle	Type 5m	10
Register (group 7,22°)		45
		90 ft equiv. lgth

The equivalent length of fittings in return ducts is computed in the same way. The results are entered in column 5 of the work sheets.

(*e*) *Combination Numbers.* Selection of a combination number from the standard combinations of sizes fixes the dimensions of the stack and the branch duct (see Tables 11.3 and 11.4). For a chosen location of intake or register it also establishes the size of these elements. Lastly it indicates the required addition to the width of a standard

8-in. deep trunk to accommodate the added capacity of the run in question. The combination is fixed by 3 factors—the number of Btuh to be supplied, the horizontal leader length, and the equivalent length of the fittings. Although the return ducts do not actually supply heat, their size is determined by the Btuh of the space served by the return and the 2 other items. To summarize in terms of the work sheets—columns 2, 4, and 5 determine the combination number shown in column 6. Column 7 and the columns following it through 10 and 11 are tabulations of the sizes indicated by the combination numbers. They are found directly below the combination numbers in the vertical columns of Tables 11.3 and 11.4.

(*f*) *Increase in Trunk Width.* For this type of design 8 in. is usually selected as the standard depth for trunk ducts. When a branch duct joins the trunk, the 8 in. deep trunk is widened one or more inches to increase its capacity. Where main trunks join, their widths are added to establish the width of the trunk to which they join. Four inches is the minimum width.

(*g*) *Sizing the Trunk Ducts.* The trunk widths and depths are indicated on the working drawings represented by Fig. 11.4*b*. At the bonnet a transition piece will usually be necessary to adapt the shallow and wide trunk to a squarer opening.

(*h*) *Selection of a Furnace.* A furnace including fan and filters is selected on the basis of the total of the heat losses from all the rooms, 61,500 Btuh. The input or bonnet capacity is greater than this net register output. The ratings of manufacturers should be consulted.

4. Warm Air Perimeter Heating. The foregoing method of warm-air distribution from high registers on warm interior walls has largely given way to the method of warm-air perimeter heating whereever it is applicable (see Figs. 11.6 and 11.7). There are several reasons for this. In the older method the cold air that was picked up at cold spots

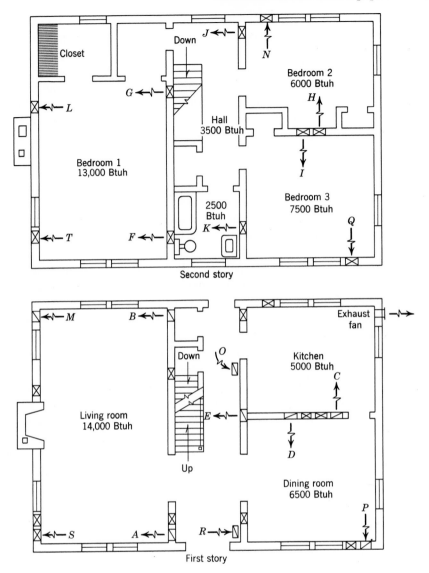

Fig. 11.4(*a*)   (Example 11.1)   Warm-air design.

near exterior walls maintained these walls in a cold condition, making them radiantly cool and increasing the condensation on glass. Perimeter heating reverses this process and warms the outside walls and glass directly. This is a distinct advantage where large glass areas are used. Open planning has minimized the use of interior partitions in which ducts were formerly placed and thin-wall construction has also helped to force a relocation. Radial or other types of duct distribution to the perimeter in a slab, crawl space, or basement leaves the story above free for flexible planning. Concrete slabs on the ground, especially in residences, need to be warmed as do wood floors above cold crawl spaces. Ducts in the concrete and ducts or warm air in the crawl space accomplish this. By warming the floor (and exterior walls) two very beneficial results

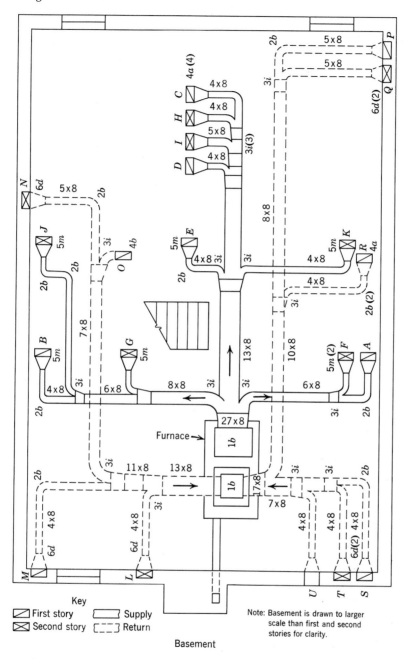

Key

First story ▱   Supply

Second story ⊠   Return ⌐ ¬

Note: Basement is drawn to larger
scale than first and second
stories for clarity.

Basement

Fig. 11.4(b) (Example 11.1) Warm-air design.

occur. The system becomes partly radiant, which is a step toward better comfort, and the air in warming these surfaces is lowered in temperature before entering the room, making it more pleasant to occupants than if the air at full temperature were delivered from interior wall registers.

Developed first for small residences, the perimeter system has found favor for use in industrial, commercial, and public build-

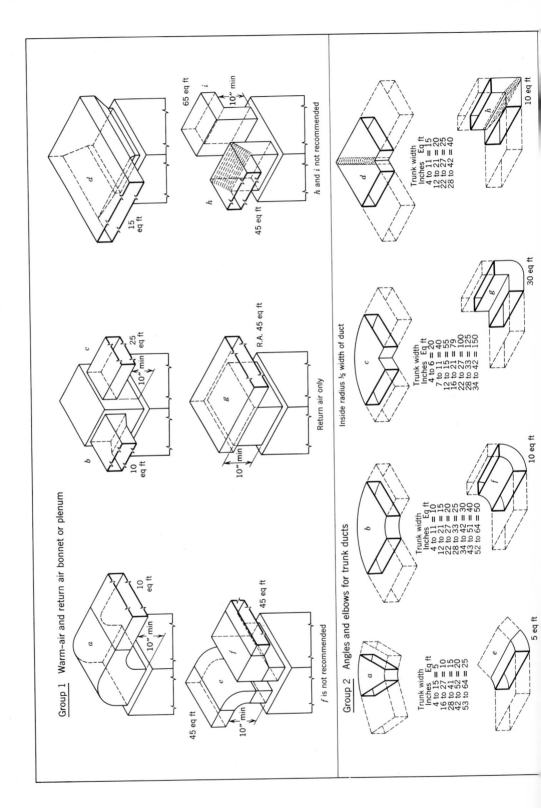

Group 1 Warm-air and return air bonnet or plenum

Group 2 Angles and elbows for trunk ducts

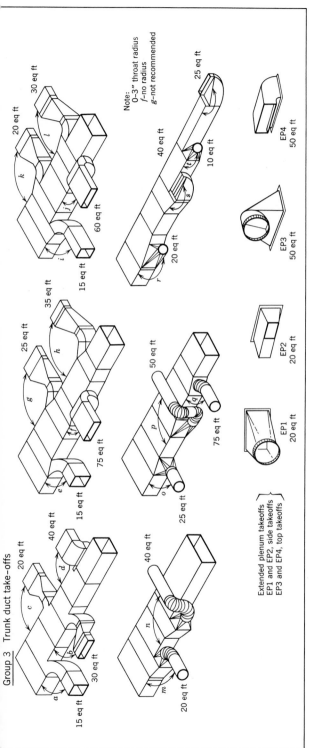

Fig. 11.5a Equivalent length of fittings and intakes. (Reprinted by permission of *ASHRAE* from the *Heating, Ventilating, Air Conditioning Guide*, 1960.)

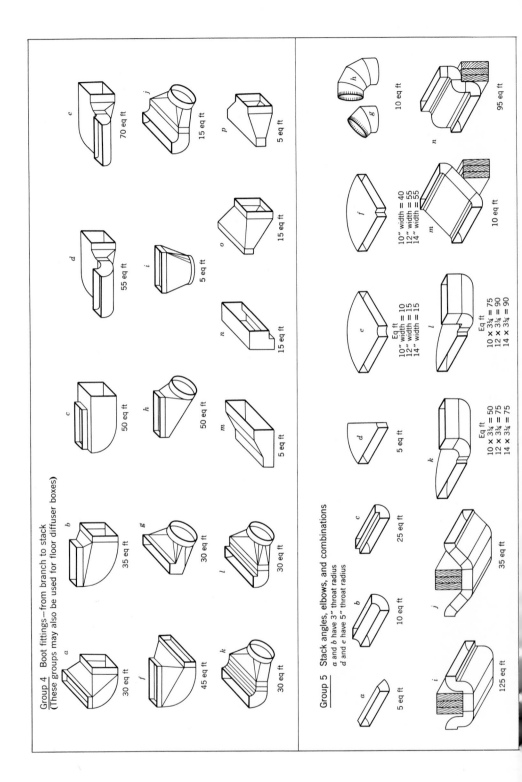

Group 4   Boot fittings—from branch to stack
(These groups may also be used for floor diffuser boxes)

a   30 eq ft
b   35 eq ft
c   50 eq ft
d   55 eq ft
e   70 eq ft

f   45 eq ft
g   30 eq ft
h   50 eq ft
i   5 eq ft
j   15 eq ft

k   30 eq ft
l   30 eq ft
m   5 eq ft
n   15 eq ft
o   15 eq ft
p   5 eq ft

Group 5   Stack angles, elbows, and combinations
a and b have 3″ throat radius
d and e have 5″ throat radius

a   5 eq ft
b   10 eq ft
c   25 eq ft

d   5 eq ft

e   Eq ft
10″ width = 10
12″ width = 15
14″ width = 15

f   Eq ft
10″ width = 40
12″ width = 55
14″ width = 55

g   h   10 eq ft

i   125 eq ft

j   35 eq ft

k   Eq ft
10 × 3¼ = 50
12 × 3¼ = 75
14 × 3¼ = 75

l   Eq ft
10 × 3¼ = 75
12 × 3¼ = 90
14 × 3¼ = 90

m   10 eq ft

n   95 eq ft

188

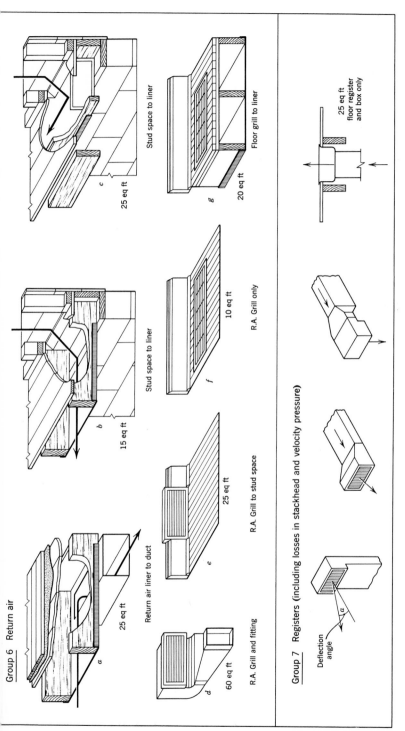

Group 6 Return air

25 eq ft

Return air liner to duct

a

60 eq ft

R.A. Grill and fitting

b

15 eq ft

Stud space to liner

c

25 eq ft

Stud space to liner

d

e

25 eq ft

R.A. Grill to stud space

f

10 eq ft

R.A. Grill only

g

20 eq ft

Floor grill to liner

25 eq ft
floor register
and box only

Group 7 Registers (including losses in stackhead and velocity pressure)

Deflection
angle

a

EQUIVALENT LENGTH FOR REGISTERS

Deflection angle A	0°	15°	22°	30°	45°
	Eq. Ft				
Baseboard, High or Low	35	40	45	60	115
Sidewall Reg.					
Floor Reg. with Box Only	25				

For 2-way deflection registers, add the vertical and horizontal deflection angles together and multiply by 0.7. Select closest angle "a" shown in Group 7 registers. Note: For equivalent length of registers, diffusers, and other types not shown, refer to Mfrs. catalog.

Fig. 11.5b Equivalent lengths of fittings and intakes (concluded). Reprinted by permission of *ASHRAE* from the *Heating, Ventilating, Air Conditioning Guide*, 1960.

189

Table 11.1 (Example 11.1) Work Sheet. Supply-Duct System Mechanical Warm Air Design (Fig. 11.4)

Reference Column Numbers

1	2	3	4	5	6	7	8	9	10
Space	Btuh	Plan Ref.	Length Horiz. Leader (ft)	Equiv. Length Ftgs. (ft)	Combi-nation Number	Stack Size (in.)	Branch Duct Size (in.)	Register* Size (in.)	Increase in Trunk (in.)
First Story									
Living Room	14,000	$\begin{cases}A\\B\end{cases}$	16 22	90 90	42 42	$10\times3\frac{1}{4}$ $10\times3\frac{1}{4}$	4×8 4×8	10×6 10×6	2 2
Kitchen	5,000	C	27	95	42	$10\times3\frac{1}{4}$	4×8	10×6	2
Dining Room	6,500	D	21	100	42	$10\times3\frac{1}{4}$	4×8	10×6	2
Lower Hall	3,000	E	17	90	41	$10\times3\frac{1}{4}$	4×8	10×6	1
Bedroom 1	13,500	$\begin{cases}F\\G\end{cases}$	14 17	95 95	42 42	$10\times3\frac{1}{4}$ $10\times3\frac{1}{4}$	4×8 4×8	10×6 10×6	2 2
Bedroom 2	6,000	H	25	95	42	$10\times3\frac{1}{4}$	4×8	10×6	2
Second Story									
Bedroom 3	7,500	I	23	100	43	$12\times3\frac{1}{4}$	5×8	12×6	3
Upper Hall	3,500	J	25	115	41	$10\times3\frac{1}{4}$	4×8	10×6	1
Bathroom	2,500	K	22	90	41	$10\times3\frac{1}{4}$	4×8	10×6	1
Total	61,500								

* All supply registers are high wall types, 22° deflection of air. Ducts are insulated metal. A and B carry 7000 Btuh each. F and G carry 6750 Btuh each.

190

Table 11.2 *(Example 11.1) Work Sheet. Return Duct System, Mechanical Warm Air Design (Fig. 11.4)*

Reference Column Numbers

	1	2	3	4	5	6	7	8	9	10	11
	Space	Btuh	Plan Ref.	Length Horiz. Leader (ft)	Equiv. Length Figs. (ft)	Combi-nation Number	Stack Size (in.)	Branch Duct Size (in.)	Intake Type	Intake Size (in.)	Increase in Trunk (in.)
First Story	Living Room	14,000	{ M	20	80	42		4 × 8	Baseboard	10 × 6	2
			S	15	80	42		4 × 8	Baseboard	10 × 6	2
	Dining Room	6,500	P	39	95	43		5 × 8	Baseboard	12 × 6	3
	Hall	9,000	R	26	75	42		4 × 8	Floor	10 × 6	2
			O	30	85	42		4 × 8	Floor	10 × 6	2
Second Story	Bedroom 1	13,500	{ L	13	85	42	$10 \times 3\frac{1}{4}$	4 × 8	Baseboard	10 × 6	2
			T	13	85	42	$10 \times 3\frac{1}{4}$	4 × 8	Baseboard	10 × 6	2
	Bedroom 2	6,000	N	35	95	43	$12 \times 3\frac{1}{4}$	5 × 8	Baseboard	12 × 6	3
	Bedroom 3	7,500	Q	37	100	43	$12 \times 3\frac{1}{4}$	5 × 8	Baseboard	12 × 6	3
Basement	Fresh air	5,000	U	9	55	41	$10 \times 3\frac{1}{4}$	4 × 8	Ext. wall	10 × 6	1
	Total	61,500									

NOTE: Ducts are insulated metal. Kitchen air, exhausted through kitchen fan, is replaced through fresh air intake. Bath and upper and lower halls are served by lower-hall returns, *R* and *O*. *M* and *S* carry 7000 Btuh each. *L* and *T* carry 6750 Btuh each.

Table 11.3 Capacity and Sizing Table—First Story
For Warm Air and Return Air Stack, Branch, and Registers

Col. a	Col. b	Col. c	Col. d	Col. e	Col. f	Col. g	Col. h	Col. i	Col. j
Equiv. Length of Fittings and Registers	Horizontal Length Furnace to Register — Ducts*	Insulated Attic Ducts	First Story Room Heat Loss—Btuh						
Up to 70 eq ft	Up to 7	Up to 5	7,200	12,500	16,000	19,100	25,000	32,000	80,000
	8–12	6–9	6,700	11,700	15,000	18,000	23,400	30,000	75,000
	13–17	10–13	6,100	10,800	14,000	17,000	21,600	28,000	70,000
	18–25	14–18	5,600	9,900	13,000	16,000	19,800	26,000	65,000
	26–35	19–25	4,800	8,500	11,000	14,200	17,000	22,600	56,500
	36–45	26–35	4,100	7,000	9,900	12,500	14,800	19,800	49,500
	46–55	36–45	3,500	6,400	8,700	11,000	12,800	17,400	43,500
	. . . .	46–55	3,000	5,500	7,700	9,600	11,000	15,400	38,500
71 to 100 eq ft	Up to 7	Up to 5	5,500	9,900	13,100	16,300	19,800	26,200	65,500
	8–12	6–9	5,100	9,200	12,300	15,400	18,400	24,600	61,500
	13–17	10–13	4,800	8,600	11,600	14,500	17,200	23,200	58,000
	18–25	14–18	4,500	8,100	10,900	13,700	16,200	21,800	54,500
	26–35	19–25	3,900	7,100	9,700	12,200	14,200	19,400	48,500
	36–45	26–35	3,400	6,200	8,500	10,800	12,400	17,000	42,500
	46–55	36–45	3,000	5,400	7,500	9,500	10,800	15,000	37,500
	. . . .	46–55	2,600	4,600	6,500	8,300	9,200	13,000	33,500
101 to 130 eq ft	Up to 7	Up to 5	4,600	8,500	11,300	14,300	17,000	22,600	56,200
	8–12	6–9	4,300	7,900	10,600	13,500	15,800	21,200	52,600
	13–17	10–13	4,100	7,400	10,000	12,700	14,800	20,000	50,200
	18–25	14–18	3,800	6,900	9,400	11,900	13,800	18,800	47,300
	26–35	19–25	3,300	6,100	8,400	10,500	12,200	16,800	42,000
	36–45	26–35	3,000	5,300	7,400	9,300	10,600	14,800	37,000
	46–55	36–45	2,700	4,700	6,500	8,300	9,400	13,000	32,400
	. . . .	46–55	2,300	4,000	5,400	7,000	8,000	10,800	27,000
131 to 165 eq ft	Up to 7	Up to 5	4,100	7,300	9,800	12,300	14,600	19,600	49,200
	8–12	6–9	3,800	6,900	9,100	11,700	13,800	18,200	45,800
	13–17	10–13	3,600	6,400	8,600	11,000	12,800	17,200	41,900
	18–25	14–18	3,400	6,000	8,100	10,300	12,000	16,200	40,300
	26–35	19–25	2,900	5,300	7,200	9,100	10,600	14,400	36,000
	36–45	26–35	2,600	4,700	6,400	8,100	9,600	12,800	31,800
	46–55	36–45	2,300	4,200	5,600	7,100	8,400	11,200	28,100
	. . . .	46–55	2,000	3,600	4,700	6,000	7,200	9,400	23,500

166 to 200 eq ft								
Up to 7	Up to 5	3,800	6,500	8,800	11,000	13,000	17,600	44,100
8–12	6–9	3,500	6,100	8,200	10,500	12,200	16,400	41,500
13–17	10–13	3,300	5,700	7,700	9,900	11,400	15,400	38,800
18–25	14–18	3,100	5,400	7,200	9,300	10,800	14,400	36,000
26–35	19–25	2,700	4,800	6,400	8,300	9,600	12,800	32,000
36–45	26–35	2,400	4,300	5,700	7,300	8,600	11,400	28,200
46–55	36–45	2,100	3,800	5,000	6,400	7,600	10,000	24,700
. . . . . .	46–55	1,700	3,000	3,900	5,100	6,000	7,800	19,500

	41	42	43	44	45	46	47
Combination number	41	42	43	44	45	46	47
Stacks:† no. (in parenthesis) and size	(1) 10 × 3¼	(1) 10 × 3¼	(1) 12 × 3¼	(1) 14 × 3¼	(2) 10 × 3¼	(2) 12 × 3¼	. . .
Rectangular branch size	3 × 8	4 × 8	5 × 8	6 × 8	8 × 8	10 × 8	15 × 8
Round branch size (diam)	5	6	7	8	9	10	12
Number of joist spaces and minimum depth return air	1 at 3	1 at 3	1 at 4	1 at 5	1 at 6 or 2 at 3	1 at 7 or 2 at 4	1 at 9 or 2 at 5
Registers: low wall, high wall, or baseboard	10 × 6	10 × 6	12 × 6	14 × 6	(2) 10 × 6 or (1) 24 × 6	(2) 12 × 6 or (1) 30 × 6	. . .
Registers: floor—warm air	8 × 10	8 × 10	9 × 12	9 × 12 or longer	10 × 12	12 × 14	. . .
Registers: floor—return air	6 × 10 or 4 × 14	6 × 10 or 4 × 14	6 × 12 or 6 × 14	6 × 14	6 × 30	6 × 30	8 × 30
Trunk duct increase, in.	1	2	3	4	5	7	12

* Uninsulated ducts in heated spaces and insulated ducts in unheated spaces.

† NOTE: For return air a 14 × 3⅝ in. stud space may be used instead of 10 × 3¼ in. stack. Where 12 × 3¼ in. or 14 × 3¼ in. stack is required, a 14 × 3⅝ in. stud space may be used only when inside of stud space is smooth and without protruding plaster keys. The number of joist spaces for combination 47 is based on 2 × 8 in. joists. One space may be used with 2 × 10 in. joists.

The limiting factor for a duct combination is the stack capacity.

Reprinted by permission of ASHRAE from the Heating, Ventilating, Air Conditioning Guide, 1960.

Table 11.4 Capacity and Sizing Table—Second Story
For Warm Air and Return Air Stack, Branch, and Registers

Equiv. Length of Fittings and Registers	Horizontal Length Furnace to Register		Second Story Room Heat Loss—Btuh						
	Ducts*	Insulated Attic Ducts							
Col. a	Col. b	Col. c	Col. d	Col. e	Col. f	Col. g	Col. h	Col. i	Col. j
	Up to 7	Up to 5	6,300	10,900	14,000	17,000	21,800	28,000	70,000
	8–12	6–9	5,700	10,000	13,000	15,900	20,000	26,000	65,000
	13–17	10–13	5,200	9,200	12,100	14,900	18,400	24,200	60,500
	18–25	14–18	4,800	8,500	11,400	13,900	17,000	22,400	57,000
Up to 70 eq ft	26–35	19–25	4,100	7,300	10,000	12,400	14,600	20,000	50,000
	36–45	26–35	3,500	6,400	8,800	11,100	12,800	17,600	44,000
	46–55	36–45	3,100	5,600	7,800	9,900	11,200	15,600	39,000
	.....	46–55	2,800	5,000	6,800	9,000	10,000	13,600	34,000
	Up to 7	Up to 5	5,000	9,000	11,900	14,800	18,000	23,900	59,500
	8–12	6–9	4,600	8,200	11,000	13,900	16,400	22,000	55,000
	13–17	10–13	4,300	7,600	10,300	13,000	15,200	20,600	51,500
	18–25	14–18	4,000	7,100	9,600	12,200	14,200	19,200	48,000
71 to 100 eq ft	26–35	19–25	3,400	6,200	8,400	10,800	12,400	16,800	42,000
	36–45	26–35	3,000	5,400	7,500	9,600	10,800	15,000	37,500
	46–55	36–45	4,700	4,700	6,700	8,500	9,400	13,400	33,500
	.....	46–55	2,300	4,200	6,000	7,500	8,400	12,000	30,000
	Up to 7	Up to 5	4,200	7,700	10,400	13,000	15,400	21,700	52,200
	8–12	6–9	3,900	7,200	9,700	12,100	14,400	19,400	48,400
	13–17	10–13	3,700	6,700	9,000	11,300	13,400	18,000	45,300
	18–25	14–18	3,500	6,200	8,400	10,600	12,400	16,800	42,300
101 to 130 eq ft	26–35	19–25	3,000	5,400	7,400	9,400	10,800	14,800	37,000
	36–45	26–35	2,600	4,700	6,500	8,300	9,400	13,000	32,500
	46–55	36–45	2,400	4,100	5,800	7,400	8,200	11,600	29,000
	.....	46–55	2,000	3,600	4,800	6,500	7,200	9,600	24,000
	Up to 7	Up to 5	3,800	6,800	9,100	11,400	13,600	18,200	45,500
	8–12	6–9	3,500	6,300	8,400	10,500	12,600	16,800	42,000
	13–17	10–13	3,200	5,800	7,900	9,800	11,600	15,800	39,600
	18–25	14–18	3,000	5,500	7,400	9,200	11,000	14,800	36,800
131 to 165 eq ft	26–35	19–25	2,700	4,800	6,300	8,100	9,600	12,600	32,200
	36–45	26–35	2,300	4,200	5,700	7,200	8,400	11,400	28,200
	46–55	36–45	1,900	3,400	4,500	5,800	6,800	9,000	22,800
	.....	46–55	1,800	3,300	4,300	5,400	6,600	8,600	21,500

166 to 200 eq ft		41	42	43	44	45	46	47
Up to 7	Up to 5	3,500	6,100	8,200	10,300	12,200	16,400	41,000
8–12	6–9	3,200	5,700	7,600	9,500	11,400	15,200	38,300
13–17	10–13	2,900	5,300	7,100	8,900	10,600	14,200	35,800
18–25	14–18	2,700	5,000	6,700	8,300	10,000	13,400	33,400
26–35	19–25	2,500	4,400	5,700	7,400	8,800	11,400	29,000
36–45	26–35	2,100	3,900	5,100	6,500	7,800	10,200	25,800
46–55	36–45	1,900	3,400	4,500	5,800	6,800	9,000	22,800
......	46–55	1,500	2,800	3,500	4,700	5,600	7,000	17,500
Combination number		41	42	43	44	45	46	47
Stacks:† no. (in parenthesis) and size		(1) 10 × 3¼	(1) 10 × 3¼	(1) 12 × 3¼	(1) 14 × 3¼	(2) 10 × 3¼	(2) 12 × 3¼	...
Rectangular branch size		3 × 8	4 × 8	5 × 8	6 × 8	8 × 8	10 × 8	15 × 8
Round branch size (diam)		5	6	7	8	9	10	12
Number of joist spaces and minimum depth return air		1 at 3	1 at 3	1 at 4	1 at 5	1 at 6 or 2 at 3	1 at 7 or 2 at 4	1 at 9 or 2 at 5
Registers: low wall, high wall or baseboard		10 × 6	10 × 6	12 × 6	14 × 6	(2) 10 × 6 or (1) 24 × 6	(2) 12 × 6 or (1) 30 × 6	...
Registers: floor—warm air		8 × 10	8 × 10	9 × 12	9 × 12 or longer	10 × 12	12 × 14	...
Registers: floor—return air		6 × 10 or 4 × 14	6 × 10 or 4 × 14	6 × 12 or 6 × 14	6 × 14	6 × 30	6 × 30	8 × 30
Trunk duct increase, in.		1	2	3	4	5	7	12

* Uninsulated ducts in heated spaces and insulated ducts in unheated spaces.

† NOTE: For return air a 14 × 3⅜ in. stud space may be used instead of 10 × 3¼ in. stack. Where 12 × 3¼ in. or 14 × 3¼ in. stack is required, a 14 × 3⅜ in. stud space may be used only when inside of stud space is smooth and without protruding plaster keys. The number of joist spaces for combination 47 is based on 2 × 8 joists. One space may be used with 2 × 10 joists.

The limiting factor for a duct combination is the stack capacity.

Reprinted by permission of ASHRAE from the *Heating, Ventilating, Air Conditioning Guide*, 1960.

Perimeter heating in crawl spaces

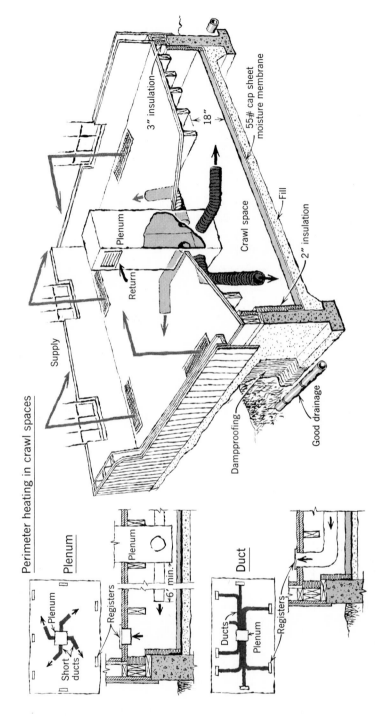

3" insulation

18"

55# cap sheet
moisture membrane

Plenum

Return

Supply

Crawl space

Fill

2" insulation

Dampproofing

Good drainage

Plenum

Plenum

Plenum

Short
ducts

Registers

6" min.

Duct

Ducts

Plenum

Registers

Registers

Fig. 11.6   Schematic view of house using crawl space plenum system. A counterflow furnace is used.
(*Progressive Architecture*)

196

Perimeter heating in concrete slab

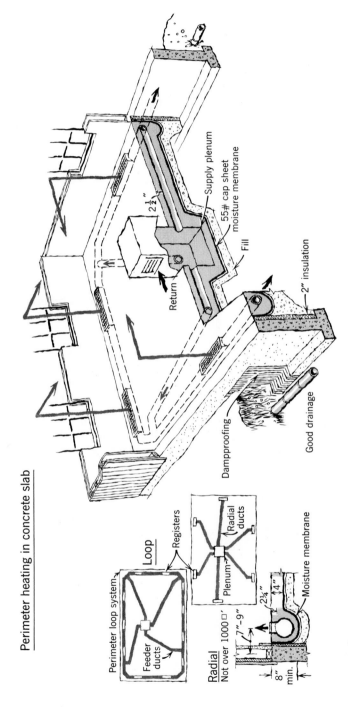

Supply plenum

55# cap sheet
moisture membrane

Fill

$2\frac{1}{2}''$

Return

2'' insulation

Dampproofing

Good drainage

Loop

Registers

Perimeter loop system

Feeder
ducts

Radial
Not over 1000 □'

Radial
ducts

Plenum

Registers

$2\frac{1}{4}''$

4''

7''–9''

Moisture membrane

8''
min.

Fig. 11.7   Schematic view of house on concrete slab using perimeter loop system. A counterflow
furnace is used. (*Progressive Architecture*)

197

ings. An example of its use is seen in Fig. 11.8. Separate furnaces serve each of two zones with different orientations. As is usual in schools, the air-handling system is arranged to circulate outside air for ventila-

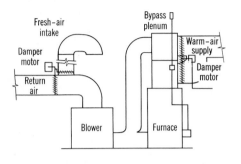

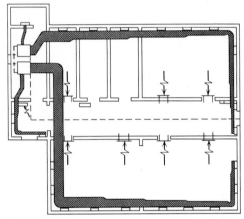

Fig. 11.8 Two-zone, two-furnace perimeter warm air system in a school near Ypsilanti, Michigan. Under-floor ducts are imbedded in concrete slab. (Reprinted from *Perimeter Warm-Air Heating and Ventilating of Industrial, Commercial, and Public Buildings, Supplement to Manual 9* of the National Warm Air Heating and Air Conditioning Association.)

tion at controlled rates during the heating season and to use up to 100 percent cool fresh air during mild weather to reduce the heat gain load which is often heavy in schools due to glass and occupants, see upper detail (Fig. 11.8).

Another illustration of the effective use of air to blanket the exterior glass is shown in Fig. 11.9. In this office building, air from a furnace (or cooling coils in summer) passes from a longitudinal basement duct to hollow masonry floor plank that carry it to perimeter floor registers below the glass. The scheme has many zones with motorized dampers to control the flow of air to the various rooms. Air returns through the corridors to the air handling units in the basement.

5. Components of a Perimeter System. When warm air perimeter heating is used for a house (or other building) on a concrete slab, it is important to select dry ground in a slightly raised location so that ground water will not collect at the structure. The heat transmission rate of earth is much increased if it is wet, increasing the heat loss from the house. Dampness, unpleasant in any case, is especially bad when one is living so close to the earth. Finally, in extreme cases and with poor construction, water might collect in the ducts. Foundation drains and dampproofing are desirable and a vapor barrier (waterproof membrane) over the earth is essential (see Fig. 11.10).

Ducts may be of terra cotta sheet metal, or asphalt fiber. Fiber is frequently used and is sufficiently rugged because all ducts must be fully imbedded in concrete. The thickness of this concrete above the duct should be $2\frac{1}{2}$ in. at the perimeter, and about 6 in. at the point where radial ducts leave the plenum. Ducts should be surrounded by not less than 2 in. of concrete at any point. The use of slab reinforcement, usually welded wire fabric, is considered good construction. The plenum is usually of concrete cast against wood or metal forms.

Air ducts — Electrical — Flexicore slab — Telephone

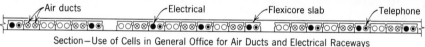

Section—Use of Cells in General Office for Air Ducts and Electrical Raceways

Double lines indicate flow of air through flexicore cells

Cooling coils — Furnace

Damper

Supply duct suspended from basement ceiling

Zone 6   Zone 11

Typical Distribution of Mixed Air (Zones 6 and 11 on First Floor Shown)

Fig. 11.9   A variation of perimeter air distribution. In this building with all-year air conditioning, air is blown laterally through self-supporting, hollow structural slab floor units to perimeter registers. (*American Concrete Institute Headquarters Building, Detroit, Michigan, Yamasaki, Leinweber, and Associates, Architects, Birmingham, Michigan.*)

A warm-air furnace consists essentially of two basic sections separated by a steel or cast iron casing through which heat is transferred from the burner-combustion-smoke-breeching side to the filter-fan and air-delivery side. The parts may be arranged in conventional form (see Fig. 11.1) or they may compose several other styles. The air to be heated may flow, not in a U-shaped path, as in Fig. 11.1, but in a straight line. The straight path may form furnaces of the upflow, downflow or horizontal type, (horizontal units find use in attics and other shallow spaces. They are known as the "stowaway" type). An appropriate furnace for warm air perimeter heating is the down-

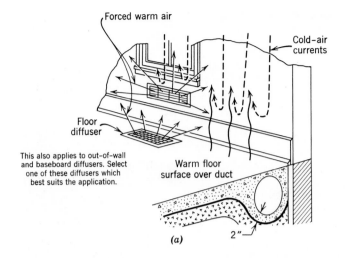

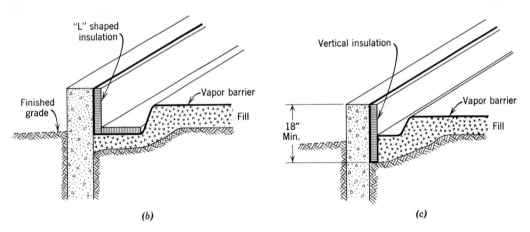

Fig. 11.10 (*a*) Perimeter duct in operation with alternate register locations. (*b*) (*c*) Two methods of preparing for placement of the duct and the concrete that surrounds it. (From *Warm-Air Perimeter Heating, Manual 4,* National Warm Air Heating and Air Conditioning Association.)

flow type (Fig. 11.11), although a plenum may be fed by a duct from any kind of furnace. Its location is usually central in the house, away from the exterior walls, and for this reason, combustion air, air to ventilate and cool the furnace, and air for house ventilation are not always easily obtainable. Sometimes copper gooseneck ducts through the roof satisfy these demands. The furnace and all its controls should be easily accessible and the unit should be kept well away from combustible construction.

In a warm air perimeter system in a concrete slab, dampers in the supply side are usually planned only at the discharge registers in each room. These longitudinal, rotating blades are adjusted for balancing the system and their limit of opening is fixed by a set screw. Thereafter, if a room occupant desires less heat, the damper can be manually operated by a small lever which adjusts it to partial or full closing.

6. **Design.** The National Warm Air Heating and Air Conditioning Association has developed design standards, (*Manual 4*) for

Warm Air Perimeter Heating, based upon its research and the testing of actual houses with heating systems in operation. Originally intended for basementless structures only, perimeter heating has been expanded to include structures with basements. The design methods are limited to structures with an hourly heat loss not exceeding 100,000 Btuh, a furnace rated at .20 in. of water static head and a range of temperature-rise of air through the furnace of 70 to 100 F. For systems on concrete slabs, a method of design for smaller buildings is also offered. For complete design information the reader is referred to *Manual 4*. A full design should not be attempted without reference to the *Manual*. A few excerpts from the *Manual* are reprinted here together with some other standards. They may be used to check a completed design, (the lower story of the Azzarone Residence) which is the subject for Example 11.2. The upper story has a ducted perimeter system in which the ducts run below the floor of that story. The lower story has a perimeter system in a concrete slab and it is fed by a duct which branches off from the general plenum at the furnace bonnet. It may be considered as separate in reviewing the design.

General guides to be considered in checking it are the following recommendations selected from *Manual 4:*

(*a*) The distance between points where feeders connect with the loop should never be more than 35 ft.

(*b*) There should not be more than 3 diffusers in the section of perimeter duct between any two feeders.

(*c*) No feeder should connect to the perimeter loop at a point less than 18 in. from the nearest diffuser. All feeders must connect to both loop and plenum at a 90° angle.

(*d*) No diffuser should be more than 15 ft from the nearest feeder.

(*e*) Run 1 feeder, if possible, under the bathroom floor.

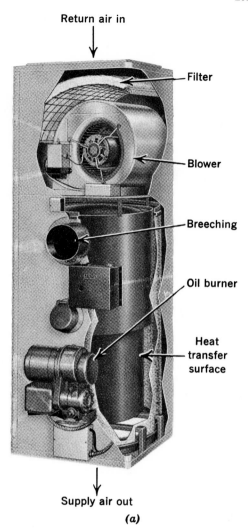

(*a*)

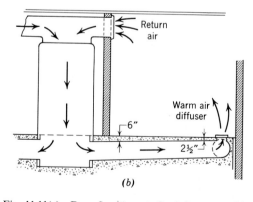

(*b*)

Fig. 11.11(*a*) Downflow (counterflow) furnace and its relation to the perimeter system, Lennox. (*b*) is from *Warm Air Perimeter Heating, Manual 4,* the National Warm Air Heating and Air Conditioning Association.

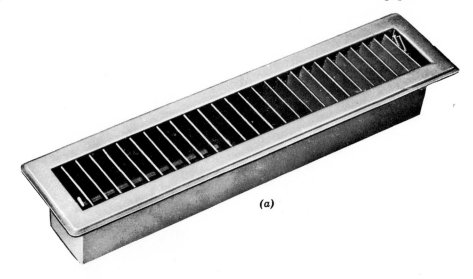

(a)

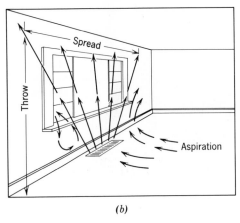

(b)

Fig. 11.12   Floor registers and their action. (*a*) A $2\frac{1}{4}$ x 12 in. floor register (diffuser). One of many sizes and shapes. It has diverting vanes for "spread" and an adjustable damper. (*b*) Concept of spread and throw. By aspiration (suction), cooler room air is induced to join the stream of warm air resulting in a bland and pleasant air stream that crosses the room.

(*f*) Avoid running a feeder under the floor of an otherwise warm room such as the utility room.

(*g*) If the distance between 2 adjacent diffusers along a section of perimeter duct between feeders is more than 20 ft, provide an additional feeder duct between these diffusers.

(*h*) A diffuser should not be installed on a feeder duct.

EXAMPLE 11.2 (Fig. 11.13). Check the design of this warm-air perimeter heating (and cooling) installation in the concrete slab of this lower story (at grade) against the foregoing recommendations (*a*) through (*h*) and by the use of Tables 11.5 through 11.8.

The following data apply to this problem:

Heat loss, lower story	33,700 Btuh
Heat loss, entire house	142,300 Btuh
Heat gain, lower story (for air quantities)	10,600 Btuh
Heat gain, entire house (for air quantities)	72,000 Btuh
Air circulated for heating, entire house	1,800 cfm
Air circulated for cooling, entire house	2,800 cfm

SOLUTION. By using the over-all dimensions of the story as a guide it will be seen that the design complies with recommendations (*a*) through (*h*).

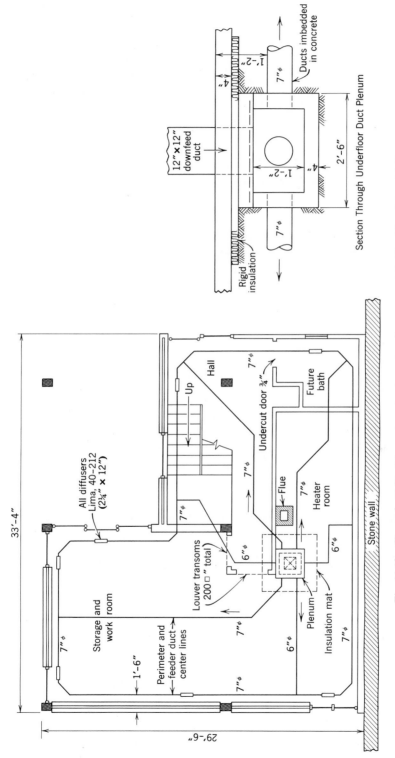

Fig. 11.13 (Example 11.2) Warm-air perimeter system in concrete slab. (See Figs. 9.4 and 9.5.) Part of heating and cooling installation (lower story), in the Azzarone residence.

Table 11.5 Diameter of Feeders when Trunk Duct is not Used

	Length of Feeder in Feet	
Btuh Per Feeder	0–15 Ft	16–30 Ft
up to 7,999	6″	6″
8,000 to 8,999	6″	7″
9,000 to 10,999	7″	7″
11,000 to 11,999	7″	8″
12,000 to 12,999	7″	8″
13,000 to 17,000	8″	8″

Reprinted from *Manual 4*, National Warm Air Heating and Air Conditioning Association.

The sizes of ducts and registers throughout this house are based upon the air that needs to be circulated for cooling, because this rate is 55 percent more than the rate needed for heating $\left(\dfrac{2800}{1800} = 1.55\right)$. The actual rate in cfm is $\dfrac{10,600}{72,000} \times 2800 = 412$ cfm. The rate for heating will be $\dfrac{33,700}{142,300} \times 1800 = 425$ cfm.

It is merely accidental that the rates are almost the same. The reason is that the heat gain in this part of the house is relatively small because of no roof, minimum east-west exposure, and shading. In the upper story (as seen in Table 9.6 and in general from the 55 percent excess found above) the cooling air rates are higher and are therefore the major influence in sizes. Since cooling and heating air-rates are about the same for the lower story, Table 11.5 applies (it is written for heating).

Feeders. Six feeder ducts are used. Each must supply $\dfrac{33,700}{6} = 5,616$ Btuh. Table 11.5 shows that 6-in. and 7-in. feeders will deliver this heat.

Air Speed. If audible sound (and friction) are to be minimized, air speeds should be generally not greater than those recommended in Table 11.6. The actual speed in the 12 in. × 12 in. square metal branch duct feeding air to this section is $\dfrac{425 \text{ cfm}}{1 \text{ sq. ft.}} = 425$ fpm. The velocity in the round feeder ducts will depend upon their aggregate area. this is:

$$3 \times \left(\frac{7}{2}\right)^2 \times 3.14 = 115$$

$$3 \times \left(\frac{6}{2}\right)^2 \times 3.14 = \underline{\ 84\ }$$
$$199 \text{ sq. in.}$$

Table 11.6 Recommended and Maximum Duct Velocities for Conventional Systems

	Recommended Velocities, fpm		
Designation	Residences	Schools, Theaters, Public Buildings	Industrial Buildings
Outdoor air intakes	500	500	500
Filters	250	300	350
Heating coils	450	500	600
Air washers	500	500	500
Fan outlets	1000–1600	1300–2000	1600–2400
Main ducts	700–900	1300–2000	1200–1800
Branch ducts	600	600–900	800–1000
Branch risers	500	600–700	800

Reprinted by permission of *ASHRAE* from the *Heating, Ventilating, and Air Conditioning Guide, 1960.*

Since this area is more than 144 sq. in. the speed will be less than it is in the general 12 × 12 in. branch duct to this system. This speed of 425 fpm is somewhat less than the 600 fpm set in Table 11.6 for branch ducts in residences. It is therefore satisfactory. These all must be considered branch ducts because they are close to people who might occupy this space, especially in its future development (see Fig. 9.5), and could be disturbed by sound.

Diffusers. Each of the 7 floor registers $(2\frac{1}{4} \times 12$ in.$)$, delivers $\frac{425}{7} = 60.7$ cfm. Table 11.8 shows that for a 60 cfm delivery the face velocity of the register is 420 fpm. Since this is less than the 500 to 750 range suggested in Table 11.7, quietness is assured. Actually it would be desirable to have a higher face velocity to produce a vertical "throw" of more than the 4 ft shown in Table 11.8. This is a problem in houses with more than the usual amount of glass. Many diffusers are needed to blanket the windows or glass, yet, as they increase in number, their power diminishes. The 4 ft throw, however, was found to be satisfactory in this case.

Heat Equation. The heat in Btuh delivered to the space may be calculated approximately, using the basic principles of physics, and the following data:

cfm for heating	412.0
Temperature rise in furnace, deg F (70 to 140)	70.0

Table 11.7 Recommended Delivery Face Velocities for Various Applications (Registers)

The sound caused by an air outlet in operation varies in direct proportion to the velocity of the air passing through it. The air velocity can be controlled by selecting outlets of proper sizes. The following recommended outlet velocities are within safe sound limits for most applications:

Application	Recommended Velometer Velocities fpm
Broadcasting studios	500
Residences	500 to 750
Apartments	500 to 750
Churches	500 to 750
Hotel bedrooms	500 to 750
Legitimate theaters	500 to 1000
Private offices, acoustically treated	500 to 1000
Motion picture theaters	1000 to 1250
Private offices, not treated	1000 to 1250
General offices	1250 to 1500
Stores, upper floors	1500
Stores, main floors	1500
Industrial buildings	1500 to 2000

Density of air	.075
Specific heat of air	.241
Conversion factor, min per hr.	60.0

$412 \times .075 \times .241 \ 70 \times 60 = 31,500$ Btuh

Table 11.8   Characteristics of 2¼ × 12 Floor Register

Heating Btuh	3045	4565	6090	7610	9515	11415	13320	15220
Cooling Btuh	855	1280	1710	2135	2670	3200	3735	4270
CFM	40	60	80	100	125	150	175	200
T.P. loss	.009	.015	.027	.037	.050	.080	.105	.134
Vertical throw	3	4	5	6	8	10	12	14
Vertical spread	6	8	10	11	14	17	22	25
Face velocity	280	420	565	705	880	1050	1230	1400

Excerpt from the *Catalog* of the Lima Register Company.

This is a close approximation to the requirement of 33,700 Btuh.

References

1. *Warm Air Perimeter Heating, Manual 4.*
2. *Code and Manual for the Design and Installation of Warm Air Winter Air Conditioning Systems, Manual 7.*
3. *Code and Manual for the Design and Installation of Warm Air Winter Air Conditioning Systems and Year-Round Air Conditioning Systems, Manual 9.*
4. *Perimeter Warm Air Heating and Ventilating, Supplement to Manual 9.*

The above four manuals are written and published by the National Warm Air Heating and Air Conditioning Association, 640 Engineers Building, Cleveland 14, Ohio.

12

Hot-Water Heating

1. Characteristics. This method of heating consists of warming the water in a boiler and circulating it by means of pumps to convectors or similar devices that warm the spaces requiring heat. Controls operate to keep the boiler water warm at all times and ready for use. It is a closed system, free from air and under a slight pressure to prevent the formation of steam. Since the water returns to its own level, the pumps, known as *circulators,* operate only to overcome the friction of water against pipes and fittings.

Early hot water systems, many of which are still operating satisfactorily, functioned by means of gravity acting by the difference in density of warm and cool water. By comparison, modern forced (mechanical) systems use smaller pipes or tubing, not necessarily pitched except for drainage. Distances are more easily overcome and the position of the boiler is a matter of choice. It can be higher than some of the convectors that it serves. It is essential that air be removed from high points and that drainage be provided at low points including locations that are *trapped* and would otherwise retain water when the general system was drained.

In residences and small buildings hot water and warm air are both suitable and may be considered competitive. Each has advantages: hot water offers silence, compactness, easy zoning, and adaptability to hot water generation by coils immersed in the boiler water. Hot water has now almost entirely replaced the 1 pipe, air-vent steam system, so often used for homes in the past.

For large buildings, hot water is competing with steam for popularity. Steam, however, is still much used and is essential, where in addition to heating, other steam-operated devices such as steam turbines, sterilizers in hospitals, steam cooking, and absorption type cooling are used. For *district* heating at campuses, airports, parts of cities, high temperature hot water (see Chap 18) is often chosen where previously steam was the universal medium.

2. Circuit Types. Copper tubing is a popular material for the water circuits. There are 3 principal methods of circulating the water. The 1-pipe system (Fig. 12.1a) is effective and the most economical of tubing. It is the one most frequently used. The reversed return, (Fig. 12.1b) is sometimes used when delivery of hot water to each

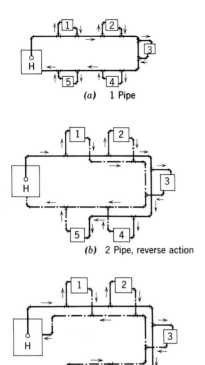

(a) 1 Pipe

(b) 2 Pipe, reverse action

(c) 2 Pipe, direct return

Fig. 12.1 Schematic diagrams of hot water piping systems.

heating unit at constant temperature is especially desired. The direct return (Fig. 12.1c) is not usually chosen because of the differ-

ence in the lengths of circuits to the near and far radiators, (Nos. 1 and 5). When, unavoidably, this kind of distribution must be used, it can be balanced by newly developed techniques.

Figure 12.2a shows the usual single-circuit 1-pipe system. Hot water is carried in the main and diverted to the several radiators. A number of special tee fittings have been devised to accomplish this. One kind (Fig. 12.3) constricts the main, forcing water into the radiator supply branch. A venturi-type jet reduces the pressure in the return fitting, inducing flow of water out of the radiator branch return. The first radiators receive slightly warmer water than the later ones in the circuit, but this difference is negligible. A double-circuit system 1-pipe (Fig. 12.2b) is sometimes used for better distribution, particularly in larger installations. Many circuits may be used off the master main. In double and multiple circuits no radiation is taken directly off the master main.

In a 2-pipe system (Fig. 12.4), no cool water from radiators is taken back into the supply main because it is collected in a separate return main. Faster heating with greater uniformity in radiator temperature is accomplished. The system shown is one employing the reversed-return principle.

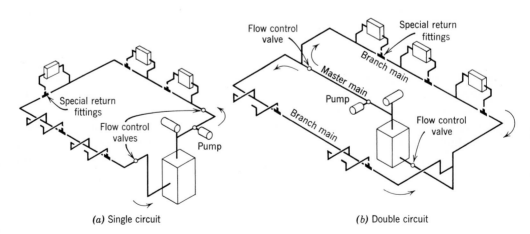

(a) Single circuit   *(b)* Double circuit

Fig. 12.2   One-pipe systems.

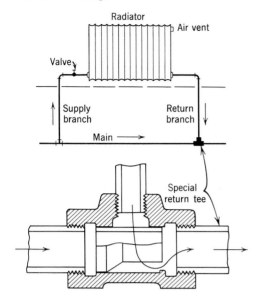

Fig. 12.3   Special fitting for 1-pipe systems. Venturi-type tee used here on the return branch connection to the main.

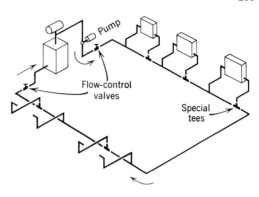

Fig. 12.5   One-pipe, downfeed system for basementless house.

The piping length from the boiler through any radiator and back to the boiler is the same, assuring equal flow because of equal friction. No special fittings are necessary because there is pressure in the supply main and suction in the return main.

Although radiator or convector heating is not generally advised for use in houses having concrete slabs on the ground, basementless houses with a crawl space below the first floor can be served well by a hot water radiator system. In this case the

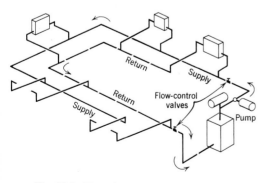

Fig. 12.4   Two-pipe reversed return system.

boiler could be at the same level or above the radiators, and there would be a downfeed supply main and upfeed branches as shown in Fig. 12.5.

Hot water heating may be used in large, multistory buildings, (see Fig. 12.6) the down-feed, 1 pipe loops serve the radiators in each *stack*. The special return tees divert the water horizontally from the vertical branch main to the radiators just as they would from a horizontal main. These special tees have the trade name of "monoflo fittings" and may be used, in reversed position as supply tees instead of return tees.

3. Zoning (Fig. 12.7). Based on the 1-pipe principle in multiple circuits, each having its own pump and flow-control (check) valves, hot water systems are very well suited to zoning. This installation comprises 3 separately heated areas—basement, first floor, and second floor. Each can be heated to different temperatures as called for by thermostats in each separate apartment. For example, if the thermostat serving the first floor (zone B) calls for heat, it turns on pump B. Flow control valves B open admitting hot water from the boiler header to main B. Flow control valves A and C remain closed, preventing flow in mains A and C. Any or all of the zones may operate at one time. The boiler keeps a supply of hot water continually ready to supply any zone upon demand. This is achieved by an aquastat (water thermostat) immersed in the boiler water. When the boiler water drops below the prescribed temperature it turns on the firing device, such as an oil burner or gas burner, which brings the water up to temperature. If an overhead main supplies downfeed, as in the basement

of this installation, special downfeed supply and return fittings are necessary. For the first and second floor zones, one special return tee is sufficient. If the designer elects to use also a special upfeed *supply* tee of the venturi type, higher outputs of the radiators will result, as indicated in Table 12.4. (See Fig. 12.8 for illustrations of special fittings). The system shown in Fig. 12.7 is a multicircuit 1-pipe system.

The diversity of occupancy and of technical functions in modern buildings has greatly increased the need for zoning. Figure 12.9 shows an arrangement that makes separate operation of many zones possible. The primary circulating pump runs continuously whenever there is any demand. Zones, by means of separate zone-pumps "pick off" hot water as needed—while protected from incidental flow by flow-control valves which close when their zone-pump stops. Connections to the primary main or the primary branch loop (as shown in the illustration) should be close together so that there will be no pressure differential large enough to cause unwanted secondary flow.

Those who are familiar with earlier design techniques will observe a change, in that the circulator is *always* placed on the supply side of the circuit to minimize drawing air into the circuit. The use of 2 flow control valves on each circuit is also a new concept.

4. Radiators, Convectors, and Baseboard Radiation. Hot water systems may be equipped with small tube-cast iron radiators, convectors, baseboard radiation or unit (blast) heaters similar to those used with steam. Radiant coils imbedded in plaster ceilings or concrete floors are also a possibility. Reference to Chapter 14 (Steam) will show that at 1 psi gauge pressure (215 F), a steam radiator emits 240 Btuh per sq ft of radiator surface. If water is maintained at an *average* temperature of 215 F, the output of the cast iron is the same,

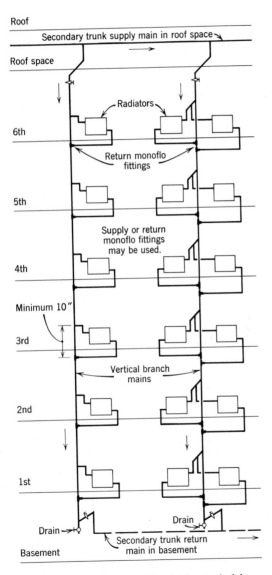

Fig. 12.6 Two 1-pipe loops (circuits) in a typical downfeed hot-water heating system for a multistory building. Monoflo fittings are those of the venturi type. Reprinted from *Engineering Manual,* Bell and Gossett Company.

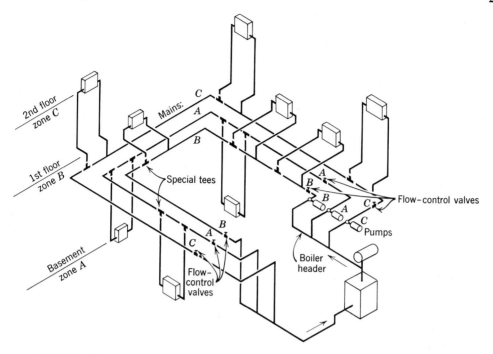

Fig. 12.7 Three-zone, multicircuit, 1-pipe system. Each radiator has connections to *one pipe*.

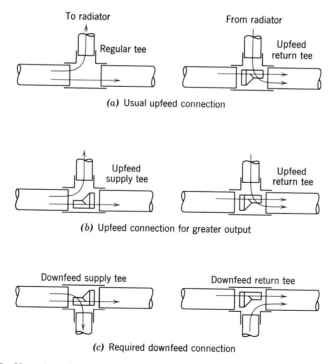

(a) Usual upfeed connection

(b) Upfeed connection for greater output

(c) Required downfeed connection

Fig. 12.8 Venturi tees in branch radiator connections in 1-pipe forced circulation systems.

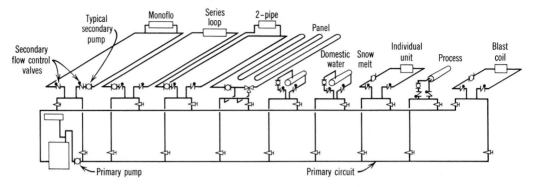

Fig. 12.9   With primary-secondary pumping, many types of secondary zones may be used. Reprinted from *Hydronic Zone Control with Primary-Secondary Pumping,* Bell and Gossett Company.

namely 240 Btuh per sq ft. Since the temperature drop in a water system is often 20 F, the boiler water temperature would be 225 F, which is a common maximum for low temperature systems. The most economical and compact installation would be based upon this temperature (215 F average in the radiator) which would permit radiators of minimum size.

More generous designs often utilize lower temperatures, (see Table 12.1), and correspondingly larger radiators. This ef-

Table 12.1   Heat Transmission Rates, Cast-Iron Radiation

(Room temperature 70°)

Average Radiator Temperature °F	Btuh per sq ft of Radiation
165	140
170	150
175	160
180	170
185	180
190	190
195	200
200	210
205	220
210	230
215	240*
220	250

* Steam at 1 psi gauge pressure.

fects milder, more dispersed heating under normal conditions and provides an extra margin of heating surface, an advantage during bitter outdoor conditions. The sq ft of radiation required for any room is found by dividing the hourly heat loss rate by the unit output rate of the radiator (selected from Table 12.1) at the radiator temperature to be maintained. If a convector is to be used, it is only necessary to select one for the same EDR (Equivalent Direct Radiation).

EXAMPLE 12.1.   (*a*) Select a small tube cast iron radiator to make up a heat loss of 7000 Btuh if the average water temperature is to be 180 F; (*b*) select a convector for the same condition; (*c*) select a baseboard heater for the same condition. Some essential reference data are found in Chap. 14.

SOLUTION. (*a*) From Table 12.1 it is found that the heat emission will be 170 Btuh per sq ft. The area of radiation required will be $\frac{7000}{170} = 42.3$ sq ft. From Table 14.2, select a 6-tube, 32-in. high section. It provides 3.7 sq ft of radiation per section. The number of sections will be $\frac{42.3}{3.7} = 11.5$ (say 12 sections). Its length will be 12 × $1\frac{3}{4} = 21$ in.

SOLUTION. (*b*) From Table 14.3 select a front-outlet type convector—6 in. deep, 40 in. long, and 38 in. high. Its Equivalent Direct Radiation (EDR) is 42.1 sq ft.

OUTPUT, BTUH PER LINEAR FOOT OF BASEBOARD

Average water temperature °F	Cast iron "Radiantrim		Nonferrous, "Heatrim"	
	Model 8	Model 10	Model N85-L	Model N85-HH
	Height 8 in.	$10\frac{3}{8}$ in.	8 in.	$10\frac{1}{4}$ in.
170	410	490	500	620
180	460	550	570	690
190	520	620	630	760
200	570	680	700	840
210	630	740	760	910
220	690	800	830	990

American-Standard, Plumbing and Heating Division

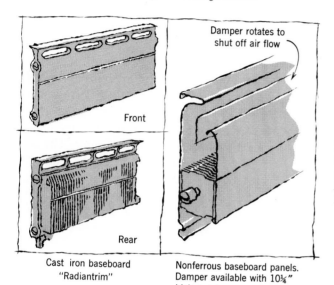

Front

Damper rotates to shut off air flow

Rear

Cast iron baseboard "Radiantrim"

Nonferrous baseboard panels. Damper available with 10¼" high panel. Copper tubing—aluminum fins "Heatrim"

Fig. 12.10   Baseboard heating elements. An example of style and output of units of one manufacturer. For ratings of others, see *Baseboard Ratings,* Institute of Boiler and Radiator Manufacturers.

In both cases, for the same output, heating units of varied proportions are available. Architectural considerations will usually be the determining factor in the choice of a unit.

SOLUTION. (c) See Fig. 12.10. If the room heat loss is divided by the output per linear ft. of the baseboard, the required number of feet of baseboard may be found. At 180 F an N85-HH baseboard panel $10\frac{1}{4}$ in. high will produce 690 Btuh per ft. Ten ft would be necessary. If a model 8 cast iron is chosen at 460 Btuh per ft, 16 ft would be required. The thermal response and heat-retaining qualities of cast iron and of sheet metal are quite different. For this reason cast iron baseboard should be used in systems where cast iron radiators are used and nonferrous baseboard panels in systems with convectors.

For houses of modern design baseboard heating units are a popular choice. They are suitable for walls in which there are picture windows or below large panels of glass. When these walls do not afford enough length to accommodate the required amount of baseboard, it may be continued on other exterior walls not having glass. If additional length is needed it may be extended to interior walls. Obviously all of the baseboard should be concentrated below the glass if possible. This favors the use of high-output elements.

The use of 2 fin-tube strips, one above the other, produces outputs higher than those shown in Fig. 12.10. Strangely enough they are not doubled, but only increased about 25 percent. There are some industrial type fin-tube units that have ratings in excess of those in Fig. 12.10. An example is the Walvector of Warren Webster used in the Sands Point residence described in this chapter.

Glass-to-the-floor and the use of sliding glass panels has pushed the convector strip below the floor level. In Fig. 12.11 industrial convector strips are used. They are 4 in. aluminum squares on $1\frac{1}{4}$ in. diameter copper tubes. The air downflow passages are 3 in. wide and the grills 8 in. wide. Cool air slipping down from the glass is drawn into the outer slot as the warm air rises in the inner one.

An automatic convector-vent is shown at the high point in Fig. 12.11. All convectors or radiators must be so vented by automatic air vents, (Fig. 12.12b) or manually operated air vents (Fig. 12.12a). High points in piping are provided with automatic vents of the type shown in Fig. 12.12c.

5. Boiler Controls (Figs. 12.13 and 12.14). In Fig. 12.13 the heating circuit can be seen in which boiler water is circulated to and from the radiators through flow-control valves which open when circulating pump g on the supply line starts. At the right is the circuit which operates the domestic hot water system. Boiler water passes through tankless heater q and back to the bottom of the boiler. The passage of this hot water heats cold water for use as domestic hot water at sinks and lavatories. Tempering valve p prevents the delivery of excessively hot water by mixing cold water as necessary. Coils in tank q facilitate the heat transfer without permitting the mixing of boiler water and domestic water. The coil shown is schematic and would be relatively longer. Above the boiler is expansion tank k and relief valve j, which, respectively, cushion expansion and relieve excessive pressure. When the boiler needs water it is

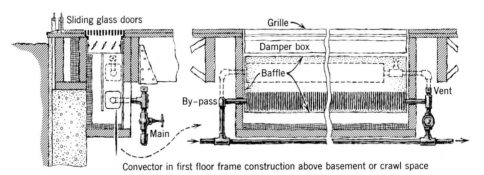

Convector in first floor frame construction above basement or crawl space

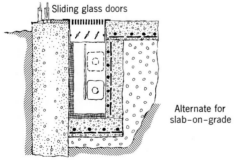

Alternate for slab-on-grade

Fig. 12.11 Convectors housed in boxes submerged in basement or crawl space, or in masonry pits for slab-on-grade conditions. Outputs in Btuh per linear foot of trench for water at 215 F are as follows:

1-finned convector strip	1570 Btuh
2-finned convector strips	1930 Btuh

From Progressive Architecture.

fed in through pressure-reducing valve *n*, backflow into the cold water main being stopped by check valve *o*. The function of each control is as follows:

(*a*) **House Thermostat.** When the room air temperature falls below the setting of the thermostat, the house thermostat turns on the pump and oil burner simultaneously. When satisfied it turns them both off.

(*b*) **Low-Limit Control.** This control turns on the oil burner when the boiler water falls below a chosen temperature (about 160 F).

(*c*) **High-Limit Control.** "Runaway" performance is prevented by this device, which turns off the oil burner when the boiler water starts to exceed a chosen high temperature (often about 200 F).

(*d*) **Reverse-Acting Control** (*optional*). To prevent the circulation of cold water in the radiators, this control stops the circulating pump when the boiler water falls below 160 F until the burner has had time to raise the temperature again to the desired degree.

(*e*) **Stack-Temperature Control.** After the burner starts, the stack-temperature control waits for the resulting rise in stack temperature. If it does not come in a short time, as a safety control it turns off the burner which has failed to ignite.

(*f*) **Junction Box and Relays.** This central control station transmits the impulses of the controls previously described.

(*g*) **Circulating Pump.** (Fig. 12.14*g*). This electrically driven centrifugal pump turns on whenever heat is called for and the boiler water is hot enough (above 160 F). Performance curves for pumps of this type are given in Fig. 12.16.

(*h*) **Oil Burner.** Reheat may be needed for a number of reasons. From lack of use the boiler water may have cooled below 160 F. The water may have been cooled in making domestic hot water. Finally, when circulation starts, cold radiator water is returned to the boiler and needs to be heated.

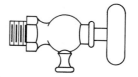

(*a*) Manual (for radiators and convectors)

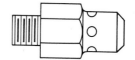

(*b*) Automatic (for radiators and convectors)

(*c*) Automatic (for piping)

Fig. 12.12   Air-vent valves.

(*i*) **Flow-Control Valves** (Fig. 12.14*i*). The precise temperature control possible in forced circulation systems is assured by the flow-control valves which close when the pump stops, thus preventing gravity circulation which would result in a further rise in room temperature. In principle they are check valves. There are 2 in each circuit.

(*j*) **Pressure-Relief Valve** (Fig. 12.14*j*). When the pressure in the system exceeds 30 psi, the spring-loaded valve opens, bleeding water out of the pipes and relieving the pressure which might otherwise cause breakage. It should be placed where its discharge will do no damage. With proper system design and adjustment it should not operate except in an emergency.

(*k*) **Expansion Tank.** This is sometimes known as a compression tank. A cushion of

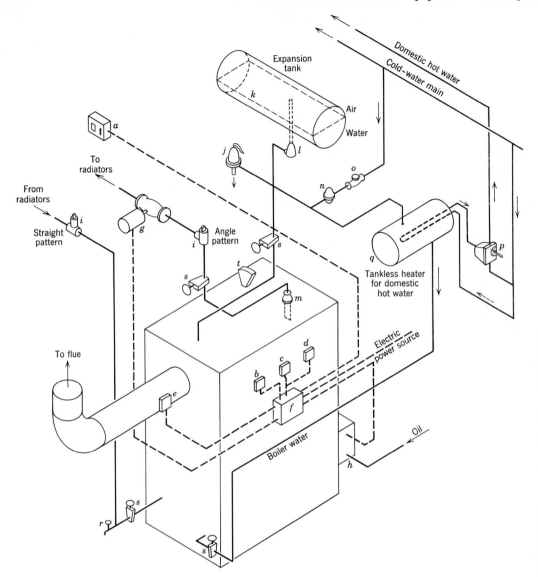

Fig. 12.13   Schematic diagram of electrical and mechanical controls for a hot-water heating plant.

air remains in the top of the tank to adjust for the varying volume of water in the system as the temperature changes.

(*l*) *and* (*m*) *Tank and Boiler Air-Control Fittings* (Fig. 12.14*l* and *m*).   Much of the air in the system is eliminated at once by these fittings, which lead the air to the expansion tank. Air accumulating in the boiler cannot leave through the dip tube *m* but

finds its way to *l*, where it is led to the top of the expansion tank.

(*n*) *Pressure-Reducing Valve* (Fig. 12.14*n*). This is the automatic fill valve. It opens when the pressure in the system drops below 12 psi and closes with a check action against higher pressures. It keeps the system full.

(*o*) *Check Valve.*   In an emergency where

pressure-relief valve *j* did not open and the pressure-reducing valve failed in its checking action, the check valve *o* prevents the boiler from putting the house cold-water system under pressure that would be dangerous.

(*p*) **Tempering Valve** (Fig. 12.14*p*). This mixing valve operates automatically by a mechanical thermostat to add cold water in sufficient quantities to deliver the domestic hot water at exactly the required temperature.

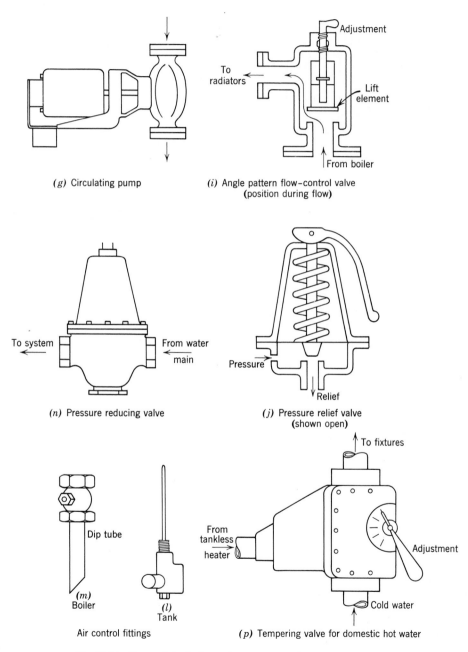

(*g*) Circulating pump

(*i*) Angle pattern flow–control valve
(position during flow)

(*n*) Pressure reducing valve

(*j*) Pressure relief valve
(shown open)

(*m*) Boiler
(*l*) Tank
Air control fittings

(*p*) Tempering valve for domestic hot water

Fig. 12.14   Some of the boiler and system controls shown in Fig. 12.13.

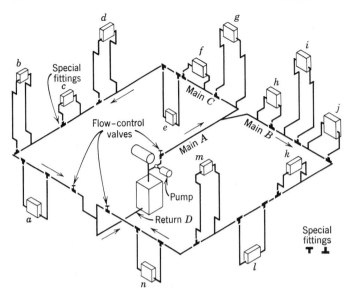

Fig. 12.15 (Example 12.2) Two-loop, 1-pipe forced circulation hot-water heating system.

Radiation in 1000 Btuh (Mbh)

Main B			Main C		
h	4		a	3	
i	3		b	4	
j	9		c	8	
k	5		d	6	
l	4		e	5	
m	6		f	4	
n	9		g	9	
Total	40 Mbh		Total	39 Mbh	

Through Main A and Return D 79 Mbh
Through Main B 40 Mbh
Through Main C 39 Mbh

(q) *Tankless Heater.* This generates domestic hot water for use in the various plumbing fixtures.

(r) *Drain.* At this and other low points, means of draining the system must be provided.

(s) *Gate Valve.* The location of gate valves is determined by the need for shutting off sections of the system for repair or servicing without draining the entire water content. Their selection in preference to globe valves is due to the smaller resistance they offer to the passage of water.

(t) *Temperature and Pressure Gauge.* The operating pressure of the system may be observed as a check on the operation and setting of the pressure-relief valve and on the cushioning effect of the compression tank. Observation of the boiler water temperature is a check on the operation of the aquastat which controls this temperature.

6. Design. For hot water heating systems the following concepts and design procedure are recommended:

(a) *Total Equivalent Length.* The length of the longest circuit through which the water is pumped plus a length equivalent to the resistance offered by the fittings, boiler, etc., is the total equivalent length.

(b) *Pressure Drop in the Pipe.* This drop due to friction, expressed in milinches of water per ft of pipe is the difference in pressure caused by friction in 1 ft of pipe and represents the static height of water in thousandths of an inch capable of being sustained by this difference in pressure.

(c) *Total Friction Head.* Expressed in feet, this head is the column of static water that could be sustained by the difference in pressure in the entire system owing to friction. Thus, if a system were 300 ft long and had a unit frictional resistance of 300 milinches per ft, the total friction head would be $\frac{300 \times 300}{1000 \times 12} = 7.5$ ft. Check this by Table 12.3.

(d) *Required Flow.* The required flow is the water flow in gpm to be circulated to make up the hourly heat loss in the building. It is determined by the hourly heat loss and the selected drop in the water temperature.

(e) *Pump Rating.* The pump size is selected on the basis of the required flow and the total friction head (Fig. 12.16).

(f) *Required Volume of Expansion Tank.* This is related to the volume of water in the system and the over-all rise in temperature from cold water supply temperature to boiler water operating temperature. For maximum rise it can be related to the sq ft of radiation in the system (Table 12.5).

The procedure may be outlined as follows:

(a) Add to the length of the longest circuit the length equivalent to fittings as taken from Table 12.2 to determine the *total* equivalent length of pipe in the longest circuit. A 90° elbow produces approximately the same friction as a straight pipe of the same diam 25 diameters long. It is, therefore, necessary to assume an average size of pipe for the system which is later checked.

(b) The rate at which the water is to be circulated is then chosen. High velocities reduce the size of pipe but increase the cost of the pump and its operation. A cooling of the water or drop of 20° has proved satisfactory and economical in average systems, on the basis of a reasonable velocity from the pump and a logical relationship between the flow and the size of pipe. A mean temperature of 215° has been found practicable for a system using forced circulation and a closed pressure tank.

(c) At the temperatures used in heating, water has a specific heat of 1.0 and a weight of about 8 lb per gal. This is an approximate "round number" to work with in preference to the *actual* 8.33. The flow in gpm to produce the total heat required in the radiators is then

$$\frac{\text{Total heat}}{\text{Drop} \times 60 \times 8} = \text{gpm}$$

or for a temperature drop of 20°

$$\frac{\text{Total heat}}{9600} = \text{gpm}$$

(d) To select the pump—the rate of flow and the pressure head must be known. From Table 12.3 a friction head and pressure head are chosen which will permit the transmission of the required heat and flow of water through the total length of piping

Table 12.2*   Iron and Copper Elbow Equivalents†

Fitting	Iron Pipe	Copper Tubing
Elbow, 90°	1.0	1.0
Elbow, 45°	0.7	0.7
Elbow, 90° long turn	0.5	0.5
Elbow, welded, 90°	0.5	0.5
Reduced coupling	0.4	0.4
Open return band	1.0	1.0
Open gate valve	0.5	0.7
Open globe valve	12.0	17.0
Angle radiator valve	2.0	3.0
Radiator or convector	3.0	4.0
Boiler or heater	3.0	4.0
Tee, percent flowing through branch:		
100	1.8	1.2
50	4.0	4.0
25	16.0	20.0

† The friction in one 90° standard elbow is approximately equal to the friction of a length of straight pipe of the same nominal size and 25 diameters long. Hence, one elbow equivalent in feet of pipe equals 25 diameters (in inches) divided by 12.
* Reprinted by permission of *ASHRAE* from the *Heating, Ventilating, Air Conditioning Guide*, 31st Edition.

Table 12.3*   *Pipe Sizing Table for Mains, Forced Circulation Hot Water Systems*

SECTION A

Booster Head Pressures (ft)	Total Equivalent Length of Pipe in Feet								
2	40	48	60	68	80	96	120	160	240
2½	50	60	75	86	100	120	150	200	300
3	60	72	90	103	120	144	180	240	360
3½	70	84	105	120	140	168	210	280	420
4	80	96	120	137	160	192	240	320	480
4½	90	108	135	154	180	216	270	360	540
5	100	120	150	171	200	240	300	400	600
5½	110	132	165	188	220	264	330	440	660
6	120	144	180	206	240	288	360	480	720
6½	130	156	195	223	260	312	390	520	780
7	140	168	210	240	280	336	420	560	840
7½	150	180	225	257	300	360	450	600	900
8	160	192	240	274	320	384	480	640	960
8½	170	204	255	291	340	408	510	680	1020
9	180	216	270	308	360	432	540	710	1080
9½	190	228	285	325	380	456	570	760	1140
10	200	240	300	342	400	480	600	800	1200
10½	210	252	315	360	420	504	630	840	1260
11	220	264	330	377	440	528	660	880	1320
11½	230	276	345	394	460	552	690	920	1380
12	240	288	360	411	480	576	720	960	1440

SECTION B *(Based on 20° Temperature Drop)*

Main Capacities *(in Thousands of Btu)*

Pipe Size (in.)	Pressure Drop in Pipe in Millinches per Foot								
	600	500	400	350	300	250	200	150	100
½	19	18	16	15	13	12	10	9	7
¾	41	37	33	30	28	26	23	20	15
1	80	71	64	59	53	48	42	37	31
1¼	170	160	140	130	118	102	90	78	63
1½	260	240	210	185	175	156	140	121	94
2	500	450	410	360	322	294	261	227	182
2½	810	750	670	610	551	523	460	385	310
3	1600	1400	1300	1150	1000	900	800	680	550
3½†	2300	2100	1850	1650	1500	1350	1190	1020	825
4†	3200	2900	2600	2300	2100	1950	1700	1350	1140

* Bell and Gossett Company.

† Trunk main capacities only. Fittings are not made larger than 3″.

NOTE: The figures shown in these tables apply to both steel pipe and Type L copper tubing, as capacity differences are not sufficient to cause design errors.

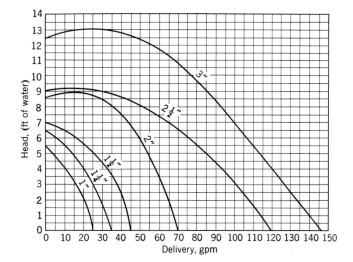

Fig. 12.16 Performance chart for circulating pump. Reprinted by permission of *ASHRAE* from the *Heating, Ventilating, Air Conditioning Guide,* 1960.

without unreasonably high or low friction and pressure. The friction head in milinches per foot of pipe is found by dividing the total pressure head in milinches by the total equivalent length of pipe; 300, 250, and 200 milinches per ft. are frequently satisfactory in systems of medium size. Higher friction heads, while permitting smaller pipe, cause high water velocity accompanied by noise. Lower friction heads require larger pipes and cause sluggish water flow.

(*e*) With the friction head in milinches, per ft. and the heat loads, the proper size of pipe for each section of the system may be determined from Table 12.3 or 12.4.

(*f*) With the rate of flow in gpm and the pressure head in feet the circulating pump may be chosen from Fig. 12.16.

(*g*) With the total radiation in the system in sq ft of cast iron a compression tank of proper size may be selected from Table 12.5.

EXAMPLE 12.2. Design piping for a 2-circuit 1-pipe forced circulation system (Fig. 12.15). In passing through the longest circuit to one of the upstairs radiators the water travels through boiler, 2 flow-control valves, radiator valve, radiator, 134 ft of pipe, 3 tees, and 18 ells. This summary would be from *working* sketches. Copper tubing is to be used. The position of special

fittings is indicated in Fig. 12.15 by heavy lines.

(*a*) From Table 12.2, friction heads in terms of 1 elbow are:

1 boiler	4
1 radiator	4
1 radiator valve	3
3 tees*	12
18 ells	18
2 flow-control valves	40 (not in Table 12.2)
	81 elbows

* Tees along the run of the main other than those serving 1 radiator are not considered as adding resistance to the flow. Assuming average pipe diam to be 1 in; $\dfrac{81 \times 25 \text{ in.}}{12} =$ 169 ft. Then $134 + 169 = 303$ ft total equivalent length.

(*b*) Select 215 F as the average temperature and a 20° drop.

(*c*) Rate of flow through the system: $\dfrac{79,000 \text{ Btuh}}{96,000} = 8.2$ gpm through main *A* and return *D*, of which (by a similar calculation) 4.15 gpm passes through main *B* and 4.05 gpm passes through main *C*.

(*d*) Select 250 milinches per ft as the pressure drop. For 303 ft equivalent length the pressure head will be $6\frac{1}{2}$ ft (Table 12.3).

Table 12.4*   *Pipe Sizing Table for Risers, 1-Pipe Forced Circulation Hot Water Systems with Special Fittings*

(Based on 20° Temperature Drop)

Capacity of Risers with 2 Fittings (In Thousands of Btu).

Pipe Size (in.)	600	500	400	350	Milinches 300	250	200	150	100
					Upfeed Risers—First Floor (See Note 1)				
A $\frac{1}{2}$	23	22	19	18	17	16	14	12	10
$\frac{3}{4}$	43	41	37	33	30	28	26	22	20
1	80	73	64	60	55	50	45	39	32
$1\frac{1}{4}$	180	140	120	110	100	93	80	74	62
					Upfeed Risers—Second Floor (See Note 2)				
B $\frac{1}{2}$	16	15	14	13	11	10	10	8	7
$\frac{3}{4}$	31	28	25	24	22	21	18	15	13
1	58	52	45	43	37	33	32	28	25
$1\frac{1}{4}$	122	108	92	90	79	72	68	59	50
					Upfeed Risers—Third Floor (See Note 2)				
C $\frac{1}{2}$	14	12	11	10	9	8	8	7	6
$\frac{3}{4}$	26	24	23	21	19	18	16	14	12
1	47	43	38	36	34	31	29	28	25
$1\frac{1}{4}$	99	91	81	77	70	66	59	56	46
					Downfeed Risers (See Note 3)				
D $\frac{1}{2}$	16	15	14	12	11	9	8	For less than 200-milinch resistance, base calculations on pump with higher head pressure	
$\frac{3}{4}$	33	30	26	24	20	18	14		
1	58	52	43	41	34	29	25		
$1\frac{1}{4}$	117	106	86	83	69	59	49		

NOTE. The figures shown in these tables apply to both steel pipe and Type L copper tubing, as capacity differences are not sufficient to cause design errors.

Capacity of Risers with 1 Fitting (In Thousands of Btu).

Pipe Size (in.)	600	500	400	350	Milinches 300	250	200	150	100
					Upfeed Risers—First Floor				
E $\frac{1}{2}$	16.5	15	13	12	11	10.6	10	9.2	8
$\frac{3}{4}$	29	27	25	24	21	19	18	17	15
1	50	48	44	41	37	35	33	31	28
$1\frac{1}{4}$	95	88	78	76	69	62	55.6	48	40
					Upfeed Risers—Second Floor				
F $\frac{1}{2}$	11	10	9	8	7	7	6	6	4
$\frac{3}{4}$	20	19	17	16	14	13	12	11	11
1	34	32	29	28	25	24	22	21	18
$1\frac{1}{4}$	70	68	59	57	51	49	45	43	36
					Upfeed Risers—Third Floor				
G $\frac{1}{2}$	9	8	7	7	6	6	6	5	4
$\frac{3}{4}$	18	16	14	14	12	12	11	10	9
1	31	29	28	27	24	22	21	20	18
$1\frac{1}{4}$	63	60	56	52	48	45	43	41	36

Read these notes carefully before sizing risers:

NOTE 1. First floor upfeed risers—Capacities shown in the table are based upon horizontal branches not more than 3 ft long, with stubs 18″ long, or a total of 9 ft of pipe. Six elbows, 1 valve and 1 union ell, and 1 C.I. radiator are added for the equivalent length. For each additional 10 equivalent ft of pipe, move 2 milinch columns to the right.

NOTE 2. Second and third floor upfeed risers—Capacities shown are based upon horizontal branches not more than 3 ft long, with risers 10 ft high and 20 ft high, respectively. Eight elbows, 1 valve and 1 union ell, and C.I. radiator are added for the equivalent length. For each additional 10 equivalent ft of pipe, move 2 milinch columns to the right.

NOTE 3. Downfeed risers—Capacities shown are based on a drop of 7 ft to the *center of the radiator,* with not over 3 ft total in horizontal branches, 6 elbows, 1 valve and 1 union ell, and 1 C.I. radiator. For every additional 2 ft of vertical drop, move 1 column to the right in milinch table.

On downfeed jobs the main *must* be pitched up and a vent installed on end of main.

* Courtesy of Bell and Gossett Company.

(e) From Table 12.3 it is found that main *A* and return *D* must be $1\frac{1}{4}$ in. Branch mains *B* and *C* will both be 1 in.

The sizes of risers (from Table 12.4) are as follows:

Second Floor (Table 12.3, F)

b	4 Mbh*	$\frac{1}{2}$ in.
d	6	$\frac{1}{2}$
g	9	$\frac{3}{4}$
i	3	$\frac{1}{2}$
m	6	$\frac{1}{2}$

* Mbh = 1000 Btuh

First Floor (Table 12.3, E)

c	8 Mbh	$\frac{1}{2}$ in.
f	4	$\frac{1}{2}$
h	4	$\frac{1}{2}$
j	9	$\frac{1}{2}$
k	5	$\frac{1}{2}$

Basement (Table 12.3, D)

a	3 Mbh	$\frac{1}{2}$ in.
e	5	$\frac{1}{2}$
l	4	$\frac{1}{2}$
n	9	$\frac{1}{2}$

(f) Reference to the pump performance curves in Fig. 12.16 indicates that a $1\frac{1}{2}$ in. pump will deliver 8.2 gpm against a friction head of $6\frac{1}{2}$ ft.

(g) 79,000 Btu ÷ 240 = 330 sq ft of radiation. Use 18-gal tank (Table 12.5).

Heating elements are selected as in Ex. 12.1.

NOTE: Tables 12.3 and 12.4 may be used for either steel pipe of Type L copper tubing, as capacity differences are not sufficient to cause design errors.

Table 12.5 * Required A.S.M.E. Size of Closed Expansion Tank

Sq Ft of Equivalent Direct Radiation Installed	Gallon Tank
Up to 350	18
Up to 450	21
Up to 650	24
Up to 900	30
Up to 1100	35
Up to 1400	40
Up to 1600	2—30
Up to 1800	2—30
Up to 2000	2—35
Up to 2400	2—40

For systems with more than 2400 sq ft of installed equivalent direct water radiation, the required capacity of the cushion tank shall be increased on the basis of one gallon tank capacity per 33 sq ft of additional equivalent direct radiation.

* Reprinted by permission of *ASHRAE* from the *Heating, Ventilating, Air Conditioning Guide*, 31st Edition.

NOTE: For tank sizes in systems other than those with cast iron radiation consult Table E, p. 34, *Engineering Manual*, Bell and Gossett Company.

References

1. *Piping Guide, Residential Heating Systems.*
2. *Baseboard Heating Systems.*
3. *One Pipe Forced Circulation Hot Water Systems.*
4. *Baseboard Ratings.*

The above four references are published by the Institute of Boiler and Radiator Manufacturers, 608 Fifth Avenue, New York 20, New York.

5. *Engineering Manual, Bell and Gossett Company,* Morton Grove, Illinois.
6. *Hydronic Zone Control with Primary-Secondary Pumping,* Bell and Gossett Company, Morton Grove, Illinois.

13

Radiant Panel Heating

1. Panel Heating in General. When heat losses in rooms are made up by means of warmed panels or sections of ceilings, walls, or floors the heating system is known as panel or radiant heating. The larger part of the heat is given off radiantly rather than by convection as in many other schemes. There are several methods of warming the panels. Hot water circulated in pipes which are imbedded in concrete or plaster and the passage of warm air in floor tiles or in the space above hung ceilings are possible methods. Electricity may be used to warm large sections of room surfaces or to provide more concentrated, smaller, radiant panels. Owing to its high temperatures, steam is unsuitable.

As in other heating systems, the function of radiant heating is not only to balance the heat losses from rooms but also to maintain bodily comfort. When the average temperature of the floor, walls, and ceiling is increased, the emission of radiant heat from the body of an occupant to those surfaces is decreased. Since the air in the room is usually cooler than in other systems, the convective body heat loss continues. Thus the occupant feels warmth and comfort while at the same time enjoying the proximity of refreshing cooler air.

Because of possible discomfort to occupants and cracking of plaster, temperatures are limited. Ceilings commonly do not exceed 115 F, and floors are often held to 85 F. Hot water is used in pipes which are laid in concrete or covered by plaster. The temperature of the water is lower than that used in conventional forced hot water heating systems, being not higher than an average of 150 F for ceilings and 140 F for floors.

For one-story or multistory buildings with basements or crawl spaces, ceiling installations consisting of thin copper tubing in the plaster are common. For one-story structures with no basement and with a concrete slab on the ground, copper tubing, or for greater ruggedness wrought iron or steel, imbedded in the concrete floor is a popular choice. The floor systems are somewhat less expensive to install. The bulk of the concrete in floors has a large thermal storage capacity and creates a slow response to change in the heating requirements in the room. Thus for steady requirements the floor system is quite suitable for structures with walls of high thermal resistance, whereas the quick changes needed in a solar house consisting of large glass areas frequently suggest the use of the faster-responding ceiling panels.

224

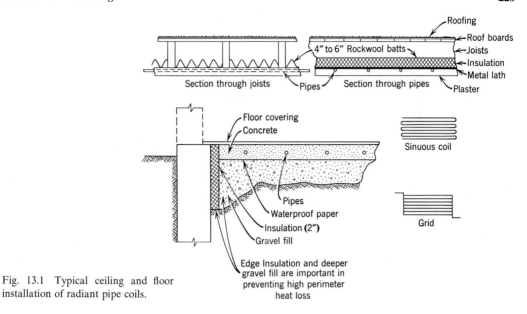

Fig. 13.1 Typical ceiling and floor installation of radiant pipe coils.

2. Advantages and Disadvantages of Radiant Heating.

For houses on concrete slabs with no crawl space or basement, radiant heating is one of the few systems that is effectively usable. From the standpoint of comfort, floor panels are preferred. In any radiant system the temperature at the floor is higher, and in general there is better temperature distribution throughout the room than in other methods of heating. No system compares with it architecturally because no heating element is visible in any living space. Lower air temperatures can be maintained which result in a superior feeling of well being and in a greater relative humidity, usually desirable in winter. Operating costs may be slightly lower because the air temperature is lower, reducing the actual heat loss from the structure. Installation costs are the same or a little more than in other systems. The lack of concentrated heating elements reduces the convection currents and prevents dirt streaking on the walls and ceiling. Floor and ceiling systems permit the shifting of partitions if the panels are planned to occupy the entire ceiling or floor space. Leaks, though not common, are costly to repair.

3. Systems Using Hot Water.

Panels and Coils. It is possible to use ceiling, wall, or floor panels in water radiant systems. The wall has not proved a very popular location. As between ceiling and floor, the ceiling is usually more expensive because of the greater trouble involved in installing the coils. The structural building plan may suggest at once the best location. From the utilitarian point of view a building with a stable heat loss can use floor coils in concrete, whereas another with speedy changes in heat loss or gain should be equipped with a ceiling installation. Greater outputs are possible in ceiling surface; therefore in an installation that is short of available panel area, ceilings are preferred. Since this difference in output calls for different water temperatures, the hotter water of the ceiling coils may have to be reduced in temperature for an auxiliary floor coil. It is, therefore, the simplest practice to use all floors or all ceilings in the same building.

Steel and wrought iron are somewhat more rugged and suitable for floor coils where injury may occur before concreting. With care copper may, however, be used in floors. Being weldable, steel or wrought iron

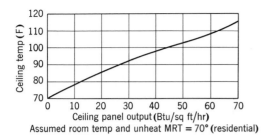

Fig. 13.2   Output at various ceiling temperatures.

is easily formed off the job into grids which are efficient in reducing friction, whereas copper is more adaptable to the sinuous loop coil. Copper tubing ($\frac{3}{8}''$) is often used for ceiling coils placed under the lath and plastered from below. Larger sizes of tube may be placed above the lath, and the plaster may be pushed through to imbed them.

The grid type with reversed return piping is efficient but it is not necessary to adhere strictly to this system. The slightly increased pumping cost caused by the friction in the loop style is not great, and if some coils are reversed return and some direct the resulting inequality of flow can be adjusted at the balancing valves. The loop coil is known also as a sinuous or serpentine coil.

Plaster, concrete, and other common surfaces emit heat about 90 percent as efficiently as a perfect radiating surface. On floors, wood in mastic, asphalt tile, or light carpeting may be used without serious interference with the efficiency. Where a great deal of heavy carpeting and much furniture

is expected a ceiling installation should be chosen. The most usual detail of imbedment of coils in plaster and concrete is shown in Fig. 13.1.

Headers, together with manual vents and adjusting valves, can all be placed in the utility room, making centralized control. In large houses mains can serve remote headers and control points located conveniently in accessible space. The best arrangement is for the hot pipes supplying each room to go directly to the most exposed wall and be led inward as the water cools.

In floor systems where the coils are below the boiler an air vent can be placed in the high piping at the boiler and at one or two remote points in the piping, rising to an air reservoir and vented there. Air that collects in ceiling systems is carried along by the high velocity of the water in the small pipes and may be released through the vent valves near the return headers. Automatic vent valves in the return headers are additional safeguards against air binding. (See Fig. 13.8.)

Coils of the sinuous type should not exceed the lengths recommended in Table 13.1; otherwise the friction becomes excessive.

4. Methods of Design. A number of variations in the selection of the panel location, size of pipes, type of coil whether grid or serpentine, water temperature, water temperature drop, and the varying temperature conditions of the surrounding surfaces are possible. The output of a panel of fixed temperature depends partly on the average

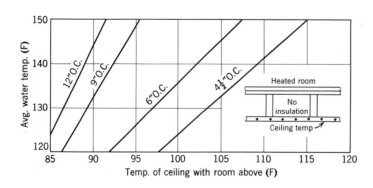

Fig. 13.3   Spacing of $\frac{3}{8}''$ tubing.

temperature of the unheated surfaces of the room. Because part of the output is convective it depends also on the air temperature. It is usual to establish an average temperature between the mean radiant temperature (MRT) of the unheated walls, and the temperature of the air. For residential design 70 F is frequently used for this purpose and is the basis of Fig. 13.2. The temperature drop in the system is usually 20 F for ceilings and 10 F for floors. Reverse flow, (thermal output) in the direction away from the planned *output surface* is subject to exact calculations and dependent upon the nature of the construction on the side of the pipes away from the room heated. For the construction of the floor above the panel in zone *A* (Fig. 13.6) and the ceiling above the panel in zone *B* (Fig. 13.7), the reverse flows are approximately 25 percent and 10 percent, respectively, of the value of the direct output and are in addition to it. Thus the direct output is used for the room below, and the reverse flow is to the credit of the room above (or lost to attic space as in zone *B*). In computing the amount of water circulated through a given panel, the amount of reverse flow must be added to the direct output to determine the total heat to be made up.

5. Typical Design of a Ceiling-Type Hot Water Radiant System.

EXAMPLE 13.1. Figure 13.5 shows a photograph and floor plans of a residence for which a design summary follows. Table 13.2 is a design schedule showing the sequence of steps. The first step is to compute the area available in each ceiling for radiant

Table 13.1   Recommended Maximum Length of Individual Loops (Sinuous Coils)

Nominal Diameter (in.)	Maximum Coil Length	
	Tube (ft)	Pipe (ft)
$\frac{3}{8}$	120	
$\frac{1}{2}$	150	250
$\frac{3}{4}$	250	350
1	500	500

panels. The heat loss is computed for each room but does *not* include the usual loss through the ceiling panel. The required output of the panel is computed from the room heat loss but the water passing through the coils must make up the output and also the reverse flow. Columns 4 and 5 list the adjustments for reverse flow. Column 6 is the design column for coils and represents the net room heat loss for the first story and the net room heat loss (*less* the gain from the lower rooms) of the rooms in the upper story. If all the ceiling areas were used for pipes, the required output would be as shown in column 7. The living room shows a need for 61 Btuhr per sq ft. Figure 13.2 indicates that this amount requires a ceiling temperature of 109 F, close to the maximum permitted which is about 115 F. Figure 13.3 indicates a required $4\frac{1}{2}$-in. spacing of $\frac{3}{8}$-in. tubes at the average water temperature of 140 F. Since this is the critical output it sets the water temperature (average) for the entire installation. Now it is possible to fill the other ceilings with pipes on wider spacings. However, for economy the pipes are

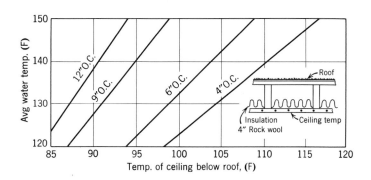

Fig. 13.4   Spacing of $\frac{3}{8}''$ tubing.

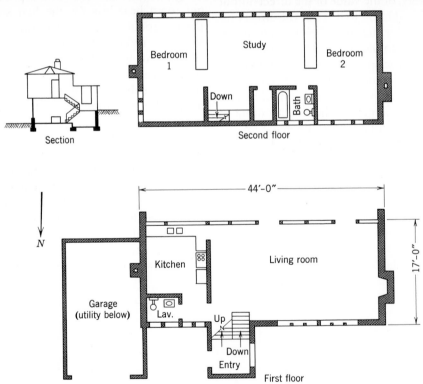

Fig. 13.5   Floor plans, design of radiant system, Example 13.1. Grossi Residence, Olindo Grossi, Architect.

Table 13.2 (Example 13.1) System Design Schedule

Average water temperature, 140 F; Temperature drop in system, 20 F; Use $\frac{3}{8}''$ copper tube

Column No.	1	2	3	4	5	6	7	8	9	10	11	12	13	14	15
	Space	Ceiling Area (sq ft)	Heat Losses (Btuh) From rooms not including reverse flow	Reverse flow from coils through roof	Reverse flow from coils to 2nd story	Corrected heat loss for coil design, (3) − (5)	Required Output if Entire Ceiling Is Used, (6) ÷ (2) (Btu/sq ft/hr)	Spacing Selected (inches o.c.)	Ceiling Panel Temperature Required, °F (Fig. 13.3)	Actual Panel Output (Btu/sq ft/hr) (Fig. 13.2)	Panel Area Required (6) ÷ (10) (sq ft)	Factor to Convert to Lin Ft of Tube (lin ft/sq ft)	Lin Ft of Tube Required	No. of Coils per Room (limit = 120')	Coil Identification Number
Zone A **First story**	Liv.-Din.	443	22,000			22,000	50	4½	109	61	360	2.67	960	8	1–8
	Kit.-Lav.	173	8,000			8,000	46	4½	109	61	131	2.67	350	3	9–11
	Entry	66	2,500	250		2,500	30	6	102	48	52	2.00	104	1	12
	Totals		32,500	250		32,500							1414		

For water circulation, zone A

$32,500 + 9110 + 250 = 41,860$ Btu

$\dfrac{41,860}{9600} = 4.36$ gpm (Fig. 13.6)

(Fig. 13.4)

		1	2	3	4	5	6	7	8	9	10	11	12	13	14	15
Zone B **Second story**	B.R. 1		200	6,000	600	2500	3,500	17	9*	95	35	100	1.33	133	2	13–14
	B.R. 2		228	6,600	620	2820	3,780	17.5	9	95	35	108	1.33	143	2	15–16
	Study		269	8,500	850	3320	5,180	19	9	95	35	148	1.33	197	2	17–18
	Bath		38	2,000	200	470	1,530	40	6	102	48	32	2.00	64	1	19
	Totals			23,100	2270	9110	13,990							537		
														1951†		

For water circulation, zone B

$23,100 + 2270 − 9110 = 16,260$ Btu

$\dfrac{16,260}{9600} = 1.70$ gpm

For boiler capacity $41,860 + 16,260 = 58,120$ Btuh net connected load (exclusive of domestic hot water demand).

*9" o.c. is maximum recommended spacing for ceiling panels.

†Total for house.

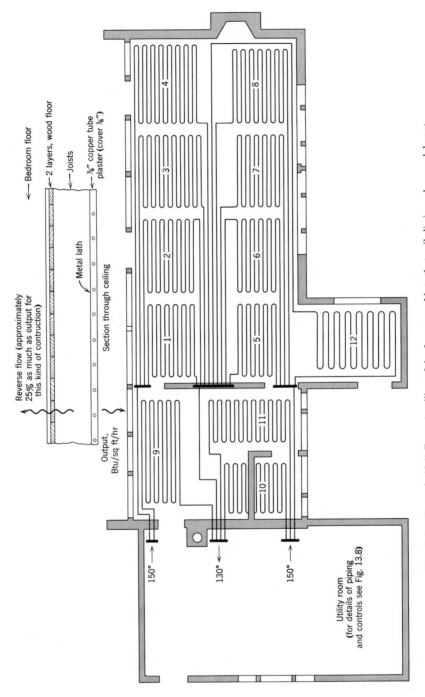

Fig. 13.6 (Example 13.1) Zone *A*, ceiling of the first story. Note that coils lie in a plane and do not cross each other.

often limited to a portion of the ceiling only, stressing the locations of greatest heat loss, as over the vicinity of large glass areas. A selection of pipe spacings is made in column 8 and the corresponding output (from Fig. 13.2) is listed in column 10 after the ceiling temperature has been established in each case (column 9). The area of panel required in each room is shown in column 11. In the living room, kitchen, entry, and upstairs bath a large percentage of the ceiling area is used, but the other rooms are served by smaller portions of their ceilings. Multiplying by the factor in column 12, the linear footage of pipe is arrived at and listed in column 13. This is useful in ordering. Limiting the coil lengths to about 120 lin ft and attempting to equalize them results in the number of coils per room shown in column 14.

The arrangement of the building will shape the coils and their connection to the headers. Figure 13.6 and 13.7 summarize the most desirable coil placement and connections. Note that the hottest water flows first along the coldest area over windows and that the return water is drawn back in the interior areas of the house. No attempt was made here to equalize exactly the length or resistance of each coil circuit or to achieve a reversed return hook-up. Equalization can be accomplished by means of the balancing valves. This house suggests the use of a 2-zone system which is one of the advantages of forced hot water radiant schemes. This is made possible by using 2 pumps and 2 sets of controls. Thus the upstairs rooms, used largely for sleeping, can be maintained at a different temperature than the downstairs living space. Coil 12 rises to an intermediate ceiling level and drops again to join the other coils in zone A. It operates with the living-space coils. (See cross section in Fig. 13.5.)

The piping arrangements from the headers to the boiler are shown in Fig. 13.8. Boiler water is maintained at about 200 F by means of an aquastat-controlled boiler-burner unit. The regulating valves use this boiler water and mix it with 130 F return water to produce the 150 F water temperature for delivery to the coils. The flow-control valves insure individual action of the zones in response to their respective pumps and prevent water flow in summer when the system is used for domestic hot water only. The balancing valves are shown as well as the manually operated vent valves to rid the system of air. Automatic vents supplement these. Changes in room temperature or outdoor temperature affect the operation of the zone pumps. Each zone indoor thermostat turns off its own pump when satisfied, and both pumps are turned on by the action of an outdoor thermostat or anticipator, which starts the system when the outside temperature drops, thus preparing the panel surface to work at higher capacity as the room heat loss increases. The calculation of water flow and the selection of main and pump sizes follow the usual procedures for hot water systems. With a 20° drop 1 gal per min delivers 9600 Btuh. Table 13.2 gives 41,860 Btuh as the requirements of zone A. Dividing by 9600, we arrive at a required flow of 4.36 gpm. In this case 1-in. pumps and 1-in. supply mains are used. Headers are often $1\frac{1}{2}$ or 2 in. for good flow.

6. Installation and Testing. Where possible the tubing should run across the joists since this makes the easiest fastening. For convenience of repair and adjustment, balancing valves, vents, boiler connections, and similar equipment must all be in accessible places, preferably the utility room. Mains, tubing, controls or vents in outside walls, attic space, or other exposed locations must be accessible and insulated to protect against freezing.

If the piping to be buried in the ceiling or floor holds a test pressure of 200 lb per sq in. for 8 or 10 hr without leakage, it can be considered safe. Other more accessible parts can be easily repaired in case of leakage. The contractor should guarantee to balance the system during the first heating season.

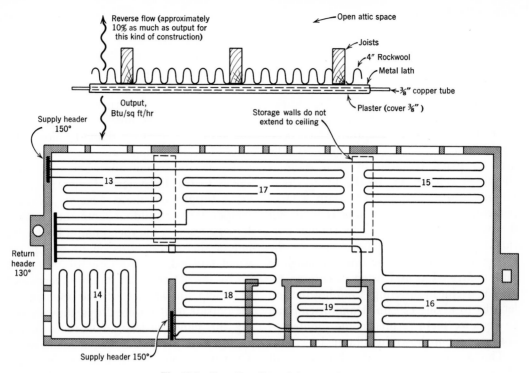

Fig. 13.7   Zone *B*, ceiling of the second story.

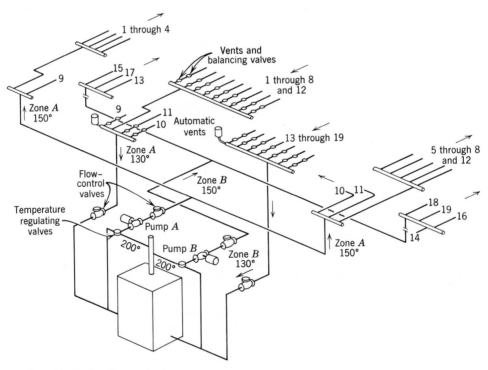

Fig. 13.8   Piping diagram for 2-zone ceiling-type radiant heating system for house shown in Fig. 13.5.

Table 13.3 (Example 13.2) Analysis of Heating Design, Residence at Sands Point (See Figs. 8.6, 13.9, and 13.10)

1 Story	2 Space	3 Heat Loss Btuh	4 Radiant Coil Nos.	5 Linear Feet of Tube	6 Radiant Output per lin ft Btuh	7 Radiant Output Btuh	8 Baseboard, Convector or Electric	9 Unit Output Btuh	10 Output, Convector, Baseboard or Electric Btuh	11 Total Output (cols 7 + 10) Btuh	12 Zone Nos. Radiant	13 Zone Nos. Convector Baseboard	14 Orientation
Upper (see Fig. 13.10)	Living Dining	20,970					22 ft Walvector	1130/ft	23,000	23,000			
	Library	4590					8¼ ft Hi-Cap	730/ft	6200	6200		4	North
	Bedroom 1	9270					16 ft Hi-Cap	730/ft	11,600	11,600		4	
	Dressing—Baths	13,070					Dunham No. 2006 (convectors) 2406 4006	3400 4200 7700	15,300	15,300		3b	South
	Kitchen Breakfast room	17,190					Dunham No. 4406 (convectors) 2406 9¼ ft HS Std	8600 4200 470/ft	17,300	17,300		3b	
Lower (see Fig. 13.9)	Playroom	13,270	4, 5, 6	480	35	16,800				16,800	1		
	Bedroom 2	4680	3	160	35	5600				5600	1		North
	Bedroom 3	11,430	1, 2	320	35	11,200				11,200	1		
	Dressing—Baths	14,470	9, 10	100	35	3500	23¼ ft HS Std	470/ft	11,100	14,600	2	3a	South
	Cellar	940	(Negligible)										
	Laundry Storage	3900	Coil Ends	120	35	4200				4200	1		North
	Maid B.R. + Bath	11,070	7, 8	260	35	9100	600 watts	3.41/watt	2000	11,100	1		North
	Entry, Well and Lounge	35,090	11, 12, 13	491	35	17,200	17 ft Hi-Cap 8 ft Walvector	730/ft 1130/ft	12,400 9000	38,600	2	3a, 3b	South

NOTES: Average water temperatures, radiant 110 F, other 180 F, all temperature drops 20 F. HS Standard and Hi-Cap are Warren Webster industrial convector strip with cover. All convectors, baseboards, and convector strips are equipped with dampers. Walvector is a Warren Webster baseboards. Walvector is a Warren Webster industrial

ZONES: 1. Radiant, north, lower story (full load) (in slab). 2. Radiant, south, lower story (partial load) (in slab). 3a. Baseboard, south, lower story (supplements radiant). 3b. Convector and baseboard, north, upper story, supplements entry radiant, full load elsewhere. 4. Baseboard and convector strip, north, upper story (full load).

233

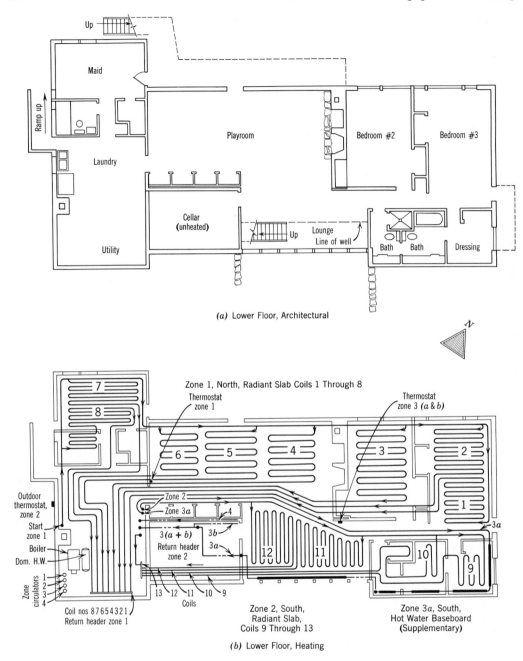

(a) Lower Floor, Architectural

(b) Lower Floor, Heating

Fig. 13.9 (Example 13.2)   Architectural and heating plans upper floor, residence at Sands Point. See Fig. 8.6. Olindo Grossi, Architect.

7. Combined Radiant and Convector Systems. Radiant heating which eliminates the need for the concentration of heating units below glass and which, by the concealed position of its coils, is so acceptable architecturally, has some shortcomings. When used in a heavy concrete slab it is sluggish. Unlike warm air or convector systems using hot water, both of which can operate at their design temperatures within 5 or 10 minutes and can be turned off as quickly, a radiant floor panel may have a time lag of one hour or more. It is common, therefore, to use radiant floor panels only where conditions are slow to change. When quick changes are expected it is sometimes

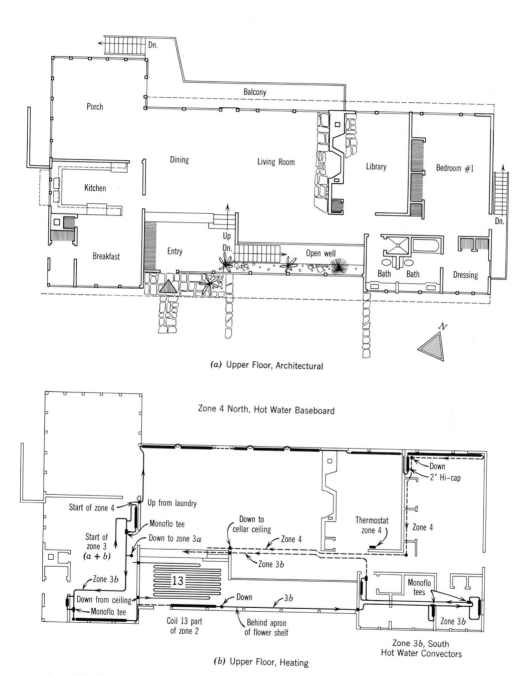

(a) Upper Floor, Architectural

(b) Upper Floor, Heating

Fig. 13.10 (Example 13.2) Architectural and heating plans, upper floor, residence at Sands Point. See Fig. 8.6. Olindo Grossi, Architect.

arranged that a stable radiant floor panel carries part of the load and a quickly responsive fin-tube system supplements it.

8. Analysis of a Combined System.

EXAMPLE 13.2 (Figs. 13.9, 13.10, 13.11, Table 13.3). The residence at Sands Point, Long Island, New York, pictured in Fig. 8.6 with heat losses calculated in Chap. 8, is an example of a design following the precepts of the foregoing article. The slab of the lower story is kept warm at all times during the heating season. It uses water that is blended part cool return-water, part boiler-water (see Figs. 13.11 and 13.12). The north slab zone, (No. 1) a stable area, not subject to the sometimes rapid on-off occurrence of sunshine and cloud-shadow, operates from its own indoor thermostat. The south slab zone (No. 2) responding to a thermostat outside of the utility room, carries only part of the thermal load, the supplementary fin-tubes of convectors and

baseboards responding promptly when the sun recedes. The slab panel operates at all times when the outside temperature is less than 60 F and the supplementary system responds to an indoor thermostat when needed. This latter zone (No. 3) has 2 loops, 3a and 3b, which are adjusted by the balancing valves at their returns. Zone 4 is a fin-tube zone which serves the upstairs north section. All fin-tubes use water at nearly boiler temperature (close to 190 F). The baseboards are connected in *loop* fashion. It is usually necessary to use larger elements at the ends of the loops because of the cooler water there. The windowless laundry-utility room, which is below grade, receives no warmth from the sun, and though its location is south, it is properly included in a north zone (zone 2), utilizing radiant coil-ends from that zone.

The unit outputs for convectors and baseboard shown in Table 13.3 are from manufacturers' ratings. It will be noted that the

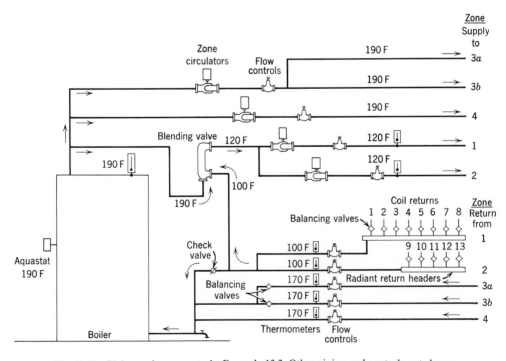

Fig. 13.11   Piping and zone controls, Example 13.2. Other piping and controls not shown.

output of the radiant slab is expressed differently from the concepts in Ex. 13.1. There are many variations in the approach to the analysis of radiant heating. For floor slabs, the output, as used here, is often stated as Btuh/l. ft of radiant coil.

The use of several zones eases the balancing problem. It is seldom, indeed, that a modern large house is controlled by only one thermostat because of the difficulty of providing comfort in all of the rooms under varying conditions.

Figure 13.11 indicates the use of 4 zone-circulators, each circuit being protected against interim flow by 2 flow-control (check) valves. The direct use of boiler water in convectors and baseboards is seen. The blended water (part return-water) at lower temperature is used by the radiant zones only. The liberal use of thermometers and balancing valves aids in the adjustment of the installation.

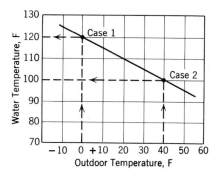

Fig. 13.12   Performance of blending valve.

References

1. *Radiant Heating,* T. Napier Adlam, The Industrial Press, New York, New York.
2. *Design of Heating and Ventilating Systems,* F. W. Hutchinson, The Industrial Press, New York, New York.
3. *Radiant Heating,* Richard W. Shoemaker, McGraw-Hill Book Company, Inc., New York, New York.

14

Heating by Steam

1. Steam Generation. When sufficient heat is supplied to water to cause it to boil and vaporize, the resulting vapor is steam. As the boiling point of water in a container is reached, bubbles of water or vapor or steam are formed in the bottom and rise to the surface where they escape. If a thermometer were placed in the container it would be seen that the temperature of the water and of the steam does not rise above the boiling point, that is 212 F at the atmospheric pressure at sea level or 14.7 psi. It is evident that bubbles of vapor will not form unless the pressure exerted outwardly by the vapor is at least equal to the exterior atmospheric pressure upon the surface of the water; otherwise the bubble would collapse at once. If the exterior pressure were greater than 14.7 psi, the heat required to form the vapor bubbles would be greater and the boiling point of the water and the temperature of the resulting steam would be above 212 F. If the exterior pressure were less than 14.7 psi, less heat would be required for boiling and the temperature of the generated steam would be below 212 F. This relationship between pressure and steam temperature is important in the study of heating because it permits temperature regulation of the steam supplied

to radiators as illustrated in the vacuum heating system. Table 14.1 shows the changes in temperature of boiling water and in the properties of steam below and above normal atmospheric pressure. Absolute pressure is the sum of the atmospheric pressure (14.7 psi) at sea level and the pressure shown on the steam gauge. Absolute pressure of 16.7 psi therefore signifies a gauge pressure of 2 psi; and absolute pressure of 10 psi, a gauge pressure of -4.7 psi or a 4.7 psi vacuum. Absolute pressure is therefore independent of elevation above sea level or atmospheric changes in pressure as indicated by barometer readings.

While steam is in contact with the water in a boiler it is called saturated steam and is at the temperature of the boiling point. It is known as wet steam or dry saturated steam according to whether it does or does not contain suspended moisture. If dry saturated steam is removed from contact with the boiler water and further heated at the same pressure, its temperature will rise above boiling and it is known as superheated steam. The steam generated in heating boilers is generally very close to wet saturated steam. It is in contact with the water and is at the boiling temperature as determined by the pressure upon it. Vapor

Table 14.1 Properties of Saturated Steam

Absolute Pressure (lb per sq in.)	Temperature (degrees F)	Heat of Liquid (Btu/lb)	Latent Heat of Evaporation (Btu/lb)	Total Heat or Enthalpy (Btu/lb)
6	170	138	996	1134
8	183	151	988	1139
10	193	161	982	1143
12	202	170	977	1146
14.7*	212	180	970	1150
15.7	215	184	967	1151
16.7	219	188	965	1153
17.7	222	190	963	1154
18.7	225	193	961	1155
19.7	228	196	959	1156

* Atmospheric pressure at sea level.

is steam at a pressure equal to or slightly above atmospheric pressure. The difference between vapor and steam is one of pressure only.

The quantity of heat contained in a pound of steam can be ascertained, and it is important since it is an evidence of the heating value of the steam. Heat added to a substance without changing its state will raise the temperature of the substance. If, however, the state of the substance is changing, as from solid to fluid or from fluid to vapor, additional heat does not increase the temperature. As an example, heat applied to water at 32° will raise its temperature to the boiling point corresponding to the surface pressure, and as more heat is applied the boiling water will be converted into steam but the temperature of the water and the steam will not be further changed. The heat of the liquid or sensible heat is the heat in Btu required to raise the temperature of 1 lb of water from 32° to the boiling point. The latent heat of evaporation is the heat in Btu required entirely to vaporize 1 lb of water at the boiling point into dry saturated steam at the same temperature. The total heat of the steam or enthalpy is the sum of the heat of the liquid and the latent heat of evaporation.

Quality of steam is the percentage of dry saturated steam in wet steam. The total heat of wet steam is consequently the sum of the heat required to raise 1 lb of water from 32° to the boiling point plus the heat required to vaporize the percentage of dry steam.

As is seen from Table 14.1, the heat of evaporation contained in steam is very large compared to the heat contained in water at the boiling point. This property renders steam a very efficient heating medium, since it may be piped to the point where heat is desired and there, while condensing each pound gives off approximately 1000 Btu, (its latent heat), the hot condensate water returning to the boiler.

2. Development of Systems. Steam heating is based upon the generation of steam in a centrally placed boiler and the transportation of the steam through pipes from the boiler to the various locations in the building where heat is desired. Upon arrival at these locations the steam gives up its latent heat by conduction through the walls of its container, heat exchanger, convector or radiator, changes its state by condensation from vapor to liquid and flows back to the boiler through the return piping.

Steam heating has had an interesting history during the past half-century which has brought many changes. Through trial and experience it has evolved from a simple one-pipe system (see Fig. 14.1) to more efficient and adaptable forms. The 1-pipe system, often described as *open,* and now almost as scarce as the steam locomotive, was a durable rugged heating method, well suited to an era in which the use of automatic controls was virtually unknown. Gradually adapted to automatic firing and controlled by thermostats, it led to the modern, more sensitive installations. When idle or not fully under pressure, its air valves were open, permitting the boiler to generate steam easily at atmospheric pressure. When steam reached the air valves integral steam traps operated and closed against its escape. Through the single pipe serving each radiator, condensed steam in the form of water began to run back against the steam flow, causing noise if the pipe were not large enough or the control valve partly shut. A mandatory full-open position of the valve left no choice between full heat or shutdown. It is obvious that large pipe sizes were needed, not only for the connecting pipe but also for the risers. In the horizontal steam main, the condensate, while not opposing the steam flow, occupied the same pipe, calling for a larger size than if steam alone were present.

As buildings increased in size, so did the

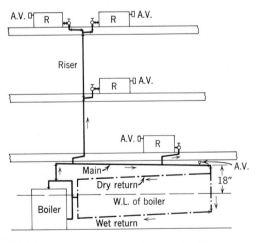

Fig. 14.1   One-pipe (air vent) steam heating system. AV = air vent; R = radiator.

1-pipe systems with pipes that became very ungainly in diameter. Variations appeared, such as downfeed of steam so that steam and condensate would flow in the same direction. Ultimately a second set of pipes were used (the 2-pipe system) to carry the condensate away from the other side of the radiators. Then it was found that, in part, steam passed *through* the radiator, condensing to give off its heat incorrectly in the return piping. This brought about the use of steam traps (Fig. 14.4b) at each return radiator connection. These closed when touched by steam and forced condensation to take place where it should—in the radiator. Later developments closed the system against the re-entry of air and permitted the sustaining of partial vacuums within the radiators and piping.

The qualities of the modern vacuum system emerged. Prior to the common use of the vacuum pump, which pulls a vacuum, eliminates air, and forces water back into the boiler, some of these functions were performed by an *alternating receiver.* With its use the name of *vapor steam* was applied to what was, except for the use of the alternating receiver instead of the pump, the essential form of the vacuum system. Like the 1-pipe system, the vapor system finds little use in new installations.

Steam, while still much used for heating by radiators and convectors, is often extended by means of heat conversion to other forms of heat distribution. By passing steam through the coils of fin-coil devices and blowing air over the fins, an adjunct warm air system may be created, or the same device may be part of a full air-conditioning system. Similarly, steam heat may be converted to hot-water heat by means of a steel shell with tubes inside of it for heat transfer between steam and water. As the cool water is pumped through the coils, it condenses the steam and acquires heat for use in the hot-water heating system, (see Fig. 14.2).

3. Vacuum System. (Fig. 14.3). The intention in the vacuum is to reduce in mild

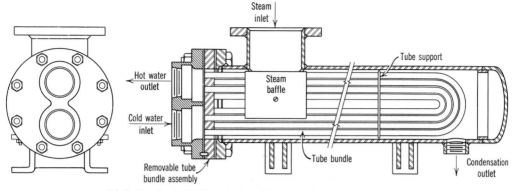

(a) Section illustrating the principle of heat transfer from steam to water.

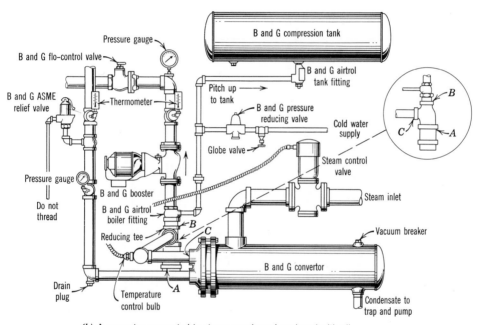

(b) A convertor connected to steam supply and equipped with all devices necessary for a complete hot water heating system.

Fig. 14.2   Conversion. Transferring heat from steam to hot water. Bell and Gossett.

weather the steam pressure in the boilers and the amount of heat emitted from the radiators and yet to maintain in cold weather a higher pressure in the boiler and increased heating effectiveness at the radiators. It is a 2-pipe system and differs from the air-vent type in that steam is admitted through air-tight packless graduated valves (see Fig. 14.4a) that may be adjusted for

regulate heat output by reducing the passage of steam through them. Their air-tightness is assured by a sealed-in expanding nonferrous bellows that contains the moving mechanism. Thermostatic valves (Fig. 14.4b) trap the steam in the radiator or convector. They operate by means of a volatile fluid that expands within a flexible hollow disc to close the exit port of the

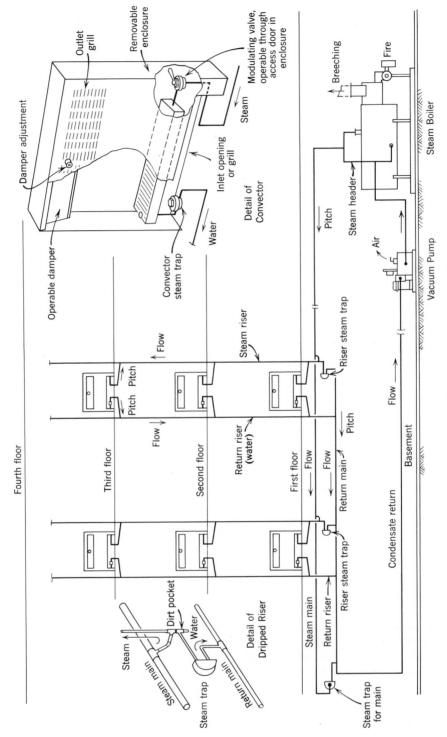

Fig. 14.3   Schematic diagram, vacuum steam heating system.

radiator when the higher temperature of the steam actuates the fluid-filled disc. Water, which is at lower temperature, passes through. By means of these air-tight devices, together with the boiler and vacuum pump, steam can be generated and circulated at low temperature and partial vacuum in conformance with the principles shown in Table 14.1.

Air-vent (one-pipe) and vapor systems are called gravity systems because the condensate flows back to the boiler by gravity. The vacuum system is known as a mechanical system because a pump is used to draw air and condensate from the return lines, producing a partial vacuum and making circulation more positive, especially in large buildings where gravity flow is difficult to accomplish owing to pressure drop in the long runs of pipe. Thermostatic traps should also be installed at the base of all risers, the ends of steam mains and at all low points of the steam distribution. In this way steam-carrying pipes are kept free of condensate. If the vacuum pump is placed at the low point in the system, radiators and convec-

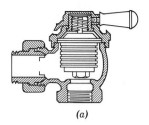

(a)

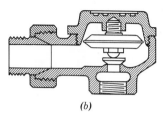

(b)

Fig. 14.4   Controls for radiator, convector or other heating element. (a) Packless radiator valve. (b) Thermostatic radiator trap.

tors may be located below the level of the boiler.

The system is air-tight and air-free. Accidentally acquired air is removed at the vacuum pump (see Fig. 14.5), where it is

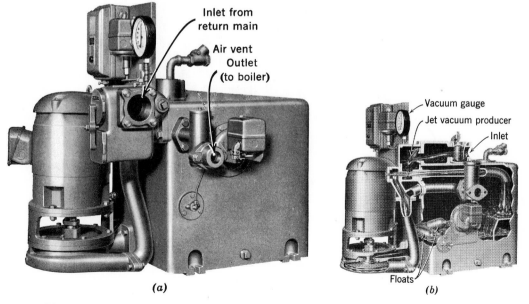

(a)

(b)

Fig. 14.5   Vertical motor vacuum pump vents out air and returns the condensed steam (condensate) to the boiler. Hoffman Specialty Mfg. Corp. (a) Exterior view. (b) Distorted section cut away to show operation.

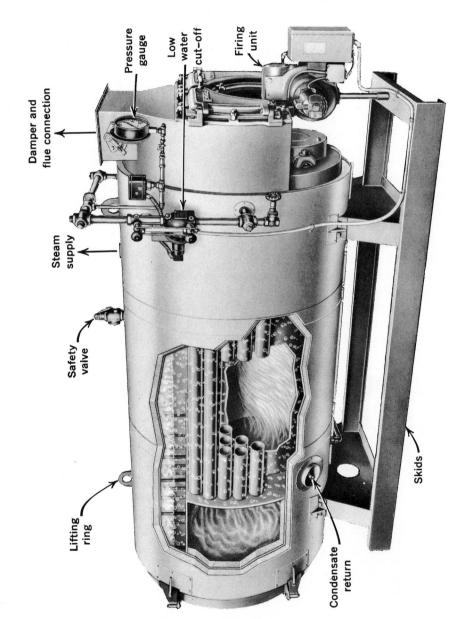

Pressure gauge

Low water cut-off

Firing unit

Damper and flue connection

Steam supply

Safety valve

Lifting ring

Condensate return

Skids

Fig. 14.6 Package-type fire-tube steam boiler. Capacity 600,000 to 3,000,000 Btuh, adaptable for oil, gas, or both. Complete with controls and all fittings.

caught in the ejector and delivered to the air-separating compartment of the receiver, and leaves through the air-vent check valve. The pump operation is electrically controlled by a float switch and a vacuum regulator switch. The float switch starts the pump when water collects in the receiver. The pump is also started when vacuum falls below a predetermined setting. It thus assures vacuum, condensate delivery to the boiler and air removal.

When used for heating, vacuum steam systems are known as low pressure systems and often operate at less than 10 psi. If steam turbines or other power devices are to be used, steam is generated at pressures generally over 100 psi. With these devices it is often more economical to use exhaust steam from the power process for heating instead of installing low pressure boilers. When the turbines are not operating the high pressure steam may be reduced to the lower pressure for heating by means of pressure reducing valves (see Fig. 14.7).

These are used when the boiler pressure, or in the case of district steam heating, the street steam main pressure, is too high for the heating system. They operate by the rising and falling of the diaphragm which is in turn actuated by the changes in pressure in the low pressure main. When the pressure becomes too high on the low pressure side, the steam pressure through the balance pipe raises the diaphragm which partially closes the valve, allowing less steam to pass from the inlet to the outlet. The degree of pressure reduction can be adjusted by moving the weight on the arm or adjusting the tension of the spring. The balance pipe is generally $\frac{1}{2}$ in. and should be connected to the low pressure pipe 15 or 20 ft from the reducing valve.

4. Piping and Equipment. Steel and wrought-iron pipes are most generally used in steam heating. For diameters up to and including 6 in. piping of steel and wrought iron is furnished with threaded ends and is screwed together. Above 6-in. diameters, these pipes are connected by flanges bolted to each other with a gasket between. Pipe drawn from a solid billet and known as seamless tubing is frequently used for high pressure, there being no welded joint to split during bending. Standard-weight black iron and steel pipe is generally employed in heating, although wrought iron and copper-bearing steel are frequently used for return lines.

Lengths of pipe are connected either in the same direction or at an angle by special pieces called fittings, made of cast iron, malleable iron, steel, or bronze. They are connected to the pipes by screw thread in sizes up to 6-in. in diameter and by flanges in sizes over 6 in. and are known as low-pressure fittings for steam up to 25 lb pressure, standard for steam up to 125 lb, and extra heavy for steam to 250 lb. Ells, (elbows) and return bends are used to change the direction of a pipeline, tees, crosses. Y's are used to take off branches,

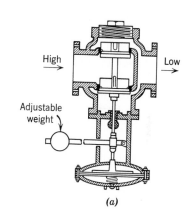

(a)

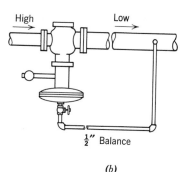

$\frac{1}{2}''$ Balance

(b)

Fig. 14.7   Pressure-reducing valve.

bushings, and reducers to reduce a threaded or tapped opening, and nipples to form short straight connections. Unions are employed to join pipe, valves, or other apparatus with easy disconnection for repairs. Screw unions are convenient for pipes up to 2 in. diam.; flanged unions are more reliable for larger sizes. Couplings are used to join the smaller sizes of pipes but do not permit disconnection as readily as unions.

Welded instead of screwed or flanged connections are becoming more used for heating work, the electric arc and oxyacetylene methods being equally successful. The pipes may be joined directly to each other or welding fittings may be used, the fittings giving the better-finished installation. The work should be entrusted to none but expert welders, and, because of the expense of the equipment and the necessity of a skilled crew of mechanics, welding is found less costly than screwed or flanged connections only in large operations. Savings in weight of pipe, insulation, and repairs, however, are possible. Socket fittings with fillet welds are used with pipe sizes of $\frac{1}{4}$ in. to 3 in., and butt welded fittings with beveled ends for 1 in. to 12 in.

In pipe detailing the following considerations should be borne in mind: economy, safety, accessibility, ease of repair, sources of possible trouble, removal of air and water, obstruction of flow, and pipe expansion. Drips, dirt pockets, thermostatic traps, easy bends, loops, and sliding joints are therefore introduced where required to improve the operation of the system. The water should be removed by drips and thermostatic traps from all points where it may accumulate and retard the flow of the steam; obstructions caused by right-angle turns should be avoided where possible, and pipe expansion under heat should be taken up in loops and swing connections.

The steam main should have a uniform slope of at least $\frac{1}{8}$ in. in 10 ft. If necessary to lift the main over a beam, doorway, or other obstruction, a drip connection with clean-out plug should be installed below

the obstruction (Fig. 14.8a). With air-vent systems an air valve was placed upon the end of the steam main as it turned down to the return (Fig. 14.8b). With vacuum systems however, there is no air valve at this point, the end of the supply main connecting through a trap to the return main (Fig. 14.8c). When mains or other horizontal steam pipes are reduced in size an eccentric fitting is used to procure a level bottom to the connection so that the flow of condensate is not impeded (Fig. 14.8d).

Branches to risers and radiators should be taken off mains in 1- and 2-pipe systems from the top of the main and should pitch $\frac{1}{2}$ in. in 10 ft toward the main when the riser is not dripped. When the riser is dripped, branches should be taken from the bottom of the main and pitch toward the riser drip (Fig. 14.8e). The foot of a riser should be dripped to the return main when more than four stories high, and dirt pockets are often installed at the lowest point (Fig. 14.8f). Elongation caused by a rise in temperature is most noticeable in the mains and risers since they contain the longest runs. Elongation resulting from an increase in temperature from 60 to 220 F in 100 ft of pipe is sufficient to produce excessive stress upon the fittings. Expansion loops and swing connections consisting of bent pipes or of a combination of straight pipe and ells (Fig. 14.8g) are introduced to take up the elongation by a bending in the loop or by a slight turning in the threaded joints.

Branches or runouts from radiator to riser should have a minimum pitch of $\frac{1}{2}$ in. in 10 ft and should be installed with a loop to protect the radiator from movement in the riser. The branch may be arranged as in Fig. 14.8h if the movement is small, and as in Fig. 14.8i when the movement is greater. First-floor radiators are often served directly from the basement main with a branch as in Fig. 14.8j. When bends and loops are not practicable to install, expansion joints consisting of a sleeve free to move in a packed gland are available or a copper bellows may be employed.

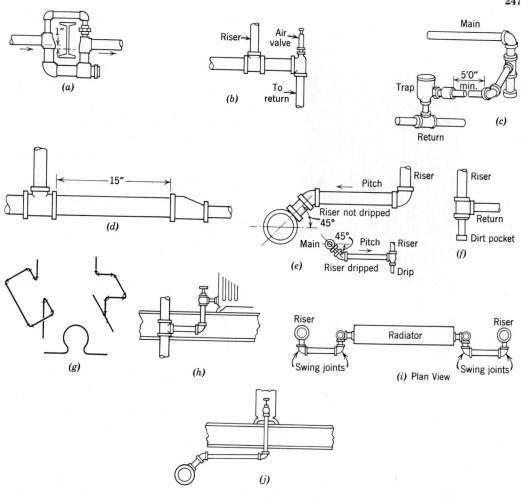

Fig. 14.8 Pipe details.

Gate, globe, check, and angle valves similar to those described for water supply are also used for steam heating systems. Gate valves are most frequently employed because they offer very little obstruction to the flow of steam and water. They must, however, be either completely open or completely closed; consequently when throttling action is desired globe valves are substituted particularly in vertical lines. The older type radiator valve with a loose spindle which required packing is now replaced by the packless type, previously described.

The heat output of cast iron radiators depends upon the number of sq ft of surface area. The term small tube distinguishes the modern radiator type from the older more bulky version which is no longer installed. The total area for any radiator is determined by the height, number of tubes, and the number of sections (each laminar section is $1\frac{3}{4}$ in. in thickness). The length of the radiator, therefore, is $1\frac{3}{4}$ × no. of sections. At 215 F steam temperature (at 1 psi) each sq ft of radiation emits 240 Btuh.

EXAMPLE 14.1 (Fig. 14.9). Select a small-tube cast-iron radiator to make up the heat loss in a room losing 5000 Btuh. Steam at 1 psi is used.

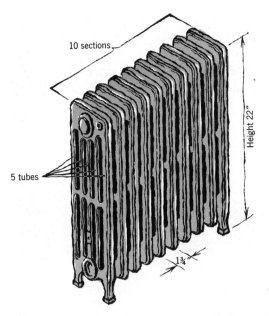

Fig. 14.9 (Example 14.1) A small-tube cast-iron radiator serving a room with an hourly heat loss of 5000 Btuh. Steam is used.

SOLUTION. Dividing the hourly heat loss of 5000 by 240 indicates a need for 20.8 sq ft of cast-iron radiation. If a 5-tube radiator is used with a height of 22 in., each section will provide 2.1 sq ft (Table 14.2). Dividing 20.8 sq ft by 2.1, it is found that 10 sections are required. Several combinations of height,

Table 14.2   Ratings: Small-Tube, Cast-Iron Radiators

(Standard section length, $1\frac{3}{4}''$)

No. of Tubes per Section	Height (in.)	Sq Ft of Radiation per Section
3	25	1.6
4	19	1.6
	22	1.8
	25	2.0
5	22	2.1
	25	2.4
6	19	2.3
	25	3.0
	32	3.7

number of tubes, and number of sections will result in the same output. A choice can be determined by window-sill height and area available for the radiator.

EXAMPLE 14.2 (Fig. 14.10). Select a convector of the front outlet type to serve a room having 5000 Btuh heat loss. Steam at 1 psi is used.

SOLUTION. As in Ex. 14.1, the equivalent of 20.8 sq ft of cast iron radiation is needed. Convectors, which have sheet metal fin-tube heating elements, are rated in Btuh or EDR, equivalent direct (cast iron) radiation, see Table 14.3. Either of the following convectors could be used.

Depth, inches	Length, inches	Nominal Height, inches	sq ft EDR
4	32	24	20.7
or 6	24	24	21.2

The above are given as typical examples of the selection of heating elements. In practice there are many variations involved. For instance, the addition of a bottom grill in a convector can reduce the heat output by as much as 14 percent. If steam at 10 psi gauge pressure is used in the convector instead of steam at 1 psi the output is increased by 25 percent. For special problems the reader is referred to design manuals or manufacturers' literature.

For the heating of large volumes as in factories, stores, and other commercial and industrial buildings unit heaters are frequently used. A fan blows air over convector elements, resulting in a large output for a fairly compact unit. Figure 14.11 shows connections for such a system when steam is used with a propeller-type fan.

Unit heaters must have a proper rating in Btuh to make up the heat loss in the space to be heated. The location of the heater is most important. It is necessary to keep the air-intake side in a location of free air circulation and to point the blower in the direction for effective use. It should be placed to create a rotary circulation in the room,

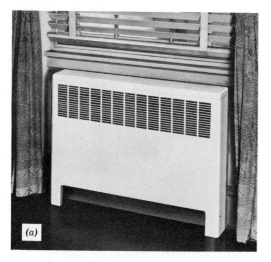 

Fig. 14.10 Two of many types of convector cabinets with integral fin-tube elements. For output at 1 psi steam pressure see Table 13.3. Warren Webster. (a) Free-Standing Cabinet Enclosure. (b) Wall-Hung Enclosure with Outlet Grille on sloped top. For ratings, see Table 14.3. Warren Webster.

starting parallel to an exterior wall. It must not blow directly on working areas and should aim above the head line.

Rapid condensation of steam is characteristic of steam unit heaters. This suggests a number of precautions shown in Fig. 14.11. Supply mains are dripped and trapped to eliminate water in the vicinity of unit heaters. The supply branch rises from the main before dropping and there is a separate return branch. This return branch is trapped to prevent the passage of steam into the return main.

5. Zoning. Very tall buildings are often divided into horizontal zones of approximately the same height in order to equalize the heating demands throughout the structure. Large structures may also be divided into zones with reference to weather exposure or to hours of occupancy. In both methods pressures, pipe sizes, and steam consumption are reduced and greater efficiency at less cost is attained.

When zoned for equalization of conditions, each section has its own vertical supply main from the boiler in the basement connected to a horizontal supply main at the top or bottom of the zone. Either up-feed or downfeed risers are taken off as con-

venient for the radiators on the various floors of the zone. The Empire State Building in New York (Shreve, Lamb and Harmon, Architects) may be taken as an example. The building comprises 86 stories and tower, with setbacks at the sixth and thirtieth stories, and is divided into 4 zones. The heating system is 2-pipe vacuum with steam-driven pumps. The zones are heated by up and downfeed risers from distributing mains in the basement and in the twenty-ninth and fifty-fourth story ceilings as shown in Fig. 14.12. Extra height is given to these stories providing additional hung-ceiling space to accommodate the horizontal piping. Even with this method of zoning

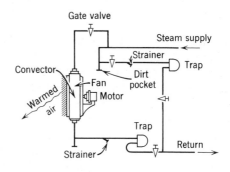

Fig. 14.11 Unit heater in a vacuum steam system.

Table 14.3   Steam Ratings in Sq Ft EDR (215 F and 65 F EAT) See Fig. 14.10

Depth Inches	Length Inches	(a) Front Outlet—Nominal Height				(b) Slope Top—Nominal Height			
		20″	24″	32″	38″	20″	24″	32″	38″
4	20	10.6	12.1	13.4	13.9	11.1	12.1	14.2	14.7
	24	13.0	14.9	16.5	17.1	13.6	14.9	17.4	18.0
	28	15.5	17.8	19.6	20.4	16.2	17.8	20.8	21.6
	32	18.1	20.7	22.9	23.8	19.0	20.7	24.3	25.2
	36	20.5	23.5	26.0	27.0	21.5	23.5	27.5	28.5
	40	23.0	26.4	29.2	30.3	24.1	26.4	30.9	32.0
	44	25.6	29.3	32.5	33.7	26.9	29.3	34.3	35.6
	48	28.0	32.1	35.5	36.9	29.4	32.1	37.6	39.0
	56	33.0	37.9	41.9	43.5	34.6	37.9	44.3	46.0
	64	38.0	43.6	48.2	50.1	39.9	43.6	51.0	53.0
6	20	14.9	17.2	18.7	19.2	19.0	20.5	23.6	24.6
	24	18.4	21.2	23.1	23.8	23.4	25.3	29.1	30.4
	28	22.0	25.4	27.7	28.4	28.1	30.3	34.9	36.4
	32	25.5	29.5	32.1	33.0	32.6	35.2	40.5	42.4
	36	29.0	33.5	36.5	37.5	37.0	40.0	46.0	48.0
	40	32.5	37.6	41.0	42.1	41.5	44.9	51.6	53.6
	44	36.1	41.7	45.4	46.7	46.1	49.8	57.3	59.9
	48	39.6	45.7	49.8	51.2	50.5	54.6	62.8	65.5
	56	46.7	53.9	58.7	60.4	59.5	64.4	74.0	77.2
	64	53.8	62.2	67.8	69.6	68.7	74.3	85.4	89.2
8	32	31.7	35.6	40.9	41.8	42.2	45.3	53.7	55.4
	36	36.0	40.5	46.5	47.5	48.0	51.5	61.0	63.0
	40	40.4	45.5	52.2	53.4	53.9	57.8	68.5	70.6
	48	49.2	55.4	63.6	64.9	65.6	70.4	83.4	86.0
	56	58.0	65.2	74.9	76.4	77.3	82.9	98.2	101.3
	64	66.9	75.3	86.5	88.2	89.2	95.8	113.4	117.1
10	36	45.5	49.0	55.0	56.5	58.0	64.5	71.5	73.5
	40	51.2	55.2	61.9	63.6	65.3	72.6	80.5	82.8
	48	62.3	67.1	75.3	77.4	79.4	88.3	97.9	100.7
	56	73.4	79.0	88.7	91.1	93.5	104.0	115.3	118.6
	64	84.5	91.0	102.2	105.0	107.7	119.8	132.8	136.7

NOTE: EDR is equivalent direct radiation, based upon cast iron. EAT is entering air temperature, the temperature of room air entering the convector for reheating. Warren Webster.

the main to the twenty-ninth story is 24 in. in diam and diminishes above. The fact that heated air rises within tall buildings due to flue action is considered in computing the heating requirements in the higher zones. Otherwise the upper floors would become overheated when the system is full of steam.

When zoned with respect to exposure, the effect of wind, sunshine, and other weather conditions, the building is often divided into 2 sections, the north and west quarters which usually require more heat and the south and east which require less. Each zone is controlled by a thermostat placed at a suitable point or key room. Parts of buildings are often used for storage and manufacturing requiring cooler temperatures, or by clubs and restaurants with short hours of occupancy. Such portions may well be divided into zones with thermostatic control. By these means a correct heating of all sections and a maximum conservation of steam may be secured.

6. Metro System (Fig. 14.13). A patented convector system, economical to install and efficient in operation, has been used in many large housing developments and also in buildings of moderate size. It is suitable for vacuum systems and is often installed as a subatmospheric system controlled by an outdoor thermostat. It can operate at 218 F under pressure to 125 F under a vacuum. The downfeed pipe supplies steam directly through the convectors on all stories of each vertical series of windows. There is no valve or trap on any convector. A common trap in the basement ahead of the connection to the return main serves the entire stack.

Control of heat in each room is possible at the individual convector as shown in Fig. 14.13*b*. An enclosure consisting of a front and sides of sheet metal is fitted tightly against the wall. The bottom is open, and there is an open grill at the top. Above the convector element there is an adjustable damper of sheet metal which can be rotated to a vertical position, permitting full convection currents to pass, or be set horizontally to cut off all air currents. When the damper is closed, uncondensed steam passes through to other convectors on the lower floors. Thus the steam always has continuous flow from top to bottom through an unvalved pipe, heat being obtained in varying degree by inducing or retarding the convection air currents in the several rooms. If desired, convectors and piping may be recessed into the wall.

Savings in pipe, traps, and valves are quite evident in this scheme. Economy of operation is the same as in any vacuum system, including the economy which is possible by means of a damper shutting off the heat in individual rooms. The servicing of traps and valves is much less frequent than in other systems and is confined to the convenient

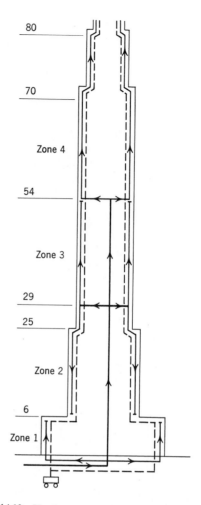

Fig. 14.12 Heating zones. Empire State Building, New York City.

location of the basement or access tunnel. Convector risers may serve 2 to 16 stories.

7. Design. For large operations such as institutions, theaters, and tall office buildings the vacuum system with mechanical condensate return and air removal by means of a pump is most generally employed. Its first cost is higher than that of the gravity systems, but its action is definite and its automatic adjustment to the varying demands of weather and of occupancy give it the preference for large installations.

The calculation of pipe sizes is affected by the relative directions of flow of the steam

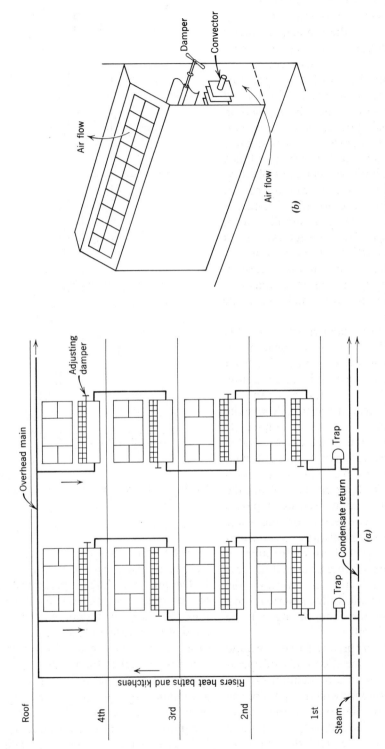

Fig. 14.13 Metro system. (*a*) Inside elevation showing down feed through convectors. (*b*) Convector and cover (with end removed) indicating air currents and adjustable damper.

and the condensed water. When they flow in the same direction the influences of pipe friction, causing pressure drop in the steam, should be considered. When they flow in opposite directions the velocity of the steam must be limited to secure proper functioning of the system.

Steam and condensate flow in the same direction in riser branches of 2-pipe systems and in downfeed supply risers of both 1- and 2-pipe installations. For satisfactory operation the supply mains and riser branches should be pitched in the direction of the steam flow and dripped, that is, connected at their low ends by a small pipe to the return main. In these cases of parallel flow the pipes must be of sufficient size to carry the steam and condensate without excessive loss of pressure due to friction. This loss is rated in ounces per sq in. per 100 ft of pipe or in ounces for the entire system. For brevity ounces per sq in. is expressed as *ounces* (as pounds per sq in. is often expressed as *pounds*).

Pressure drop should not exceed half the initial or gauge pressure and should not cause such velocities as impede counterflowing condensate. Steam heating should be designed with low initial pressures of not over 2 to 5 lb gauge and with small pressure drops, usually taken for air vent and vapor types at not over 1 oz in 100 ft of pipe or 2 to 4 oz total for the entire system, and at not over 4 to 8 oz total for the vacuum type, depending upon the equivalent length of pipe.

The condensate flows in the opposite direction to the steam in the upfeed risers of 1-pipe systems and in the upfeed risers and riser branches of 2-pipe systems when not dripped. With a low steam velocity the condensate runs down the sides of the pipe and the steam flows up the center with little interference between them. As the steam velocity becomes greater, however, the quantities of both steam and condensate increases until a critical velocity is reached at which the steam stops the water and forces it back into the radiator, causing un-

pleasant noises, water hammer, and resistance to steam flow in pipes and radiators. The critical velocity depends upon the size of pipe, the friction, and the quantity of condensate. It is lower in horizontal and sloping pipes than in vertical pipes. Branches to risers and radiators should, therefore, be relatively larger than vertical risers. Upfeed risers in 2-pipe systems also carry some counterflowing water condensed in the pipes themselves, but the volume is small compared to that from the radiators, and, when dripped and the pipes designed for a low pressure drop, no interference should occur.

It is seen, then, that pipe sizes are determined by either one of two considerations, pressure loss or steam velocity, depending upon the circumstances of the design, and that these considerations are related since a higher velocity produces a greater friction with the same quantity of flow. In order to simplify the design of steam heating systems, tables based upon tests for critical velocities have been prepared by the American Society of Heating, Refrigerating, and Air Conditioning Engineers. These tables are here reproduced with the permission of the Society.

The general procedure consists in first calculating the heat losses which must be supplied by the radiators in the rooms as explained in Chapter 8. By dividing the heat loss from each room by 240 Btu the sq ft of radiation for that room is determined. The sum of these radiations gives the total radiation for the building. The distance is then measured from the boiler to the farthest radiator. To this distance or run must be added the resistance of the fittings in equivalent lengths of straight pipe. Since the resistance of fittings varies with the pipe size, it is necessary either to assume an average pipe size for the system and to calculate the resistance of the fittings in equivalent lengths of pipe, or to assume a total length of pipe including both the actual length to farthest radiator and the equivalent lengths corresponding to the resistance of the fit-

Table 14.4   Steam Pipe Capacities for Low Pressure Systems

(Reference to this table will be by column letter *A* through *L*)

*This table is based on pipe size data developed through the research investigations of the American Society of Heating, Refrigerating, and Air Conditioning, Engineers**

	Capacities of Steam Mains and Risers — Direction of Condensate Flow in Pipe Line								Special Capacities for 1-Pipe Systems Only		
	With the Steam in 1-Pipe and 2-Pipe Systems						Against the Steam 2-Pipe Only		Radiator Valves and Vertical Supply Risers Upfeed	Radiator and Riser Runouts
Pipe Size (in.)	$\frac{1}{32}$ psi or $\frac{1}{2}$ oz Drop	$\frac{1}{24}$ psi or $\frac{2}{3}$ oz Drop	$\frac{1}{16}$ psi or 1 oz Drop	$\frac{1}{8}$ psi or 2 oz Drop	$\frac{1}{4}$ psi or 4 oz Drop	$\frac{1}{2}$ psi or 8 oz Drop	Vertical	Horizontal	Supply Risers Upfeed	Vertical Connections	Radiator and Riser Runouts
A	*B*	*C*	*D*	*E*	*F*	*G*	*H*†	*I*§	*J*‡	*K*	*L*§
					Capacity Expressed in Square Feet EDR						
$\frac{3}{4}$	...	...	30	...	...	...	30	...	25	...	...
1	39	46	56	79	111	157	56	34	45	28	28
1$\frac{1}{4}$	87	100	122	173	245	346	122	75	98	62	62
1$\frac{1}{2}$	134	155	190	269	380	538	190	108	152	93	93
2	273	315	386	546	771	1,091	386	195	288	169	169
2$\frac{1}{2}$	449	518	635	898	1,270	1,800	635	395	464	...	260
3	822	948	1,160	1,650	2,330	3,290	1,130	700	800	...	475
3$\frac{1}{2}$	1,230	1,420	1,740	2,460	3,470	4,910	1,550	1,150	1140	...	745
4	1,740	2,010	2,460	3,480	4,910	6,950	2,040	1,700	1520	...	1110
5	3,210	3,710	4,550	6,430	9,090	12,900	4,200	3,150	...	...	2180
6	5,280	6,100	7,460	10,550	14,900	21,100	7,200	5,600	...	...	...
8	11,000	12,700	15,500	21,970	31,070	43,900	15,000	12,000	...	...	...
10	20,000	23,100	28,300	40,100	56,700	80,200	28,000	23,000	...	...	...
12	32,000	37,100	45,500	64,300	91,000	129,000	46,000	38,000	...	...	...
16	61,000	69,700	84,800	121,000	170,000	242,000	88,000	76,000	...	...	...
	All Horizontal Mains and Downfeed Risers						Upfeed Risers	Mains and Un-dripped Run-outs	Upfeed Risers	Radiator Con-nec-tions	Run-outs Not Dripped

NOTE: Steam at an average pressure of 1 psig is used as a basis for calculating capacities. All drops shown are in psi per 100 ft of equivalent run—based on pipe properly reamed.

† Do not use Column *H* for drops of $\frac{1}{24}$ or $\frac{1}{32}$ psi; substitute Column *C* or Column *B* as required.

‡ Do not use Column *J* for drop $\frac{1}{32}$ psi except on sizes 3 in. and over; below 3 in. substitute Column *B*.

§ On radiator runouts over 8 ft long increase one pipe size over that shown in Table 14.4.

* Extracted by permission from the *Heating, Ventilating, Air Conditioning Guide*, 34th Edition.

Table 14.5 Return Pipe Capacities for Low Pressure Systems

Capacity Expressed in Square Feet of Equivalent Radiation

(Reference to this table will be by column letter M through EE)

*This table is based on pipe size data developed through the research investigations of the American Society of Heating, Refrigerating and Air Conditioning Engineers**

Capacity of Return Mains and Risers

Mains

Pipe Size (in.)	$\frac{3}{32}$ psi or $\frac{1}{2}$ oz Drop per 100 ft			$\frac{1}{24}$ psi or $\frac{2}{3}$ oz Drop per 100 ft			$\frac{1}{16}$ psi or 1 oz Drop per 100 ft			$\frac{1}{8}$ psi or 2 oz Drop per 100 ft			$\frac{1}{4}$ psi or 4 oz Drop per 100 ft			$\frac{1}{2}$ psi or 8 oz Drop per 100 ft		
	Wet	Dry	Vac.	Wet	Dry	Vac.	Wet	Dry	Vac.	Wet	Dry	Vac.	Wet	Dry	Vac.	Wet	Dry	Vac.
M	N	O	P	Q	R	S	T	U	V	W	X	Y	Z	AA	BB	CC	DD	EE
$\frac{3}{4}$	....	....	....	....	....	326	....	....	400	....	....	568	....	....	800	....	....	1,130
1	500	248	....	580	285	570	700	320	700	1,000	412	994	1,400	460	1,400	....	....	1,980
1$\frac{1}{4}$	850	520	....	990	595	976	1,200	670	1,200	1,700	868	1,700	2,400	962	2,400	....	....	3,390
1$\frac{1}{2}$	1,350	822	....	1,570	943	1,550	1,900	1,060	1,900	2,700	1,360	2,700	3,800	1,510	3,800	....	....	5,370
2	2,800	1,880	....	3,240	2,140	3,260	4,000	2,300	4,000	5,600	2,960	5,680	8,000	3,300	8,000	....	....	11,300
2$\frac{1}{2}$	4,700	3,040	....	5,300	3,470	5,450	6,700	3,800	6,700	9,400	4,900	9,510	13,400	5,450	13,400	....	....	18,900
3	7,500	5,840	....	8,500	6,250	8,710	10,700	7,000	10,700	15,000	9,000	15,200	21,400	10,000	21,400	....	....	30,200
3$\frac{1}{2}$	11,000	7,880	....	13,200	8,800	13,000	16,000	10,000	16,000	22,000	12,900	22,700	32,000	14,300	32,000	....	....	45,200
4	15,500	11,700	....	18,300	13,400	18,000	22,000	15,000	22,000	31,000	19,300	31,200	44,000	21,500	44,000	....	....	62,190
5	....	....	....	....	....	31,500	....	....	38,700	....	....	54,900	....	....	77,400	....	....	109,000
6	....	....	....	....	....	50,450	....	....	62,000	....	....	88,000	....	....	124,000	....	....	175,000

Risers

Pipe Size (in.)	N	O	P	Q	R	S	T	U	V	W	X	Y	Z	AA	BB	CC	DD	EE
$\frac{3}{4}$	....	190	....	....	190	570	....	190	700	....	190	994	....	190	1,400	....	....	1,980
1	....	450	....	....	450	976	....	450	1,200	....	450	1,700	....	450	2,400	....	....	3,390
1$\frac{1}{4}$	....	990	....	....	990	1,550	....	990	1,900	....	990	2,700	....	990	3,800	....	....	5,370
1$\frac{1}{2}$	....	1,500	....	....	1,500	3,260	....	1,500	4,000	....	1,500	5,680	....	1,500	8,000	....	....	11,300
2	....	3,000	....	....	3,000	5,450	....	3,000	6,700	....	3,000	9,510	....	3,000	13,400	....	....	18,900
2$\frac{1}{2}$	....	....	....	....	....	8,710	....	....	10,700	....	....	15,200	....	....	21,400	....	....	30,200
3	....	....	....	....	....	13,000	....	....	16,000	....	....	22,700	....	....	32,000	....	....	45,200
3$\frac{1}{2}$	....	....	....	....	....	17,900	....	....	22,000	....	....	31,200	....	....	44,000	....	....	62,200
4	....	....	....	....	....	31,500	....	....	38,700	....	....	54,900	....	....	77,400	....	....	109,000
5	....	....	....	....	....	50,500	....	....	62,000	....	....	88,000	....	....	124,000	....	....	175,000

*Reprinted by permission of ASHRAE from the Heating, Ventilating, Air Conditioning Guide, 34th Edition.

tings. In both cases the assumptions must be verified after the pipe sizes are obtained. The second method is found to be more reliable, the length of run to the farthest radiator usually being doubled to allow for the resistance of the fittings. Thus if the length to the farthest radiator were 200 ft a total equivalent length of 400 ft would be selected for purposes of design. The total allowable pressure drop must then be chosen.

As stated, the modern tendency is toward low initial pressure at the boiler and small pressure drops in the piping. Far better operation is obtained in average weather under low pressure, and likewise no difficulty is encountered when higher pressures are required. The total pressure drop is divided by the total equivalent length of pipe in hundreds of feet to obtain the pressure drop per 100 ft. Thus, if the selected total drop is 4 oz and the equivalent length 400 ft, the drop per 100 ft will be $\frac{4}{4} = 1$ oz or $\frac{1}{16}$ lb. Likewise if the total drop is 2 oz and the equivalent length 300 ft the drop per 100 ft will be $\frac{2}{3} = 0.66$ oz or $\frac{1}{24}$ lb. The same pressure drop is customarily used in both the steam supply and return sides of a system.

EXAMPLE 14.3. The initial gauge pressure at the boiler is limited to 1 lb and the run of pipe to the farthest radiator is 400 ft. What pressure drop per 100 ft should be used?

The total drop should not exceed $\frac{1}{2}$ the gauge pressure or $\frac{1}{2}$ lb. Double the longest run to obtain total equivalent run including resistance of fittings. This is a common approximation. $400 \times 2 = 800$. Drop per 100 ft is $\frac{1}{2} \div 8 = \frac{1}{16}$ lb. Answer.

With the total equivalent direct radiation and the pressure drop per 100 ft of pipe. Table 14.4 is consulted to determine the steam pipe sizes and Table 14.5 for the return pipe sizes.

The pipe capacities in the tables are based upon $\frac{1}{4}$ lb of condensation per hr per sq ft of equivalent direct radiation (EDR) and upon actual diameters of reamed standard pipe. Proper reaming of pipe after cutting is important, tests showing that unreamed pipe may reduce the capacity of a 1 in. riser as much as 28.7 percent. In using the tables the following considerations should be noted for practical reasons:

(a) Radiator runouts over 8 ft long should be increased 1 pipe size.

(b) Pitch of mains should be not less than $\frac{1}{8}$ in. in 10 ft.

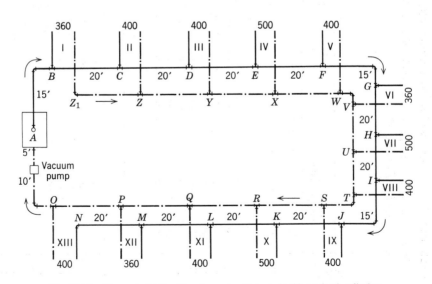

Fig. 14.14 (Example 14.3) Numbers at radiators signify sq ft of radiation.

(c) Pitch of horizontal runouts to risers and radiators should not be less than $\frac{1}{2}$ in. in 10 ft.

EXAMPLE 14.4 (Fig. 14.4). Two-Pipe Vacuum. Select sizes of mains, risers, and runouts. Radiation 5380 sq ft. Longest equivalent run, $320 \times 2 = 640$ ft. Drop per 100 ft $\frac{1}{2} \div 6.4 =$ less than $\frac{1}{12}$ lb. Use $\frac{1}{16}$ lb. Riser runouts dripped.

Pipe Section	Radiation (sq ft)	Pipe Size (in.)
Supply mains		
AB	5380	6
BC	5020	6
CD	4620	5
DE	4220	5
EF	3720	5
FG	3320	5
GH	2960	5
HI	2460	4
IJ	2060	4
JK	1660	$3\frac{1}{2}$
KL	1160	3
LM	760	3
MN	400	$2\frac{1}{2}$
Supply risers, I, VI, XII	360	2
II, III, V, VIII, IX,		
XI, XIII	400	$2\frac{1}{2}$
IV, VII, X	500	$2\frac{1}{2}$
Riser runouts, I, VI, XII	360	2
II, III, V, VIII, IX,		
XI, XIII	400	$2\frac{1}{2}$
IV, VII, X	500	$2\frac{1}{2}$

All of the above sizes are selected from Column D of Table 14.4.

Return mains		
ZZ	360	$\frac{3}{4}$
ZY	760	$1\frac{1}{4}$
YX	1160	$1\frac{1}{2}$
XW	1660	2
WV	2060	2
VU	2420	2

UT	2920	2
TS	3320	2
SR	3720	$2\frac{1}{2}$
RQ	4220	$2\frac{1}{2}$
QP	4620	$2\frac{1}{2}$
PO	4980	$2\frac{1}{2}$
OA	5380	$2\frac{1}{2}$
Return risers, I, VI, XII	360	$\frac{3}{4}$
II, III, V, VIII, IX,		
XI, XIII	400	$\frac{3}{4}$
IV, VII, X	500	$\frac{3}{4}$

All of the above sizes are selected from Column V of Table 14.5.

In vacuum systems as in the other systems low pressure-drops should also be employed. Since this system, however, is generally used in large buildings with long runs of pipe, a saving in pipe size and consequently in cost is attained by using drops of not less than $\frac{1}{24}$ lb per 100 ft. Thus, if the longest equivalent run were 900 ft and the desired drop per 100 ft were $\frac{1}{24}$ lb, the system would be designed for a total drop of $\frac{9}{24}$ or $\frac{3}{8}$ lb. The total pressure-drop should not exceed 1 lb, however, nor $\frac{1}{8}$ lb drop per 100 ft of equivalent run.

The supply main should not be less than 2 in. When it is 3 in. or over at the boiler or pressure-reducing valve it should be at least $2\frac{1}{2}$ in. at the far end. Supply mains, supply risers, and riser branches should be dripped separately through a thermostatic trap into the vacuum return.

References

1. *Heating, Ventilating and Air Conditioning Fundamentals,* Severns and Fellows, John Wiley & Sons, Inc., New York, New York.
2. *Heating Design and Practice.* Robert Henderson Emerick, McGraw-Hill Book Company, Inc., New York, New York.

15

Heating by Electricity

1. Nature of Electric Heating. Cleanliness, silence, individual room control, and fire safety are some of the good qualities of heating by electricity. Flameless operation precludes the need for air to support combustion and neither chimney nor fuel storage space is required. In some cases, notably that of the heat pump and the electric furnace, a central unit is used; but in most other instances the system can be extremely compact with neither a central heat source nor a heat-distribution network. Thus many electric systems consist of a central electrical control panel, concealed electric distribution feeders and the heating elements in the rooms. Usually electric systems are less expensive to install than those that burn gas or oil, especially when the cost of the chimney is considered and, in the case of oil, the cost of the fuel storage tank.

On the debit side, and under discussion here, the cost of operation can sometimes be high. It can vary from a cost equivalent to, or lower than, that of fossil fuels to a value several times that cost. An exception exists in the use of the heat pump whose power demands are less than those of *resistance* heating.

When economy is a consideration, electric heating should be compared in cost with other possible systems. This involves evalua-tion of the cost of chimneys and the variations in insulation. The cost of installation and the yearly costs for fuel or electric energy are not a complete study. Yearly service charges and the cost of replacing deteriorated parts must be considered. These items generally favor electric heating which is reasonably free of maintenance problems. Electric heating has many advantages and will often be chosen at comparable or even higher costs.

As population density increases, it is quite logical to assume that the generation of heat or power will be delegated more often to central utility companies where it can be handled by trained specialists. Elimination of flame from the home has a strong appeal on the basis of safety. Rapidly increasing use of electricity for heating and the strong interest of electric utility management in a new sales market, forecast greater activity in this field.

2. Present Status. At the time of this writing there are in the United States more than a million dwelling units, including apartments, that are heated electrically. Of the new dwelling units constructed during the current year, 15 percent have electric heating. As may be seen in Table 15.1 the number of electrically heated homes has increased almost threefold in 5 years.

258

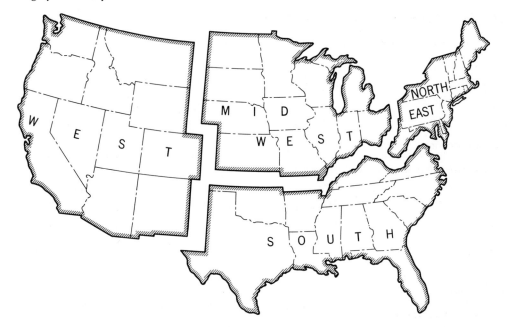

Fig. 15.1 Regional divisions of the United States for the tabulation of statistics about electrically heated homes. See Table 15.1. Adapted from *Electric Heat and Air Conditioning.*

Almost one half of all electrically heated homes are in the south (see Table 15.1). Five years earlier this percentage was more nearly two thirds. On the other hand, the number of such installations in the northeast where rates are higher has increased fivefold during the same period. Table 15.2 shows a variation of from 0.65¢ to 2.10¢ per kwh in the United States, which accounts for a persisting localization in the popularity

Table 15.1

913,583 Homes Fully Heated January 1, 1962 (See Fig. 15.1)

	Number in Use				
	Jan. 1, 1962	*Sept. 1, 1960*	*Sept. 1, 1959*	*Sept. 1, 1958*	*Sept. 1, 1957*
Northeast	25,070	15,974	9,553	6,819	4,924
South	455,953	375,375	316,929	275,399	236,782
Midwest	91,696	72,998	54,461	36,081	26,403
West	340,864	254,953	210,757	181,844	104,110
All Sections	913,583	719,300	591,700	500,143	372,219
	Percent of Total Number in Use				
	1962	*1960*	*1959*	*1958*	*1957*
Northeast	2.7%	2.2%	1.6%	1.4%	1.4%
South	49.0	52.2	53.6	55.1	63.6
Midwest	10.1	10.2	9.2	7.2	7.1
West	37.3	35.4	35.6	36.3	27.9

Reprinted from *Electric Heat and Air Conditioning.*

Table 15.2 *Rates and Heating Costs: Electric Heating*

Electric Home Heating Rates National Average Now 1.15¢ kwh

	Highest	Lowest	Average
Northeast	2.10¢	1.40¢	1.70¢
South	2.00	0.7	1.09
Midwest	2.10	1.00	1.55
West	2.00	0.65	1.08
1962 All Sections	2.01¢	0.73¢	1.15¢

These Utilities Raised or Lowered Heating Rates

			Net Change	
	Reduced	Increased	Previous	Now
Northeast	21%	. . .	1.78¢	1.60¢
South	13	. . .	1.55	1.35
Midwest	22	. . .	1.55	1.47
West	3	4	1.00	1.09
All Sections	10%	1%	1.35¢	1.27¢

Average Seasonal Heating Cost $154

	Annual kwh for Heating	Average Rate per kwh	Average Annual Cost	Average* Degree Days	Cost per Degree Day
Northeast	14,365	1.70¢	$244	5620	4.34¢
South	12,358	1.09	135	2771	4.87
Midwest	14,961	1.55	232	6054	3.83
West	14,277	1.08	154	4125	3.73
1962 All Sections	13,370	1.15¢	$154	3686	4.17¢

Reprinted from *Electric Heat and Air Conditioning.*
* For degree-days in various locations, see Fig. 15.23.

of electric heating. As costs tend to equalize, this method of heating may become more widespread.

The change in utility rates is seen in Table 15.2 which shows that they have had a periodic decrease. This is the general trend. Electric rates have either remained steady or dropped in recent years while the prices of fossil fuels have increased. This fact, together with the 100 percent efficiency of electric heating has been another spur to its increasing use.

Electric power companies like to produce and sell power at a steady rate throughout the year. In the early days of electric use, the peak load was nearly always in the winter when industrial activity and lighting im-

posed heavy demands. As summer air conditioning became popular, especially in the south, the peak load shifted to the summer. Among the companies that have reported the season of their peak loads (Table 15.3), one finds that in the northeast 70 percent of such organizations have a heavy winter load and look for summer air conditioning customers instead of increasing their winter peak by electric heating. As their air conditioning patronage grows these utilities will be in a better position to offer their power at more favorable rates for winter heating. In quite an opposite position, 56 percent of southern companies report heavy summer loads and are therefore happy to keep their plants and staffs busy

Table 15.3 Peaks and Valleys of Demand by Regions and Months
(percent of companies reporting)

	Northeast		South		Midwest		West	
	Highest	Lowest	Highest	Lowest	Highest	Lowest	Highest	Lowest
January	15%	...	22%	2%	13%	2%	22%	4%
February	...	6%	2	14	10	15	...	3
March	...	3	...	14	...	5	...	7
April	...	24	...	19	...	10	...	8
May	...	12	...	26	...	18	...	15
June	...	10	...	12	...	6	3	7
July	...	36	2	9	7	24	11	19
August	12	9	43	...	21	7	11	30
September	18	...	11	...	4	8	4	...
October	...	...	2	...	2	5	...	3
November	...	...	...	2	...	...	...	4
December	55	...	18	2	43	...	49	...
Total Co.'s with Winter Peaks— Dec.–Jan.–Feb.	70%		29%		66%		71%	
with Summer Peaks—July– Aug.–Sept.	30		56		32		26	

Reprinted from *Electric Heat and Air Conditioning*.

in the winter to furnish power for heating at attractive rates. This explains the regional nature of electric heating costs and the influence of the local utility companies on the growth of this method of heating.

A few decades ago almost all of the electric heating in the United States was in the vicinity of public utility companies which could offer low rates because of government sponsorship and efficient power gen-

Table 15.4 More Home Heating by Private Utilities

	Private Companies				Public Companies			
	Percent of Co.'s	Meter Connections	Heating—In Use	Share Added 1961	Percent of Co.'s	Meter Connections	Heating—In Use	Share Added 1961
Northeast	86%	99%	98%	99%	14%	1%	2%	1%
South	62	87	38	80	38	13	62	20
Midwest	54	94	93	91	46	6	7	9
West	50	64	70	73	50	36	30	27
1962 All Sections	57%	80%	57%	79%	43%	20%	43%	21%
1960 All Sections	60	89	49	62	40	11	51	38

Reprinted from *Electric Heat and Air Conditioning*.

Table 15.5   Nonresidential Electric Heating Installations in Use Jan. 1, 1962

	Northeast	Midwest	South	West	Total
Commercial					
Resistance	1,548	4,277	14,641	10,064	30,530
Commercial					
Heat Pumps	380	811	17,389	3,929	22,509
Motel Rooms	6,874	8,301	37,386	21,446	74,007
Apartment Units	2,179	6,745	7,581	79,829	96,334
Schools	53	281	142	259	735

Reprinted from *Electric Heat and Air Conditioning.*

eration. Communities with houses entirely heated by electricity sprang up in the region surrounding the Tennessee Valley Authority and similar projects. While these public companies continue to expand as shown in Table 15.4, private companies are extending their facilities even faster. In the current year private companies have 57 percent of the total business and 79 percent of the new business that was acquired during the previous year.

Much use of electric heating is made in nonresidential installations (see Table 15.5). It is especially appropriate in motels and schools where long periods of nonuse permit its being turned down or off.

3. Thermal Design. Because electric heating in its early stages was found to be expensive, great pains were taken to design houses for minimum heat loss. This attention to thermal planning was more intensive than it had ever been before. The program succeeded in making electric heating economically competitive by reducing both its initial cost and the cost of operation, often producing a favorable economic balance-sheet even when the extra cost of insulation and multiple glazing were included. Recommendations in a joint report of the Edison Electric Institute (EEI) and the National Electrical Manufacturers Association (NEMA) for thermal planning are usually followed in addition to regulations of the local authorities and of the Federal Housing Administration where they apply. Ad-

herence to the report results in such an efficient thermal design that it could well be followed by designers of all projects regardless of the fuel contemplated.

A significant index of the thermal efficiency of the house is to divide its total heat loss by the floor area as directed in Table 15.6. This number, its unit heat loss, should be not greater than the amount listed there for the number of degree days of the geographic region in which the house is located.

Table 15.6   Maximum Heat Loss Values

When based on an infiltration rate of three-quarters air change per hour, the total calculated heat loss shall not exceed the values in this table. These values are expressed in Btuh (or watts) per sq ft of floor area of the space to be heated to the comfort level, measured to the outside of exterior walls.

Maximum Heat Loss Values

Degree Days*	Btuh/sq ft of Floor Area	Watts/sq ft
Over 8000	36	10.6
7001 to 8000	34	10.0
6001 to 7000	32	9.5
4501 to 6000	31	9.2
3001 to 4500	30	8.9
Under 3001	29	8.4

Data to aid in attaining these values are tabulated in Table 15.7.
(Reprinted from EEI-NEMA Joint Report.)
* For degree days in various locations, see Fig. 15.23.

Table 15.7 Thermal Performance Values Including Insulation

Type of Wall Construction	Ceiling Installed Insulation U-Value	Resistance	Opaque Wall Installed Insulation U-Value	Resistance	Floor Over Vented Crawl Space Installed Insulation U-Value	Resistance	Floor Over Unheated Basement Installed Insulation U-Value	Resistance	Perimeter Insulation Resistance
Frame; nominal 4″ studs (with shingle, siding or masonry veneer exterior)	.05	19.*	.07	11.*	.07	13.*	.09	9.*	5.–6.
Frame; nominal 2″ studs (with shingle, siding or masonry veneer exterior)	.04	24.	.11	6.	.05	19.	.07	13.	5.–6.
Masonry; (8″ light weight block or brick cavity)†	.04	24.	.15	—	.05	19.	.07	13.	5.–6.

Use of greater amounts of insulation than indicated above in building sections will result in lower heat loss per sq ft values than are listed in Table 15.6.
Slab edge heat loss in Btuh per exposed linear foot may be determined from data described in the Minimum Property Standards of the FHA for One and Two Living Units.
* Standard minimum resistance values, (R).
† Representative constructions fitting this category include:
1. Brick cavity; 2¼ inch cavity, with granular fill insulation in cavity.
2. 8 inch lightweight concrete block; core is filled with granular fill insulation, ¾ inch furring and ½ inch gypsum board interior finish.
3. 4 inch split block exterior and 4 inch lightweight concrete block interior cavity wall; with 2⅝ inch cavity filled with granular fill insulation.
(Reprinted from EEI-NEMA Joint Report.)

263

Wall units, decreasing 33%

Heat pumps, growing 12%

5% ← Furnace and in-duct, growing

Baseboard, Fast growing 22%

Cable, steady 28%

Fig. 15.2 Approximate relative use of the principal methods of electric heating indicating general market trends as of 1963.

Table 15.8   Output of Some Electrical Resistance Heating Units

Voltage Ratings 120–208 and 240 V

(a) Baseboard Heaters	(b) Wall Heaters	(c) Heating Cable
Output in Watts		
250	750	400
500	1000	600
750	1250	800
1000	1500	1000
1250	2000	1200
1500	2500	1400
2000	4000	1700
3000	5000	
		2000
		2300
		2700
Maximum Outlet		3200
Temperature 200 F		3800
		4300
		4800

(120, 208 and 240 Volts for the upper group; 208 and 240 Volts for the lower group)

Standards to be developed for floor furnaces and portables.

Reprinted from *Standards Publication, Electric Comfort Heating Equipment*, National Electric Manufacturer's Association.

Tables 15.6 and 15.7 are the core of the design procedure, but other recommendations are made by the EEI-NEMA Joint Report, which is here transcribed directly.

GENERAL DISCUSSION OF THERMAL DESIGN

The U-values listed in Table 15.7 are intended as a guide to the thermal design of the home. They may be used with flexibility to suit particular design or climatic conditions. For example, if the design of a nominal 4-in. frame wall structure is such as to limit the wall area which may be insulated to less than about 70–75% of the entire wall area, the calculated heat loss may prove to exceed the values in Table 15.6. The use of multiple glazing on windows and doors will significantly reduce this over-all total. Further reductions, if desired, may be obtained using a ceiling U-value of .04 (installed insulation R-24) and a floor

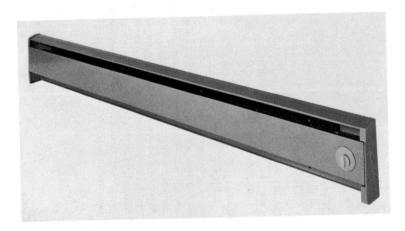

Fig. 15.3 Electric baseboard heater. Markel Electric Products, Inc.

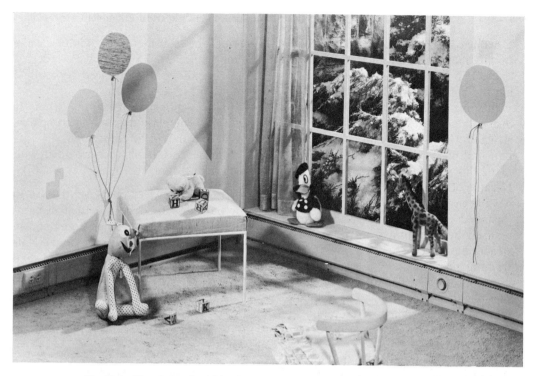

Fig. 15.4   Electric baseboard in place. Hunter Division, Robbins and Myers, Inc.

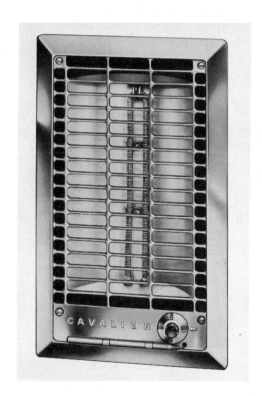

Fig. 15.5   Recessed wall heater. Cavalier Corporation.

Fig. 15.6   Recessed wall-type electric heater with integral fan for forced air. Markel Electric Products, Inc.

U-value of .05 (installed insulation R-19). In this manner, the limits established in Table 15.6 may be satisfied without altering the basic design of the structure.

In some areas, structures with very low over-all heat losses have been constructed. Using combinations of standard batt and fill insulations, ceiling U-values of .02 (installed insulation R-49) and floor U-value of .04 (installed insulation R-24) have been provided. Wall U-values of .05 (installed insulation R-19) have been realized by deviating from normal construction practices. The use of 2×6 wall framing members on 24-in. centers, is one example of this. The cost of construction changes in relation to estimated reductions in equipment required and lowered operating costs should be carefully considered.

Weatherstripping and multiple glazing should be used on doors and windows for improved comfort, economy, and as required to meet the values in Table 15.6. Double glazing should be used if degree days are above 4500. Triple glazing

should be considered if winter design temperature is -15 F or lower, or degree days are above 7000. Degree days will be found in Fig. 15.23.

For sections separating regularly heated from periodically heated spaces, insulation should be considered.

Fire places should be provided with tight-fitting dampers.

VENTILATION. Mechanical ventilation to the outside should be provided in bathrooms (12 air changes per hour) and in kitchens (15 air changes per hour). Natural ventilation of structural spaces shall meet the requirements of the Minimum Property Standards of the FHA for One and Two Living Units.

END OF TRANSCRIPTION FROM EEI-NEMA JOINT REPORT

The standards in Table 15.7 of 19, 11, 13, and 9 as the resistances, (R) of installed insulation in ceiling, walls, floor over vented crawl space, and floor over unheated basement, respectively, are stated in this way

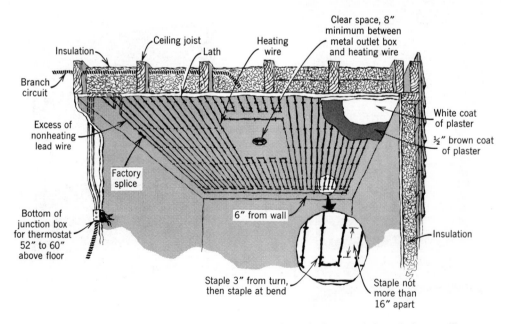

Fig. 15.7 Typical installation of radiant heating cable ready for completion of plaster ceiling. General Electric.

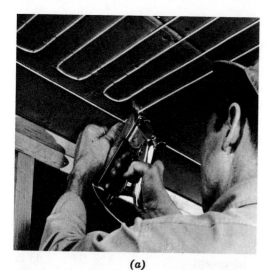

(a)

(b)

(c)

Fig. 15.8 Wiring and controls in an electric cable-type ceiling radiant heating installation. (a) Stapling radiant heating wire to gypsum lath. (b) Checking for continuity of cable after its installation in the ceiling and prior to installing the thermostat and switch. (c) Thermostat in each room controls the performance of the imbedded wires to maintain the desired temperature in the room. (General Electric Company)

Fig. 15.9 Recessed ceiling heater. Projection $1\frac{1}{4}$ in. Three types available: heater only; heater and light combination; heater, light, and exhaust combination. Markel Electric Products, Inc.

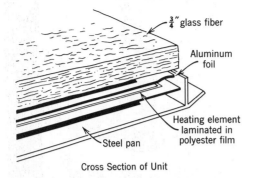

Cross Section of Unit

Fig. 15.10   Electric radiant ceiling panel. Electric radiant ceiling panels feature a new exclusive resistive wire grid heating element imbedded in a tough plastic sheet. This provides parallel paths of wire covering the entire panel surface for even, efficient distribution of heat. Exterior surface is formed of durable lightweight steel; over-all size $5' \times 2' \times \frac{13}{16}''$. The panel is backed by a dense $\frac{3}{4}''$ glass fiber blanket insulation. Rating 700 W. (General Electric Company)

instead of in inches of thickness to allow for variations in the k-value of insulating material. If, for instance, the k-value were .27 the thickness (x inches) would be calculated as $x = Rk \left(\text{since } R = \dfrac{x}{k} \right)$. (See Chap. 8.) The results would be as follows:

Ceiling	$x = 19 \times .27 = 5.12$ in.
Walls	$x = 11 \times .27 = 2.97$ in.
Floor over vented crawl space	$x = 13 \times .27 = 3.50$ in.
Floor over unheated basement	$x = 9 \times .27 = 2.43$ in.

Vapor barriers, of course, are extremely important to prevent house-moisture from reaching cold locations where it could condense and wet the insulation, reducing its efficiency.

Fig. 15.11   Appropriate use of the electric ceiling radiant panel shown in Fig. 15.10. (General Electric Company)

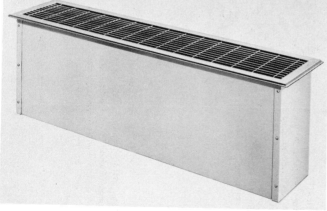

Fig. 15.12 Floor-type drop-in convective electrical resistance units. Ratings of this type:

Watts	Btuh	Width	Length
350	1194	$7\frac{3}{4}$ in.	14 in.
750	2559	$7\frac{3}{4}$ in.	30 in.
2000	6824	$7\frac{3}{4}$ in.	62 in.

(Edwin L. Wiegand Company)

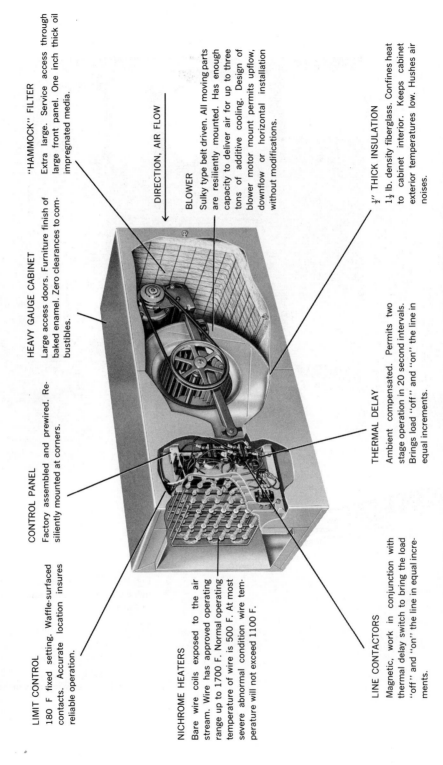

LIMIT CONTROL
180 F fixed setting. Waffle-surfaced contacts. Accurate location insures reliable operation.

NICHROME HEATERS
Bare wire coils exposed to the air stream. Wire has approved operating range up to 1700 F. Normal operating temperature of wire is 500 F. At most severe abnormal condition wire temperature will not exceed 1100 F.

CONTROL PANEL
Factory assembled and prewired. Resiliently mounted at corners.

LINE CONTACTORS
Magnetic, work in conjunction with thermal delay switch to bring the load "off" and "on" the line in equal increments.

HEAVY GAUGE CABINET
Large access doors. Furniture finish of baked enamel. Zero clearances to combustibles.

THERMAL DELAY
Ambient compensated. Permits two stage operation in 20 second intervals. Brings load "off" and "on" the line in equal increments.

"HAMMOCK" FILTER
Extra large. Service access through large front panel. One inch thick oil impregnated media.

DIRECTION, AIR FLOW

BLOWER
Sulky type belt driven. All moving parts are resiliently mounted. Has enough capacity to deliver air for up to three tons of additive cooling. Design of blower motor mount permits upflow, downflow or horizontal installation without modifications.

$\frac{1}{4}$" THICK INSULATION
1$\frac{1}{2}$ lb. density fiberglass. Confines heat to cabinet interior. Keeps cabinet exterior temperatures low. Hushes air noises.

Fig. 15.13 Electric central warm-air furnace. Rating up to 12.41 kw (42,500 Btuh). Lenox Industries, Inc.

CONTROL RELAY

Isolates EDTI transformer from Heat Pump or air conditioning transformer eliminating the need for transformer phasing.

TRANSFORMER

Class 2, 24 volt internally protected. It has capacity to operate up to three additional ED1 or ED2 units.

HEATING RELAY

Two-pole normally open contacts. Low wattage coil.

TERMINAL STRIP

High-voltage. Three 1.9 KW elements are connected for single phase, can be field connected for three phase operation.

TERMINAL STRIP

Low voltage. Permits quick and simple thermostat connection.

NICHROME HEATERS

Bare wire heaters exposed directly to air stream. Wire has approved operating range up to 1700 F. Normal operating temperature of wire is 500 F. At the most severe abnormal conditions, wire temperature will not exceed 1100 F.

PORCELAIN INSULATORS

Accurately located and spaced for best operation of heaters.

ELEMENT SUPPORT BARS

Nickel plated. Heat reflective.

LIMIT CONTROL

Surface type with enclosed bimetal. Accurately located. 175 F. Fixed setting with 30 F. differential.

DUCT FLANGE

Secures to duct with metal screws.

ELEMENT SUPPORT

Rugged construction. Coated with heat reflecting aluminum paint.

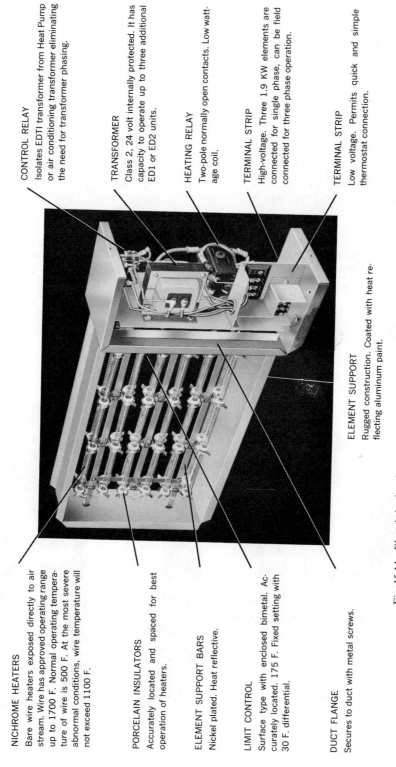

Fig. 15.14   Electric in-duct heater. It warms the air circulated by a central fan. Placed in duct before room register. Capacities up to 6.20 kw (21,250 Btuh). Lennox Industries, Inc.

Fig. 15.15 Electric unit ventilator in school classroom, with electric baseboard heat supplied behind bookshelves for window downdraft protection. (Edwin L. Wiegand Company)

Fig. 15.16 Electric unit heaters find wide use in storage, garage, and other large service areas. High mounting reduces draughts.

Fig. 15.17 Overhead electric infrared spot heater minimizes discomfort of worker in otherwise unheated buildings. (Edwin L. Wiegand Company)

Fig. 15.18 Air-to-air heat pump, its controls, an indoor view and its operating characteristics.

Capacity, Btuh	RB581B/c	RB781B/c
Heating	9,500	14,000
Cooling	10,000	15,000

General Electric.

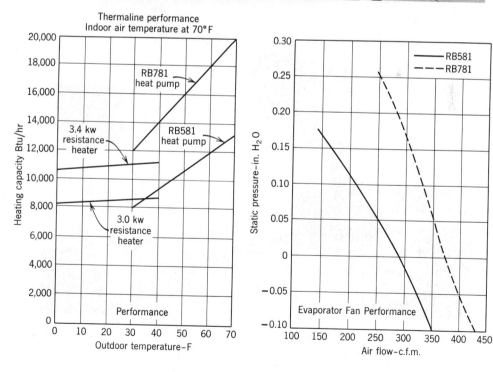

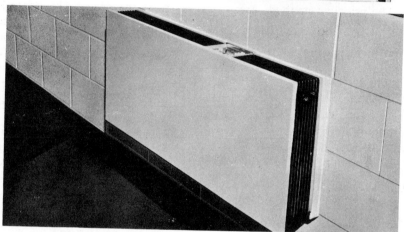

4. Methods and Equipment. Quite a variety of heating methods are available to suit diverse architectural conditions. Voltages of 120, 208, and 240 are used, the higher voltages usually chosen for units of larger output. Heating elements are placed at locations of greatest heat loss or to avoid heat concentrations where people are gathered. Temperatures are low enough to avoid danger of fire or discomfort to the touch. The principal methods are:

(a) Baseboard
(b) Wall units
(c) Cable
(d) Ceiling units
(e) Floor units
(f) Central furnaces
(g) In-duct heaters
(h) School and industrial heaters
(i) The heat pump

The National Electric Manufacturer's Association sets many standards of performance and output. Some of these for items a, b, and c of the foregoing list are included in Table 15.8. Most manufacturers conform.

(a) **Baseboards.** Increasing in popularity and effective in their location below areas of heat loss, baseboards may be had in a variety of sizes, lengths (1 ft through 10 ft), and outputs. As in the case of all electric heaters, the wattage should balance the wattage equivalent to the heat loss rate from the space. The control can be by a thermostat and switch in each room or the baseboard elements may be individually controlled. Outputs per lin ft in the larger capacities equal those of hot water fin-tube baseboard elements. Thus it is often possible to localize the baseboard on exterior walls only.

(b) **Wall Units.** These may be of the type having wires imbedded in glass or ceramic or they may be of the recessed type with depth sufficient to enclose resistance coils and sometimes fans. Among their many uses they are quite suitable for motels

Fig. 15.19 This heat pump in a living room is quite self-contained. It has an electrical connection and access in a separate chamber to outdoor air. It heats the room in winter and cools it in summer. Indoor air is handled in and out through the edges. It is the same unit as pictured in Fig. 15.18. General Electric.

Fig. 15.20*a*   In this application of the heat pump, a panel set forward of the exterior wall line allows the pump to inhale and exhale outdoor air around the panel edges. In summer it discharges warm air and, in winter, cool air. (General Electric Company)

Fig. 15.20*b*   Interior cabinet details and depth serve the heat pump. Room air is taken back as shown and discharged (after cooling or heating) upwards across the glass surface. (General Electric Company)

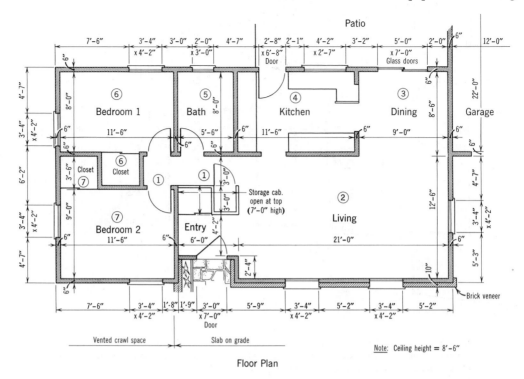

Fig. 15.21 Small house divided into room areas for design of electric heating installation based upon calculations developed by the National Mineral Wool Insulation Association. See Fig. 15.22 and Tables 15.9 and 15.10.

where the guest may adjust the degree of heat by the manually set thermostat which is usually part of the heater. The wall heater in Fig. 15.5 is of stainless steel, 1250 Watts (4629 Btuh) and is suitable for bathrooms, kitchens, attic rooms, playrooms, or any small room, the heat loss of which does not exceed the rating of the unit.

A fan type forced-air recessed electric wall heater is shown in Fig. 15.6. It is 16 in. wide, 20 in. high, and projects $1\frac{1}{2}$ in. into the room. It is obtainable in wattages up to 4800 (16,387 Btuh) and has in integral thermostat.

(c) *Cable.* The only invisible electric heating system is one using electric cable imbedded in plaster ceilings. The cables come in specific lengths and wattages. Usually one cable serves each room. They have nonheating leads which terminate at switch and thermostat and each complete wire-and-lead assembly must be used as received and not cut or altered in any way.

This method of electric heating by low-temperature wire provides all of the advantages of any radiant heating installation with extremely simple room controls. Each room constitutes an individual zone. Branch circuits connect to a general power center at a convenient location often near the electric service entry and main switch.

A radiant *floor* may be used by setting the cables on a masonry base below a concrete floor. The ceiling location is preferred because of its smaller thermal capacity which facilitates a faster response.

(d) *Ceiling Units.* A convenient location for a heating unit is the ceiling. For use in bathrooms and kitchens the unit in Fig. 15.9 is especially appropriate since it can be specified to supply heat, light, and ventilation. Its electrical ratings for heat are 1000 and 1500 W (3412 and 5118 Btuh). Figure 15.10 represents an element which may be used to advantage for a concentration of warmth above areas that otherwise would be cold. (See also Fig. 15.11.)

(*e*) *Floor Units.* When glass is carried to the floor it is usually brought as close to that level as possible. As in the case of hot water convectors and warm air delivery ducts, the acceptance of floor registers above submerged electric heating elements has often been the lesser of two evils and preferred to raising the glass to accommodate a baseboard unit (see Fig. 15.12).

(*f*) *Central Furnaces.* The many advantages of a duct system and moving air can be had by use of a central electric air furnace. The one shown in Fig. 15.13 is of the horizontal type, but upflow and downflow furnaces are also available. Not the least of the advantages is the possibility of utilizing the same duct system for air conditioning.

(*g*) *In-duct Heaters.* A very flexible method of warming air is by the use of an in-duct electrical resistance element such as that shown in Fig. 15.14. The use of these heaters eliminates the central furnace. In-duct heaters are part of a modern trend to warm (or cool) air by the use of conditioning elements located in the ducts that sup-

Table 15.9   Excerpt from "Electric Comfort Estimate Based Upon Joint EEI-NEMA Recommendations, Developed by the National Mineral Wool Insulation Association. Annual Cost, Electric Heating, House in Fig. 15.10. Rate from Fig. 15.22.

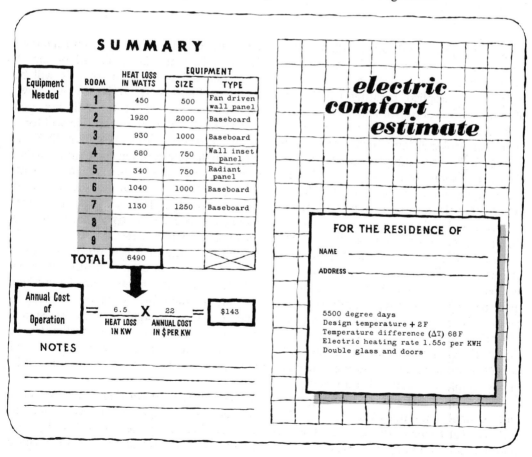

SUMMARY

Equipment Needed	ROOM	HEAT LOSS IN WATTS	EQUIPMENT	
			SIZE	TYPE
	1	450	500	Fan driven wall panel
	2	1920	2000	Baseboard
	3	930	1000	Baseboard
	4	680	750	Wall inset panel
	5	340	750	Radiant panel
	6	1040	1000	Baseboard
	7	1130	1250	Baseboard
	8			
	9			
TOTAL		6490		

Annual Cost of Operation = 6.5 X 22 = $143

HEAT LOSS IN KW   ANNUAL COST IN $ PER KW

NOTES

electric comfort estimate

FOR THE RESIDENCE OF

NAME _____

ADDRESS _____

5500 degree days
Design temperature + 2F
Temperature difference (ΔT) 68F
Electric heating rate 1.55c per KWH
Double glass and doors

Table 15.10 Calculation of Heat Loss in Btuh Converted to Watts to Check Itemized Summary of Table 15.9. For house in Fig. 15.21.

Section (Entire House)	U-Value, Infiltration, or Edge-Units	×	Volume, Area, or Length	×	Temperature Difference ΔT	=	Btuh Heat Loss
Ceiling	.05		805 sq ft		68		2,737.0
Glass	.61		149 sq ft		68		6,180.5
Doors	.31		38.8 sq ft		68		817.9
Floor (slab)	FHA M.P.S. table		77'–4" at 16½ Btu/ft*				1276.0
Floor (over ventilated crawl space)	.07		241.5 sq ft		68		1,149.5
Infiltration (¾ of an air change per hr)	.0135		6842.5 cu ft		68		6,281.4
Net wall	.07		871.9		68		4,150.2
					Total		22,592.5 Btuh

Conversion to watts $\dfrac{22,592.5}{3.41} = 6619.5$ watts (1 watt = 3.41 Btuh)

* Special edge insulation.

ply certain spaces with air circulated by a central fan. Cooling coils or in-duct heaters can respond to thermostats in the spaces to which air is supplied, creating a multitude of individually controlled zones.

(h) *School and Industrial Heaters.* Conventional bookshelf and convector units in schools have been adapted to the use of electricity. Some forced-air electric types are rated as high as 36 KW (123,000 Btuh). School officials in some regions have found that electric heating is less in over-all cost than heating by other fuels locally available.

Electric heaters of the unit type have proved to be effective in industrial buildings as space heaters (see Fig. 15.16). When space heating is not provided, infrared units can supply radiant energy for the comfort of workers in these unheated buildings (see Fig. 15.17). Gymnasium buildings have been heated by infrared units, and they are commonly employed under theatre marquees, below outdoor shelters in shopping areas and for similar outdoor uses.

(i) *The Heat Pump.* By reversing the conventional refrigeration cycle, the evaporator coils can cool the outdoor air and the condenser coils can warm the indoor air. A more detailed explanation of this will be found in Chapter 16. It is obvious, however, that if the evaporator coils are used to refrigerate the outdoor air, ice will form when the outdoor air is less than 32 F. At this time the refrigeration cycle turns off and electrical resistance elements take over with less efficiency. When air is used as a heat source with supplemental resistance elements, the device is partly a heat pump and partly a resistance heater.

Although the heat pump is generally listed as a form of electric heating it draws a large part of its energy from the outdoor air and is therefore more economical to operate than straight electric resistance heating, especially in southern climates. In summer, by a reversal of the evaporator and condenser operations, it is an air conditioner.

5. **Cost of Electric Heating.** Electrical contractors are frequently called upon to estimate the yearly cost of heating by electricity. Joint efforts of the Edison Electric

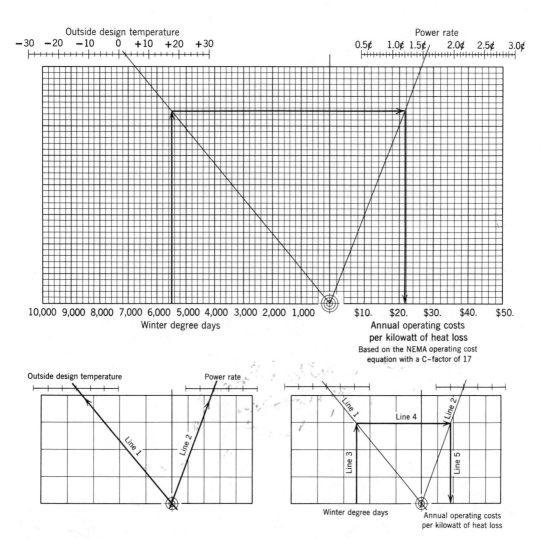

Fig. 15.22   Excerpt from "Electric Comfort Calculator." Method of finding annual heating cost per kilowatt of heat loss. Developed by the National Mineral Wool Insulation Association.

To draw lines 1 and 2:

Draw line 1 from the center of the target to the number on the "Outside Design Temperature" scale for your climate, upper left.

Draw line 2 from the center of the target to the number on the "Power Rate" scale for your area, upper right.

To draw lines 3, 4, and 5:

From a point on the left, bottom scale indicating the number of winter degree days for your area, draw Line 3 straight up to join line 1.

From where Lines 3 and 1 meet, draw Line 4 horizontally across the chart until it meets Line 2.

From where Lines 4 and 2 meet, draw Line 5 straight down. Where it crosses the bottom scale indicates the annual operating cost per kilowatt of heat loss for your climate and your rate.

The conditions shown here apply to Fig. 15.21 and Table 15.9.

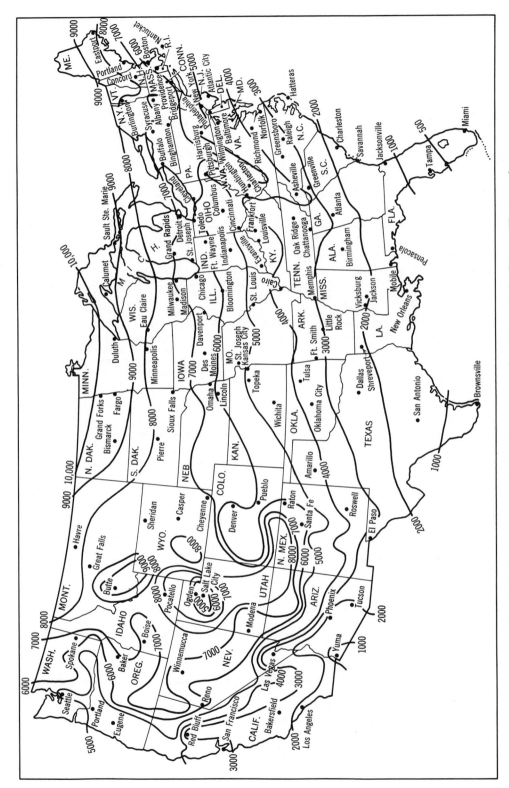

Fig. 15.23   Normal number of degree days per year. Adapted from *Air Conditioning, Heating, and Ventilating*.

Institute, the National Electrical Manufacturer's Association, and the National Mineral Wool Insulation Association have resulted in a simplified method of doing this. It begins with room-by-room calculations of heat loss. These are expressed directly in watts. Though the calculations are not shown here, their totals are summarized for a house (Fig. 15.21) in Table 15.9, together with notes about equipment to heat the several rooms, making a generous allowance for the bathroom. Table 15.10 is a check calculation in Btuh for the whole house to verify the room-by-room breakdown. Using the conversion factor 1 watt = 3.41 Btuh, there is close agreement.

The yearly cost of electric heating for this house in a 5500 degree day area and by electricity costing 1.55¢ per kwh is $143 (see Table 15.9). This is based upon the annual kilowatt use (Table 15.9) and the annual cost per kilowatt found by the use of Fig. 15.22. Approximate degree days are selected from Fig. 15.23.

References

1. *Electric Heating Fact Book,* Published by Electric Heating Journal, 2132 Foredem Avenue, Madison 1, Wisconsin.
2. *Electric Warmth,* Edison Electric Institute, 750 Third Avenue, New York 17, New York.
3. *Home Heating with Electricity,* H. H. Beaty, University of Illinois, College of Agriculture.
4. *Electric House Heating,* Rural Electrification Administration, U. S. Department of Agriculture, Superintendent of Documents, Washington, D.C.
5. *Standards Publication,* Electric Comfort Heating Equipment, National Electrical Manufacturer's Association, 155 East 44th Street, New York 17, New York.
6. *Manual for Electric House Heating,* National Electrical Manufacturer's Association, 155 East 44th Street, New York 17, New York.

16

Principles of
Air Conditioning

1. Scope. Air conditioning in its full meaning is a system of complete all-year climate control. It is not just *summer cooling* but involves, throughout the year, control of indoor air temperature, the regulation of the humidity (water vapor) content of the air, the introduction of fresh, outdoor air at controlled rates, and the cleaning, circulation, and proper distribution of the air. Complete air conditioning requires a source of heating such as a boiler or furnace, methods of cooling such as the refrigeration cycle, equipment for introducing moisture and for removing it, filters or air-washing devices to clean the air and, for proper air distribution, blowers, ducts, and registers. Fresh air is introduced on the intake side of the conditioning equipment so that it may be treated before entering the space. An equal or slightly smaller amount of indoor air is exhausted from points of odor concentration such as kitchens, toilets, and smoking rooms. Obviously, partial systems are sometimes used that do not afford the completeness of service just described. Yet in most modern buildings of importance in which air conditioning is employed, the sys-tem generally conforms to the foregoing specifications.

2. Cooling by Compressive Refrigeration. Since methods of heating have already been discussed in foregoing chapters, it is now necessary to consider the means for producing cool air, or the chilled water by which air may be cooled. Occasionally ground water is obtainable at temperatures low enough for direct use, but generally the use of a refrigeration machine or other special cooling device is necessary. As shown in Fig. 16.1 the compressive refrigeration cycle is a scheme for transferring heat from one circulated water system (chilled water) to another (condenser water). The means for doing this is the liquification and evaporation of a refrigerant, usually Freon, during which processes it respectively gives off and takes on heat. The heat that it gives off must be disposed of (except in the heat pump) but the heat that it acquires is drawn out of the circulated water known as the chilled water, which is the medium for subsequent cooling processes.

Freon, a gas at normal temperatures and pressures, must be compressed and liquified

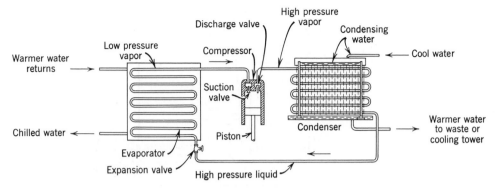

Fig. 16.1   Schematic arrangement of a compressive refrigeration cycle.

to be of service later as a heat absorber. In order to liquify it (see Fig. 16.1), it is first compressed to a high pressure vapor, then, by means of cool water, latent heat is extracted from the Freon, which condenses it to a liquid. This product, high-pressure liquid Freon is a potential heat absorber, for when it is released through an expansion valve it springs mechanically to gaseous form. In this change of state it must take on latent heat which it does by drawing heat out of the circulated water of the chilled water system. It may be said that the refrigeration cycle pumps the heat out of the chilled water system into the condenser water system. Indeed, by special (reverse cycle) arrangements of the water systems a *heat pump* is the result. So the refrigeration cycle is the basis for the cooling in air conditioning systems that have fossil fuel sources of heat, and the basis for both heating and cooling in the heat pump.

The piston in the schematic drawing of Fig. 16.1 suggests a reciprocating compressor, a type often used in smaller compressor sizes. Larger chilled water "packages" usually employ centrifugal compressors such as the types of Figs. 16.2 and 16.3. Application of the principle of Fig. 16.1 is seen in Fig. 16.2 and in its final form as a piece of tangible equipment, in Fig. 16.3. Compressor, condenser, and cooler (evaporator) are usually assembled as a unit package. When the compressor is steam-turbine driven, the exhaust steam is often used as an energy source for an auxiliary absorption refrigeration machine, the principle of which is described in the following article. These two devices make an efficient combination, and the use of steam for cooling can employ, for summer operation, the steam plant which is used for heating in winter. Economic studies to compare the relative costs of steam, electricity, or other power sources should be made independently for each project.

Unit of Refrigeration. A ton of refrigeration is the cooling effect obtained when 1 ton of 32 F ice melts to water at 32 F in 24 hrs. Since the latent heat of fusion of ice is 144 Btu per lb, the cooling effect or rate of 1 ton of refrigeration (2000 lb) is taken as 144 × 2000 = 288,000 Btu per day of 24 hr or 12,000 Btuh. The requisite capacity of a refrigerating machine in tons may therefore be found by dividing the total heat gain in a building in Btuh by 12,000.

Of the materials tried out as refrigerating media, comparatively few combine economy, efficiency, and safety. Two of these in general use will be noted here.

(a) *Monofluorotrichloromethane* (CCl_3F) is also known as Freon 11. Its critical pressure is 535 psi, and its saturation temperature at this pressure is 388 F. The boiling point at standard atmospheric pressure is 74.7 F and the freezing point is − 168 F. It is

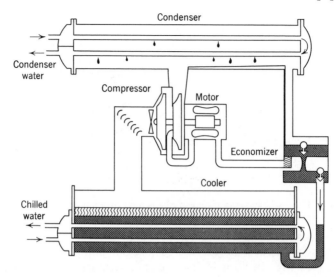

Fig. 16.2 Diagrammatic section of chilled-water producer. A centrifugal compressor (center) delivers the high pressure refrigerant gas to the condenser (top) where it condenses, giving up its latent heat to the condenser water. In the cooler (bottom) it expands to a gas absorbing heat from the water of the chilled water cycle. (Carrier Corporation)

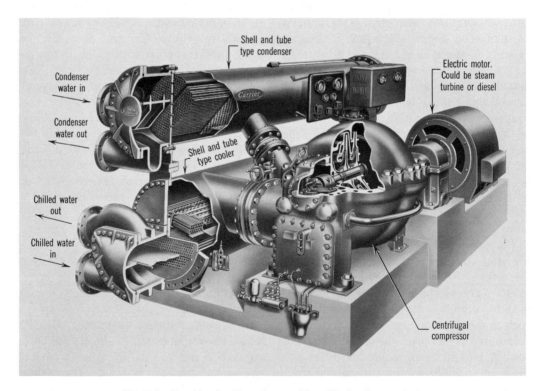

Fig. 16.3 Centrifugal refrigeration machine. (Carrier Corporation)

very slightly toxic and is not explosive or corrosive and well adapted to centrifugal machines. This refrigerant has been largely used by the Carrier Corporation under the name of Carrene No. 2.

(b) *Dichlorodifluoromethane* (CCl_2F_2) is also known as Freon 12. Its critical pressure is 582 psi, and its saturation temperature at this pressure is 232 F. At standard atmospheric pressure the boiling and freezing points are, respectively -21.6 F and -247 F. It is very slightly toxic and is not explosive or corrosive. It is satisfactory in all types of reciprocating compressors.

Ammonia has several desirable properties and has been used in the past, but, because it is explosive, corrosive, and very toxic, leakage is highly dangerous and it is seldom employed in air conditioning at the present time.

3. Cooling by Absorption. A form of water chiller recently developed is the absorption machine (see Fig. 16.4). Suitable for installations up to 1000 tons capacity, the external connections of this device are similar to those of the refrigeration machine shown in Fig. 16.3. It produces chilled water and has a cycle of hot condensing water that must be cooled. Its motive power is steam, but instead of driving a turbine to run a compressor, the steam is used in a regenerative process to strengthen a salt solution. Though similar in external connections, its interior functioning is very different from the compressor-type refrigeration machine and the steps of the process are explained in Fig. 16.4. The absorption machine has become very popular. It is often economically competitive with the compression machine, has fewer moving parts, is quieter and demands somewhat less attention. The cooling principle, shown in Step 1 of Fig. 16.4, consists of drawing vapor away from a body of water. The change of state from water to vapor requires the acquisition of latent heat. This heat is drawn from the sensible heat of the remaining water, cooling it. The uses of chilled water in cooling coils to produce cool air are described in later articles.

4. Thermoelectric Cooling. In an effort to create an even simpler and quieter method of cooling, the thermoelectric principle has recently been refined and developed. Prior to Lord Kelvin's investigation in 1850 of the refrigeration cycle, Jean Peltier had made some interesting discoveries in 1834 concerning electricity, heat, and the dissimilar metals of a thermo-couple. He found that if a direct current is sent through the circuit of a thermo-couple, heat is given off at 1 junction and absorbed at the other. This effect is due to the fact that at one junction the current opposes the potential difference between the 2 metals and hence work is done by the current and this electric energy appears as heat. At the other junction the potential difference of the 2 metals acts *with* the current and the effect is cooling. This device will, of course, act in reverse and the thermo-couple is well known as an instrument for determining temperatures by measuring their electrical effect in the conductors.

For many years little was done to utilize the thermal effects that Peltier found when passing a current through the apparatus. Recently, however, by the selection of appropriate metals and other aids, devices have been perfected that maintain steady low temperatures in vital control equipment of missiles. This specialized use has been expanded to solve other and larger cooling problems. One of the companies that has been involved in this transition is the York Division of Borg-Warner Corporation. It has recently announced the development and imminent marketing of a refrigerator, an ice-cube maker, and an air conditioner. The conditioner is only of small capacity but larger units of several hundred tons capacity are contemplated. The present cost of such air conditioners is high but they are expected to be economically competitive at a later stage of development. Assets are silence and the absence of moving parts. Alternating current is rectified to provide the necessary direct current.

5. Air, Moisture, and Heat. Air and water vapor are the media by which air-conditioning systems operate. The qualities and characteristics of these two gases must be understood if we are to gain a working knowledge of air-conditioning processes. Water vapor in varying amounts always exists in air, and the regulation of this mois-

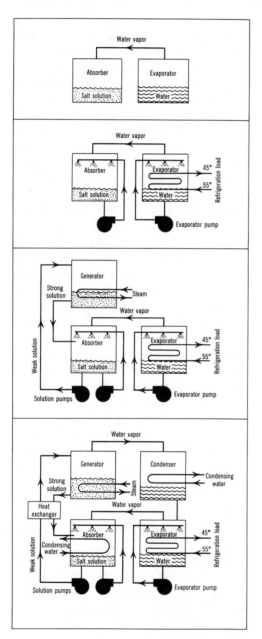

1 Evaporator and absorber

Consider two connected, closed tanks with a salt solution (lithium bromide) in one and water in the other. Just as common table salt absorbs water on a damp day, the salt solution in the absorber soaks up some of the water in the evaporator. The water remaining is thereby cooled by evaporation.

2 Evaporator coil and pump added

This refrigeration effect is utilized by putting a coil in the evaporator tank. Water from this tank is pumped to a spray header which wets the coil. The spray's evaporation chills water in the coil as it circulates to the refrigeration load. Solution pumped to spray in absorber raises efficiency.

3 Solution pumps and generator added

In an actual operating cycle, the salt solution is continuously absorbing water vapor. To keep the salt solution at proper concentration, part of it is pumped directly to a generator where excess water vapor is boiled off. The reconcentrated salt solution is returned to the absorber tank where it mixes with the solution sprayed to absorber in step 2.

4 Condenser and heat exchanger added

Water vapor boiled off from the weak solution is condensed and returned to the evaporator. A heat exchanger uses the hot, concentrated salt solution leaving the generator to preheat the cooler, weak solution coming from the absorber. Finally, condensing water circulating through the absorber and condenser coils removes the waste heat.

Fig. 16.4   Absorption refrigeration unit. For external view of machine, see Fig. 17.9. Connected systems are steam, condensing water and chilled water (Refrigeration load). (Carrier Corporation)

ture content and of the temperature of the vapor-air mixture is the problem posed to the designer of air conditioning. The principles of physics and their development in the *ASHRAE Guide and Data Book* are an aid to a deeper understanding of these matters. A few brief definitions and statements of physical relationships given here will serve as an introduction to the subject.

DRY-BULB TEMPERATURE (DB). The temperature of the air–water vapor mixture measured in the normal way with a Fahrenheit thermometer.

WET-BULB TEMPERATURE (WB) (see Fig. 16.5). The temperature shown by a thermometer with a wetted bulb rotated rapidly in the air to cause evaporation of its moisture. In dry air the moisture evaporates and, in acquiring latent heat, draws heat out of the thermometer to produce a large *wet-bulb depression* (difference between dry- and wet-bulb temperatures). This is an index of low relative humidity. Slow evaporation when the air is already moisture-laden results in a small wet-bulb depression and indicates a condition of high relative humidity.

RELATIVE HUMIDITY (RH). The ratio of the partial pressure of the actual water vapor in a mixture to the pressure of a saturated mixture *at the same temperature.* The quantity of moisture showing 40 percent RH at 40 F would only produce about 13 percent at 75 F.

DEW POINT (DP). The temperature at which an air–water vapor mixture will become saturated and begin to yield drops of condensed water. The moisture collecting on the exterior of an uncovered cold-water pipe indicates that the pipe surface temperature is below the dew point of the surrounding mixture. This phenomenon, usually called "sweating," would more correctly be called "condensing."

HUMIDITY RATIO (HR). The weight of the actual water vapor in a mixture per pound of dry air.

ENTHALPY. The total heat in the mixture

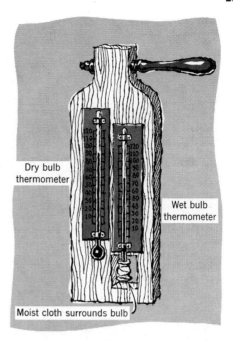

Fig. 16.5   Principle of the sling psychrometer.

measured above zero degrees Fahrenheit and including the latent heat of the water vapor.

SPECIFIC HEAT. The number of Btu required to raise 1 lb of a substance 1 F. For air 0.241 may be used and for water vapor 0.444.

DENSITY. For approximate calculations 0.075 lb per cu ft may be used as the density of air.

6. The Psychrometric Chart. The qualities of mixtures of air and water vapor are summarized graphically in the psychrometric chart. Figure 16.6 is an abridgement of a more complete presentation known as Chart II of the 1961 *ASHRAE Guide and Data Book.* Its use is explained in Fig. 16.7. If, for a selected location (New York City for example), outdoor design conditions are selected (see Table 9.1), other data may be found from Fig. 16.6 as explained in Fig. 16.7. Dry and wet bulb temperatures of 90 F and 76 F respectively will fix values as shown in Fig. 16.7 for dew point, humidity ratio, relative humidity, and

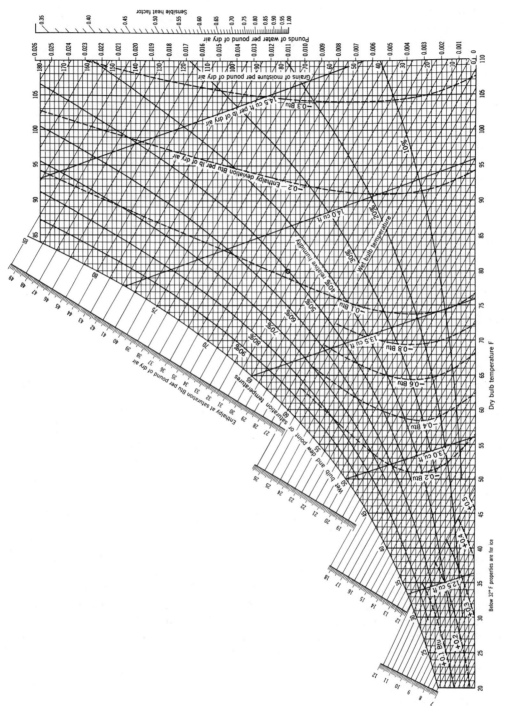

Fig. 16.6   The Psychrometric Chart. (Carrier Corporation)

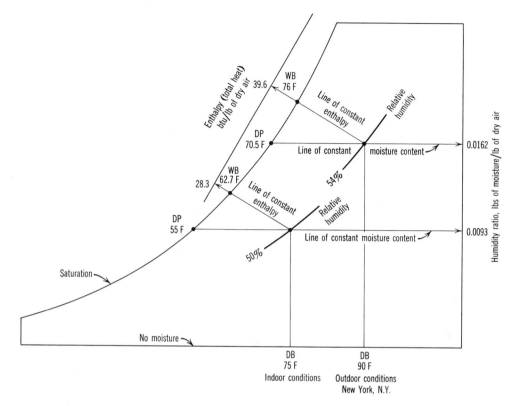

Fig. 16.7   Use of the Psychrometric Chart. Typical indoor and outdoor conditions in summer.

enthalpy. For comparison, indoor conditions are shown on the same drawing.

The psychrometric chart is the working diagram of the air-conditioning engineer. Assume the simple case of a once-through system, using 100 percent outdoor air, all of which is discarded. This method is not as economical as when most of the air is recirculated, but it is used in special cases such as for hospital surgical suites. For every pound of "dry" air (it is not really dry, but the values are based upon the weight of the air alone) that is cooled and dehumidified, 39.6 − 28.3 = 11.3 Btu must be extracted. Similarly, for every pound of air so treated, .0162 − .0093 = .0069 lbs of condensed moisture must be disposed of. The conditioned air must be introduced to the space at conditions of temperature and relative humidity less in value than those of the indoor conditions so that the entering air may "soak up" heat and moisture

Table 16.1   Verification of the Enthalpy Values of Fig. 16.7

Item	Indoor Conditions	Outdoor Conditions
Latent heat, vapor	.0093 × 1061* = 9.90	.0162 × 1061* = 17.25
Sensible heat, vapor	.0093 × .444 × 75 = .31	.0162 × .444 × 90 = .65
Sensible heat, air (1 lb)	1 × .241 × 75 = 18.10	1 × .241 × 90 = 21.70
	Enthalpy (Total Heat) 28.30	39.60

* Latent heat of vaporization Btu/lb (approximate).

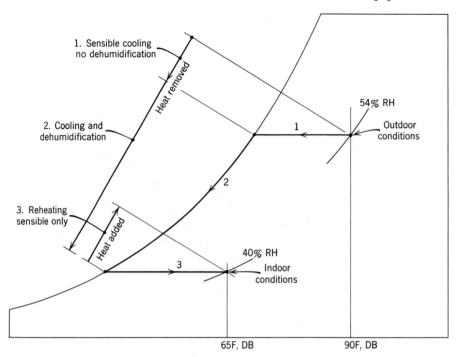

Fig. 16.8   Cooling and dehumidifying outdoor air, summer conditions.

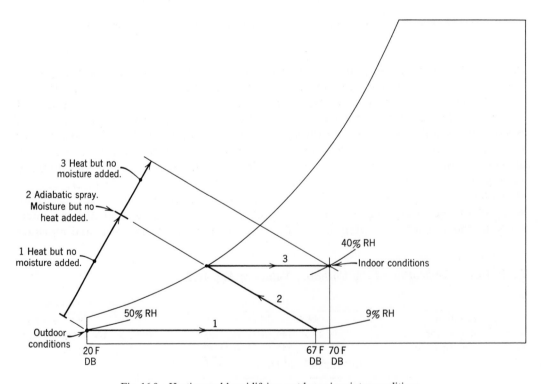

Fig. 16.9   Heating and humidifying, outdoor air, winter conditions.

and leave through the return grills no worse than the design characteristics of 75 F and 50 percent relative humidity. So another set of conditions lower in dry bulb and humidity ratio will be established and the values will depend on the rates at which the air is introduced and the amounts of heat and moisture to be absorbed by the air passing through. This heat and moisture is, of course, the sensible, and latent heat gain of the space to be conditioned.

Each pound of moist air contains heat which is, by custom, measured above the value of zero degrees Fahrenheit. It consists of the sensible heat of the air and the water vapor and the latent heat of the water vapor.

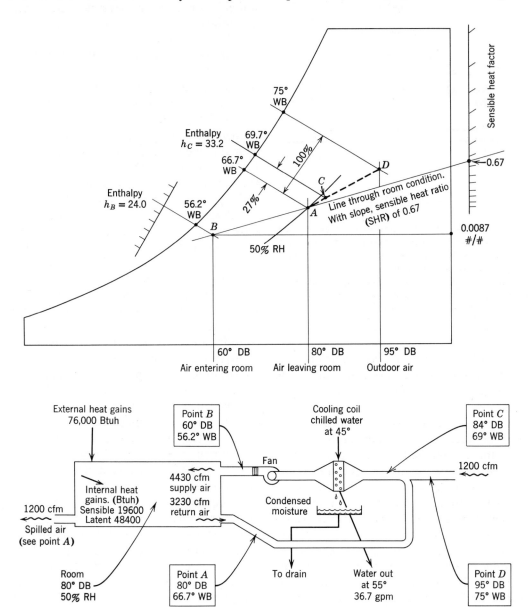

Fig. 16.10 (Example 16.1) Air-handling and cooling calculations for a room for public gatherings. A central station installation is used.

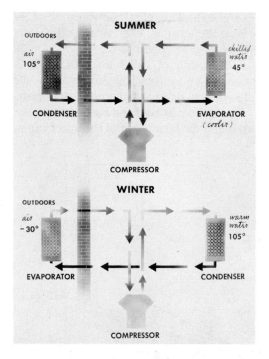

SUMMER

OUTDOORS

air 105°

CONDENSER

EVAPORATOR (cooler)

chilled water 45°

COMPRESSOR

WINTER

OUTDOORS

air -30°

EVAPORATOR

CONDENSER

warm water 105°

COMPRESSOR

Fig. 16.11 An air source heat pump that produces chilled water or hot water for indoor cooling or heating. By an arrangement of valves not shown in this simple diagram, the routing of the refrigerant can be reversed to switch the evaporative and condensing processes between apparatus that remains fixed. (York Division, Borg-Warner Corporation, York, Pa.)

Using 1061 Btu as an average value of latent heat per lb of moisture, one may check the enthalpy values of Fig. 16.7 as shown in Table 16.1.

The cycles of the mixture of air and moisture between the conditioning equipment and the conditioned space bear a resemblance to those of the refrigeration cycle. They are similar in the fact that they each carry heat from one location to another, but different because only the moisture passes through a change of state while the air itself is subject only to *sensible* cooling or heating as evidenced by its change in temperature. In most cases, for economy, the room air is recirculated and only a small amount of fresh outdoor air is added and stale air exhausted. For simplicity, let us consider again a once-through system using all outdoor air for the purpose of further explaining the cycles in both summer and winter. Figure 16.8 shows schematically the lines that trace the possible summer cooling and dehumidifying steps. Air is cooled without loss of moisture until it reaches a temperature at which it is saturated (its dew point). The cooling then continues. The air which had been losing sensible heat in step 1 continues to lose it in step 2, but additionally, moisture is condensed, which also requires the extraction of heat. When step 3 begins (it is known as a reheating process), the remaining smaller amount of moisture and the air are both heated to a condition at which the air temperature and moisture content are slightly below the conditions to be maintained in the room. The changes in the heat content of the air and moisture at the various stages are measured along the enthalpy line. Now refer to Fig. 16.9.

Reference to the psychrometric chart shows that air at low temperatures in winter always has a humidity ratio so low that this moisture content would be unsatisfactory when the mixture was warmed to acceptable room temperature. Moisture must be added. Often this is in the form of a warm spray. For our purpose, however, consider an adiabatic spray (no gain or loss of total heat) accomplished by first warming the outdoor air and vapor to a predetermined temperature, in this case 67 F (step 1). Then it is sprayed with water at room temperature to saturation. During this process (step 2) the added water which is evaporated mechanically draws sensible heat from the air, cooling it. The water acquires an equal amount of latent heat for its change of state to vapor. Thus the value at the enthalpy scale does not change. The saturated mixture is then heated (step 3) with no addition of moisture until, at 70 F, it has a reasonably suitable relative humidity. Again the heat changes are read on the enthalpy scale. The action in Fig. 16.8 is known as cooling and dehumidifying with a reheat process. Fig. 16.9 illustrates a preheat, spray, and reheat arrangement.

7. Air Handling. The use of the psychrometric chart in computing the relationships of heat and air flow when planning the cooling processes of a central station air conditioner is illustrated in the following example:

EXAMPLE 16.1 (Fig. 16.10). A room is used for public gatherings such as cocktail parties and dances. The design requirements are as follows:

Room conditions (summer)	80 F DB, 50% RH
Number of occupants	80 people
Activity	Dancing
Ventilation required	15 cfm per person (Recommendation, 1960 ASHRAE Guide)
Conditions, outdoor air	95 F DB, 75 F WB (New York City, for buildings with occupancy other than residential)

Heat gains in the room	*Sensible Heat (SH)*	*Latent Heat (LH)*
80 people dancing (see Table 9.10)		
80 × 245	19,600	
80 × 605		48,400
Total transmission and solar gain	76,000	
	95,600	48,400
	Room sensible heat (RSH)	Room latent heat (RLH)
		95,600
Total heat gains in room		143,000 Btuh (RSH + RLH)

SOLUTION. Sensible heat ratio

$$(SHR) = \frac{RSH}{RSH + RLH} = \frac{95,600}{143,000} = .67 \quad (1)$$

Point A. Worst condition of air in the room when returned for reprocessing 80 F DB, 50% RH, 66.7 F WB.

Point B. 60 F DB. Air leaving the cooling condition, (assuming a 20F differential). Then read 56.2 F WB and .0087 #/# moisture content.

Air quantity required

$$cfm = \frac{RSH}{1.08 \times \Delta t} = \frac{95,600}{1.08 \times (80 - 60)}$$
$$= 4430 \text{ cfm} \quad (2)$$

1.08 is factor (60 min/hr
    × .075 lb/c.f. avg. air density
    × .241 Btu/lb specific heat of air) = 1.08

Ventilation rate

$$80 \times 15 \text{ cfm/person} = 1200 \text{ cfm} \quad (3)$$

Percentage, outdoor air to total air

$$\frac{1200}{4430} = 27\% \text{ at } 95 \text{ F DB, } 75 \text{ F WB,}$$
$$\text{(Point D)} \quad (4)$$

Establish point B (condition of air entering the room) by connecting point A with .67 on the sensible heat factor scale and extending this sloping line to the vertical line through 60 F DB. Enthalpy (h_B) = 24.0 Btu/lb.

Establish point C (condition of air entering the cooling coil). Connect points A and D and plot point C = 27% of the distance from A to D. Point C represents the condition of the mixture of outdoor air and recirculated air.

Establish temperatures of air mixture

Air air entering the coil (Point C)
DB   .27 × 95F (outdoor)   = 25.6
    .73 × 80F (recirculated = 58.4
                            84.0F DB
WB   .27 × 75F   = 20.3
    .73 × 66.7F   = 48.7
                            69.0F WB

Enthalpy (h_C) of mixture = 33.2 Btu/lb

Heat to be removed
   Cooling coil must remove the following grand total heat (GTH)

$$GTH = 4.5 \times cfm \times (h_C - h_B) \quad (5)$$
$$= 4.5 \times 4430 \times (33.2 - 24.0)$$
$$= 183,500 \text{ Btuh}$$

4.5 is a factor, (60 min/hr
    × .075 lb/cf average air density) = 4.5

Fig. 16.12 The air heat exchanger. This is the outdoor "breathing" element of an air source heat pump at the Miller Fluid Power Division of the Flick-Reedy Corporation plant and offices at Bensenville, Illinois. Six axial-flow suction fans draw air through the brick grill, pass it over finned coils behind the solid wall and eject it above the roof. In summer this air condenses the compressed gas refrigerant which has absorbed the indoor heat. The air is discarded at 105 F. In winter the air gives up some of its heat to the evaporating refrigerant which yields it indoors during the condensing process. The outdoor air is thus refrigerated and wasted at −30 F. The air heat exchanger discards heat in summer and collects it in winter. It is an integral part of the architecture of the building. (York Division, Borg-Warner Corporation.) (From *Progressive Architecture*)

Refrigeration required

$$\frac{183,000}{12,000 \text{ Btuh/ton}} = 15.3 \text{ tons}$$

Chilled water flow rate
   Water enters coil at 45 F, leaves at 55 F (10 F differential)

$$\frac{183,500}{8.33 \text{ lb/gal} \times 60 \text{ min/hr} \times 10 \text{ Btu/lb*}}$$
$$= 36.7 \text{ gpm} \quad (7)$$

   * Specific heat of water = 1 Btu/lb for each 1° F.

8. The Heat Pump. This is a combined air conditioning and heating device powered by electricity and (for heating) drawing a large part of its heat energy from air, water or the ground, making them cooler. As an air conditioner, excess heat taken from the building is "pumped" to these media and disposed of by making them warmer. Thus, to serve the purposes of the building, the *exterior* environment (air, water or earth) is chilled in winter and warmed in summer.

   Each of these three energy sources has been used satisfactorily and each has inherent advantages and disadvantages. The air-source heat pump appears to have been developed more than the other two types. For this reason and for brevity it will be the only one discussed here. In Chapter 15 brief mention was made of the air-source heat pump because it is usually considered a form of electric heating. Some small, individual through-the-wall type units were illustrated and described. They are complete and self-contained, including a compressor, inside and outside heat exchangers, and reversible routing for the refrigerant. They have two shortcomings which have been solved in larger, centralized installations. One is the icing of the outdoor coils in freezing weather. Small units switch to the less efficient resistance heating, but large installations (see Fig. 16.13) use defrosting and continue to use the refrigeration cycle. The other disadvantage is the reduction of efficiency when the temperature of outdoor air drops. Here again the small unit operates by resistance elements, but the principle of multiple (2-stage) compression permits large heat pump installations to continue the refrigeration cycle with good efficiency to temperatures below zero.

The elimination of fuel, flame, chimneys,

Fig. 16.13 Interior view of the outdoor air-heat exchanger. Air enters this chamber through the brick grill, performs its heat exchange function at the finned tubes above and leaves through the roof. The photograph shows a winter condition. As the air is chilled, ice forms. Periodic defrosting is automatic. (York Division, Borg-Warner Corporation.)

Fig. 16.14 Indoor apparatus of the heat pump. (a) Control panels. Supervisory Data Center. See Fig. 16.15. (b) Compressors, arranged in groups of three. See diagram in Fig. 16.15. (c) Cooler-condensers. The refrigerant is evaporated or condensed in these *indoor* heat exchangers to produce chilled (45 F) or warm (105 F) water. (d) Masonry wall encloses outdoor air heat exchanger (Fig. 16.13), the heat transfer elements of which seasonally change their function as do the indoor heat exchangers directly to the left. In this air-to-water installation, chilled or heated water is produced for use in indoor air handling units. It is thus really an air-to-water-to-air installation. The final product is cool or warm air. Note air ducts above. (York Division, Borg-Warner Corporation.)

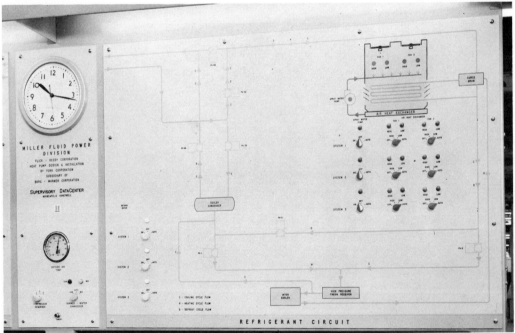

Fig. 16.15 Minneapolis-Honeywell Supervisory Data Center renders the entire heat pump almost entirely automatic. Note symbol for rotary compressor No. 3 which starts up to supplement the others for multiple compression when the temperature drops below 15 F. This center is at station (a) in Fig. 16.14.

and combustion air and at an operating cost, in general, less than that of electric resistance heating has made the heat pump popular. In many cases where fossil-fuel heating and full air conditioning were contemplated, comprehensive economic studies of the cost of installation, fuel, power, and maintenance have shown the heat pump to be equal or less in cost. Such was the case at the Miller Fluid Division of the Flick-Reedy Corporation plant and offices at Bensenville, Illinois, (Figs. 16.12, 16.13, 16.14, 16.15).

This plant, using only electric power and air, is fully air conditioned in summer and heated in winter. One of the largest in the world, the system serves an industrial and office area of 220,000 sq ft and has an air-conditioning capacity of 640 tons. It has 4 distinct circulation systems. One is the circulation of outdoor air, (see Fig. 16.12), which contributes or accepts heat and is then discarded through the roof. A second is the refrigeration cycle, basically similar to Fig. 16.1, except that it has water on one end (indoors) and air on the other (outdoors). It comprises compressors and heat exchangers, (shell-tube units indoors and fin-tube units outdoors). The indoor shell-tube heat exchangers which, in winter, provide hot water by condensing the refrigerant, operate in summer to chill water which is cooled by the evaporative process which takes place within them at that time. The chilled or heated water forms a third circuit which is pumped between the shell-tube units and the heat-exchange coils of air-handling units. Here there is a heat exchange between water and the air which is circulated by fans to form a fourth series of circulating systems. There are 16 air zones responding to local thermostats.

The compressors, of which there are 3 groups, consist of 2 of the reciprocating type and one of the rotary type in each group. The reciprocating compressors cut in sequentially as the demand increases. In series with them are the rotary compressors which start up when the outdoor air drops below 15 F. This constitutes the 2-stage compression developed by the York Division of Borg-Warner Corporation and adapted in this case by Zay Smith and Associates.

Reference

ASHRAE Guide and Data Book, 1962, American Society of Heating, Air Conditioning and Refrigerating Engineers, 345 East 47 Street, New York 17, New York.

17

Air-Conditioning

Systems

1. Air-to-Air Principles and Application. Figure 16.1 of the *previous* chapter illustrates the basic arrangement of the compression refrigerating cycle. Surrounding both coils (evaporator and condenser) there are systems of circulated water. The evaporator cools the circulated water flowing over it, and the condenser warms the water of the circuit within which it is enclosed. It is not essential to use water for these purposes and, for small local units, air is much more suitable. Air may be circulated freely or in ducts to perform both of the necessary heat-transfer functions. Furthermore, if convenient or necessary, air may be used in one circuit and water in the other. Indeed, this is the case of the air-source heat pump described in Chapter 16. Air passes the coils of Fig. 16.13 of the outdoor heat exchanger, while water in shell-tube units effects the indoor heat exchange (Fig. 16.15c).

Perhaps the simplest of all air-conditioning devices is the through-the-wall conditioner shown in Fig. 17.1. It uses nonducted air taken from the room and blown over the evaporator coils and returned directly to the room, passing up across the glass or generally upward toward the ceiling to avoid causing draughts on occupants. Air for condensing the refrigerant is taken from outdoors and blown across the coils where it picks up the heat rejected by the unit. A baffle separates the two circuits except for a small opening to admit fresh outdoor air for ventilation. Through-the-wall units have largely replaced window units which operate on exactly the same principle.

A good example of one of these individual self-contained room conditioners is given in Fig. 17.2. It is typical in principle of most conditioners of this kind. Note that the compressor is placed on the outdoor side of the baffle which helps to muffle the sound which it makes. These units have been quite popular for use in apartment houses and motels and are being adapted to use in some office buildings. Their good features include the following: Control is in the hands of the occupant or tenant, relieving the management of complaints, making every room an individual zone. If a unit needs servicing it is easy to remove the defective element and insert another. Cooling towers, central chillers, pumps, and pip-

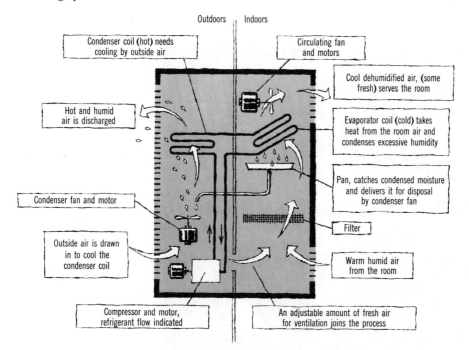

Outdoors | Indoors

Condenser coil (hot) needs cooling by outside air

Circulating fan and motors

Cool dehumidified air, (some fresh) serves the room

Hot and humid air is discharged

Evaporator coil (cold) takes heat from the room air and condenses excessive humidity

Condenser fan and motor

Pan, catches condensed moisture and delivers it for disposal by condenser fan

Outside air is drawn in to cool the condenser coil

Filter

Warm humid air from the room

Compressor and motor, refrigerant flow indicated

An adjustable amount of fresh air for ventilation joins the process

Fig. 17.1 Schematic diagram of the operation of a through-the-wall, air-to-air, conditioning unit. Direct heat-exchange occurs between air and the processes of evaporation or condensation of the refrigerant. The unit is quite self-contained requiring only access to outdoor air and an electrical connection that powers the motors of 2 fans and a compressor. The usual capacities are about 1 or 2 tons of refrigeration (12,000 or 24,000 Btuh).

ing for chilled and condenser water are all avoided, saving space and making unnecessary the services of a resident operating engineer. Among the disadvantages, the following may be listed: A compressor so close to the occupied space will always create some sounds while a remote central chiller would be inaudible. Room units have a somewhat shorter useful life than that of central plants. Large outdoor grills sometimes present problems in architectural design.

Central air-conditioning units in parallel with warm air furnaces are frequently chosen for use in residences. These are of a design similar to that of through-the-wall units but are usually manufactured for larger tonnages. They are arranged to have the condenser-half of the unit projecting beyond the buildings line and a fan on the evaporator-half of sufficient power to cope

with the static head of a conventional duct system. Reference is made to the Azzarone Residence (see Figs. 17.3, 9.4, 9.5 and 11.13). The heat gain calculations for this house made in Chapter 9 show that 72,000 Btuh should be removed. Since about half of this is the gain in the living-dining-kitchen area, two 3-ton units were chosen, one for this area generally south and one for the balance of the house, generally north including the lower story (Fig. 11.13), a perimeter-duct section of this cooling and heating system. The horizontal ducts serving the upper story from a position at the ceiling below it are shallow and well insulated underneath, especially where they pass above outdoor areas. The terminal branches turn up into floor registers below glass in the upper story. By means of this 2-zone conditioning system, either or both of the units can operate in response to thermo-

(*a*) Equipment assembly swung out from the wall sleeve.

(*b*) View of the mechanism of the unit seen from the room side.

Fig. 17.2   An air-to-air unit applying the principle diagrammed in Fig. 17.1. The addition of a steam coil (6) just above the cooling coil makes this unit operable for both summer and winter comfort. Control of both is at panel (8). Steam and condensate pipes of the building serve coil (6). Numbered parts are further identified on the opposite page. (American Standard.)

stats that control the 2 divisions of the house. Air is drawn back from only 2 locations—a side-wall grill in the lower hall and from a plenum below the guest coat closet in the upper hall.

Louvers *A* and *B* operate to close on light air pressure from the corresponding cooling unit, which channels the effect of the unit into its own zone. During the heating season, both *A* and *B* open to pass warm air from the furnace to supply all ducts. Air speeds are higher in summer than in winter because of the greater cfm required for cooling. This was discussed in Ex. 11.2.

In this residence it was convenient and inconspicuous to have the cabinets project through a heavy masonry wall below an overhang. When such a projection is undesirable, a divided unit may be obtained. The evaporator-half is then located in the utility room and the condenser-half remotely located on the roof or behind garden planting. Connection between halves is by 2 lengths of small copper tubing which carries the refrigerant.

2. Water as a Vehicle for Heat Transfer. In architecture, compactness of equipment is a highly valuable quality. Air moving in ductwork at normal velocities (900 to 1200 fpm) calls for ducts of rather bulky proportions. Piped water is a much more convenient method of transferring heat, especially where considerable distance is involved. Except in the case of high velocity air systems, (see Art. 4), central air handling units and the ducts that relate to them must necessarily be somewhat limited in scope. In large buildings, therefore, it is customary to pipe chilled water to dispersed air-handling assemblies that distribute and recirculate air quite locally.

Space is at a great premium in apartment

Manufacturer's Statement of Design Features

1. Wall sleeve with integral flashing pan and anodized aluminum louver permits standardized installation regardless of application. This assembly becomes "part of the building." The flashing pan provides a solid base for the chassis and a moisture-proof drain surface for masonry protection.

2. Air-cooled condenser has an extra-large surface area for maximum cooling capacity with minimum power consumption. Design complies with ARI requirements governing cooling performance under high outside temperatures and undervoltage conditions.

3. Condenser fan is equipped with a slinger ring (SR), for atomizing condensate over the warm condenser. With the SR unit there is no condensate drip, under the severe conditions set up by the ARI code on condensate disposal.

4. Hermetically sealed motor-compressor assembly is spring mounted and located in the wall for quiet operation.

5. Removable Chassis is sturdily constructed, with gussetted corners for added strength, and designed for balanced component arrangement. Chassis center for gravity is within the wall sleeve. Insulated bulkhead is a sound and thermal barrier and isolates the compressor and condenser from the room.

REFER TO FIG. 17.2.

6. Universal header-type steam-heating coil, directly above the evaporator coil, has provision for either right or left and upfeed or downfeed connections. Concealed flared copper tube connections are made inside the cabinet. A separate coil of serpentine construction is furnished for hot water applications, in place of the steam coil. The heating coil is *not* immediately under the discharge grill, contributing to a lower temperature of the exposed metal cabinet and grill.

7. Quiet operating evaporator fan assembly consists of 2 double-inlet, statically and dynamically balanced, large, slow-speed centrifugal fans mounted directly on the motor shaft. Slow fan speed provides superior heating performance.

8. Built-in control panel is always located on the right hand side of chassis. Access is through a flush-mounted door, from the top or front, dependent on cabinet style.

9. Conditioned air outlet has adjustable louvers in the cabinet, to permit adjustable air deflection with top discharge models. Front outlet models with fixed cabinet grill are also available. On the top outlet models, the adjustable grills are removable by taking out four screws, a handy feature allowing easy cleaning out of any foreign matter that might fall through the grill. Fresh and return air are filtered and mixed before passing over *both* the heating and the cooling coils with both models.

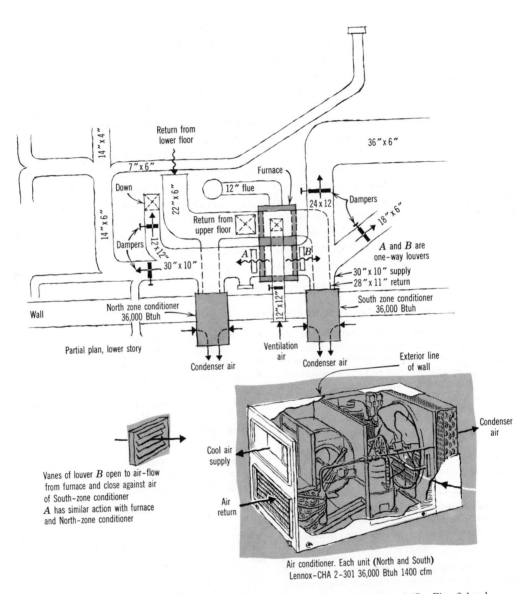

Return from
lower floor

14" x 4"

36" x 6"

7" x 6"

Down

22" x 9"

12" flue

Furnace

24 x 12

Dampers

14" x 6"

Return from
upper floor

18" x 6"

Dampers

12x12"

30" x 10"

A

B

A and B are
one-way louvers

30" x 10" supply
28" x 11" return

Wall

North zone conditioner
36,000 Btuh

12"x12"

South zone conditioner
36,000 Btuh

Partial plan, lower story

Ventilation
air

Condenser air

Condenser air

Exterior line
of wall

Condenser
air

Cool air
supply

Vanes of louver B open to air-flow
from furnace and close against air
of South-zone conditioner
A has similar action with furnace
and North-zone conditioner

Air
return

Air conditioner. Each unit (North and South)
Lennox-CHA 2-301 36,000 Btuh 1400 cfm

Fig. 17.3   Air conditioning, Azzarone residence. (Bentel and Bentel, Architects) (See Figs. 9.4 and 9.5.)

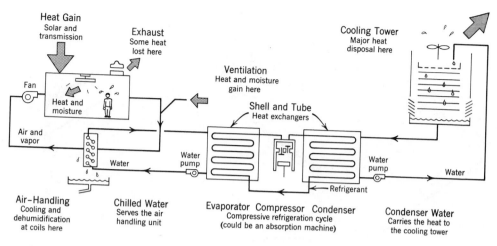

Fig. 17.4   In most large central systems, water is the vehicle that extends the effects of the refrigeration cycle. Circulated water carries heat from the room via the air-handling unit to the refrigeration unit and a similar water circuit carries it to the cooling tower for disposal. *This* diagram includes only the *cooling* processes of an air conditioning system. For appearance of absorption machine, water pumps and cooling tower, see Figs. 17.9, 17.10, and 17.11.

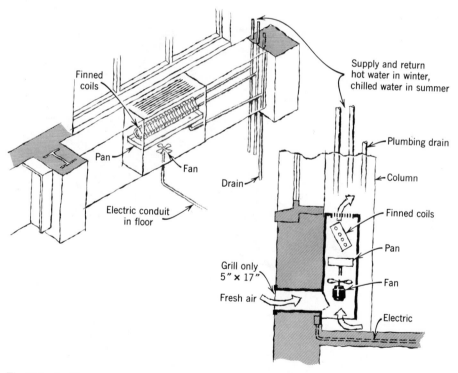

Fig. 17.5   In this case the air-handling unit is a cabinet in a below-the-sill element. A small fresh-air grill provides ventilation, but the major air motion is recirculation of room air for cooling (or heating). For simplicity of presentation, valves and controls are omitted. In contrast to through-the-wall operation, this central system takes the compressor out of the room-unit to supply chilled water from its central (utility room) location.

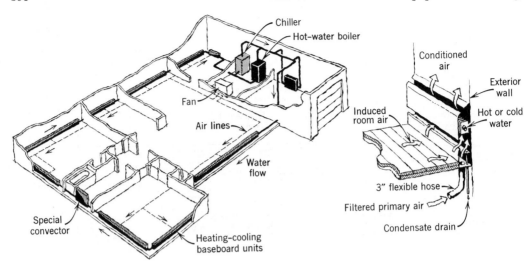

Fig. 17.6 A *hydronic* (heating and cooling by piped water) installation utilizing finned baseboard. A small amount of outdoor primary air doubles to afford ventilation and also to provide induction for better circulation of the room-air over the fins of the baseboard tubing. This is one of many contributions to air-conditioning progress promoted by the Better Heating Cooling Council.

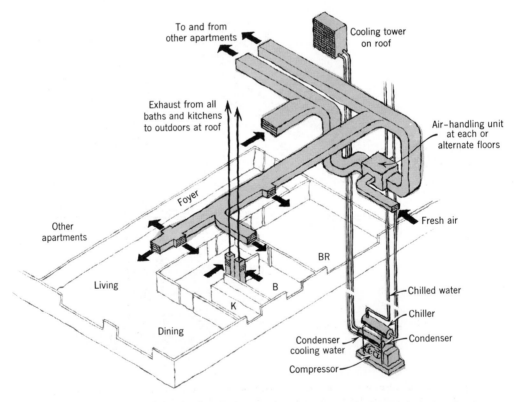

Fig. 17.7   The compactness of water-to-terminal-cabinet systems (see Fig. 17.5), is lost when ducts are used as shown here. Bulkiness of horizontal ductwork has made this method little used in apartment houses though it is suitable in office buildings where furred ceiling space is needed for other reasons (recessed lighting and sprinklers).

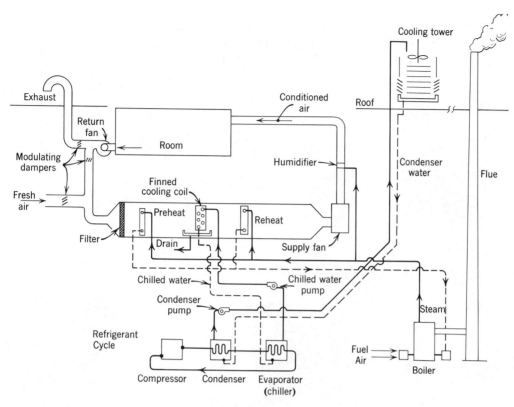

Fig. 17.8   Schematic diagram of some of the principal components of a central station air conditioning plant for year-round operation.

buildings, where dropped ceilings are not favored. Figure 17.5 shows a cabinet containing a fan-coil unit. It may be classified as an air-handling unit of very small scale. With no ducts at all, it has also the advantage of quieter operation than that of through-the-wall units with compressors. The small dimensions of the outdoor grill may be favored over the size of the grill for units which need to draw in and discharge condenser air.

There can be great variations in the relative distances to be traversed by ductwork, chilled water circuits, and condenser water circuits. Their lengths will depend upon the placing of the components that they serve. Every installation involves special study and the field is wide open for imaginative planning. Using Fig. 17.4 as a basic frame of reference, it is possible to interpret and ap-

praise existing systems and to plan new ones. There are a great many possible variations. Absorption can replace compression. River water can supplant the cooling tower (see Fig. 18.13), and high-velocity air can be used instead of low-velocity air. Air-conditioning methods are in a continual state of change and improvement. Better methods can appear for the solution of any problem, and certain systems lend themselves more appropriately than others to special architectural conditions. The mechanical engineer can contribute much in the early stages of planning.

3. Central Station Systems. A complete air-conditioning system for summer and winter use, employing chilled water and steam in a central station plant is shown in Fig. 17.8. The space designated as "room" represents the entire building and the single

Fig. 17.9   An absorption machine for producing chilled water. Carrier Corporation. Courtesy of Ingersoll-Rand.

supply and return ducts are symbolic of an entire network of ducts.

Chilled water may be supplied by a compression refrigeration cycle employing a centrifugal compressor of the type pictured in Fig. 16.3 and included in Fig. 17.8, or by an absorption machine. One of these appears in Fig. 17.9.

Pumps of the centrifugal type are commonly used to circulate chilled water and condenser water. A construction photograph (Fig. 17.10), shows some of these in place.

Cooling towers of the type shown in Fig. 17.11 use up (vaporize) some water to cool the balance of the circulated condenser water. An arrangement is therefore needed to add *make-up water* as required. Despite this *small* water use, the cooling tower is considered to conserve city water supplies which must not be squandered in large air conditioning plants for once-through condenser cooling and then be wasted.

4. High Velocity Systems. If air is delivered at a velocity of 3000 or more fpm (ft per min) instead of the more usual 1000 to 1500 fpm, ducts can be very much smaller. Obviously fans must be more powerful and problems are faced concerning noises that can be caused by this fast moving air. These are solved by routing the air through a box performing a function similar to an automobile muffler. These units lined with acoustically absorbent material reduce the sounds to acceptable levels before the air is discharged into the room (see Fig. 17.13).

The dual-duct high velocity system (see Figs. 17.12 through 17.15) solves a lot of general problems that had existed in tall buildings as well as in buildings of moderate size. In addition to the much smaller size of ducts, it has the unique characteristic of making both heating and cooling available in different (often closely adjacent) parts of a building. The need for this can occur when, on a reasonably mild day of about 40 F, sun through east or west glass can make cooling necessary while the north (sunless) glass can lose heat so rapidly that heating will be required. Another instance is at midwinter on a very cold cloudy day. All perimeter elements are providing heat. Concurrently, in a crowded interior conference room or auditorium the heat and moisture gain from people can require cooling to maintain comfortable conditions. These selections can be made when cool air is delivered at all seasons together with warm air at room temperature in summer and warmer than this in winter. This is done by a thermostat and implemented by the high velocity attenuation and blending units, (Fig. 17.13), each of which delivers air at a temperature called for by the local thermostat that controls it. Thus small zones are created which deal with localized heat gains or losses.

The small high velocity ducts are a great advantage in tall buildings, permitting vertical risers of many stories without excessive bulk. Return air at normal velocities and pressures is often exhausted through ceil-

Fig. 17.10 Electric motors drive these centrifugal pumps for circulation of condenser water and chilled water. Ingersoll-Rand Corporation.

Fig. 17.11   A cooling tower serving a large building. Condenser water is delivered to this unit by pumps. (Ingersoll-Rand Corporation.)

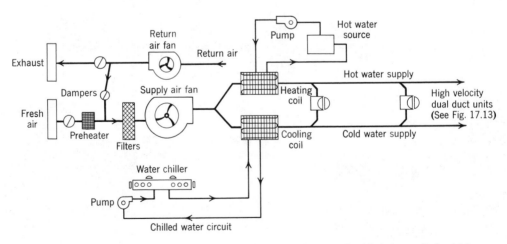

Fig. 17.12   Principle of the dual-duct high velocity method. Hot and cold air is supplied at high velocity through small ducts. Return air is drawn back by its own fan at low velocity (larger ducts). Fresh air, exhaust, and recirculation are all provided for. (Anemostat Corporation of America.)

Fig. 17.13 High-velocity dual-duct unit. Terminal mixing and attenuation (pressure and sound reduction) unit for dual-duct high-velocity systems. Pneumatically controlled from a thermostat, it blends and delivers air at selected temperature. These constant volume units provide accurate constant volumetric delivery at each outlet of the system even though the pressure in the hot and cold ducts may vary widely. The units have simple automatic controls, consisting of a thermostat and a pressure sensitive membrane, both acting through a system of simple mechanical linkages. (Anemostat Corporation of America.)

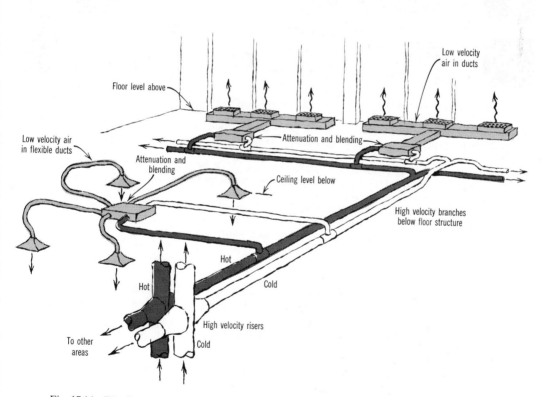

Fig. 17.14 Distribution of high velocity dual ducted air for use at perimeter (above) and interior spaces (at left) through attenuation boxes (see Fig. 17.13). Air streams are mixed and diffused after reduction of sound and velocity. Each blending unit serves a separately controllable zone. Three zones are shown here. (Anemostat Corporation of America)

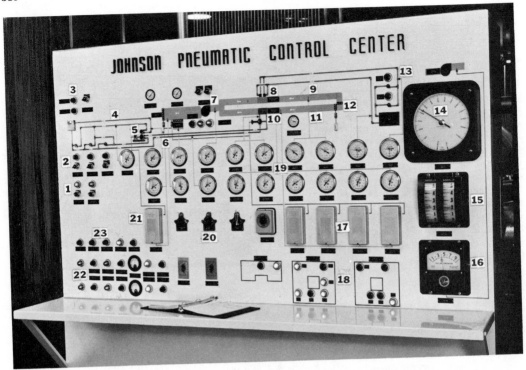

Fig. 17.15 Dual-duct high-velocity control center. The operating engineer no longer has to make trips to remote equipment, dials and gauges. All are assembled in a single panel. Pneumatically operated center for supervision and control, Dorr-Oliver Building, Stamford, Conn. 1. Exhaust-fan controls. 2. Pump controls. 3. Cooling-tower controls. 4. Refrigerant circuit. 5. Compressors. 6. Chilled-water circuit. 7. Fans (Nos. 1 and 2). 8. Heating coils. 9. Hot air (hot "deck"). 10. Cooling coils. 11. Cold air (cold "deck"). 12. Air blending. 13. Fuel-oil system. 14. Fuel-oil gauge. 15. Draft over the fire. 16. Flue temperature. 17. Automatic-damper controls. 18. Lights come on to indicate operation of major air zones. 19. Twenty dials (temperatures): outdoor air, recirculated air, hot air, cold air, chilled water, condensed water, etc. 20. Switches: winter-summer, day-night, clock operation. 21. Chilled-water temperature regulator. 22. Blower control. 23. Air compressor pilot lights, (Compressed air operates this *pneumatic* control system).

ing grills into a plenum between ceiling and the floor structure above it, or by systems of return ducts of conventional size. Vertical return ducts, also of conventional size, carry the air, usually through the building core, to the return air fan. From there it is recirculated or exhausted. A characteristic of modern air-conditioning systems is the flexibility possible in the flow rates of fresh outdoor air, recirculated air and exhausted air.

Round ducts offer small frictional resistance and are commonly used in this system.

The flexibility of those serving the interior areas allows for office changes with easy relocation of ceiling diffusers. Two common methods of air delivery are the ceiling diffuser, which creates a plane of conditioned and induced air at the ceiling without draughts on occupants, and the floor registers near exterior glass for delivery of air to cope directly with solar heat gains or losses.

The central control panel (see Fig. 17.15), similar in principle to such panels for any modern mechanical system, illustrates

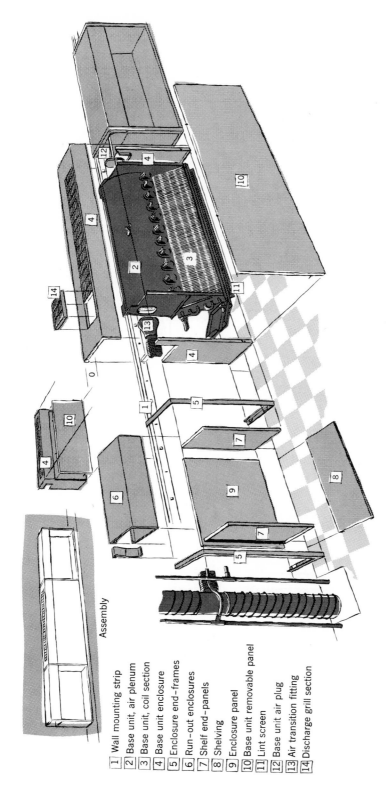

Assembly

1 Wall mounting strip
2 Base unit, air plenum
3 Base unit, coil section
4 Base unit enclosure
5 Enclosure end–frames
6 Run–out enclosures
7 Shelf end–panels
8 Shelving
9 Enclosure panel
10 Base unit removable panel
11 Lint screen
12 Base unit air plug
13 Air transition fitting
14 Discharge grill section

Fig. 17.16 High-velocity induction system. Conditioned outdoor air for ventilation and to induce circulation of room air is brought in through a single high-velocity duct. It is attenuated and silenced in the chamber (2) and then, through jets in the front of this plenum, it induces flow of room air which is heated or cooled at finned coil (3). (Carrier Corporation)

311

Fig. 17.17 General distribution systems of the high-velocity induction method of air conditioning. Conditioned fresh air (once through, *not* recirculated) provides ventilation, controls air quality and humidity, and induces, through jets, the secondary circulation of room air. This air-flow at the cabinet is warmed or cooled to selected temperature by hot or chilled water at controlled rates. (Carrier Corporation)

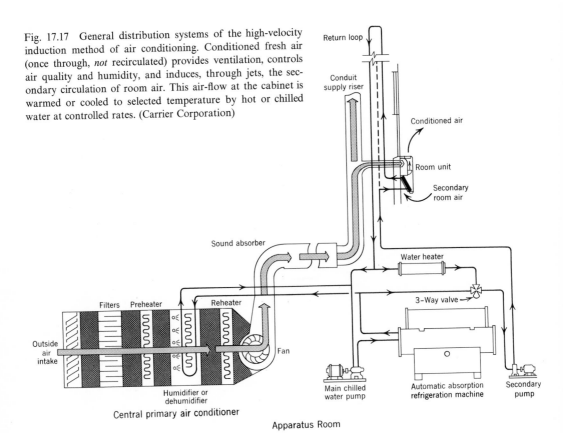

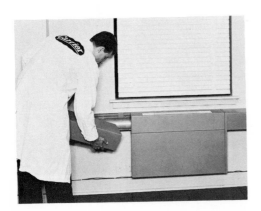

Fig. 17.18 Placing the lateral branch of the high-velocity duct that conveys ventilation air to the central induction unit through which room air is circulated and conditioned.

Fig. 17.19 Induction unit assembled as part of bookshelf arrangement.

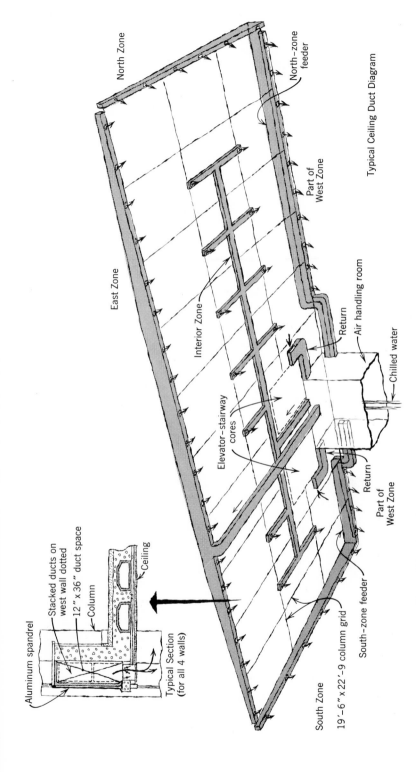

Fig. 17.20 Luz Electrica Building, Caracas, Venezuela. Lathrop Douglass, Architect; Sidney Barbanel, Mechanical Engineer. The classic four-zone perimeter distribution of conditioned air is achieved in this building by ducts entirely outside the structural spandrels and above the structural soffit of each ceiling. In a space between the upturned spandrel beam and an exterior skin of insulated aluminum, the ducts distribute air laterally. The windows are blanketed by a down-flow from grills that are flush with the ceiling. By a careful choice of a location for the air-handling room on each floor, only the eastern zone required a supply duct that crossed from the core to the spandrel laterals. In this way an uncluttered ceiling was assured.

313

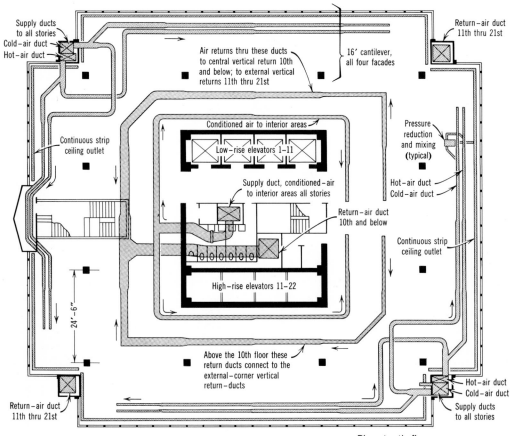

Supply ducts
to all stories
Cold–air duct
Hot–air duct

Air returns thru these ducts
to central vertical return 10th
and below; to external vertical
returns 11th thru 21st

16' cantilever,
all four facades

Return–air duct
11th thru 21st

Continuous strip
ceiling outlet

Conditioned air to interior areas

Low–rise elevators 1–11

Pressure
reduction
and mixing
(typical)

Hot–air duct
Cold–air duct

Supply duct, conditioned–air
to interior areas all stories

Return–air duct
10th and below

Continuous strip
ceiling outlet

24' – 6"

High–rise elevators 11–22

Above the 10th floor these
return ducts connect to the
external–corner vertical
return–ducts

Hot–air duct
Cold–air duct

Supply ducts
to all stories

Return–air duct
11th thru 21st

Plan, tenth floor

the inter-relation of the various elements and the methods of checking and controlling them. These parts include boiler, refrigeration, cooling tower, air handling, as well as the controlling elements in and near the conditioned spaces.

A very interesting, compact and efficient high velocity air-conditioning method is the induction system (see Figs. 17.16 through 17.19). Instead of carrying all of the air back to a central air handling unit as is done in the dual duct system, room air is recirculated through a cabinet below a window. A small amount of fully conditioned outdoor air for ventilation is brought in through a single high velocity duct. After attention it flows through jets to induce circulation and permit temperature regulation of room air. In principle this resembles the method shown in Fig. 17.5 except that the ventilation air makes the fan unnecessary and eliminates the need for an outdoor ventilating grill for fresh air. Similarity to Fig. 17.6 may also be noted. In that scheme, primary fresh air induces flow of room air over finned baseboard which is heated or cooled according to season.

5. Air Distribution in Buildings. Consider a small office somewhere in the massive bulk of a modern office building. Air for its use is often treated in a remote spot in the penthouse or in a mechanical floor. Then it has to be delivered past structural floors, hung ceilings, core partitions, and office partitions to the air-conditioned room. After use it has to be returned just as surely to the air-handling unit. Except in the most special cases, air is never used just once and then discarded. Even after use the air is much more valuable thermally than outside air.

Economics demands its re-use. Ducts to and from the small office are bulky.

There is a continuous struggle to avoid the bulk of the passages through which air must flow. Various solutions have appeared. High velocity has reduced duct sizes. Additional mechanical floors have been added so that the central apparatus could be closer to the spaces served. Supplying just a little (ventilation) air and recirculating the air already in the room has been developed (see Figs. 17.5, 17.6, and 17.16). Using a central air-handling unit on each floor (see Fig. 17.7) makes vertical ducts unnecessary.

The last mentioned solution, that of placing air handling at each story to eliminate major vertical feeders was used in the Luz Electrica Building (see Fig. 17.20). One of the first large buildings in Caracas to be fully air-conditioned, it follows the South American trend to the use of reinforced concrete. Since little use was made of hung ceilings, the horizontal ducts were efficiently enclosed in spaces between an upturned concrete spandrel beam and an aluminum skin. The ceiling is left quite clear except for one feeder to the east zone and a small neat duct-pattern of the interior zone and the returns.

Three other schemes using vertical, high velocity feeder ducts have offered new solutions to this space problem. The first (see Fig. 17.21) is in the International Building where the dual-duct feeders are enclosed in nonstructural vertical towers at diagonally opposite corners of the building. At the alternate corners, air is returned through matching vertical elements. Pressure reducing and mixing boxes at the perimeter ceiling serve, not individual diffusers, but a con-

---

←——— Fig. 17.21 International Building, San Francisco, California. Anshen and Allen, Architects; Eagelson, Engineers (Charles Krieger, E.E.), Mechanical Designers. In this ingenious scheme, the major supply arteries for conditioned air have been located in alternate corners. In diagonally opposite locations, supply risers are placed in large square enclosures. Though nonstructural, each enclosure is emphasized as a distinct vertical design element. Each encloses both hot- and cold-air ducts which supply two separately controlled orientations on all of the 21 stories. Conditioned air originates at an intermediate floor, the third. In the opposite two corners, similar ducts return much of the air to the equipment story. The balance is returned through duct risers in the core.

Fig. 17.22   Blue Cross-Blue Shield Building, Boston, Massachusetts. Anderson, Beckwith and
Haible and Paul Rudolph, Associated Architects; Stressenger, Adams, Maguire and Reidy,
Mechanical and Electrical Engineers. The two-story Y-shaped forms are structural columns which
divide at mezzanine level and continue to rise in pairs to form the exterior skeleton frame. Hollow
channels on the exterior of each pair enclose, individually, a hot-air supply duct and a cold-air
supply duct. These round, high-velocity ducts join for mixing and velocity reduction in attenuation
boxes, located between columns at each floor. Conditioned air is discharged upward from a window-
sill grill above the box. A mullion between each pair of structural columns originates at the second-
floor level and extends to the mechanical story at the roof. This mullion encloses a return-air duct
which draws air through grills in the sills of the two adjacent windows on each story. Thus the air is
delivered at the exterior, accomplishes its mission at that surface, and returns in the same vertical
plane to the suction side of fans on the roof.

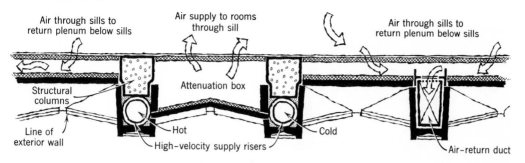

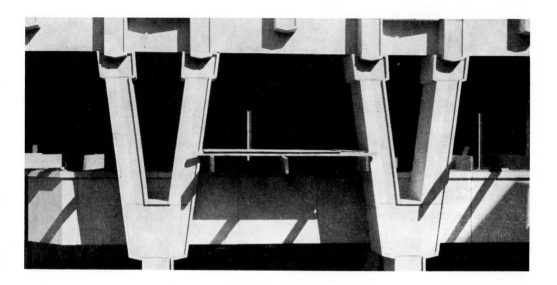

tinuous strip ceiling outlet that downfeeds air directly in the plane of the glass. Interior spaces are supplied and exhausted by concealed lateral ducts connected to vertical low-velocity ducts in the core.

In the Blue Cross–Blue Shield Building (Fig. 17.22), all of the ducts that supply the perimeter are overlaid in a vertical pattern on the *outside* of the structure. It bears some resemblance in principle to the Luz Electrica solution (Fig. 17.20), except that, instead of a horizontal pattern of exterior low velocity supply ducts, it presents a vertical pattern of exterior high-velocity (hot and cold) supply ducts as well as low-velocity return ducts. Each column and mullion is utilized.

Designers have found that there is usually too much bulk involved in the ducts for the air needed at glass facades to route them all to and from the central interior building core shaft across and above hung ceilings. One sees in the Medical Towers Building (Fig. 17.23) a solution, in which vertical feeders are *at* the perimeters. In this case they are at both *ends* of a long narrow tower. Four pairs of verticals supply four pairs of laterals at each story. In this and other buildings using the dual-duct method, divisions in the horizontal distributions systems are largely for convenience and are not considered zones in quite the same sense as when a single stream of air is delivered. Since the final choice of a temperature can

Fig. 17.23 Medical Towers Building, Houston, Texas, Goleman and Rolfe, Houston, with Skidmore, Owings and Merrill, Consulting Architects; Bernard Johnson and Associates, Consulting Engineers. Air conditioning for the tower section of this building originates in 2 air-handling units in the tall top story. Downfeed vertical supply ducts fit into vertical planes at the ends of the building. Below each floor in a horizontal plane are the lateral distribution branch ducts. A dual-duct high velocity system, it comprises pairs (one hot, one cold) of downfeed supplies and dual horizontal branches for each quarter of the building. At offices, all air is distributed down from the ceiling after attenuation and blending. Return air at low velocity flows through ceiling plenums to vertical ducts at the core for return to the penthouse units which are supplied with steam and chilled water from the basement.

be made by the thermostat that controls the dual-duct blending unit, the zoning arrangement is a little more independent of orientation, the importance of which is so much in evidence in the Luz Electrica Building (Fig. 17.20).

6. Rooftop Equipment. Reference is made to the photograph opposite the title page of this book. On the roof of the Chase Manhattan Bank Building and screened by the three-story louvered enclosure, a mechanical "village" can be seen. Predominant are nine cooling towers. It also includes a diesel-powered emergency electric generator, enclosures for elevator hoisting machinery and for condenser-water pumps, water storage tanks, and kitchen exhaust vent. Circling them all is a railroad which provides tracks for a window-washing rig that is lowered from cantilever cranes to permit cleaning of the glass facades. Consulting engineers for this building were Jaros, Baum and Bolles.

NOTE: Figures 17.1, 17.5, 17.6, 17.7, 17.15, 17.20, 17.21, 17.22, and 17.23, were reprinted by courtesy of *Progressive Architecture* from the monthly page "Mechanical Engineering Critique" and from other articles.

References

1. *Residential and Commercial Air Conditioning,* Charles H. Burkhardt, McGraw-Hill Book Company, Inc., New York.
2. *Air Conditioning and Refrigeration,* Severns-Fellows, John Wiley and Sons, Inc., New York.

18

District Heating
and Cooling

1. Reasons for Greater Centralization. Counting the chimney pots of a residence built before the advent of central heating, one finds that there was a flue for a fireplace in nearly every room. Though an open fire is a romantic and charming thing, much used up to the present day, the problems of fuel distribution, ash removal, house cleaning, chimney cleaning, and fire hazard were very great when winter comfort depended solely on open fires. Centralization into a single fire in each building with heat distribution by steam, air, or water is now taken for granted. Extending this principle, central plants now serve, not merely the rooms of a single building, but many buildings in a group or even in a city. When a related group of buildings operate under the same ownership or even when separate owners agree to pay a metered rate for heating, central plants are built to supply steam or high temperature water for heating and, more recently, chilled water for the cooling processes of air conditioning.

The economies and efficiencies are obvious. One chimney or a very small group of them replace a multitude of individual chimneys which often disgorge soot from smoky fires. Trained personnel on a round-the-clock basis can take pride in efficient and smoke-free combustion and the dignity of a large operation. In the case of dispersed, small heating plants, the care of each is a part time and often an unpleasant chore for janitors and custodians busy with many other responsibilities. Economical purchases of fuel in wholesale quantities and bulk deliveries are advantages. Most important to the owners and operators of the buildings that are served is the elimination of the chimney, fuel storage space, boilers, and boiler rooms. Cleanliness and the release of valuable space open up new possibilities in building management. These developments have changed the architecture of buildings by eliminating bulky mechanical elements and the service requirements of space and access for their maintenance. This has been even more advantageous in the recent distribution of chilled water, resulting in free space at the building that would otherwise be cluttered by water chillers and

Fig. 18.1   Steam distribution system. New York City. Ellipses indicate extensions. Ten waterfront steam generating stations are shown. (Consolidated Edison Co. of New York, Inc.)

the bulky and troublesome cooling towers that serve them.

The educational and administrative buildings at Harvard, over 200 in number, are heated by exhaust steam from a nearby utility power plant with economic advantages to both institutions. Campuses and hospital groups are typically suitable for centralized heating, the pipe distribution network of which is often routed along walk-through tunnels available for service personnel and sometimes for general personnel. Groups of high-rise low-cost housing units in cities are invariably heated from a plant in only one of the several buildings. Utility companies in cities here and abroad sell steam to customers along the routes of their mains. Air Force bases and airports utilize central plants, usually supplying high temperature hot water, and in one city, Hartford, Connecticut, the sale of piped chilled water has taken its place beside the more usual distribution and sale of metered district steam.

2. Steam Distribution in Cities. In many cities in the United States and abroad, building owners find it more economical to buy steam which is generated and distributed by a utility company than to maintain their own plants. A typical example of steam service to users in a large city is that of the Consolidated Edison Company of New York whose elaborate distribution system and many power stations on the island

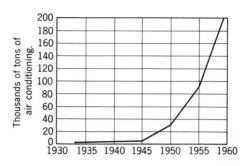

Fig. 18.2   Increase in demand for district steam supplied by Consolidated Edison Company of New York, Inc., for *air-conditioning* purposes (steam-driven compressors and absorption machines).

of Manhattan are shown in Fig. 18.1. This network with its currently proposed extensions shows a tremendous increase since its inception in 1882 when it served 62 buildings, all south of City Hall Park, which may be seen near the lower tip of the island. It is interesting to learn that this early steam system went into operation shortly before electricity was similarly distributed. The growth of a steam utility invariably follows the development of big buildings, though small buildings often make use of the service if they are on the route of an established supply main. The New York system serves three general areas, (1) the financial district which practically coincides with the limits of the entire original nineteenth century network, (2) the more northerly commercial,

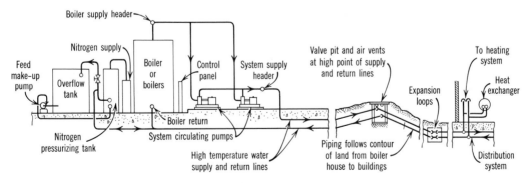

Fig. 18.3   Typical arrangement of a HTW system reprinted from "High-temperature Water Systems," Industrial Press. By Courtesy of author Owen S. Lieberg, Consulting Engineer.

Fig. 18.4   John F. Kennedy International Airport. The central heating and cooling plant is to the
left of the central pool. It is identified as an L-shaped building with a spherical oil-storage tank in its
foreground. (Port of New York Authority.) Drawing by Raniero Corbelletti.

shopping, residential, and hotel area from 14th to 60th Street and (3) the residential areas east and west of the lower part of Central Park where there are many high-rise apartment houses.

The high cost of extending underground mains limits extensions to locations where large consumption may be expected. The original system followed and fostered the development of the skyscraper and its extensions still follow the trend of heavy demand. Unlike electricity and water, the service is not universally available. Since 1945 almost all of the new large commercial buildings along the routes of established mains have chosen this purchased steam for heating and most of them have taken it for cooling (steam refrigeration compressors and absorption machines). Most of the new hotels and apartment houses have done the same. Since a large part of the economy is in the elimination of chimneys and the space for boilers, very few of these new buildings have chimneys or standby equipment of their own or space allocated to the future installation of either. Conversely,

Consolidated Edison Company does not supply standby or breakdown service to buildings already equipped with systems of their own.

An interesting example of the rapid changes that can occur within a utility is seen in Fig. 18.2. This summer load helps to balance the winter seasonal demand and to assure a more uniform operating rate and sales volume throughout the year.

Mains that interconnect between stations supply steam to consumers at 125 psi and in a dry condition. They may use it for power equipment, or, in the case of hospitals, at somewhat reduced pressure for cooking, laundering, sterilization, and, by heat transfer, for domestic hot water. For comfort heating, the entry pressure of 125 psi is often reduced in 2 stages by pressure reducing valves to 5 psi or less which is usual in low-pressure steam heating systems. Conversion to hot water for heating or direct use in steam coils to produce warm air is also possible.

In private plants the water resulting from the condensing of the steam is returned to the boiler for reuse, but in this network distance is a major factor and very little of the condensate is recovered. The user cools it by preheating domestic hot water and by other useful heat recovery operations and then disposes of it, at reduced temperature, to the sewer.

3. High-Temperature Water and Chilled Water for Airports. Though long-distance steam distribution has been used for almost a century, the development of the *high-temperature water* (HTW) principle is measured in several decades and is limited in the United States mostly to the past 10 years. Offering many advantages (though steam is still frequently chosen for city distribution—see Article 4), circulated high-temperature, high-pressure hot water in closed systems has found great favor in Air Force bases and airports, and for groups of buildings such as hospital complexes and those of college campuses. Water will not flash into steam if kept at sufficiently high pressure. It may then be circulated by pumps through supply and return mains and through branches to heat exchangers which

Fig. 18.5   Heating and cooling plant at John F. Kennedy International Airport, New York, N.Y. At left, spherical fuel oil storage tank. Four stacks serve the high-temperature water boilers. Five of the nine absorption refrigeration machines appear through glass at the right. Six cells identify the two cooling tower structures in the rear. Architects: Skidmore, Owings, and Merrill. Engineers: Seelye, Stevenson, Value, and Knecht. (Port of New York Authority.)

Fig. 18.6   Night view of the heating-cooling plant at the John F. Kennedy International Airport. Distinctive colors identify the piping connections to the refrigeration absorption machines. Chilled water, condenser water and, in this case, high temperature water instead of steam, comprise the 3 circuits connected to each of the 9 machines. (Port of New York Authority.)

operate conventional low-pressure hot water systems, generate steam, and perform numerous other thermal tasks. Pressures are of the order of 400 psig (lb per sq in., gauge) and temperatures are about 300 F. During its circuit the water will sometimes lose about 150 F and 60 psig in pressure.

High temperature water has a number of advantages over steam which favor it for certain installations. It is a 2-pipe system and the temperature drop in the *supply* main is often as little as 10 F. By the use of reasonably high water velocities, mains can be reduced to almost half the size of those required for steam distribution. Simplicity results from the lack of need for steam traps and pressure-reducing valves. The pipes need not pitch to low points as in the case of steam but may follow the contours of the ground. Though installation costs are greater, operational costs are less than for steam. Feed water treatment is negligible and corrosion is at a minimum. Underground problems of expansion and insulation are the same as in other subterranean systems. Large sweep-type loops accommodate expansion between fixed points and underground piping is imbedded in special thermally efficient insulative fill.

In planning the heating and cooling for complete air conditioning in the principal buildings of the Kennedy International Airport at Idlewild, the original concept was to have the facilities located in utility space in each of the buildings. However, the advantages of centralizing the basic equipment for both heating and cooling soon became apparent. Under the guidance of Mr. Charles Broder, Mechanical Engineer of the Port of New York Authority, planning moved in this direction. A central heating-cooling plant was designed by Architects Skidmore, Owings, and Merrill and engineered by Seelye, Stevenson, Value, and Knecht. In the final scheme (see Figs. 18.4 and 18.5) all facilities except air handling and ducts were assembled in the central

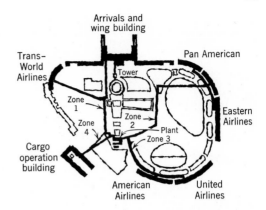

Fig. 18.7 Control terminal area of the John F. Kennedy International Airport showing location of heating and cooling plant and the four zones of distribution for high temperature water and chilled water. Reprinted from "Heating and Air Conditioning a Civilian Airport," by Charles Broder, in *High Temperature Water*, a Symposium Bulletin published by the American Society of Heating and Air-Conditioning Engineers.

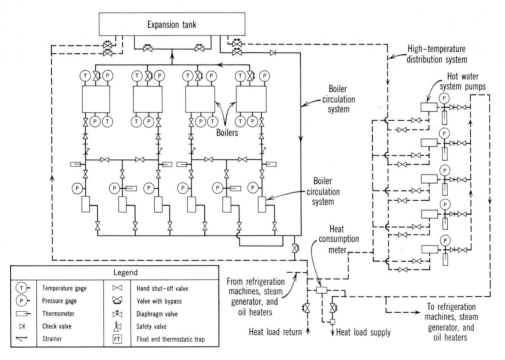

Fig. 18.8 Piping diagram for high-temperature water system showing circulation through boilers and expansion tank and connection to heating load and refrigeration load. John F. Kennedy International Airport, New York. From "Space Heating at Idlewild" by Charles Broder, M.E. in *Industry Power*.

Fig. 18.9   Automatic panels control operation of the Arrivals Building at New York's John F. Kennedy International Airport. Panels at right: central circular dials indicate temperatures of various rooms and of air leaving the local conditioners. Reset of the latter is possible at the dial. Square recorders at top register permanently these temperatures and those of domestic hot water. Panels at left: Motors are started by switches. Their operation is indicated by lights. Panels at left also control all lighting inside and outside of the building. A trouble alarm calls attention to possible difficulties. (Controls by Johnson Service Company and IBM's T. E. Division, recently acquired by Simplex Time Recorder Company.) (Port of New York Authority.)

plant. The elimination of a multitude of stacks, boilers, fuel storage, water chillers, and cooling towers at each building was considered to be a great step forward in the release of valuable space and for cleanliness, control, and architectural freedom. Moreover, it proved to be economically advantageous.

Four La Mont-type International Boiler Works Company high temperature water boilers supply the heating needs and also serve the Carrier absorption refrigeration machines. These were specially adapted to use this high-temperature water instead of steam. Thus the boilers are active throughout the year, burning gas or oil. The latter, No. 6 oil, is stored in the 210,000 gallon spheroid tank adjacent to the plant. Boilers, chillers, and cooling towers are all in close proximity.

Statistics for the plant are as follows:

(*a*) *Hot water:*   160,000,000 Btuh, 1,140,000 lb per hr pump capacity, 160 ft head, 380 F flow, 240 F return.

Fig. 18.10 Aerial perspective of downtown Hartford, Connecticut, shows route of pipelines through which cooling and heating service are supplied from a new Hartford Gas Company plant in the southeast section of the city (upper left). The Connecticut River is at the far left and Constitution Plaza, the city's new $40,000,000 redevelopment project is the dark complex of buildings at the lower left. Other dark-shaded structures to be served include the Travelers Insurance Company Building, the city's tallest structure, in the center of the drawing. Gray buildings at upper right (Bushnell Plaza), top (proposed Federal Building), and upper left, (Riverview Apartments), and others connected by dotted lines indicate new and existing construction which will probably be served by extending the pipelines. Lightly shaded buildings are nearby structures offering a potential area of growth for this service.

Fig. 18.11 Architect's rendering of the heating and cooling plant which contains boilers and refrigeration equipment. Its location with respect to its customer-buildings is shown in Fig. 18.10. Architect: Charles Du Bose, Engineers: Seelye, Stevenson, Value, and Knecht.

(*b*) *Chilled water:* 6210 tons, 16,800 gpm pump capacity, 150 ft head, 55 F to 45 F cooling range.

(*c*) *Condenser water:* 24,600 gpm pump capacity, cooling tower capacity for rated flow from 102.4 F to 85 F with wet bulb at 78 F.

At the ends of the 4 zones for water-distribution, namely the various buildings of the airport group, chilled water and hot water are used in the coils of air-handling units from which conditioned air is circulated for complete climate control. The latest in electronic control equipment was used (see Fig. 18.9 for the panel of the Arrivals Building). Checked periodically, this equipment is all but completely automatic in its regulation of the temperature and humidity throughout the building. Expansion to the central heating and cooling plant is now in progress.

4. District Heating and Cooling. With the growth of new cities and the strong trend toward urban renewal there is every reason to believe that the centralization of mechanical services will increase. Expanding from modest beginnings, private utility companies, as well as muncipal and sometimes state and federal organizations, have assumed responsibility for many vital building services. Gradually buildings have become connected for gas, steam, electricity, telephone and other communications, water supply, and the removal and disposal of sanitary and storm drainage. Counter to the increasing intricacy of modern mechanical equipment, each of these central utility services has *lightened* the burden for building owners and managers and has freed the architect for more flexible designs. A recent development in this movement is the distribution of chilled water, a service which eliminates refrigeration and cooling towers from the building site.

The first instance of district cooling in a city occurred in Hartford, Connecticut.

There the Hartford Gas Company and its subsidiaries have added a service that pumps chilled water through a network of mains for the cooling needs of air-conditioning systems in many buildings. This new medium is purchased by consumers on a metered basis. To make the service complete, steam from the central plant is also piped in parallel fashion. A building owner may purchase steam and chilled water to free his building from a large part of the basic equipment for all-year climate control (see Fig. 18.14). There were several reasons for the choice of steam instead of high-temperature water as the heat-conveying medium. Economic studies showed that the availability of water from the Connecticut River as condensing water made the use

of steam more favorable than high-temperature water. Moreover, the contours of the ground were favorable to the slope and pitch needed in a steam and condensate system. It is an interesting fact that Dr. Willis H. Carrier predicted in 1940 that within 25 years, air-conditioning facilities would be piped to buildings and purchased in a manner similar to that of water or electricity. Hartford reached this goal 3 years before the predicted date.

The impetus for this new movement at Hartford was given by extensive city improvements, planned over a period of 12 years and nearing completion concurrently with the opening of the new plant and its piping system. A number of established buildings, including that of the Travelers

Fig. 18.12 Diagram at left indicates route of underground pipelines through which the world's first utility-operated air-conditioning plant supplies cooling and heating to a large segment of downtown Hartford, Connecticut. At right is one of four Carrier refrigerating machines which provide the chilled water used to cool office buildings located nearly one mile from the plant. Turbine is driven by steam from gas-fired boilers.

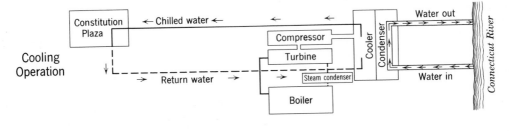

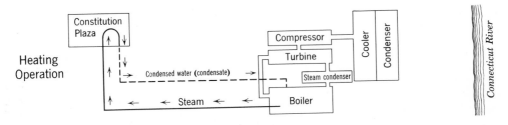

Fig. 18.13 The Connecticut River takes the place of a master cooling tower in the cooling operation of this district heating and cooling service, a departure for the Hartford Gas Company. Its service to the city of Hartford began in 1848 when gas was first distributed.

Insurance Company, the tallest building in the city, use the new service, while further along the line, Constitution Plaza, a group of 6 large new buildings will add to the customer list. Major financing for the Constitution Plaza project was by the Travelers Insurance Company.

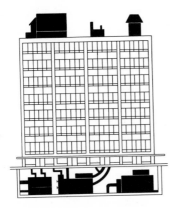

Fig. 18.14 The central system eliminates bulky cooling towers employed in conventional air conditioning. Boiler room equipment and chimneys, are also eliminated, making this space available for other uses.

The scheme not only provides numerous buildings with an economical and labor saving service, it also solves a problem for the Hartford Gas Company. Two Combustion Engineering Company steam boilers with a total output of 150,000,000 Btuh operate *summer and winter* on gas. Gas use in summer has increased sevenfold to equalize seasonal demand. Both boilers are equipped for oil burning to be used occasionally in winter during heavy gas demand by customers. In winter the steam is piped directly to the buildings (see Fig. 18.13). In summer it is used in Carrier refrigeration machines having a total capacity of 6500 tons. They comprise 1 turbine-driven centrifugal machine of 3000 tons capacity, 2 additional turbine-driven centrifugal machines at 1500 tons each, and 1 absorption machine of 500 tons. It will be noted that these capacities for both heating and cooling compare approximately with the corresponding loads at the John F. Kennedy International Airport (see Article 3). Increases in both installations are contem-

Fig. 18.15 Air-conditioning service from the central plant, the first installation of a utility-metered cooling source, has been initiated for buildings in and near Constitution Plaza. Left to right, clockwise: Phoenix Mutual Insurance Company, One Constitution Plaza, 100 Constitution Plaza, North Office Building, Hotel America, and Broadcast House. This model includes minor changes from original scheme of Fig. 18.10. Associated Architects: Charles Du Bose, Emery Roth and Sons.

plated. At Hartford, a jump to 15,000 tons is expected, which may make it the largest single cooling plant in the world.

Insulated underground piping for the chilled water is of 24 in. diam for both supply and return, while the insulated underground pipes for steam and for the condensate return are 12 in. and 5 in. respectively. All lines are buried at depths varying from 2 to 10 ft below the surface. The cost of the initial plant installation with its equipment and distribution piping was about $4,500,000.

Figures 18.9 and 18.10 are from *Progressive Architecture*.

References

1. "Steam Talk," Consolidated Edison Company, 4 Irving Place, New York, New York.
2. *High-Temperature Water*, a Symposium Bulletin, American Society of Heating, Air Conditioning, and Refrigerating Engineers, 345 East 47 Street, New York 17, New York.
3. "High Temperature Water Systems," Owen S. Lieberg, The Industrial Press, New York, New York.

19

Lighting

Fundamentals

1. Light and Architecture. An artificial dichotomy exists in the field of lighting design dividing it into two distinct parts; utilitarian lighting and architectural lighting. Architects often somewhat condescendingly declare the former to be the province of engineers and the latter theirs, and vice versa. Yet this separation need not, and in fact should not, exist. The competent lighting designer will make his utilitarian lighting complement the architecture, since architectural lighting often serves a utilitarian purpose, as well as aesthetic. The distinction between the two types of lighting thus disappears and the ultimate actual purpose, i.e. to utilize light as an architectural building material in the construction of a utilitarian space, is realized.

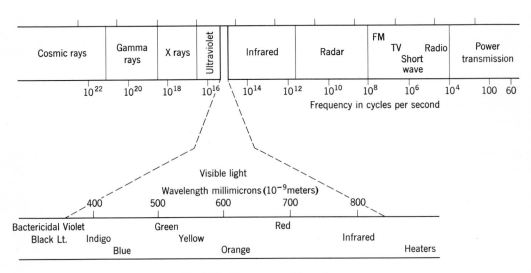

Fig. 19.1   Electromagnetic spectrum.

To touch upon only a few of the usual items in dispute between the utilitarian and architectural points of view, we maintain that absolute uniformity of lighting is neither required nor in many cases desirable, that fixtures can be chosen and arranged to efficiently perform their task without dominating or detracting from the architecture, that brightnesses and shadows can be readily controlled and that an over-all integrated effect is possible which is both aesthetically pleasing and utilitarian. We will return to this subject at a later point. At this stage however, if we are to become proficient in the use of lighting as a design material, we must be fully conversant with its characteristics, effects, and means of generation, in addition to its application and utilization. To this end this chapter is directed.

2. Light as Radiant Energy. The Illuminating Engineering Society, hereafter referred to as the IES, defines light as "visually evaluated radiant energy" or more simply, a form of energy which permits us to see. If light is considered as a wave, similar to a radio wave or an alternating current wave, it has a frequency and a wave length. Figure 19.1 shows the position of light in the wave spectrum with relation to other wave phenomena of various frequencies.

From the chart we see that even the longest wave length light (red) is a much higher frequency than radio and radar, and that visible light comprises only a very small part of the wave energy forms. Yet it is this energy which makes possible our sight and with which we are here concerned. Color is determined by wave length; starting at the longest wave lengths with red, we proceed through the spectrum of orange, yellow, green, blue, indigo, and violet to arrive at the shortest visible wave lengths (highest frequency).

When a light source produces energy over the entire visible spectrum in approximately equal quantities, the combination of the colored lights produces white such as is the case with the sun, whereas a source produc-

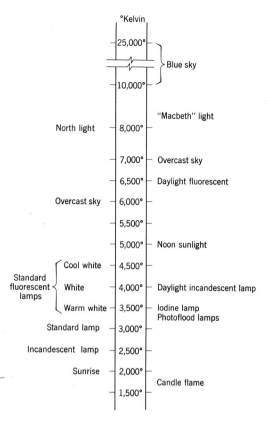

Fig. 19.2   Color temperature scale.

ing energy over only a small section of the spectrum produces its characteristic colored light. Examples are the blue-green mercury lamp and the yellow sodium lamp.

3. Color Temperature. A light source is often designated with a "color temperature" such as 3400°K for iodine lamps, 4500°K for cool white fluorescent tubes, etc. This nomenclature is derived from the fact that when a light-absorbing body (normally called a black body) is heated it will first turn deep red, then cherry red, then orange until it finally becomes blue-white hot. The color of the light radiated—red from a red hot body, white from a white hot body—is thus related to its temperature. Therefore by developing a black body color temperature scale, we can compare the color of a light source to this scale and assign to it an approximate "color temperature," i.e., the

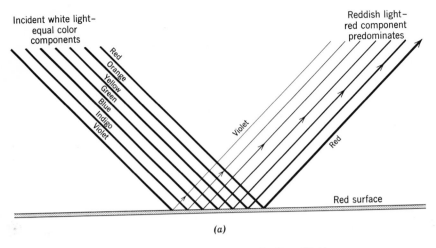

Fig. 19.3*a*   Selective absorption of reflected light.

temperature to which a black body must be heated to radiate a light approximating the color of the source in question. Temperature is measured in degrees Kelvin, which is a scale that has its zero point at minus 456° Fahrenheit. Figure 19.2 shows the assigned color temperature of some common light sources.

It must be understood, of course, that color temperature of a light source is an indication of the color of the light produced and not of the actual source temperature. Certain colors, such as green, are not radiated by an incandescent black body as its temperature is raised, and therefore green lamps are not assigned a color temperature. However, since most common light sources are designed to deliver "white light," an approximate color temperature may be given.

4. Fundamental Laws of Light. Design of lighting installations is possible because light is predictable; i.e. it follows certain laws and exhibits certain fixed characteristics. Although some of these are so well known as to appear self-evident, a review is in order. When a composite light such as white falls on a surface other than black or white, selective absorption occurs. The component colors are absorbed in different proportions so that the light reflected or transmitted is composed of a new combination of the same colors as had impinged on

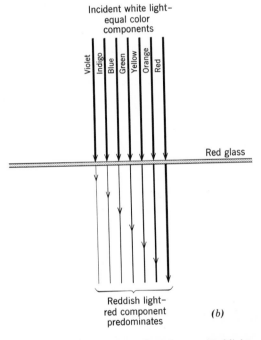

Fig. 19.3*b*   Selective absorption of transmitted light.

the surface. Thus a white light reflected from a red wall has a red tint since the component colors of the white light other than red were absorbed in greater proportion than the red. When recombined the red light took prominence thus giving the reflected light a red tint. This is illustrated in Fig. 19.3*a*.

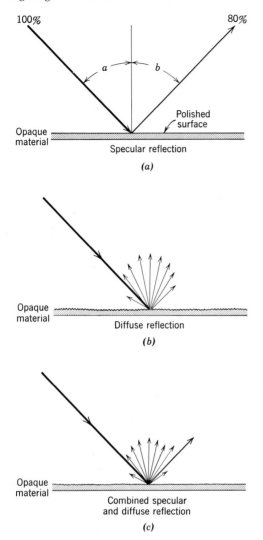

100%   80%

Polished
surface

Opaque
material
Specular reflection

(a)

Opaque
material
Diffuse reflection

(b)

Opaque
material
Combined specular
and diffuse reflection

(c)

Fig. 19.4 Reflection characteristics. (*a*) In specular reflection, angle of incidence equals angle of reflection
(*a = b*). Since 80 percent of light is reflected, reflectance
factor is 80 percent; 20 percent of light is absorbed.
(*b*) In diffuse reflection, incident light is spread in all
directions by multiple reflections on the unpolished surface. Such surfaces appear equally bright from all viewing angles. (*c*) Most materials exhibit a combination of
specular and diffuse reflection. Such a surface will mirror
the source while producing a bright background.

Similarly, a white light when passed
through a piece of red glass emerges as a
reddish light since the other components
were absorbed in much greater proportion
than the red. This well known phenomenon
is illustrated in Fig. 19.3*b*.

It is this phenomenon which allows us to
see color at all; the individual object pig-
mentation absorbs all other colors of light
and reflects or transmits to the eye only its
own hue.

The luminous transmittance of a material
such as a fixture lens or diffuser is a measure of its capability to transmit incident
light. By definition, this quantity known
variously as luminous transmittance, transmission factor, or coefficient of transmission
is the ratio of the total emitted light to the
total incident light. In the case of incident
light containing several components passing
through a material which displays selective
absorption, this factor becomes an average
of the individual transmittances for the
various components and must be used
cautiously. A piece of milk white glass and
a piece of red glass may both have a 70 percent transmission factor but obviously affect
the incident light differently. In general
then, transmission factors should normally
be used only when referring to materials
displaying nonselective absorption. Clear
glass for instance displays a luminous transmittance between 80 and 90 percent, frosted
glass between 70 and 85 percent, and solid
opal glass between 15 and 40 percent.

Similarly, the ratio of reflected to incident
light is variously called reflectance, reflectance factor, and reflectance coefficient.

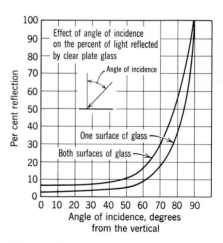

Effect of angle of incidence
on the percent of light reflected
by clear plate glass

Angle of incidence

One surface of glass
Both surfaces of glass

Per cent reflection

Angle of incidence, degrees
from the vertical

Fig. 19.5 Relation between angle of incidence and percent of reflection.

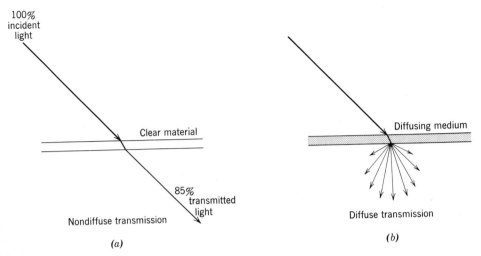

Fig. 19.6   Transmission characteristics. (*a*) In nondiffuse transmission, the light is refracted (bent) but emerges in the same beam as it enters. Clear materials such as glass, water, and certain plastics exhibit this type of transmission. In the instance illustrated the transmission factor is 85 percent. The source of light is clearly visible through the transmitting medium. (*b*) With diffuse transmission, the source of light is not visible and in the case of multiple sources, the diffusing surface will exhibit generally uniform brightness if the spacing between the light sources does not exceed 1½ times their distance from the material.

Thus if half the amount of light incident on a surface is bounced back, the reflectance is 50 percent or 0.50. The remainder is absorbed in the case of an opaque material. The amount of absorption and reflection depends upon the type of material and the angle of light incidence (see Fig. 19.5), since light impinging upon a surface at small (grazing) angles tends to be reflected rather than absorbed or transmitted. An example of almost perfect reflection from an opaque surface would be that from a well-silvered mirror while almost complete absorption takes place on an object covered with lamp black or matte finish black paint. The effect of the material finish on reflection is shown in Fig. 19.4*a*, *b*, and *c*.

If the reflection takes place on a smooth surface such as polished glass or stone it is called *specular* reflection, as shown in Fig. 19.4*a*. If the surface is rough, multiple reflections take place on the many small projections on the surface, and the light is diffused as shown in Fig. 19.4*b*. Since the reflection factor is a measure of total light reflected, it does not depend upon whether the reflection is specular or diffuse, or a combination of both, as shown in Fig. 19.4*c*. Diffuse transmission takes place through any translucent source such as frosted glass, white glass, milky plexiglas, tissue paper, etc. This diffusing principle is widely employed in lighting fixtures to spread the light generated by the bulb or tube within the fixture. Diffuse and nondiffuse transmission are illustrated in Fig. 19.6*a* and *b*.

VISION AND LIGHT

5. The Eye.   Since all discussion of light and lighting techniques is irrelevant to our purposes unless ultimately related to vision, we turn to a cursory examination of the workings of the human eye before proceeding further with discussions of lighting.

Light impinging upon the eye enters through the pupil, the size of which is controlled by the iris, thereby controlling the amount of light entering the eye. The lens focuses the image on the retina from which the optic nerve conveys the visual message by electric impulse to the brain. Figure 19.7 shows the structure of the eye and the parallel structure of a camera.

The central portion of the eye, near the fovea, contains light-sensitive cells called "cones" because of their shape. The cones are responsible for the ability to discriminate detail and also give us our sensation of color. As we proceed outward from the fovea a second type of cell is encountered called a "rod" cell, also after its shape. These cells are extremely light-sensitive, giving response to light 1/10,000th as bright as that required by cone cells. Rod cells however lack color sensitivity, thus accounting for the fact that in dim light (rod vision) we have no color perception and all colors appear as varying shades of gray. Rod cells also lack detail discrimination, making "night vision" quite poor. Finally, rod cells are slower acting than cone cells and therefore have a low degree of flicker fusion, or, stated conversely, they are highly motion-sensitive. Since these cells occur at the outer portions of the retina, their motion

sensitivity results in our being best able to detect movement when looking out of the "corner of the eye."

VISUAL ACUITY

6. Factors. Investigation has demonstrated that there are 4 basic characteristics of each visual task with which the eye is confronted; the brightness, contrast, size, and time exposure of the object or area being viewed. There are other minor considerations which affect visual acuity, such as the pattern of the background, peripheral glare, pupil accommodation, and chromaticity; but these can generally be considered secondary.

The basic visual tasks are the perception of low contrast, fine detail, and brightness gradient. These abilities are all dependent on the 4 basic conditions stated above, the interrelated effects of which have been determined by large numbers of field tests.

7. Size of Visual Object. Visual acuity is generally proportional to the physical size of the object being viewed given fixed brightness, contrast and exposure time. Since the

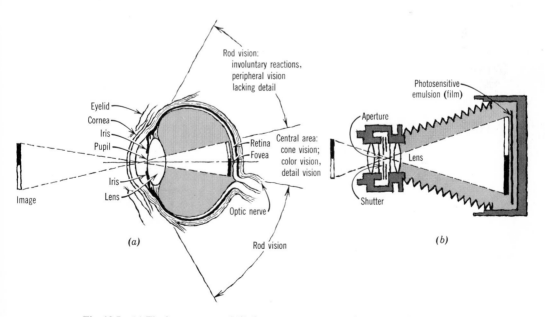

Fig. 19.7 (a) The human eye and (b) the camera operate on the same optic principles.

Fig. 19.8 Relationship between object size and visibility is demonstrated by comparison of subtended angles *a* and *b*.

actual parameter is not physical size but subtended visual angle, visual ability can be increased by bringing the object nearer the eye. (See Fig. 19.8.)

8. Brightness. Brightness is probably the most discussed and least understood factor in visibility.

The sensation of vision, as explained above, is caused by light entering the eye. This light may be thought of as a group of convergent rays, each ray coming from a different point in space and therefore carrying different visual information. The composite of these rays comprises the entire visual picture which the eye sees and the

brain comprehends. The individual rays differ from each other in intensity and chromaticity depending upon the part of the viewed object from which they were reflected. The intensity of these pencils of light determine and describe the *brightness* of the object being viewed. (See Fig. 19.9.) If the surface reflectance of the object being viewed is uniform and the illumination is also uniform then the reflected rays of light will be equal in intensity and we will see an object of uniform brightness. If however, as is generally the case, either the object or the illumination is non-uniform we will see an object of varied brightness. Mathematically then, the brightness of a non-luminous diffusely reflecting surface is equal to the product of the illumination falling on the surface and the reflectance of the surface. That is, 1 foot-candle of illumination falling upon a surface of 1.0 reflectance factor produces a brightness of 1 footlambert. If the reflectance factor were 0.5, and the illumination 50 foot-candles, the resulting brightness would be 25.0 footlamberts.

$$\text{Brightness} = \text{illumination} \times \text{reflectance,}$$
$$\text{or}$$
$$\text{footlamberts} = \text{footcandles} \times \text{reflectance factor, or}$$
$$\text{F.L.} = \text{F.C.} \times \text{R.F.}$$

The above discussion concerns itself with

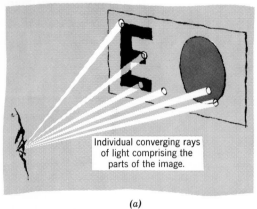

(a)

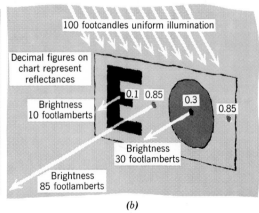

(b)

Fig. 19.9   (*a*) Composition of the visual image. (*b*) Brightness of a nonuniform surface.

Table 19.1 Typical Brightnesses

Object	Brightness in Footlamberts
Black glove on cloudy night	0.0001
Snow in moonlight	0.015
Asphalt road—street lighting	0.05
This sheet of paper lit by a candle	0.75
Floor brightness in a poorly lighted office	2.0
Wall brightness in a well lighted office	50.0
Luminous ceiling	200.
Asphalt paving—overcast day	400.
North sky	1,000.
Moon, candle flame	1,500.
Asphalt paving—sunny day	2,000.
Fluorescent tube	2,000.
Kerosene flame	2,500.
Hazy sky or day fog	4,500.
Snow in sunlight	10,000.
40 watt I.F. lamp	15,000.
500 watt inside frost incand. lamp	95,000.
Sun	450,000,000.

(Full Color — Human Eyes — Blink or Squint)

reflecting surfaces which derive their brightness from incident illumination and are therefore known as secondary sources. Primary sources are those which generate their own light and transmit directly to the eye. The largest and best known primary and secondary brightness sources are the sun and the moon respectively.

The human eye detects brightness over an astonishing range of more than 100 million to 1, the lower levels being accomplished after an accommodation period, called adaptation time. This period varies from 2 minutes for cone vision to up to 40 minutes for rod vision for dark adaptation, but is much faster for both types for bright adaptation (going from dark to light). Table 19.1 lists some typical brightnesses of every day visual tasks.

Returning then, to the primary consideration of visual acuity as affected by brightness, we can state that in general, visual performance increases with object brightness. A great deal however depends upon the background against which an object is viewed and the consequent contrast in brightness between the object being viewed and its surroundings.

9. Contrast. In order to properly evaluate the effect of contrast (brightness ratio) we must first determine the nature of the visual task or, more simply, exactly what it is that we are trying to see. As stated before, the basic visual tasks are detail descrimination and detection of low contrast. An example of the former task is reading of fine print, while of the latter would be examination of surface textures.

High contrast is helpful in delineating outline, size and detail as shown in Fig. 19.10. High background brightness makes the object viewed look darker and therefore assists in outline detail descrimination, as

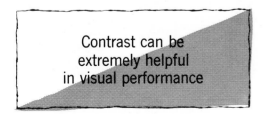

Contrast can be extremely helpful in visual performance

Fig. 19.10 Effect of contrast on visual acuity. Where contrast is high, even low brightness is sufficient for high visual performance.

Fig. 19.11   The effect of high background brightness on delineation of silhouette is demonstrated
by the tree whereas the high reflectance of the building allows fairly good surface detail vision.
(RCA Building, Rockefeller Center)

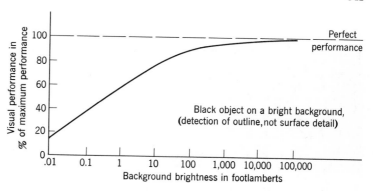

Fig. 19.12 Visual performance as a function of background brightness. Since
reading of print is essentially
a task in silhouette recognition, high background brightness is helpful. (*IES Lighting
Handbook, 3rd edition*)

shown in Fig. 19.11. Figure 19.12 shows a
chart of actual visual performance in a high
contrast (black on white) situation, demonstrating graphically that when contrast is
high visual accuracy is good even when
brightness is low.

When however, our task depends upon
surface contrast descrimination, as would
be the case in examining the leaves and bark
of the tree in Fig. 19.11, high background
illumination is a definite hindrance since the
eyes automatically adjust to the *average*
brightness of a scene. It is well known that
when using an electric-eye camera to photograph a dark object on a light background
such as a person in a snow scene, it is necessary to manually increase the camera

aperture in order to obtain additional light
so as to photograph the detail of the darker
object. Since we cannot control voluntarily
the aperture of our eyes, we must compensate for the detrimental affect of high background brightness in another way, namely
by increasing the surface brightness of the
visual task. Ideally, the brightness of the
task should be the same as that of the background, but ratios of up to 3 to 1 are
acceptable in most circumstances. Thus,
looking again at Fig. 19.11, we see that the
building which is light-colored (high reflectance) and well illuminated has a brightness
approaching that of the background, and
therefore surface visibility is good. The
detrimental effect of high background

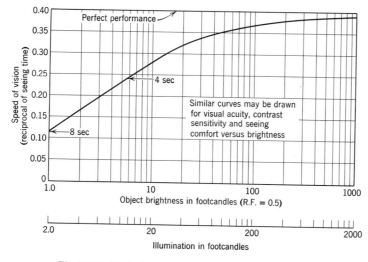

Fig. 19.13 Typical curve of visual speed vs. brightness.

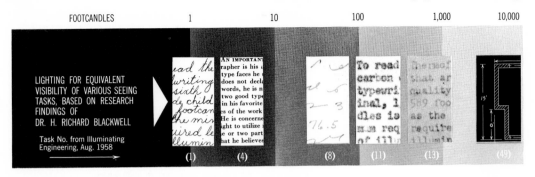

Fig. 19.14   Typical seeing tasks used in tests by H. R. Blackwell. See Table 19.2 for task descriptions.

brightness or glare is thus overcome by an increase in the surface brightness of the object being viewed.

10. Exposure Time. Registering a meaningful visual image is not an instantaneous process, but one which requires finite amounts of time. Just as in photography a "photo" can be taken in dim light by using a longer exposure, so too the human eye can distinguish and discriminate fine detail in poor light given enough time (and neglecting eyestrain). Figure 19.13 is a plot of seeing time versus illumination for a given visual task. Of course, time depends upon the type of task, and different curves can be plotted for different tasks, but the principle of shorter time at higher illumination remains the same. This is particularly true when the object being viewed is not static, but in motion.

This curve shows that by increasing the brightness by a factor of six we can halve the seeing time, whereas a further increase of sixfold in brightness only reduces the time approximately 20 percent. Thus, as in the case of increasing background brightness, we reach a point of diminishing returns.

As stated above, brightness, contrast, size, and exposure are the four basic factors which affect visual performance. Generally, exposure time and size are not readily controllable parameters, leaving brightness and contrast to be manipulated by the lighting designer in such a way as to give a

comfortable and efficient visual environment. Such an environment must be efficient in the sense that it provides for optimal performance of a given task, and comfortable in the sense that this visual task performance takes place with minimum fatigue, whether conscious or not.

11. Determination of Lighting Levels. The factors discussed above have been widely known for many years and numerous attempts have been made to relate them to actual seeing tasks in order to establish brightness requirements and thereby illumination levels for various seeing tasks so that practical design use can be made of the laboratory experimental data. The best known and most successful of these attempts from an acceptance viewpoint has been the continuing work of Dr. H. R. Blackwell at Ohio State University. Blackwell used as his basic experimental visual task the detection of a circular target on a field of uniform brightness, the variable parameters being the size, brightness, and exposure time of the target. The result of these tests was the determination of contrast requirements for various accuracies of sightings. Blackwell's problem was then to relate these laboratory findings to actual practical seeing tasks. By means of an empirical "field factor" and a device known as a Field Task Simulator he was able to accomplish this. Several of Blackwell's sample tasks are shown in Fig. 19.14. The resultant footcandle illumination figures for these and other tasks are tabulated in Table 19.2.

Although some of the figures seem at first glance to be inordinately high, it must be remembered these values were derived using a fixed "field factor" and 5 exposures per second. We are all aware that we can read poor reproductions with less than 589 foot-

Table 19.2   Typical Blackwell Illumination Data

Task	Required Footcandles
SCHOOL	
1. Sample of ink writing	1.4
4. 6-point text type	3.0
57. Average of 8 samples of spirit duplicated material— (difficult)	684.0
OFFICE	
8. Sample of shorthand copy with #3 pencil	76.5
11. Typed carbon, 5th copy	133.0
13. Thermal reproduced copy, poor quality	589.0
49. White line on blueprint, tracing paper overlay	5,090.0
GARMENT INDUSTRY	
15. White chalk mark on blue serge cloth	10.0
20. Gray stitching on gray silk vertical stitching	4,160.0
horizontal stitching	10,000.0
STORE TASKS	
29. Price tag, pencil	241.0
30. Price tag, ink	3.1

IES Lighting Handbook 3rd Edition

candles, but the reading process is much slower and fatigue may well result. On the whole however, Blackwell's data when used judiciously, provides a useful guide to the illumination required for different tasks.

The results of Blackwell's tests as well as those of others have been evaluated by illumination engineers and specialists and classified by type; i.e., school, office, industrial, etc. Since the type of tasks performed in these areas are known and the required brightnesses are calculated from the test results, footcandle illumination data for these tasks can be derived, utilizing either known or recommended reflectances. These illumination levels will generally provide acceptable minimum illumination in the specified area for the various activities in progress. This of course presupposes an acceptable design so as to provide good quality lighting at this minimum intensity. A list of the minimum footcandle levels recommended by the IES Committee on Recommendations for Quality and Quantity of Illumination, appears in Chapter 21. The lighting designer will at one time or another undoubtedly encounter a written or verbal statement to the effect that footcandle levels are meaningless since the eye perceives brightnesses and not luminous flux density. The latter part of this statement is, of course, correct and the criticism would be valid if the same illumination were provided for diverse activities occurring in a given space e.g., a manufacturing process and an inspection procedure. For such a situation, a proper lighting design would take cognizance of the individual task requirements by providing varied illumination within the single space.

QUALITY OF LIGHTING

12. Considerations of Quality. Quality of lighting is a term used to describe all the factors in a lighting installation not directly concerned with quantity of illumination. Certainly it is obvious that if a given room is alternatively lit with a bare bulb and with a luminous ceiling, both giving the same quantitative illumination (in terms of lumen output), there is a vast difference in the two lighting systems. This difference is in the quality of the lighting, a term which describes the brightness ratios, diffusion, and chromaticity of the lighting. Since uncomfortable brightness ratios are commonly referred to as glare, the quality of the lighting system is also a description of the visual comfort and seeing efficiency of the system.

When the discomfort glare is caused by light sources in the field of vision it is known as direct glare. When, however, the glare is caused by reflection of a light source in a viewed surface it is known as reflected glare or "veiling reflection." (See Fig. 19.15.)

13. Direct Glare. All direct glare produces discomfort and interference with vision. However, whether or not a specific light source constitutes or produces objectionable

direct line of vision, the glare produced by a source depends upon its position in the field of view.

We indicated in Section 9 above that one way to decrease the detrimental effect of high background brightness was to increase the task brightness. This technique is also effective in reverse, with a source of glare since the amount of discomfort glare produced by a source is inversely proportional to the background or field brightness (also known as eye adaptation level). Therefore, a 500-footlambert source which would be highly objectionable in a space with an

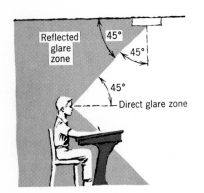

The direct and reflected glare zones are delineated on the diagram although the zones overlap considerably. Keeping direct and reflected glare at a minimum is mandatory. Placement of fixtures, room size, ceiling height, paint finishes, windows, etc., also affect brightness ratios, and thereby glare.

Fig. 19.15   Glare zones with student in a head-up position.

glare is determined by several factors: brightness, size and position of the source, and surrounding or background brightness. Although the brightness of fixtures will be discussed in detail in Chapter 21, we can say here that the higher the brightness of the fixture or other source, the greater the glare.

The size of the source which is defined with respect to the viewer by the angle subtended by the source at the eye, is the second parameter to which glare is directly proportional. However a large low brightness source may produce much less glare than a very bright point source.

Since glare decreases rapidly as the brightness source is moved away from the

eye adaptation level of 10 footlamberts would not be a source of discomfort glare in a space with a field brightness of for example 300 footlamberts. Generally then, direct glare can be controlled by reducing source brightness and size, positioning sources outside the direct line of view and raising background brightnesses. A common technique for accomplishing this latter result is to use diffuse high reflectance paints or materials in light colors on upper walls and ceilings.

Although the foregoing analysis of direct glare has been entirely qualitative, a number of systems have been developed to quantitatively analyze the discomfort due

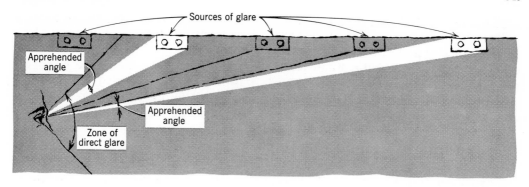

Fig. 19.16   Glare factor determination. The glare contribution of each source depends upon its size (apprehended angle), brightness, and location in the field of view. Glare will be much more objectionable with a dark background than with a light one; therefore light-colored paints on ceilings and upper walls are recommended.

to direct glare, to the extent possible with an inherently subjective factor. The method usually employed is to calculate the glare from the least favorable position in a room with multiple direct glare sources, using factors to compute the glare contribution of bright areas at various locations in the field of view. (See Fig. 19.16.) The result is then generally expressed, numerically, as the percentage of *normal* observers who would experience no visual discomfort in this room, and is usually referred to as a Visual Comfort Index, or Visual Comfort Factor. Conversely, the result can be expressed as an empirical figure known as Glare Factor, which is an indication of the amount of glare present in the room. It must always be borne in mind however, in the evaluation of a direct glare situation that the result is quite literally in the eye of the beholder, and that even a well-designed installation may not please all the occupants of the space.

14. Reflected Glare. The problem of reflected glare is somewhat more complex than that of direct glare in that we have the additional consideration of the nature of the object being viewed. Although there is no generally accepted convention with respect to nomenclature, many persons refer to reflected glare when dealing with specular

(polished or mirror) surfaces and to veiling reflections when considering source reflections in dull or semimatte finish surfaces, which always exhibit some degree of specularity. In all cases the result is a distinct loss of contrast due to the veiling of the image by the reflection of the light source. The sources of reflected glare are brightnesses within the geometry of reflected vision as shown in Fig. 19.17, and the ef-

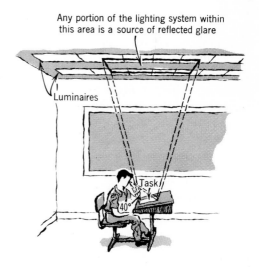

Fig. 19.17   A method for determining the zone in which potential reflected glare sources may be located. See Fig. 21.23.
IES Standard Guide for School Lighting—1962.

fects are shown in Figs. 19.18 and 19.19.

Table 19.3 lists a few sample reflectance figures to demonstrate that most materials exhibit both a specular and a diffuse reflectance.

Since the causes of veiling reflections are well understood it would seem that a solu-

illumination, means the use of more or larger low brightness luminaires. This is illustrated in Fig. 19.21.

(c) As discussed in Section 13, loss of contrast can be compensated for (and glare eliminated) by increased over-all illumination. What we are doing is simply making

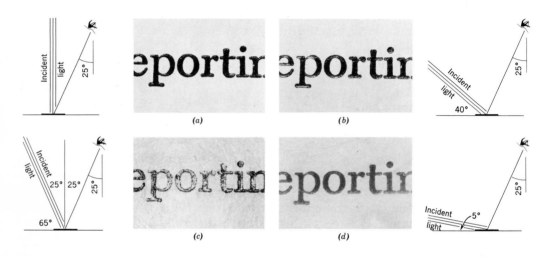

Fig. 19.18   Veiling reflection increases the difficulty of the seeing task. Note that the reflected glare is worst at c (25°), where angle of incidence equals viewing angle. Veiling is pronounced at the 5° glancing angle even on a matte-finish surface. *IES Lighting Handbook*, 3rd ed.

tion to the problem should by now have been adduced. Unfortunately, this is not the case. Although there is no known lighting method or material which will completely eliminate veiling reflections, there are a number of techniques which can be employed to reduce the contrast loss due to these reflections.

(a) Since veiling reflections are most pronounced at certain angles of light incidence, if practicable, the light source should be located so as to avoid this situation, as in Fig. 19.20.

(b) The reflected brightness which causes loss of contrast is proportional to the luminaire brightness. It is apparent then that glare may be reduced by reducing luminaire brightness, which, if we are to maintain

Fig. 19.19   The reflected glare from luminaires disappears when a piece of light diffuse linoleum is placed over the dark, polished desk top. Light-colored desk tops with a 25 percent to 40 percent reflectance result in task to background ratios within the 3 to 1 recommended range. (From IES, Recommended Practice for Office Lighting.)

the task brighter so as to eliminate the detrimental veiling reflection. Figure 19.22 is a curve which quantitatively relates the 2 parameters. In the particular instance shown in the curve, a 300 percent brightness in-

initial comparison of lighting schemes, i.e., a single bulb versus a luminous ceiling, it is also immediately apparent that the quality of lighting is affected by the direction from which the light emanates or its diffuseness.

Table 19.3   Typical Reflectances

Material	Reflectance	
	Specular	Diffuse
Matte black paper	.0005	.04
Matte white paper	.0030	.77
Newspaper	.0065	.68
Very glossy white photo paper	.048	.83
Metallic paper— copper	.11	.28
Dull black ink	.006	.045
Super gloss black ink	.039	.016

IES Lighting Handbook, 3rd Edition.

crease is required to compensate for the loss of contrast experienced. This can in many instances be most practically accomplished not by an increase in over-all room illumination but by addition of a supplementary source as in (*a*) above so arranged as to be inherently free of reflected glare. Thus, in Fig. 19.20, addition of a properly chosen down light at *B* would mitigate the difficulty. **15. Diffuseness of Light.** Returning to our

Fig. 19.20   Lighting fixture at *a* will produce more glare than one at *b* due to the geometry of the light rays. Desk finish and luminaire brightness can be chosen to minimize loss of contrast.

Diffusion is a function of the number of directions from which light impinges on a particular point and is therefore measurable by the shadows cast. In a room with well-diffused illumination, sharp shadows

Fig. 19.21   Varying degrees of detrimental specular light. Largest concentration of light downward (left) produces largest amount of reflected glare. As number of light sources is increased (center), reflected glare is decreased. Least glare is from all luminous ceiling (right). (*IES Std. on School Lighting*)

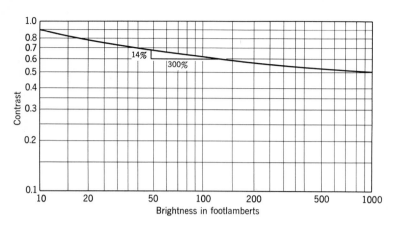

Fig. 19.22 A loss in contrast can be compensated by increasing the background brightness. Here a 14 percent loss in contrast (.7 to .6) due to glare may be eliminated by a 300 percent increase in brightness. (Contrast in this curve is quantitatively defined as the ratio of minimum detectable change in brightness of the task to background brightness.) *Graphs from IES Lighting Handbook, 3rd Edition*

are absent and vice versa. (See Fig. 19.23.)

There is a widely held but erroneous belief that diffuse lighting is better than directional lighting for all installations. Although this is certainly true for offices, schoolrooms, machine shops, and drafting rooms where shadows would be highly disturbing and could be dangerous (as in the case of a machine shop), it is decidedly not the case where texture must be examined, surface imperfections detected by grazing angle reflections, or in any installation where the flat monotony of diffuse lighting is undesirable. For this reason, some directional lighting is often introduced as an adjunct to diffuse general lighting to lend interest by producing soft shadows and brightness variations. As a matter of fact,

the only naturally occurring example of perfectly diffuse lighting is a daytime fog which we know to be extremely disturbing to the eye, demonstrating that some directivity is desirable. (See Fig. 19.24.)

16. Color. The color of the illuminant (light) and correspondingly the coloration of the objects within a space constitute an important facet of the lighting quality. The two factors however must not be considered separately since by definition the color of an object is its ability to modify the color of light incident upon it. It does this, as mentioned earlier, by a process of selective absorption, absorbing most of the light and reflecting or transmitting a spectrally modified light rich in a single hue, as shown in Fig. 19.3. The color reflected or transmitted

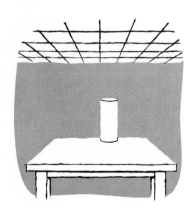

Fig. 19.23 Diffuse illumination. The luminous ceiling installation provides shadowless, almost perfectly diffuse lighting. By comparison, the single ceiling bulb produces sharp shadows and very little light diffusion.

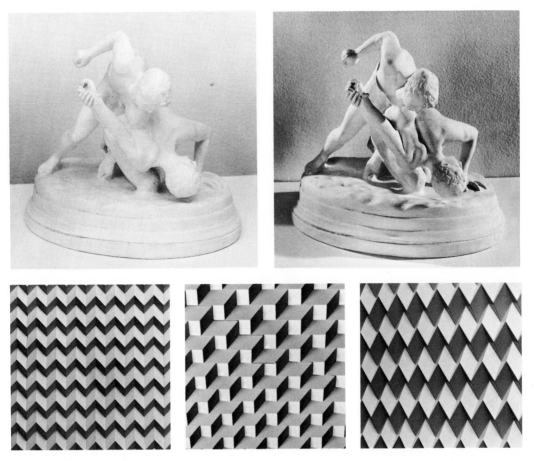

Fig. 19.24 Totally diffuse lighting (*a*) destroys texture, whereas a combination of diffuse and directional lighting (*b*) produces the required modeling shadows. Figs. (*c*), (*d*), and (*e*) demonstrate how visual patterns can be altered by changes in directional lighting of the same material. (*a, b,* Holophone Company. *c, d, e, Architectural and Engineering News,* August, 1963)

is apprehended by the eye as the color of the object. An object is said to be colorless when it does not exhibit selective absorption, reflecting and absorbing the various components of the incident light nonselectively. Thus, white, black, and all shades of gray are colorless, neutral, achromatic, or more precisely, lack hue.

Hue is defined as that attribute by which we recognize and therefore describe colors as red, yellow, green, blue, etc. Just as it is possible to form a series from white to black with the intermediate greys, so it is also possible to do the same with a hue. The difference between the resultant colors of the same hue so arranged, is called *brilliance or value*. White is the most brilliant of the neutral colors and black the least, pink is a more brilliant red hue than ruby, and golden yellow a more brilliant (lighter) yellow hue than raw umber.

Colors of the same hue and brilliance may still differ from each other in *saturation*, which is an indication of the vividness of hue or the difference of the color from gray. Thus pure gray has no hue; as we add color

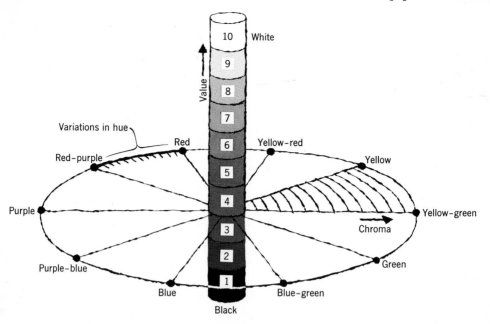

Fig. 19.25   Munsell color system.

we change the saturation without changing the brilliance. The 3 characteristics then which define a particular coloration are hue, brilliance, and saturation. Using these terms we may define "bay" as a color red-yellow in hue of low saturation and low brilliance; while carmine is a color, red in hue, of very high saturation and low brilliance.

Various systems of color classification have been devised, including the Maerz and Paul Color Dictionary, the Munsell Color System, the Ostwald Color System, and the I. C. I. Chromaticity Diagram. In the Munsell color system (see Fig. 19.25) brilliance is referred to as "value" and saturation as "chroma"; thus a color is defined by hue, value, and chroma. The brilliance (value) of a pigment or coloration is related to its reflectance to white light. The higher the brilliance or value, the higher the reflectance factor as might be predicted when one considers that white and black are the poles of brilliance. Chroma or saturation may be thought of as

either the difference from gray or the purity of the color. Spectral colors have 100 percent purity and therefore maximum chroma.

Where white is added to a pigment, it produces a *tint;* adding black produces a *shade.* When pigments are mixed to produce a particular color, we create this color by a subtractive process. That is, each pigment absorbs certain proportions of white light; when mixed the absorptions combine to subtract (absorb) various colors of the white spectra, and leave only those colors which finally constitute the hue, value, and chroma of the pigment. This subtractive effect is also utilized when producing colors by filtering white light. Contrariwise, when the three primary colors of red, green, and blue are combined they form white by an additive process. (See Fig. 19.26.)

The additive and subtractive primary colors are complimentary; they combine to give a white or neutral grey respectively. Thus, red and blue-green, blue and yellow, and green and magenta are complimentary.

Light of a particular hue (other than

white) is rarely used for general illumination except to create a special atmosphere. When a space is lit with colored light, the eye adapts by a phenomena known as "color constancy" so that it can recognize colors of objects despite the spectral quality of the illuminant. However, the eyes become more sensitive to the missing colors which would make up white light. This phenomenon could be used to make meat look redder on a butcher counter by using blue-rich, red-poor cool white lighting in the remainder of the store. A similar phenomenon occurs when the eye is exposed to a monochromatic scene where the chromaticity is due to coloration of the objects, rather than the illumination. The eye in such a situation becomes sensitized to the *complimentary* color; thus if after looking at a green surface one shifts the gaze to a white surface, one sees the complimentary red color. Returning to our meat market, the use of green paint on the walls also enhances the redness of the meat. This effect in reverse also accounts for the extensive use of green for paints, linens, and gowns, etc., in operating rooms in that the eyes of the surgeons and nurses when diverted from the redness of the surgical area will be more comfortable seeing green on a green background than on a white one. A similar effect is apparent object color differences when background color is changed. Thus a green object looks somewhat blue-green on a yellow background because the eye is supplying the complimentary color to yellow— namely blue. Similarly the same green object looks slightly yellow-green when on a blue background, the eye supplying the yellow.

Apparent brightness of a color is a function of its hue, in that light colors appear lighter than dark colors even when measured brightness is the same. Thus spaces may be defined by color within an area of equal illumination. Too, all colors tend to appear less saturated or "washed-out" when illumination is high, thus pigments of high saturation (chroma) must be used in well-lit spaces if they are to be effective although extensive use of saturated colors is generally best avoided. Other well-known psychological effects of colors are the coolness of blues and greens and the warmth of reds and yellows. Similarly, red and yellow are "advancing" colors because objects lit with them tend to "advance" toward the observer, giving the appearance of becom-

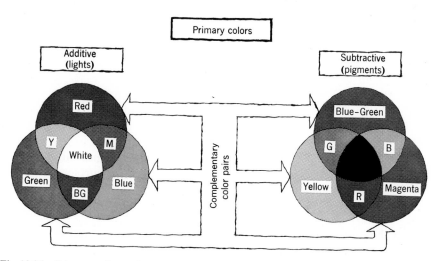

Fig. 19.26 Primary and complementary colors. Complementary color pairs are shown by arrows. Pigments form color by an absorptive (subtractive) process; colored lights form colors by a reflective (additive) process.

ing larger. The opposite effect is noted with blue and green, accounting for their being known as receding colors. Thus cool colors might well be used in a fur salon and warm colors in a display of summer wear.

In an atmosphere which is designed to be calm and restful, greens should generally predominate either in illuminant color, object color, or both, except in eating areas, which should be lit with reds and yellows since cool colors are definitely unappetizing.

A further discussion of color control and color matching will be found in Chap. 20, Section 7 dealing with spectral energy distribution of sources.

LIGHT: CHARACTERISTICS AND MEASUREMENTS

17. Terminology and Definitions. We have discussed in some detail many of the characteristics of light including color temperature, transmission, reflection, absorption, and color classification, and have touched upon nomenclature such as lumens, footcandles, footlamberts, etc. We cannot, however, expect to gain the facility with these parameters that is required of a lighting designer until we thoroughly understand their definitions and interrelation. This then is the burden of the following paragraphs.

The *candlepower,* abbreviated C.P. is the unit of *luminous intensity*. It is analogous to pressure in a hydraulic system and voltage in an electric system and represents the force which generates the light that we see. An ordinary wax candle has a luminous intensity horizontally of approximately one candlepower, whence the name. A source of one candlepower intensity produces a total light output in all direction of 12.57 (4π) lumens.

The *lumen* is the unit of luminous flux or quantity of light. It is analogous to flow in hydraulic systems and to current in electrical systems, and is a measure of the amount of light generated by a luminous source.

The *footcandle* is the unit used to measure the density of luminous flux and is therefore equal to lumens per sq ft. If we were to consider a light bulb to be analogous to a sprinkler head, then the amount of water released would be the lumens and the amount of water per sq ft of floor area would be the footcandles.

$$\text{Footcandles} = \frac{\text{Lumens}}{\text{Square feet of area.}}$$

Therefore, 1 lumen falling on an area of one sq ft produces an illumination of one footcandle. Similarly, 250 lumens falling uniformly on a floor 5 ft wide by 10 ft long produces an illumination of 5 footcandles.

$$\text{F.C.} = \frac{250 \text{ Lumens}}{5 \times 10 \text{ sq ft}} = 5$$

Footcandle illumination at a point can also be computed from candlepower as will be shown in the section which discusses candlepower and distribution curves.

A *footlambert,* abbreviated F.L., is the unit of brightness or luminance and is defined as the brightness of a surface *emitting* or *reflecting* one lumen per sq ft, in that direction. This unit has no readily conceivable mechanical or electrical analogy. By definition, 1 lumen falling uniformly on an area of 1 sq ft produces an illumination on the surface of 1 footcandle. If the surface has a 100 percent reflection factor, it will have a brightness of 1 F.L., as previously explained.

With respect to luminous sources, if we have a luminous ceiling installation of 100 F.L. average brightness, then it produces 100 lumens per sq ft.

Expressed mathematically:

(*a*) For a reflecting surface

$$\text{Brightness (F.L.)} = \text{footcandles} \\ \times \text{reflectance factor}$$

$$= \frac{\text{incident lumens}}{\text{sq ft}} \times \text{reflectance}$$

(*b*) For a luminous surface

$$\text{Brightness (F.L.)} = \\ \text{lumens emitted per sq ft}$$

18. Footcandle Measurements. Measurements of illumination levels are most commonly made with one or another of the available portable footcandle meters, some of which are illustrated in Fig. 19.27. These cells comprise a light-sensitive material connected to a microammeter, and calibrated in footcandles. The smaller portable units are convenient to use but accuracy is generally not better than ±5 percent and fairly frequent recalibration is advisable. If greater accuracy is desired, the larger units should be employed.

The human eye is not equally sensitive to the various wave lengths, i.e., colors. Maximum sensitivity is in the yellow-green area (wave length of 5550 A°) while sensitivity at the red and blue ends of the spectrum is quite low. This effect is so pronounced that 10 units of blue energy at 4700 A° are required to produce the same visual effect as 1 unit of yellow-green. Therefore, if a meter is to be useful in terms of human eye response, its inherent response, which is quite different from that of the human eye must be corrected to correspond to the eye. For

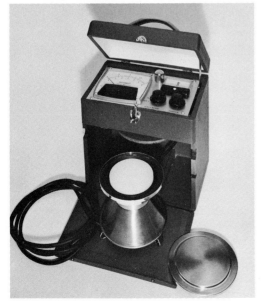

Fig. 19.27   (Above) Typical light flux meters. Note footcandle scales. (Weston Electric Instrument Corp.) (At left) Low range light meter with a scale of 0–2 footcandles. This type of meter is useful for checking outdoor lighting levels in such areas as streets, walkways, parking lots and highways. (General Electric)

this reason most modern meters are "color corrected." The effects described above are shown graphically in Fig. 19.28.

The cells (meters) must also be corrected for light incident at oblique angles which does not reach the cell due to reflection from the surface glass and shielding of the light-sensitive cell by the meter housing. This correction is known as cosine correction. A good meter must therefore be (and it will plainly so indicate) color and cosine corrected.

When taking actual readings meters

should be placed on a stable surface and readings taken after the needle stabilizes. For determining average room illumination a number of readings should be taken and an average computed. Where no definite height is specified, readings are taken at 30 in. above the floor. The meter must always be held with the cell *parallel* to the plane of the test. Thus to measure wall illumination, the meter must be held with the cell vertical. If nighttime illumination readings are desired and the test is being conducted during daylight hours, readings should be taken with and without the artificial illumination and the results subtracted. Detailed instructions for conducting field surveys are contained in the I. E. S. publication, "Recommendations for a Standard Method for Measuring and Reporting Illumination from Artificial Sources in Building Interiors."

19. Brightness Measurements. A number of different types of meters are available for taking direct brightness readings. These

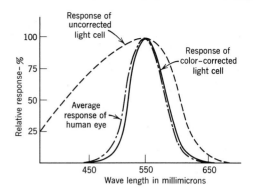

Fig. 19.28   Response of color-corrected cells.

meters are not direct reading in that the operator must make a brightness equivalency judgment of target on background. For this reason, it is advisable to take at least 2 readings for each point and average them.

An approximation of the brightness of a reflecting or luminous source can be obtained using a footcandle meter of the type

Fig. 19.29   Brightness measurements of luminous sources with (*a*) a direct reading comparator type of brightness meter, and (*b*) with a footcandle meter. The latter, when held in contact with the luminous source, will read brightness in footlamberts directly, on the footcandle scale. In Fig. (*a*) the author is checking brightness of a louver which utilizes parabolic wedges to form the individual cells, giving low brightness above 45°. This is readily apparent in comparison to the adjacent fixture which utilizes a prismatic lens diffuser. (Photos by Stein)

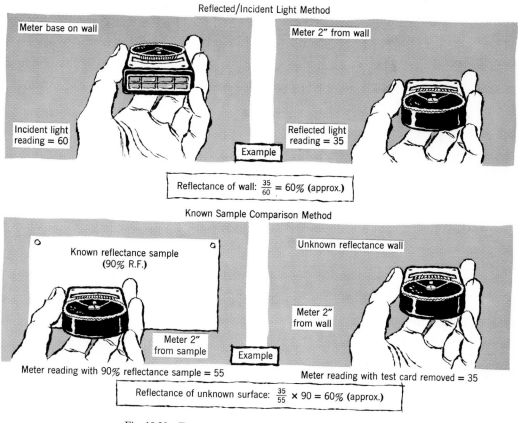

Reflected/Incident Light Method

Meter base on wall

Incident light
reading = 60

Meter 2″ from wall

Reflected light
reading = 35

Example

Reflectance of wall: $\frac{35}{60} = 60\%$ (approx.)

Known Sample Comparison Method

Known reflectance sample
(90% R.F.)

Meter 2″
from sample

Unknown reflectance wall

Meter 2″
from wall

Example

Meter reading with 90% reflectance sample = 55

Meter reading with test card removed = 35

Reflectance of unknown surface: $\frac{35}{55} \times 90 = 60\%$ (approx.)

Fig. 19.30   Two methods of measuring reflectance factors.

shown in Fig. 19.27. For diffuse reflecting surfaces the cell of the meter is placed against the surface and then slowly retracted 2 to 4 in. until a constant reading is obtained. The brightness is then 1.25 times the reading in footcandles, the 1.25 factor compensating for wide angle losses.

For a luminous source, the cell of the meter is placed directly (see Fig. 19.29) against the surface; the reading in footcandles is the brightness in footlamberts. (Because footlamberts = lumens per area and incident lumens per area = footcandles.)

20. Reflectance Measurements. It is often desirable to know the reflectance of a given surface since brightnesses can then be readily computed (F.L. = F.C. × R.F.). Two methods of measuring reflectance are shown in Fig. 19.30; the known sample and

the light ratio method. If a sample of known reflectance factor (R.F.) is available, this method should be used since it yields more accurate results than the ratio method. The sample should be no smaller than 8 in. square.

It is well for a budding lighting designer to determine the reflectance, brightnesses, and illumination levels of spaces and surfaces familiar to him, such as his office desk, adjoining wall, etc.—even to the extent of marking these figures on the respective surfaces in order that he develop an appreciation of and a memory for these parameters.

This will enable him to visualize the result of his lighting design and should be of considerable assistance.

21. Candlepower Measurements. Candlepower cannot be measured directly but must be computed from its illumination ef-

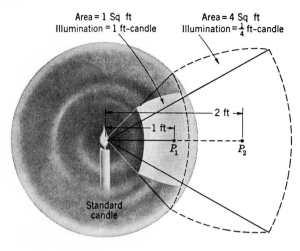

Area = 1 Sq ft
Illumination = 1 ft-candle

Area = 4 Sq ft
Illumination = $\frac{1}{4}$ ft-candle

2 ft

1 ft

P_1

P_2

Standard
candle

Fig. 19.31 Relations between candlepower, lumens, and footcandles defined with reference to a standard light source of 1 mean spherical candlepower located at the center of a sphere.

fects. Since candlepower is not uniform in all directions from anything but an ideal point source, the average of the candlepowers in all directions is used, and is commonly referred to as the "mean spherical candlepower." When a lamp is rated at 10 C.P. it does not mean that the candlepower is 10 in every direction, but that the average is 10 or that the mean spherical candlepower (M.S.C.P.) is 10. If a light source of 1 M.S.C.P. is assumed to be placed at the center of a hollow sphere of 1-ft radius (see Fig. 19.31), by definition the illumination at any point on the sphere will be 1 footcandle (1 F.C.). However, we already know that an illumination of 1 footcandle is produced by 1-lumen incident per sq ft. Referring to Fig. 19.31, since the sphere has a total surface area of 12.57 sq ft ($4\pi r^2$), and there is 1-lumen incident on each sq ft, the source of 1 M.S.C.P. produces a total of 12.57 lumens.

Referring again to Fig. 19.31, if we consider a sphere of 2-ft radius and similarly calculate the illumination, we will find it to be $\frac{1}{4}$ F.C. This establishes the inverse square law which stated simply is

$$\text{F.C.} = \frac{\text{C.P.}}{\text{D}^2}$$

That is, the illumination in footcandles of a point due to a light source at distance D ft away is equal to the candlepower of the source divided by the square of the distance.

This relation gives us a convenient way to measure candlepower of an unknown source; we measure the F.C. illumination produced on a plane at right angles to the source, at a known distance; then C.P. = F.C. × D². For accurate measurement the distance should be at least 5 times the maximum dimension of the source. If we plot on polar coordinate axes our resultant C.P. figures measured at various angles we obtain what is called a candlepower distribution curve. The steps in making such a curve are shown in Fig. 19.32.

22. Candlepower Distribution Curves. Assuming a 1-candlepower source, and referring to Fig. 19.33a it may be seen that if a band having 1 sq ft of area is drawn on the unit sphere it will intercept 1 lumen. If the sphere is now divided into bands or zones of 10° each (see Fig. 19.33b), the number of lumens in each zone is equal to 1 candlepower times the area of the zone in sq ft. Note that zones near the 90° positions have a larger area than those near the 0° and 180° positions, which become very small. The value of these areas may be calculated

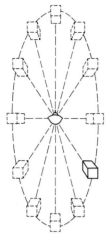

Photocell is rotated around luminaire at a specific distance to measure footcandles at specified angles

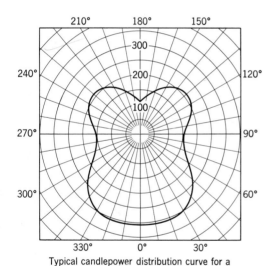

Candlepower values computed from footcandle values at each angle are plotted on polar coordinate graph

Typical candlepower distribution curve for a general diffuse type of luminaire

Fig. 19.32   Steps in producing a candlepower distribution curve. Sylvania Electric Products Inc.

by geometry. Thus for a 1-candlepower source the 0 to 10° zone has 0.10 sq ft of area and therefore receives 0.10 lumen while the 80 to 90° zone has 1.09 sq ft of area and therefore receives 1.09 lumens. For an actual source the lumens in each zone would be equal to the above values times the candlepower of the source. Given fixture distribution curves of the type shown in Fig. 19.33d, developed as explained in Section 21 above,

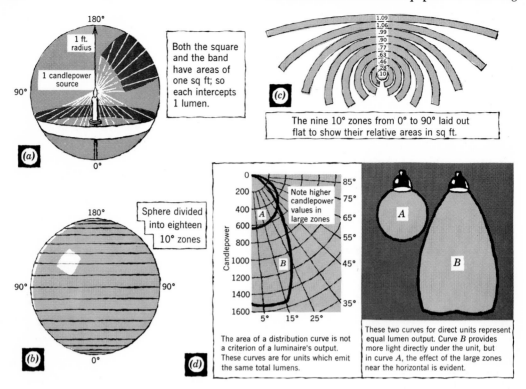

Fig. 19.33   Standard method of dividing 1-ft sphere to get candlepower distribution curves.

the lumen output in each zone can be calculated using the zonal constants of Table 19.4. These values are useful in determining the fixture efficiency and coefficient; quantities discussed in Chapter 21, section 11. It should be noted that the area of the

Table 19.4   Zonal Factors

Zone	Zonal Constant	Zone	Zonal Constant	% of Lumens in each Band
0°–10°	.10	170°–180°	.10	0.8
10°–20°	.28	160°–170°	.28	2.2
20°–30°	.46	150°–160°	.46	3.7
30°–40°	.63	140°–150°	.63	5.0
40°–50°	.77	130°–140°	.77	6.1
50°–60°	.90	120°–130°	.90	7.2
60°–70°	.99	110°–120°	.99	7.9
70°–80°	1.06	100°–110°	1.06	8.4
80°–90°	1.09	90°–100°	1.09	8.7
Total	6.28	Total	6.28	50.0%
		Grand Total	12.56	100% in both halves

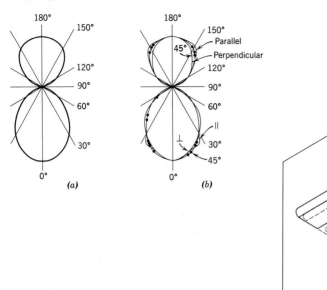

Fig. 19.34 Three planes are used in testing a fluorescent luminaire, within each of which a candlepower distribution curve (*a*) is measured and plotted at a given uniform distance from the common central point (*p*) of plane intersection. The 3 resulting curves are then plotted as shown in (*b*).

curve is not a measure of the lumen output, since a source which gives high candlepower near the vertical has its lumens in this direction spread over only a small area.

In making candlepower distribution curves of a nonsymmetrical source such as a fluorescent luminaire, it is necessary to choose specific planes in which the values will be taken. It is standard practice to choose 3 planes—a perpendicular, a parallel, and 45° plane (see Fig. 19.34).

References

See bibliography following Chapter 21, page 438.

20

Light Sources and Their Characteristics

Long before the dawn of recorded history man discovered the double blessing of fire; heat and light. Even today in our sophisticated space age, fire is still used almost universally as the source of heat, and in a large proportion of the world's dwellings, as the source of light. Recently there has been a resurgence of interest in gas as a light source to the extent that a number of small cities have within the past several years put in installations of street lighting luminaires burning natural gas. Electrical lighting had its real beginning in about 1870 with the development of commercially usable arc lamps and was given greater impetus some 9 years later by Edison's first practical incandescent lamp. Today's electric light sources fall into 3 generic classifications; the incandescent lamp, the gaseous discharge lamp (which includes fluorescent, mercury, sodium, and neon lamps), and the newer electroluminescent lamps. A glance at Table 20.1 will show that none of these sources exhibit a high over-all efficiency (the most efficient fluorescent lamp on the market today converts less than 25 percent of its power input into visible light and throws off the rest as invisible light and heat), although progress in recent years has been great and will probably continue so. The efficiency of filament incandescent

Table 20.1   Efficiency of Various Light Sources

Source	Lumens per Watt*
Candle	0.1
Oil lamp	0.3
Original Edison lamp	1.4
1910 Edison lamp	4.5
Modern 100 watt lamp	17.5
Modern 1000 watt lamp	23.0
Modern 400 watt silver-white mercury lamp†	60.0
Modern 40 watt rapid start fluorescent lamp, warm white†	80.0
Modern 96 watt high output fluorescent lamp†	89.5

NOTE: Maximum theoretical efficiency of an incandescent source is approximately 200 lumens/watt.
* Efficiency of light sources is normally stated in lumens produced per watt of power consumed.
† Initial lumens; ballast losses not included.

lamps has trebled in the last 40 years although it is doubtful that much greater efficiency is possible from what is an inherently inefficient source. On the other hand electroluminescent and gaseous discharge sources of various types are fruitful research fields which are being actively pursued. We feel quite safe in predicting that in the near future new light sources will drastically alter the present lamp and luminaire perspective of lighting design.

1. The Incandescent Filament Lamp—Construction. Although available in a large variety of shapes, sizes, wattages, and colors, every incandescent filament lamp comprises basically a sealed glass envelope containing a filament; it produces light by virtue of the filament being heated to incandescence by an electric current pass-

ing through it. Since the basic principle of lamp operation requires that the tungsten filament be heated until it glows, the lamp is, as mentioned above, inherently inefficient, converting only about 10 to 12 percent of its input power to light and wasting the remainder as heat. Tungsten is used for the filament material because of its high melting point and slow evaporation. Evaporation of the filament results in the familiar bulb blackening and finally in filament rupture, or bulb burnout. The diameter of the filament wire is proportional to the wattage rating of the lamp. Since heavy filaments may be operated at higher temperatures than thin ones, with a correspondingly higher efficiency, higher wattage lamps are more efficient than low wattage units. For example, a 100-watt

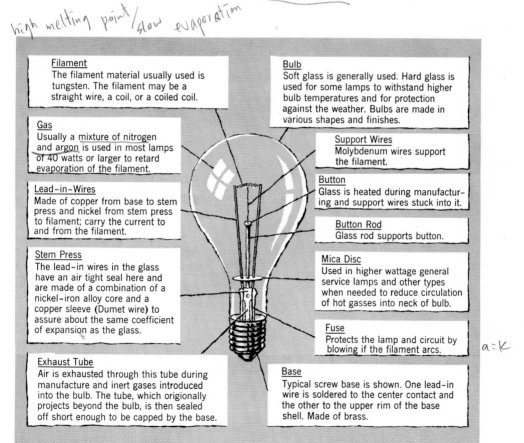

Fig. 20.1　Typical incandescent lamp.

Filament
The filament material usually used is tungsten. The filament may be a straight wire, a coil, or a coiled coil.

Gas
Usually a mixture of nitrogen and argon is used in most lamps of 40 watts or larger to retard evaporation of the filament.

Lead-in-Wires
Made of copper from base to stem press and nickel from stem press to filament; carry the current to and from the filament.

Stem Press
The lead-in wires in the glass have an air tight seal here and are made of a combination of a nickel-iron alloy core and a copper sleeve (Dumet wire) to assure about the same coefficient of expansion as the glass.

Exhaust Tube
Air is exhausted through this tube during manufacture and inert gases introduced into the bulb. The tube, which origionally projects beyond the bulb, is then sealed off short enough to be capped by the base.

Bulb
Soft glass is generally used. Hard glass is used for some lamps to withstand higher bulb temperatures and for protection against the weather. Bulbs are made in various shapes and finishes.

Support Wires
Molybdenum wires support the filament.

Button
Glass is heated during manufacturing and support wires stuck into it.

Button Rod
Glass rod supports button.

Mica Disc
Used in higher wattage general service lamps and other types when needed to reduce circulation of hot gasses into neck of bulb.

Fuse
Protects the lamp and circuit by blowing if the filament arcs.

Base
Typical screw base is shown. One lead-in wire is soldered to the center contact and the other to the upper rim of the base shell. Made of brass.

120-volt general service lamp produces 1750 lumens whereas two 50 watt lamps produce only 1280 lumens. (See Fig. 20.1.)

The glass envelope, normally called the bulb, comes in a variety of shapes and sizes, some of which are illustrated in Fig. 20.2. The bulb nomenclature indicates the type and size; the letter being an abbreviation of the shape and the number equal to the maximum diameter in eighths of an inch. Thus a PS-52 is a pear shaped bulb, $6\frac{1}{2}$ ($\frac{52}{8}$) in. in diameter and an R-40 is a reflector lamp 5 ($\frac{40}{8}$) in diameter. The bulb is normally of soft glass except for high tem-perature units such as projection lamps or units which must withstand sudden tem-perature changes, such as outdoor flood lights. These lamps have hard glass bulbs.

To diffuse the light, most bulbs are either etched on the inside (inside frosted) or are coated inside with white silica. The silica coating provides almost complete light diffusion at a cost of approximately 2 to 3 percent of the light output, whereas inside frosted bulbs provide only partial diffusion but do not reduce light output. Inside frosted bulbs are normally supplied for general service use unless other types are

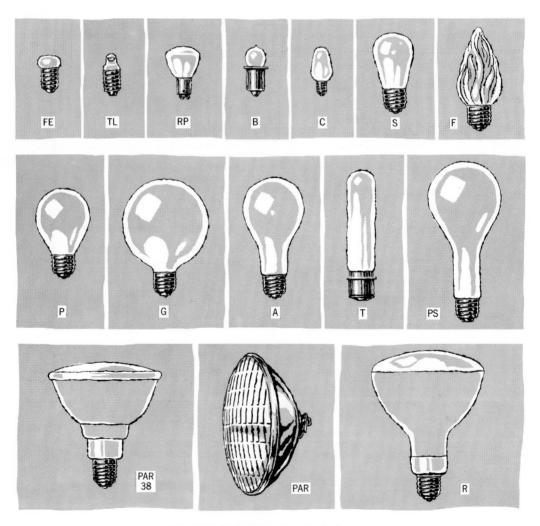

Fig. 20.2 Incandescent lamp bulb shapes.

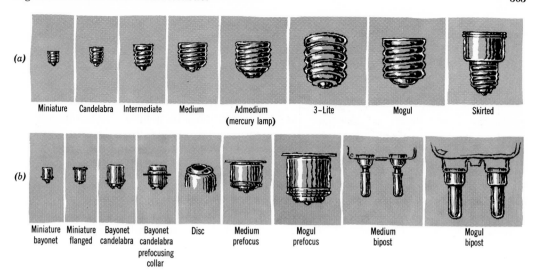

(a) Miniature   Candelabra   Intermediate   Medium   Admedium (mercury lamp)   3–Lite   Mogul   Skirted

(b) Miniature bayonet   Miniature flanged   Bayonet candelabra   Bayonet candelabra prefocusing collar   Disc   Medium prefocus   Mogul prefocus   Medium bipost   Mogul bipost

Fig. 20.3 Incandescent lamp base types: *(a)* screw types; *(b)* accurate positioning types. (Illustrations are shown in relative scale only)

specified. Colored light is also readily available from either coated bulbs or bulbs of colored glass. The most widely used of these is the common daylight blue bulb which produce its daylight color by filtering a portion of the preponderant red and yellow output of the filament. This filtering reduces lamp light output about $\frac{1}{3}$, which, combined with the additional expense of this lamp, makes its use uneconomical except where its special color is required.

The lamp base is the means by which connection is made to the socket and thereby to the source of electric current. Most lamps are made with screw bases of various sizes, the most common being the medium screw base. General service lamps of 300 watts and larger use the mogul screw base. Where exact positioning of the filament is important as it is when lamps are placed in precise reflectors, or in lens systems, a screw base cannot be used. Lamps designed for such use are furnished with one of the special bases illustrated in Fig. 20.3*b*.

2. Operating Characteristics of Incandescent Lamps. The operating characteristics of a filament lamp are critically dependent on filament temperature. Since tempera-

ture is proportional to the current passing through the filament and therefore to impressed voltage, the life, output, and efficiency of a lamp can be markedly altered by even a small change in operating voltage, as illustrated by Fig. 20.4.

For example, burning a 120-volt lamp at 125 volts (104.2%) means approximately:

16% more light (lumens)
 7% more power consumption (watts)
 8% more efficiency (lumens per watt)
42% less life (hours)

whereas;

Burning a 120-volt lamp at 115 volts (95.8%) means approximately:

15% less light (lumens)
 7% less power consumption (watts)
 8% less efficiency (lumens per watt)
72% more life (hours)

Particular note should be taken of the effect of voltage on lamp life. In installations where lamp replacement is difficult and (or) expensive, lamps may be burned slightly under voltage and life prolonged, thereby decreasing the frequency of replacement. However, since efficiency is decreased by

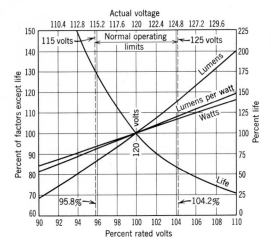

Fig. 20.4   Operating characteristics of a standard 120 volt incandescent lamp.

burnout on a group replacement system and initial installation cost per footcandle and (or) energy costs are high, lamps may be burned over voltage thereby increasing output and efficiency but shortening life. This procedure is normal in sports-lighting installations. In general, however, it is advisable to operate incandescent lamps at rated voltage, accepting balanced efficiency, output, and life. The commonest exception to rated voltage operation is dimming by reduced voltage supply. A brief list of conventional incandescent lamps and their physical and operating characteristics is given in Table 20.2.

this procedure and since energy cost is normally a major cost in any lighting installation over the life of the installation, a detailed cost analysis, which is beyond the scope of this book, should be made by the consulting engineer involved. Conversely, where lamps are replaced before

3. The Fluorescent Lamp—Basic Data. The second major category of light sources is that of electric discharge lamps of which the fluorescent lamps is the best known and most widely used type. It has become so popular since its major introduction in 1937 that it has almost completely supplanted the incandescent lamp in all fields except specialty lighting and residential use. The typical fluorescent lamp comprises a cylindrical glass tube sealed at both ends and

Table 20.2   Incandescent Lamp Data

(Listing a few of many sizes and types of 115-, 120-, and 125-volt lamps)

Watts and Life		Lumens		Physical data	
Lamp Watts*	Av'g Rated Life (hr)	Initial Lumens	Lumens per Watt	Shape of Bulb†	Base
60 A	1000	835	13.9	A-19	Med
60 A/W	1000	835	13.9	A-19	Med
75 A	750	1150	15.4	A-19	Med
100 AX	750	1750	17.5	A-19	Med
100 AX/W	750	1710	17.1	A-19	Med
100 A/SB	1000	1450	14.5	A-21	Med
150 A	750	2700	18.0	A-23	Med
200/A	750	4000	20.4	A-23	Med
200/SBIF	1000	3300	16.5	PS-30	Med
300/IFA	1000	5750	19.2	PS-35	Mog
300/SBIF	1000	5250	17.5	PS-35	Mog

* Figures in this column designate the input watts, and the letters identify the treatment of the glass bulb; thus: 60 A means 60 watts, A means inside frosted. The other letters have these meanings: A/W, inside frosted, white; A/SB, inside frosted, silver bowl; SBIF, silver bowl, inside frosted; IF, inside frosted.

† Bulb Designations. Bulb designations consist of a letter to indicate its shape and a figure to indicate the approximate maximum diameter in eighths of an inch.

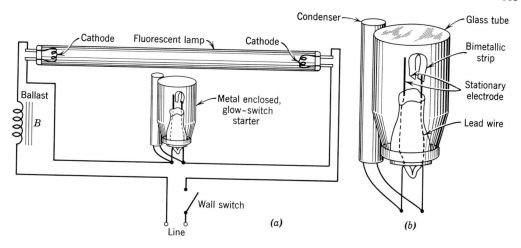

Fig. 20.5 (a) Fluorescent lamp, operating auxiliaries and circuit connections. (b) Enlarged details of the glow switch starter.

containing a mixture of an inert gas, generally argon, and low pressure mercury vapor. Built into each end is a cathode which supplies the electrons to start and maintain the mercury arc, or gaseous discharge. The short wave ultraviolet light, which is produced by the mercury arc, is absorbed by the phosphors with which the inside of the tube is coated and reradiated

in the visible light range. The fluorescent lamp is so called because its phosphors fluoresce, or radiate light, when exposed to ultraviolet light. The particular mixture of phosphors used governs the spectral quality of the light output.

The 2 ends of the lamp are of identical construction. Figures 20.5 and 20.6 show a preheat-starting lamp and its operating

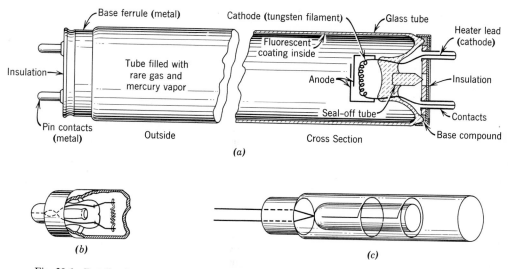

Fig. 20.6 Details of constructions of standard fluorescent lamps. The 2 ends of the lamp are of identical construction. Type (a) hot cathode for preheat-starting; (b) hot cathode for instant starting; (c) cold cathode for instant starting.

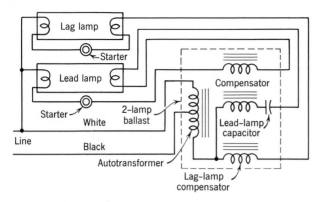

Fig. 20.7 Wiring for a 2-lamp preheat high-power factor, lead-lag fluorescent circuit. The 2-lamp ballast contains the line autotransformer, lamp compensators and the capacitor.

auxiliaries. The glow switch contacts are open when the lamp is off. To start the lamp, the wall switch is closed. The voltage across the starter is sufficient to produce corona or glow discharge between the bimetal and the center electrode. The heat of this discharge causes the bimetal to expand and to close the starter contacts, thus completing the series circuit through the lamp cathodes at both ends of the lamp and preheating the cathodes during the time that residual heat keeps the contacts closed. Because the glow discharge is shorted out, the bimetallic strip cools and the contacts open, at which time the inductive kick of the ballast starts the arc and

normal lamp operation commences. The voltage at the starter contacts is insufficient thereafter to cause the contacts to close while the lamp is in operation and the starter therefore consumes no energy during normal operation. The glow starter is self-contained in a small tubular jacket with terminals to provide easy replacement in case of failure (outer jacket not shown in Fig. 20.5).

The ballast serves the double function of supplying the high voltage necessary to start the arc and of limiting the current in the arc after it is struck. Ballasts are often supplied for operating 2 preheat lamps in a lead-lag circuit. Such a ballast, shown in Fig. 20.7, in addition to starting and current-limiting duty also provides high power factor and causes a marked decrease in the stroboscopic effect of the light output. Since the development of the rapid-start lamp and ballast, the preheat lamp and ballast have fallen into disuse and at this time are certainly, as pertains to all new construction, obsolete. The 48 in. 40-watt 430 ma. T-12 rapid-start lamp may be used as a replacement for preheat lamps in existing preheat circuits.

The major disadvantage of the preheat circuit is the 2- to 5-second starting delay; this failing is overcome by the rapid start circuit of Fig. 20.8 (known as the series-sequence circuit) which gives approximately 1-second starting. Cathode current flows continuously from a separate ballast winding, even when the lamps are lighted.

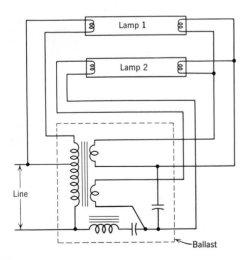

Fig. 20.8 Two-lamp rapid-start series sequence circuit. Ballast rating must correspond to lamp current rating, i.e., 430 ma, 800 ma, or 1500 ma.

Table 20.3 Typical Fluorescent Lamp Operating Data

Lamp Wattage, Diam., Length	Color	Current in Milliamps (ma)	Total Wattage (including ballast)				Rated Life Hours	Initial Lumen Output Per Lamp	Remarks
			Single Lamp		Two Lamps				
			Low PF	Hi PF	Series	Lead-lag			
PREHEAT									
40w T-12 48"	White	...	49	50	...	96	6000	2750	
RAPID START									
30w T-12 36"	Warm white	430	45	50	80	...	9000	2350	Normal output
40w T-12 48"	Warm white	430	47	50	92	...	12000	3250	Normal output
35w T-12 24"	Cool white	800	...	...	95	...	7500	1600	Hi output
60w T-12 48"	Cool white	800	...	85	147	...	7500	3800	Hi output
85w T-12 72"	Cool white	800	...	115	214	...	7500	6500	Hi output
110w T-12 96"	Cool white	800	...	140	254	...	9000	9000	Hi output
110w T-12 48"	Cool white	1500	...	145	252	...	7500	6900	Very hi output
160w T-12 72"	Cool white	1500	...	235	455	...	7500	10900	Very hi output
215w T-12 96"	Cool white	1500	...	235	455	...	7500	15000	Very hi output
SLIMLINE									
25w T-6 42"	Cool white	200	41	39	...	80	7500	1750	
37w T-8 72"	Cool white	200	56	53	...	99	7500	2700	
50w T-8 96"	Cool white	200	...	69	...	132	7500	3750	
21w ⎱ T-12 48"	Cool white	200	...	34	...	63	7500	...	
38w ⎰		425	...	58	108	99	7500	2820	
30w ⎱ T-12 72"	Cool white	200	...	46	...	85	7500	...	
56w ⎰		425	...	83	139	144	7500	4250	
40w ⎱ T-12 96"	Cool white	200	...	56	...	105	9000	...	
74w ⎰		425	...	101	175	180	9000	5850	

No starter is used, the open circuit voltage being sufficient to strike the arc after a short preheat. The rapid start circuit is a very flexible one, lamps and ballasts being readily available for operation at above 430 ma. The higher current lamps which operate at 800 ma. and 1500 ma. are called High Output and Very High Output respectively. These lamps are made in 48, 72, and 96 in. lengths and produce 40 and 250 percent more light than their 430 ma. relatives, respectively.

Instant-start fluorescent lamps, of which Slimline lamps are the best known variety, use a high-voltage transformer to strike the arc without any cathode preheating. These lamps have only a single pin at each end which also act as a switch to break the ballast circuit when the lamp is removed, thus lessening the shock hazard. The lamps are generally operated in 2-lamp circuits at various currents; normal currents being 200 ma. and 430 ma. and normal lengths 42, 48, 64, 72, and 96 in. These lamps are actually hot cathode instant-start lamps, differentiating them from the high-voltage cold cathode type. Slimline lamps and ballasts are more expensive than rapid-start and somewhat less efficient. They are manufactured however in certain sizes and

currents not made in rapid start (e.g., 96 in. 430 ma.) and they have the additional advantage of being able to start in much lower ambient temperature (below 50 F) than rapid start circuits. This starting characteristic makes the instant-start circuit particularly applicable to outdoor use.

The true cold cathode tube uses a large thimble shaped cathode and a high-voltage transformer which literally tears the electrons out of the large cathode, to strike the arc. These lamps have a very long life which, in contradistinction to hot cathode lamps, is virtually unaffected by the number of starts. Cold cathode lamps have a lower over-all efficiency than the hot cathode types and are normally used where long continuous runs are required, as in architectural type lighting rather than in lighting fixtures. Cold cathode lamps are readily dimmed and also operate well at varying ambient temperatures.

4. The Fluorescent Lamp—Operating Characteristics. *Lamp Life* of a fluorescent tube is greatly dependent on the burning hours per start. The figure listed in Table 20.3 and in the lamp catalogs for lamp life is based on a burning cycle of 3 hrs. per start and represents the average life of a group of lamps, i.e., half the lamps of any group will

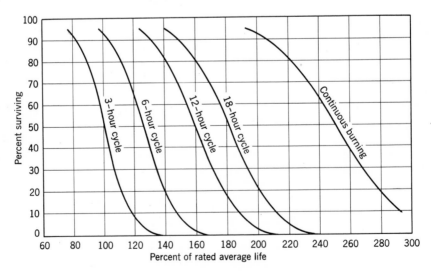

Fig. 20.9   Mortality curves of fluorescent lamps.

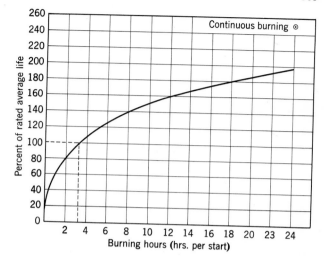

Fig. 20.10 Effect of burning hours on fluorescent lamp life. Note that at 3 burning hours per start the average lamp life is 100% of the nominal catalog figure. This can be doubled by continuous burning or halved by averaging $\frac{1}{2}$ hour burning per start.

have burned out at this time. Typical lamp mortality curves are shown in Fig. 20.9, and the effect of burning hours per start in Fig. 20.10.

Since lamp life and therefore replacement costs are so critically dependent on burning cycles, in some instances it is more economical to leave a lamp burning rather than shut it for a short time. An economic analysis by the engineers involved, based on power, lamp, and labor costs, will answer questions of this type.

Lumen Output of a fluorescent tube decreases rapidly during the first 100 hours of burning and thereafter much more slowly. For this reason the tabulated initial lumen figures represent output after 100 hrs. of burning. Data is also generally published on the lumen output at 40 percent of average rated life. This figure is approximately 85 to 90 percent of the 100 hour initial value.

Temperature of the tube which is also an important factor in light output, is affected by the ambient temperature. Maximum efficiency occurs with the tube operating at a bulb temperature of 100 to 120 F with output reduction above and below these values. For outdoor use where starting below 50 F is a requirement rapid start lamps require special low temperature ballasts. Slimline lamps with normal ballasts will

start readily down to 20 F, and by using the next higher voltage ballast, starting at −20 F is possible.

Voltage either above or below rating adversely affects life, unlike the effect of low voltage on the incandescent lamp. The results of operation at other than rated voltage are shown graphically in Fig. 20.11. The development of special dimming ballasts has made dimming of fluorescent lamps possible. These ballasts, which can dim only a single lamp allow fairly smooth dimming of tubes down to about 1 percent output, at which point the lamp extinguishes. The dimming however is not nearly as smooth nor as complete as is possible with incandescent lamps, and the over-all equipment cost is much higher per KW of dimming load. Normal operating voltage range for ballasts is 110 to 125 volts on 120-volt circuits and 240 to 270 volts on 256-volt circuits.

Frequency is the parameter which will probably see the largest future change inasmuch as operation at frequencies higher than 60 cycles increases lamp efficiency, decreases ballast size, weight, losses, and cost, lowers maintenance costs, and results in smaller air-conditioning systems. Each large job should be the subject of a cost analysis to determine whether installation and operation of a high frequencies system

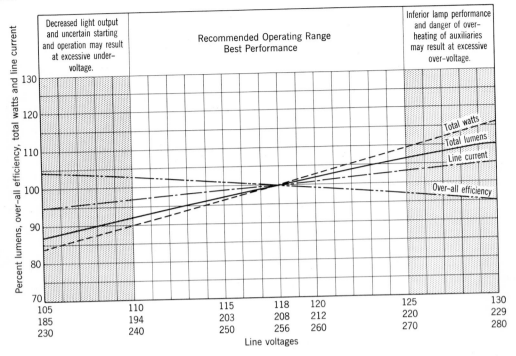

Fig. 20.11 Recommended operating ranges of circuit voltages for most satisfactory operation. The curves indicate the percentage changes in output lumens, efficiency, total watts, and current for line-voltage changes from the rated value. The nominal circuit voltages are 120, 208, and 256 volts.

is feasible and practical. Standard frequencies are 360 cps, 420 cps, 840 cps, 1500 cps, and 3000 cps with higher frequencies in the offing.

5. Other Discharge Lamps. Neon-vapor lamps consist of exhausted glass tubes filled with neon gas which is ionized and conducts an electric current through the tube. A high voltage is required because of the large voltage drop at the cathode, and consequently a transformer is a necessary part of the equipment. A step-up from 115 to 6000 or 10,000 volts may be required. Neon light has a pink to dark-red color, depending upon the gas pressure. The tubes are commonly used in street and window signs as well as indoor signs. Different colors may be obtained by the use of helium gas instead of neon or mixtures of the two, as well as by colored glass tubing.

Mercury- and sodium-vapor lamps are used principally in industrial and street-lighting applications and are therefore not discussed in this book.

6. Electroluminescent Sources. The fluorescent lamp produces light by exciting phosphors with ultraviolet light; the electroluminescent source eliminates the "middleman" by producing light directly from electric energy. The phosphors in the lamp glow when excited by the electric field produced by the applied voltage. Though now in early stages of development, the potential advantages of simplicity of construction, flexibility of shape, brightness control, low operating temperature, long life, and stability are extremely attractive. Present uses are road sign illumination, night lights, and other applications requiring low brightness, maintenance free illumination. The color generally used commercially is green, due to the high sensitivity of the eyes to light of this hue.

7. Spectral Distribution of Light Sources.

In Section 16, Chapter 19 we discussed color as an absolute characteristic of both pigments and light; we defined it, classified it, and reviewed some of the salient optical and psychological characteristics. At this point we are ready to discuss the interrelation between illuminant and pigment since it has been truly observed that "color is how you light it." It behooves the lighting designer to choose the light source with the particular color characteristic which will accomplish his purpose. To do this, it is necessary that he be familiar with the color composition or spectral distribution of the various sources, and their apparent effect (with respect to the eye) on various pigments. If we were to separate each illuminant under consideration into its compo-

nent colors and plot the relative amounts of energy on a wavelength axis, the results would be somewhat as shown in Fig. 20.12. The results are not surprising; we know that north light is very blue, noon daylight white, light from an incandescent lamp yellow-orange, and that light from fluorescent tubes varies with the type of tube.

We have tabulated the energy emission of the various color bands for the 8 types of fluorescent tubes manufactured by Sylvania Electric Products, Inc. and for a 100-watt general service incandescent lamp. Similar lamps of other manufacturers correspond very closely to these figures. (See Table 20.4.)

8. Lighting and Color Rendering. Since the intensity of illumination influences the appearance of colors it must be considered in

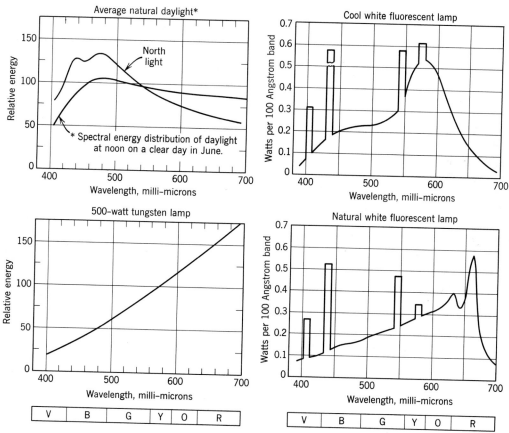

Fig. 20.12 Spectral quality of light sources. Note the extreme blueness of north light and the red-orange quality of the incandescent. (Sylvania Electric Products, Inc.)

Table 20.4 *Energy Emission in Color Bands* (In percent of total emission)

	Angstroms	Daylight	Cool White	White	Warm White	Soft White	Cool White Deluxe	Warm White Deluxe	Natural White	500w Incand.
Ultra Violet	<3800	2.15%	1.70%	1.96%	1.54%	6.96%	5.34%	7.24%	3.58%	.....
Violet	3800–4300	9.60	7.63	6.40	5.23	7.09	9.42	5.20	7.03	2.9%
Blue	4300–4900	27.91	20.95	15.97	13.11	18.73	17.97	10.76	15.49	8.8
Green	4900–5600	27.38	24.88	23.11	20.55	20.80	22.44	22.10	21.32	15.7
Yellow	5600–5900	14.53	18.42	21.11	23.54	12.25	11.77	14.54	10.93	14.6
Orange	5900–6300	13.21	17.89	21.07	24.32	19.01	15.74	24.68	16.30	18.4
Red	6300–7000	5.22	8.53	10.38	11.71	15.16	17.32	15.48	25.35	39.6
Total		100.00	100.00	100.00	100.00	100.00	100.00	100.00	100.00	100.0

choosing object colors. As intensity is increased, reflection increases, particularly with pale tints (high value) which contain much white pigment, thus tending to wash out color. Therefore, with high-intensity lighting, saturation of colors should be high and spectral quality should enhance the object color for true, brilliant color rendition.

Color rendering is defined as the degree to which perceived colors of objects illuminated by a source conform to the colors of the same objects when illuminated by a standard source. In other words, assuming the standard to be an evenly balanced white light, e.g., noon daylight, a good color rendering source must possess a well-balanced spectral distribution in order that it render red as red, yellow as yellow, blue as blue, etc. with no marked color distortion throughout the spectrum. Its own appearance on a neutral surface will depend on its own spectral content but if the observer is placed in a space illuminated with this source, the eye after a short exposure time will become adapted to the source color and will detect only a degree of whiteness rather than an actual tint. Table 20.5 lists the color characteristics of the major sources.

Where it is necessary to detect small color differences between 2 objects, a light poor in object color, or complementary to the object color, should be used, along with a relatively high illumination level. It should be remembered in all considerations of color comparison, matching and rendering, that object color depends upon the spectral energy distribution of the light source (illuminant) and therefore any change in the spectral content will change the object appearance. Two sources of the same color temperature and therefore apparent whiteness can have quite different spectral content and will therefore render object colors differently. A case in point would be a 3500° K warm-white fluorescent tube and an incandescent lamp (500-watt photoflood) of approximately the same color temperature. Color temperature is an expression of dominant color, not spectral distribution.

9. Selection of Light Source. The previous section familiarized the reader with the color characteristics of the various sources so that these characteristics can be intelligently considered and weighed in the choice of a source. This choice, which is one of the early decisions in any lighting design, involves a number of factors of which color is only one. The others are discussed below.

First Cost. Incandescent sources and their fixtures are generally cheaper than fluorescent for the same lighting intensity. However, since the wattage of the incandescent source is approximately $2\frac{1}{2}$ times that of the fluorescent, this cost advantage is reduced as lighting levels are increased due to wiring systems cost, and the advantage shifts to the fluorescent when air conditioning enters the picture, since the addi-

tional wattage is radiated as heat which must be removed by the air conditioning system.

Total Cost. When total costs are reckoned either for an annual figure or longer, including cost of power, it can generally be

Table 20.5 *Color Characteristics of Fluorescent and Incandescent Lamps*

Lamp	Colors Brightened	Colors Greyed	Appear-ance	Color Rendering	Remarks
Daylight	Blue Green	Yellow Orange Red	Blue-White	Fair	Creates very cool atmosphere. Unflattering to skin and other warm tones. Blends with cool white.
Cool White	Blue Green Orange	Yellow Red	White with Blue Tint	Good	Blends with daylight and gives a cool atmosphere. May be used at high illumination levels.
White	Green Yellow Orange	Blue	White with Yellow Tint	Fair	May be used interchangeably with warm white or cool white.
Warm White	Yellow Orange	Blue	Yellow-White	Fair	Blends well with incandescent to create warm atmosphere. Not generally appropriate for levels above 100 F.C.
Soft White	Orange Red	Blue Green Yellow	White with Pink Tint	Good	Blends with deluxe tubes and enhances skin tones. Best applied at low levels, yielding a warm, friendly atmosphere.
Cool White Deluxe	All	None	White	Excellent	Best color rendering. Mixes well with cool white and provides a cool atmosphere. Excellent at high levels.
Warm White Deluxe	Yellow Orange Red	Blue	White	Good	Blends well with warm white, creating a warm atmosphere, flattering to skin tones.
Natural White	Red	None	White with Pink Tint	Excellent	Blends well with incandescent and warm white. Creates a warm, friendly atmosphere with excellent color rendering.
Incan-descent	Yellow Orange Red	Blue Green	Yellow-White	Fair	Useful at low levels to create warm atmosphere, flattering to skin. Blends well with warm white.

Table 20.6 Cost Comparison of Various Lighting Systems for a Typical School Classroom—22 ft × 30 ft × 10 ft

Lighting Layout

	Incandescent	RAPID START 40W. T-12 48"				SLIMLINE 96" T-12 425ma.	
		Indirect	Direct-Indirect with Metal Side Panels	Semi-Indirect	Direct 12" Wide	Direct-Indirect Metal Side Panels	
1. Type of lamp	Incandescent	◄——— RAPID START ———►				◄— SLIMLINE	
2. Lamp description	500 Watt Silver Bowl	40W. T-12 48"				96" T-12 425ma.	
3. Type of luminaire*		Indirect	Direct-Indirect with Metal Side Panels	Semi-Indirect	Direct 12" Wide	Direct-Indirect Metal Side Panels	
4. Luminaire description		Concentric Ring Louver	35° Crosswise × 25° Lengthwise Louver	Plastic Diffuser	Refracting Enclosure	35° Crosswise × 25° Lengthwise Louver	
5. Number of lamps per luminaire	1	4	2	4	2	2	4
6. Rated initial lamp lumens per luminaire	9100	11200	5600	11200	5600	78400/row	11200
7. Watts per luminaire (including ballast)	500	188	94	188	94	1256/row	178
8. Number of luminaires	12	6	14	14	25	2 rows	9
9. Total watts connected	6000	1128	1316	2632	2350	2512	1602
10. Average footcandle maintained†	39	35	42	53	66	82	54
11. Total initial lamp cost	$14.40	$18.00	$21.00	$42.00	$37.50	$52.10	$34.55
12. Total initial cost	371.00	424.00	497.00	855.00	1000.00	694.20	601.00
13. Total initial cost less lamps (12 − 11)	356.60	406.00	476.00	813.00	962.50	642.10	566.45

Line									
14. Annual fixed charges (15% × 13)‡	53.54	60.90	71.50	97.70	121.95	144.45	84.95	96.30
15. Annual cost of replacement lamps§	14.40	2.25	3.00	4.50	5.25	5.25	5.80	8.45
16. Annual cleaning cost	6.00	4.80	7.00	10.50	25.20	12.50	9.00	10.60
17. Total annual maintenance cost (15 + 16)‖	20.40	7.05	10.00	15.00	30.45	17.75	14.80	19.05
18. Annual energy cost (9 × 1000 hrs × .02 ÷ 1000)**	120.00	22.55	26.30	39.45	52.65	47.00	32.05	50.30
19. Total annual operating cost (17 + 18)	140.40	29.60	36.30	54.45	83.10	64.75	46.85	69.35
20. Total annual cost (14 + 19)	193.94	90.50	107.80	152.15	205.05	209.20	131.80	165.65
21. Relative annual cost	2.14	1.00	1.19	1.68	2.27	2.32	1.46	1.83
22. Annual cost per footcandle (20 ÷ 10)	5.01	2.59	2.56	2.42	3.87	3.14	2.44	2.02
22a. Initial cost per footcandle (12 ÷ 10)	9.5	12.1	11.8	10.8	16.2	15.1	11.1	8.5
23. Relative annual cost per footcandle	2.48	1.28	1.27	1.20	1.92	1.56	1.21	1.00
24. Satisfies IES average brightness limitations	Yes	Yes	Yes	Yes	Yes	No	Yes	Yes
25. Uniformity of illumination	Good	Fair	Fair	Good	Satisfactory	Excellent	Good	Fair

* All Indirect and Semi-Indirect units suspended 18″; Direct-Indirect units suspended 12″; Semi-Direct units suspended 12″; Direct units surface mounted; Direct units recessed.
† Based on Medium Maintenance and Reflectances; Ceiling 80%; Walls 30%; Floor 30%.
‡ 10 year amortization plus 5% for interest, insurance, etc.
§ 1000 hours of operation per year.
‖ Labor of replacing lamps done by salaried employee; no separate charge.
** $0.02 per kilowatt-hour.

Electrical Construction and Maintenance, copyright 1959, McGraw-Hill Publishing Co., Inc.

shown that even without consideration of air conditioning the advantage lies with fluorescent fixtures. Table 20.6 shows a typical cost comparison which demonstrates this point.

Operating Costs. The smaller wattage consumed by the more efficient fluorescent source and the lower maintenance cost due to increased lamp life makes the operating cost of fluorescent installations generally the lower one.

Brightness and Glare. Although good fixture designs are readily available for both sources, the fluorescent lends itself more readily to large-area lighting (e.g., luminous ceiling), whereas the incandescent, being a point source, lends itself to greater control, e.g., accurate downlighting. However, it is generally easier to control glare with the inherently lower brightness fluorescent source than with the very bright incandescent source.

Noise. The fluorescent ballast produces a hum which in certain cases can be objectionable. This sound problem can be mitigated by the use of special ballasts, soundproof cases or by remotely mounting the ballasts. All of these procedures, of course, involve additional expense.

Radio Interference. In addition to audible noise, a fluorescent fixture also produces radio noise, or radio interference. This in-terference is of 2 kinds, direct radiation from the lamp and wiring, and conducted interference induced in the power-line wiring. Although this interference is usually small to negligible, it is sufficient to rule out the use of fluorescent lighting in many commercial, industrial, and military electronic laboratory installations. Cold-cathode fluorescent lighting produces considerably less radio noise than conventional fluorescent tubes and is therefore applicable where the radio noise restrictions are less stringent. Direct radiation can be reduced by distance separation or by metallic shielding; conducted interference can be mitigated by special filters which are built into the fixtures. The problem of radio noise does not exist with incandescent fixtures.

Pattern. Due to the large size of fluorescent lamps, they cannot readily be used where unobtrusiveness is paramount; at best they can be designed to blend with the architecture so as to avoid dominating an area. Incandescent lamps, being much smaller, can more readily be "hidden" or used in indirect systems requiring beams of light.

References

See bibliography following Chapter 21, page 438.

21

Lighting Design

1. General. The contents of this chapter belie its title, for having completely absorbed all the data in this and the preceding lighting chapters, the neophyte lighting designer becomes fairly well informed—but remains a neophyte. Lighting design is a combination of applied art and applied science. There can be many solutions to the same lighting problem, all of which will satisfy the minimum requirements, yet some will be dull and pedestrian while others will display ingenuity and resourcefulness. The competent lighting designer approaches each problem afresh, bringing to it a knowledge of current technology and years of background and experience, yet rarely being satisfied with a carbon copy of a previous design. And it is these years of background with their successful and not-so-successful designs coupled with a constant striving for improvements that are the characteristics which differentiate the lighting consultant, designer, or engineer from the design hack who attempts to force each new job into the unwilling mold of a previous design.

Because of the large number of interrelated factors in lighting no single design is the correct one, and for this very reason it is not entirely desirable to solve a lighting problem with a step-by-step technique.

However, since this technique is the only avenue of approach open to the uninitiate who lacks the experience necessary to view an entire solution, we have adopted this approach.

2. Goals of a Lighting Design. Most simply stated, the goal of lighting is to create an efficient and pleasing interior. That these 2 requirements, that is, the utilitarian and architectural, are not antithetical is demonstrated by every good lighting design. Light can and should be used as an architectural material.

(*a*) Lighting levels should be adequate for efficient seeing, yet absolute uniformity is not required. On the contrary, moderate variations within acceptable brightness ratios in a given field of view are desirable to avoid monotony and to create perspective effects.

(*b*) Lighting equipment should be unobtrusive, but this does not mean invisible. Fixtures can be chosen and arranged in various ways to complement the architecture or to create dominant or minor architectural features or patterns. Fixtures may also be decorative and thus enhance the interior design.

(*c*) Lighting should have the proper quality as discussed previously. Accent

Courtesy of T.A.C., Louis Reens

Photo by Dearborn-Massar

Fig. 21.1 Treatment of dominant architectural patterns. In each case the lighting designer was faced with essentially the same problem viz, a low-level seeing task in a large space with a dominant architectural ceiling. Three different solutions were arrived at, each of which is consonant with the architectural ceiling. (*a*) and (*c*) accomplish this by following the dominant line, (*b*) by complementing it.

Photo by M. E. Warren

lighting, directional lighting and other highlighting techniques increase the utilitarian as well as architectural quality of a space. With these goals before us we can write a lighting design procedure, keeping in mind that the order of steps shown is not necessarily the same in each lighting problem and that since all of the factors are closely interrelated it is often necessary to apprehend several of the stages simultaneously before arriving at a decision.

1. Analyze the Lighting Problem
   Consider occupancy, tasks, and arrive at brightnesses, reflectances, lighting levels, and quality of light.

2. Select the Lighting System
   Select type of light source, distribution characteristic of fixture(s) or area source, consider effects of daylighting, economics, and electric loads.

3. Calculate the Lighting Requirements
   Use the applicable calculation method; establish the fixture pattern, considering the architectural effects.

4. Design the Supplemental Lighting
   The decision as to the requirement for supplemental lighting falls under step 1.

5. Review the Resultant Design
   Check the design for quality,

quantity, esthetic effect, and originality. Try at least one alternate scheme.

3. The Lighting Problem. Each space presents a unique lighting problem which must be studied with two principal considerations in mind; the physical characteristics of the space and its occupancy and usage. Under the former category are not only such readily apparent factors as dimensions and proportions of the space, but also architectural treatment and dominant structural or architectural characteristics. Dimensions and proportions will often determine spacing and mountings of fixtures unless dominant architectural elements govern the choice, as in Fig. 21.1.

With respect to occupancy of the space a number of questions must be asked:

(*a*) Is the usage uniform or are different areas utilized for seeing tasks of varying severity? A private office may have a work area and a conference area which may very well be treated differently (see Fig. 21.2).

(*b*) Will the area be used during both daylight hours and at night and if so, are the seeing tasks the same? A schoolroom which has a large daylighting contribution need not be as well artificially illuminated if its nighttime use will be as a meeting room rather than as a classroom. The effect of fenestration will be discussed below.

(*c*) What are the actual seeing tasks? The answer to this question will allow us to de-

Fig. 21.2 Office lighting showing nonuniform approach. Lighting of a space should correspond to the seeing task; thus the protracted close work area (desk) is lighted much more intensely than the relaxation-conference area on the right. The cornice lighting reduces uncomfortable brightness ratios. *IES Recommended Practice for Office Lighting.*

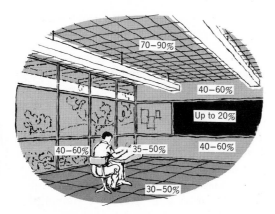

Fig. 21.3 Recommended reflectances for surfaces and furnishings in the classroom. (Note control media is used at windows to reduce exterior brightness so that they are in balance with interior brightness.) *IES Standard Guide for School Lighting.*

Table 21.1   *Recommended Brightness Ratios*

To achieve a comfortable brightness balance, it is desirable and practical to limit brightness ratios between areas of appreciable size from normal viewpoints as follows:

1 to 1/3	Between task and adjacent surroundings
1 to 1/10	Between task and more remote darker surfaces
1 to 10	Between task and more remote lighter surfaces
20 to 1	Between luminaires (or fenestration) and surfaces adjacent to them
40 to 1	Anywhere within the normal field of view

These ratios are recommended as maximums; reductions are generally beneficial.

termine recommended illumination levels from the IES tabulations. These levels must then be adjusted for reductions in visual acuity caused by high brightness ratios and direct and reflected glare. In other words, the proper quantity and quality of light must be established for the particular seeing task involved.

4. Illumination, Brightness, and Reflection Factors. As stated above, by studying individual tasks and their required brightnesses,

a value of required illumination may be arrived at, given the reflectances involved. If the tabulation is made by area type, the most difficult seeing task in the area is used to establish the illumination level for such a typical area. In all cases average reflectance factors are used and brightness ratios are assumed to be within specified limits. The tabulation which follows in Table 21.2 was developed as described above. It cannot be emphasized too strongly that this data must be modified as explained before

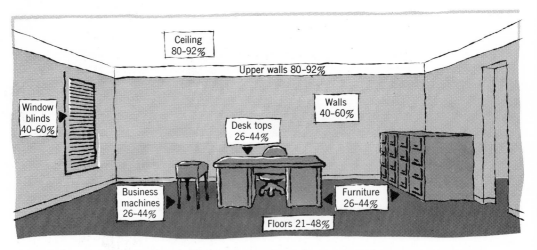

Fig. 21.4   Recommended reflectances for room and furniture surfaces in offices. *IES Recommended Practice for Office Lighting.*

Fig. 21.5 Dark desk tops of this character have reflectances of 4 to 7 per cent. Brightness ratios between the work and such tops are frequently 10 to one or greater. *IES Recommended Practice for Office Lighting.*

in situations where excessive brightness ratios, glare, or incorrect reflectance factors cause a loss of contrast. Figures 21.3 and 21.4 show the recommended reflectance factors for a classroom and an office, while Table 21.1 establishes the general criteria for acceptable brightness ratios.

It must be borne in mind that illumination near a wall, column, or other light-absorbing surface will be less than that found in the center of the room; fixtures should be arranged or designed to overcome this if the seeing task for which we are designing occurs near the wall. The values listed in Table 21.2 represent the required illumination on the surface in question whether horizontal, vertical, or in between.

Since the flux method of calculating illumination normally yields the 30 in. horizontal plane illumination level, it is necessary to be cognizant of the ratio of horizontal to vertical illumination for various lighting systems. This ratio is approximately 3:1 for narrow distribution direct and semi-direct lighting; 2.5:1 for wide distribution luminaires of the same type, and 1.5:1 for indirect, general diffuse lighting.

The figures given in Table 21.2 are minimum standards and should be used as such. Where illumination in excess of 150 to 200 F.C. is required, supplemental lighting is generally indicated, since systems of general area illumination in excess of 200 F.C. will often produce excessive direct and

Fig. 21.6 Desk tops of recommended 35 per cent reflectance result in brightness ratios between the work and these surfaces of two to one. Under conditions of extreme dirt accumulation on such tops, the ratio will seldom exceed three to one. *IES Recommended Practice of Office Lighting.*

Table 21.2   Illumination Levels

	Recommended Minimum Footcandles		Recommended Minimum Footcandles
INDUSTRIAL		Tanks for cooking, extractors, percolators, nitrators, electrolytic cells	50
Airplane Manufacturing			
Stock parts		***Clay Products and Cements***	
Production	100	Molding, pressing, cleaning, and trimming	30
Inspection	200	Color and glazing—rough work	100
Parts manufacturing		Color and glazing—fine work	300
Drilling, riveting, and screw fastening	70		
Spray booths	100	***Cloth Products***	
Welding		Cloth inspection	2000
General illumination	50	Cutting	300
Supplementary illumination	1000	Sewing	500
Final assembly		Pressing	300
Placing of motors, propellers, wing sections, and landing gear	100	***Dairy Products***	
		Fluid milk industry	
Airplane Hangars		Boiler room	30
Repair service only	100	Bottle storage	30
		Can washers	30
Assembly		Filling: inspection	100
Rough easy seeing	30		
Rough difficult seeing	50	***Electrical Equipment Manufacturing***	
Medium	100	Impregnating	50
Fine	500	Insulating: coil winding	100
Extra fine	1000	Testing	100
Automobile Manufacturing		***Exterior Areas***	
Frame assembly	50	Entrances	
Body manufacturing		Active (pedestrian and/or conveyance)	5
Parts	70	Inactive (normally locked, infrequently used)	1
Assembly	100	Vital locations or structures	5
Bakeries		Building surrounds	1
Mixing room	50	Active shipping area surrounds	5
Face of shelves (vertical illumination)	30	Storage areas—active	20
Inside of mixing bowl (vertical mixers)	100	Storage areas—inactive	1
Oven room	30	Loading and unloading platforms	20
Fillings and other ingredients	50		
Wrapping room	30	***Forge Shops***	50
Book Binding		***Foundries***	
Cutting, punching, and stitching	70	Core making (fine)	100
Embossing and inspecting	200	Inspection (fine)	500
		Molding (medium)	100
Breweries			
Brew house	30	***Garages—Automobile and Truck***	
Filling (bottles, cans, kegs)	50	Service garages	
		Repairs	100
Chemical Works		Active traffic areas	20
Hand furnaces, boiling tanks, stationary driers, stationary and gravity crystallizers	30		

Table 21.2 (Continued)

	Recommended Minimum Footcandles		Recommended Minimum Footcandles
Parking garages		*Plating*	30
Entrance	50	*Polishing and Burnishing*	100
Traffic lanes	10	*Printing Industries*	
Storage	5	Printing plants	
Inspection		Color inspection and appraisal	200
Ordinary	50	Machine composition	100
Difficult	100	Composing room	100
Highly difficult	200	Presses	70
Very difficult	500	Imposing stones	150
Most difficult	1000	Proof reading	150
Laundries		Electrotyping	
Washing	30	Molding, finishing, leveling molds, routing, trimming	150
Flatwork ironing, weighing, listing, and marking	50	Blocking, tinning	50
Machine and press finishing, sorting	70	Electroplating, washing, backing	50
Fine hand-ironing	100	*Receiving and Shipping*	
Leather Manufacturing		(See Materials Handling)	
Cleaning, tanning, and stretching, vats	30	*Sheet Metal Works*	
Cutting, fleshing, and stuffing	50	Miscellaneous machines, ordinary bench work	50
Finishing and scarfing	100	Presses, shears, stamps, spinning, medium bench work	50
Locker Rooms	30	Punches	50
Lumber Grading (redwood)	300	Tin plate inspection, galvanized	200
Machine Shops		Scribing	200
Rough bench and machine work	50	*Shipyards*	
Medium bench and machine work, ordinary automatic machines, rough grinding, medium buffing, and polishing	100	General	5
		Ways	10
Fine bench and machine work, fine automatic machines, medium grinding, fine buffing, and polishing	500	Fabricating areas	30
		Stairways, Corridors, and Other Service Areas	20
Extra fine bench and machine work, grinding—fine work	1000	*Storage Rooms or Warehouses*	
Materials Handling		Inactive	5
Wrapping, packing, labeling	50	Active	
Picking stock, classifying	30	Rough bulky	10
Loading, trucking	20	Medium	20
Inside truck bodies and freight cars	10	Fine	50
Paint Shops		*Testing*	
Dipping, simple spraying, firing	50	General	50
Rubbing, ordinary hand painting and finishing art, stencil and special spraying	50	Extra fine instruments, scales, etc.	200
Fine hand painting and finishing	100	*Textile Mills* (Cotton)	
Extra fine hand painting and finishing (automobile bodies, piano cases, etc.)	300	Beaming and slashing on comb	
		Grey goods	50
		Denims	150

Table 21.2 (Continued)

	Recommended Minimum Footcandles		Recommended Minimum Footcandles
Textile Mills (Cotton) (Continued)		**Barber and Beauty Shops**	100
Inspection		**Churches**	
Grey goods (hand turning)	100		
Denims (rapidly moving)	500	Altar, Ark, Reredos	100
Automatic tying-in	150	Pews	20
Drawing-in by hand	200	Pulpit (supplementary)	50
Weaving	100	**Club Reading Rooms**	30
Tobacco Products		**Courtrooms**	
Drying, stripping, general	30		
Grading and sorting	200	Seating area	30
		Court activity area	70
Toilets and Washrooms	30		
Upholstering—Automobile, Coach, Furniture	100	**Depots, Terminals and Stations—** (*See Rail Transportation*)	
Watch and Jewelry Manufacturing	500	**Hospitals**	
Warehouse (*see Storage*)		Autopsy	
Welding		General	100
General illumination	50	Supplementary	2500
Precision manual arc welding	1000	Corridors	10
		Emergency Rooms	
Woodworking		General	100
Rough sawing and bench work	30	Supplementary	2000
Sizing, planing, rough sanding, medium quality machine and bench work, glueing, veneering, cooperage	50	Examination and Treatment Rooms	
		General	50
		Examining table	100
Fine bench and machine work, fine sanding, and finishing	100	Laboratories	
		General	30
STORES, OFFICES, AND INSTITUTIONS		Close work	100
		Library, Consultation Rooms, Kitchen	70
Art Galleries		Obstetrics	
General	30	General (delivery room)	100
On paintings (supplementary)	30	Delivery table	2500
Dark paintings with fine detail may require 2 or 3 times as much illumination.		Patients' Rooms	
		General	10
On statuary	100	Supplementary for reading	30
In some cases, much more illumination is necessary to reveal the beauty of statuary.		Supplementary for examination	100
		Recovery Rooms	30
		Surgery	
Auditoriums		General	100
Assembly only	15	Supplementary on table	2500
Exhibitions	30	Toilets	10
Social activities	5	Waiting Rooms	30
Banks (*See also Offices*)		**Hotels and Motels**	
Lobby	50	Auditoriums	
Writing areas in lobby	70	Assembly only	15
Teller's stations	150	Exhibitions	30
		Dancing	5

Table 21.2 (Continued)

	Recommended Minimum Footcandles		Recommended Minimum Footcandles
Bars and cocktail lounges (see Restaurants)		Washrooms	30
Bathrooms		Medical and Dental	
General	10	Waiting room	30
Bedrooms		Medical examination room	
Reading (books, magazines, newspapers)	30	General	50
General	10	Examining table	100
Corridors, elevators, and stairs	20	Dental office (General)	70
Entrance foyer	30	Dental chair (oral cavity)	1000
Linen room			
Sewing	100	***Post Offices***	
General	20	Lobby, on tables	30
Lobby		Sorting, mailing, etc.	100
General lighting	10	Storage	20
Reading and working areas	30	Files (see Offices)	
Offices		Corridors and stairways	20
Accounting	150		
General	100	***Restaurants***	
Power Plant		Dining Areas	
Boiler room	10	Cashier	50
Equipment room	20	Intimate type	
Storerooms	10	Light environment	10
		Subdued environment	3
Libraries		Leisure type	
Reading rooms and carrells	70	Light environment	30
Stacks	30	Subdued environment	15
Book repair and binding	70	Quick service type	
Check-in and check-out, catalogs, card files	70	Bright surroundings	100
		Normal surroundings	50
Municipal Buildings		NOTE: Footcandle levels in dining areas are highly variable. Variations depend on such factors as time of day, desired atmosphere, individuality, and attractiveness.	
Municipal offices (see Offices)			
Police			
Identification records	150		
Jail cells and interrogation rooms	30		
Fire Houses		Food Displays—twice the general levels but not under	50
Dormitory	20	Kitchen—commercial, hospital, hotel	
Recreation room	30	Inspection, checking, and pricing	70
Wagon room	30	Other areas	30
Offices		***Schools***	
General		Auditoriums	
Cartography, designing, detailed drafting	200	Assembly only	30
Accounting, auditing, tabulating, bookkeeping, business machine operation	150	Study halls	70
Regular office work—reading, transcribing, active filing, mail sorting, etc.	100	Classrooms	
		Regular classroom work	70
Corridors, elevators, escalators, stairways	20	Chalkboards (supplementary illumination)	150
(Or, not less than $\frac{1}{5}$ the level in adjacent areas.)		Drafting rooms	100

Table 21.2 (Continued)

	Recommended Minimum Footcandles		Recommended Minimum Footcandles
Schools (Continued)		Rest rooms	30
		Stockrooms	30
Laboratories		Parking areas (convenience lots lighted for	
General work	70	customer attraction)	5
Close work	150		
Lecture rooms		**Studios**	
General	70		
Special exhibits and demonstrations	150	Broadcasting	70
Lipreading classes	150	Television	
Manual arts	100	In studio	
Sewing rooms	150	General (circulation areas)	30
Sightsaving classes	150	Black and white studio	50–150
Study halls	70	Color studio	350–700
Corridors and stairs	20	Industrial, sports, special events	
Gymnasiums		Black and white	25–200
General exercising	30	Color	250–1000
Exhibition games	50	NOTE: Above footcandle recommendations are for scenes not involving special lighting or special pictorial effects.	
Service Stations		**Theaters**	
Exterior		Auditoriums	
Yard	5	During intermission	5
Street entrances	10	During performance or presentation	0.1
NOTE: Illumination level at entrances should be at least twice yard level for customer attraction and for safe entry and exit.		Foyer	5
		Entrance lobby	20
Pump island	100	**RESIDENTIAL**	
Building faces	20		
Interior		**Kitchen Activities**	
Sales room	100	Sink	70
Displays	200	Range and work surfaces	50
Service bays	100		
		Laundry Activities	
Stores		Trays, ironing board, ironer	50
NOTE: Color rendition of fluorescent lamps is important. Incandescent and fluorescent lighting usually are combined for best appearance of merchandise.		**Reading at any Location**	
		Prolonged periods	
Store interiors		Small type—low contrast	70
Circulation areas	30	Large type—high contrast	50
Merchandising areas		Casual periods	
Service stores	100	Small type—low contrast	50
Self-service stores	200	Large type—high contrast	30
Showcases and wall cases		**Sewing**	
Service stores	200	Dark fabric (fine detail, low contrast)	200
Self-service stores	500	Prolonged periods (light to medium fabric)	100
Feature displays		Occasional periods (light fabric)	50
Service stores	500	**Facial Grooming**	
Self-service stores	1000	Shaving—Make-up	50

Table 21.2 (Continued)

	Recommended Minimum Footcandles
Study—Flat Top Desk	
Concentrated and prolonged	70
Writing—Flat Top or Dropleaf Desk	
Casual letter writing	30
Table Games	30
Work Shop	
Bench work	70
General Illumination	
NOTE: General lighting in residential areas need not be uniform in character.	
Entrances, hallways, stairways, stair landings	10
Living room, dining room, family room, bedroom, sun room, library, game, or recreation room	10
Kitchen, laundry, bathroom	30

TRANSPORTATION

AIR TRANSPORTATION

	Recommended Minimum Footcandles
Airplanes	
Passenger compartment	
General	5
Reading (at seat)	20
Airplane Repair Service Hangars	100
Hangar Aprons, to approximately 50 ft out	
Maintained at not less than	1
Terminal Aprons, to approximately 200 ft out	
Maintained at not less than	0.5
Central area—area of heavy vehicular and passenger activity. Minimum	2

RAIL TRANSPORTATION

	Recommended Minimum Footcandles
Depots, Terminals and Stations	
Ticket offices, ticket racks, counters, general	100
Waiting rooms, rest rooms, smoking rooms, washrooms	30

	Recommended Minimum Footcandles
Baggage checking	50
Storage	20
Concourse	10
Platforms	20

OUTDOOR FLOODLIGHTING

	Recommended Minimum Footcandles
Building	
Construction	10
Excavation	2

Bulletins and Poster Panels

	Surroundings	
	Dark	Bright
Light surfaces	20	50
Dark surfaces	50	100

Building Exteriors, and Monuments (Floodlighted)

	Surroundings	
	Dark	Bright
Light surfaces	5	15
Medium—dark surfaces	10	20
Dark surfaces	20	50

	Recommended Minimum Footcandles
Flags	50

Industrial Properties—Exterior Areas

	Recommended Minimum Footcandles
Entrances	
Active (pedestrian and/or conveyance)	5
Inactive (normally locked, infrequently used)	1
Vital locations or structures	5
Building surrounds	1
Active shipping area surrounds	5
Storage areas	
Active	20
Inactive	1
Loading and unloading platforms	20

Parking Lots

	Recommended Minimum Footcandles
Self-parking	1
Attendant parking	2
Shopping centers (customer attraction device)	5

Adapted from *IES Lighting Handbook,* 3rd Edition.

Table 21.3 Approximate Reflection Factors, (for medium value colors)

White	83%	Tan	50–30%
Gray	70–44	Brown	40–20
French gray	40	Green	55–20
Dark gray	19	Olive green	20
Ivory white	80	Azure blue	55
Caen stone	78	Sky blue	37
Ivory	71–63	Shell pink	54
Pearl gray	72	Pink	70–50
Buff	70–40	Cardinal red	20
Buff stone	20	Red	40–15

reflected glare and will thus defeat the purpose of the increased illumination. Too, location of supplemental lighting sources can generally be controlled to fall outside

the geometry of either direct or reflected glare, in addition to the obvious economic considerations.

The table is generally an extract from current IES Standards with some changes and additions. For more complete data refer to IES handbook, 3rd Edition.

5. Quality of Lighting. Having established a footcandle intensity level, reflectance factors, and brightness of surfaces, the lighting designer in conjunction with the interior specialist may select the finishes of the ceiling and walls. Table 21.3 is an abbreviated list of reflection factors which may be helpful in this connection.

In the case of semi-indirect or indirect lighting, where the light undergoes a number of wall and ceiling reflections before

Table 21.4 Visual Comfort Table

Holoflux with four F40T12/RS lamps per four foot section in rooms having reflection factors as follows:—Ceiling 80%, Walls 50%, Floor 30%.

Room Width (in feet)	Room Length (in feet)	Crosswise				Lengthwise			
		Ceiling Height (in feet)							
		8½′	10′	13′	16′	8½′	10′	13′	16′
15	20	95	97	99	100	96	96	95	94
	30	95	96	98	100	96	96	95	94
	40	94	95	96	99	95	95	94	94
	60	94	95	97	99	95	95	94	94
20	20	95	97	98	100	96	95	95	94
	30	95	96	98	99	96	95	95	95
	40	95	95	98	99	96	95	95	95
	60	94	95	97	98	95	95	95	95
	80	94	95	97	98	95	95	95	95
30	40	94	96	98	99	95	95	95	95
	60	94	95	97	98	94	95	95	95
	80	93	95	96	97	94	95	95	96
	100	92	94	95	96	94	95	96	96
40	40	94	96	97	98	95	95	95	95
	60	94	96	96	97	95	95	95	96
	80	93	95	96	97	95	96	96	97
	100	93	95	96	97	95	96	96	97
60	60	93	94	95	97	95	96	97	97
	120	95	95	95	96	95	97	98	99

This table indicates the percentage of normal observers who may be expected to experience visual comfort when seated in the least favorable visual positions in the room. *Holophane Co.*

reaching the working surface, greater illumination will be obtained if those surfaces are colored than if they are grays of the same luminous reflectance. The difference can be as much as 100 percent depending upon the number of reflections and the luminous reflectance. With an 80 percent R.F. paint the difference is 2 percent for 1 reflection and 10 percent for 5 reflections.

The factors affecting quality of lighting were discussed in detail in Chapter 19 and will not be repeated here except for a few general remarks. Reflected glare is a greater problem at low lighting intensities than at high, since in systems of 70 F.C. and above, room brightnesses are generally within a factor of 3 to 1 to the brightness of the source, at the reflecting angle. Direct glare on the other hand *may* be a problem in a high intensity installation if fixture brightnesses are not carefully controlled. Although no single universally acceptable method has been developed for evaluating direct glare, the problem has for some years been the subject of intensive study by individual researchers and by subcommittees of the IES. In addition to the Visual Comfort Index and the Visual Comfort Factor mentioned in Section 19.13, other formulations of the same type such as Glare Factor, Visual Comfort Probability and Discomfort Glare Ratio have been proposed. A new method for computing comfort in a visual field has been developed by the Direct Glare Study Group of the IES. At this writing, this method is not sufficiently simple to allow ready application. It is our recommendation therefore, that pending the appearance of a simple accurate method, the manufacturers glare—comfort data be utilized. A typical table of this type is shown in Table 21.4. The degree of diffuseness (amount of shadow) also effects the quality of the lighting as previously discussed. Methods of accomplishing varying degrees of diffuse lighting will be studied under Section 7, "Types of Lighting Systems."

A comparison of sources i.e., incandescent and fluorescent, was discussed at some length previously. The recommendations in Table 21.5 offer a quick first solution which may then be reviewed in detail.

6. Illumination Methods. There are 3 methods of illumination: general, local and combined general and local.

(*a*) *General Lighting* is a system designed to give uniform and generally, though not necessarily, diffuse lighting throughout the area under consideration. The method of accomplishing this result varies from the use of luminous ceiling to properly spaced and chosen downlights, but the resultant lighting *on the horizontal working plane* must be the same, i.e., reasonably uniform, and sufficient for the tasks.

(*b*) *Local Lighting* is a system of lighting which results in restricted areas of high intensity with generally larger areas of low intensity from spill light. Luminaires are normally of the direct type, placed immediately over the work area. Typical applications of this method would be at factory machine or bench locations, merchandise counters, billiard tables, and other restricted area usages. This type of lighting is also used in offices and other business areas to add interest and to highlight selected areas. See Fig. 21.28. This system may result in unacceptable brightness ratios between task and surroundings and is therefore often combined with general lighting.

(*c*) *Combined General and Local Lighting* is used in areas where the general seeing task is low—but local high-intensity lighting, in such instance called supplementary lighting, is required. An excellent example is the department store where circulation requires low-level lighting (30 F.C.), while merchandising areas and show cases require up to 500 F.C. The indicated solution for such a problem is a general lighting system which will provide 30 F.C. of uniform, diffuse lighting of the proper color, and supplementary local lighting in restricted areas. The quality of the local

Table 21.5   Recommended Light Source for Various Uses

For Industry

In Production Areas

Fluorescent	Cool White, Daylight, White, Warm White
Incandescent	Inside Frosted, Clear
Mercury	Silver White, Clear, Color Improved, True-Tone

In Laboratories, Drafting and Engineering Areas

Fluorescent	White, Warm White, Cool White, Daylight

For Business

In General Offices

Fluorescent	Warm White, Cool White, White, Natural White
Incandescent	Soft White

For Private Offices, Conference and Reception Rooms

Fluorescent	Natural White, Deluxe Warm White, Deluxe Cool White
Incandescent	Soft White

For Retail Stores

Selling General Merchandise, Apparel, Foods, Flowers

Fluorescent	Natural White, Deluxe Warm White, Deluxe Cool White, Warm White
Incandescent	Soft White, Inside Frosted

For Home Furnishings, Furniture, Draperies

Fluorescent	Deluxe Warm White, Warm White, Natural White
Incandescent	Soft White, Inside Frosted

For Furs

Fluorescent	Cool White, Daylight, or both combined

For Beauty Shops

Fluorescent	Natural White, Deluxe Cool White, Deluxe Warm White

For Items Needing Close Matching, Threads, etc.

Fluorescent	Deluxe Cool White, Daylight

For Restaurants, Cafeterias, Cocktail Lounges

In Customer Areas

Fluorescent	Natural White, Deluxe Warm White, Deluxe Cool White
Incandescent	Soft White, Softlight

In Kitchens, Food Preparation Areas

Fluorescent	White, Warm White
Incandescent	Inside Frosted, Soft White

For Schools and Colleges

In Classrooms, Lecture Halls, Libraries, Laboratories, Workshops

Fluorescent	Cool White, Warm White, White
Incandescent	Soft White

In Cafeterias, Art Rooms, Home Economics Areas, Auditoriums

Fluorescent	Natural White, Deluxe Warm White, Deluxe Cool White
Incandescent	Soft White

For Homes, Hotels, Motels

In General Lighting Fixtures, Floor, Wall and Table Lamps

Incandescent	Soft White, Softlight, Cool-Light Inside Frosted

In Built-in Architectural Valance, Cove and Cornice Lighting

Fluorescent	Natural White, Deluxe Warm White, Deluxe Cool White

In Utility Areas, Workshops, Laundries, Commercial Kitchens

Fluorescent	Warm White, White

lighting supplied depends upon the particular item being displayed.

These 3 methods of illumination can be accomplished in many ways by the use of fixtures of different types, since the illumination method is primarily a function of fixture placement and arrangement and only secondarily of the inherent fixture lighting distribution. The term used to describe the type of lighting obtained from the inherent design of the fixture is referred to as the "lighting system."

7. Types of Lighting Systems. No one lighting system can be said to be the single choice in a given instance; on the contrary, the designer will normally have a choice of at least 2 systems which will, if utilized properly, yield illumination of adequate quantity and good quality. However, other factors, such as harmonization with the architecture and economics, will usually tip the balance in favor of one or the other. The 5 generic types of lighting systems are: Indirect, Semi-Indirect, Diffuse or Direct-Indirect, Semi-Direct, and Direct.

(*a*) *Indirect.* 90 to 100 percent of the light output of the luminaires is directed to the ceiling and upper walls of the room. The system is called indirect because practically all of the light reaches the horizontal working plane indirectly, that is, via reflection from the ceiling and upper walls. *Therefore, the ceiling and upper walls in effect become the light source* and if these surfaces have a high reflectance finish, the room illumination is quite diffuse (shadowless). Since the source must be suspended at least 18 in., this system requires a minimum ceiling height of 9 ft. 6 in.

In addition to diffuseness, the resultant illumination is generally uniform, and direct and reflected glare are low. In order to avoid an unacceptable (greater than 20 to 1) brightness ratio between the luminaire and its surrounding field, the luminaire is made translucent, at least on the bottom surfaces and sometimes on the sides. This type is known as "luminous indirect" in contra-

distinction to metal reflectors, which are totally indirect. Architectural coves and valances also may be classed as indirect lighting. See Figs. 21.7*a* and 21.8.

In all cases, but most particularly in the instance of high-level illumination, the luminaire spacing and suspension length and the cove or valance dimensions must be carefully chosen to avoid excessive ceiling brightness. Generally 75 F.C. is considered the maximum horizontal plane illumination attainable without exceeding ceiling brightness limits. Ceiling brightness should not exceed 400 footlamberts. In general, the desirable light quality produced in this system tends to offset its inherent inefficiency, and makes it an excellent choice for schools, offices, drafting rooms, and other locations requiring shadowless light. This system also has the advantage, inherent in all diffuse systems, of high vertical surface illumination.

(*b*) *Semi-Indirect.* 60 to 90 percent of the light is directed upwards to the ceiling and upper walls. This distribution is similar to the indirect, except that it is somewhat more efficient and allows higher levels of illumination without undesirable brightness contrast between fixture and surroundings. A typical fixture employs a translucent diffusing element through which the downward component shines, and is illustrated in Fig. 21.10. The ceiling remains the principal radiating source and the diffuse character of room-lighting remains. In both indirect and semi-indirect systems, it is often desirable to add accent lighting or down lighting in order to break the monotony inherent in these systems, and to establish a visual point of interest, or to create required modeling shadows.

(*c*) *General Diffuse or Direct-Indirect.* This type provides approximately equal distribution of light upwards and downwards, resulting in a bright ceiling and upper wall background for the luminaire. For this reason brightness ratios in the upper vision zone are usually not a problem, although direct and reflected glare *may* be troublesome at high illumination levels (100 F.C. and above). Since the ceiling is a major though secondary source of room illumination, diffuseness will be good, with resultant satisfactory vertical-plane illumination. Light falling on a horizontal surface will derive principally (65–75 percent) from the luminaire and secondarily from the ceiling (25 to 35 percent), the exact ratio being dependent on the ceiling reflectance and the fixture characteristic.

The difference between general diffuse (e.g., an opal diffusing globe) and direct-indirect (e.g., an open-top luminous side and bottom luminaire) lies in the fixture characteristic; diffuse fixtures give light in all directions, whereas direct-indirect have little horizontal component. See Figs. 21.7*c*, *d*, 21.9 and 21.11. Stems should be of sufficient length to avoid excessive ceiling brightness; generally not less than 18 in.

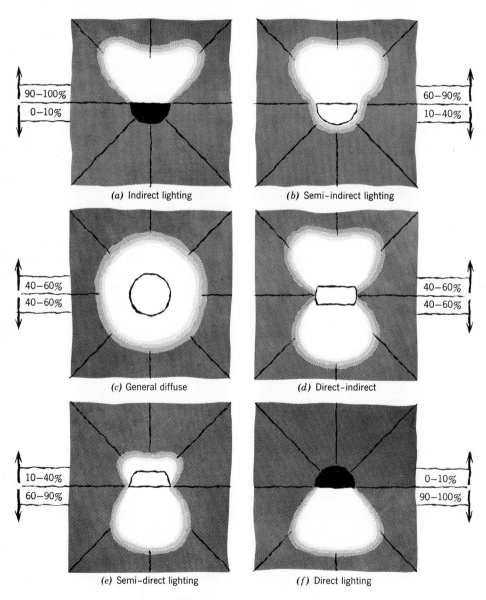

(a) Indirect lighting

(b) Semi-indirect lighting

(c) General diffuse

(d) Direct-indirect

(e) Semi-direct lighting

(f) Direct lighting

Fig. 21.7　Lighting systems.

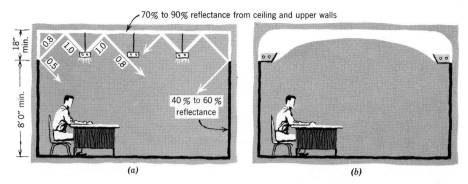

70% to 90% reflectance from ceiling and upper walls

Fig. 21.8 Indirect lighting. The white surfaces of the room represent the areas which are illuminated by the indirect fixtures, and in turn illuminate the room. (*a*) Indirect luminaires give uniformly bright ceiling. (*b*) Use of architectural coves gives brightness gradient on ceiling and if properly designed, uniform illumination in the room.

Fig. 21.9 (*a*) General diffuse lighting. Note that all room surfaces are illuminated and become secondary sources; the primary source of illuminant is the direct radiation from the fixture. The floor contribution is low due to its normally low reflectance. (*b*) Direct-indirect lighting. Upper and lower room surfaces are luminous but center of walls is not because of the lack of horizontal light from fixtures. Principal light on working plane comes from luminaire directly.

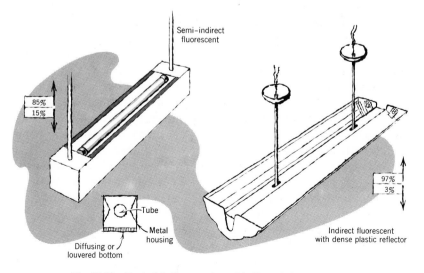

Fig. 21.10 Typical indirect and semi-indirect lighting fixtures.

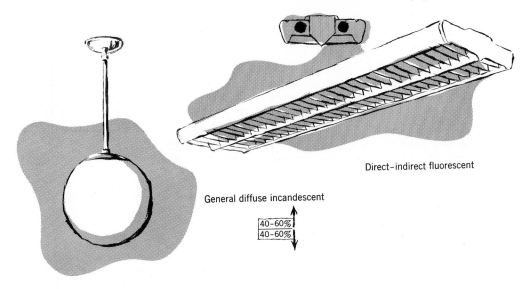

Direct–indirect fluorescent

General diffuse incandescent

40–60%
40–60%

Fig. 21.11   Typical general diffuse and direct-indirect fixtures.

(*d*) *Semi-Direct Lighting.* Since with this lighting system 60 to 90 percent of the fixture output is directed downward, the ceiling component is small and the room lighting lacks diffuseness. This may result in annoying shadows unless a large number of fixtures or large area sources are used. In the former case, since reflected glare may very well be a problem, surfaces of room furnishings should have a high reflectance diffuse finish (e.g., matte white or beige). Ceiling brightness serves generally to eliminate the possibility of objectionable brightness ratios between the luminaire and its background. Since the major portion of the light is directed downward it is important to use a high reflectance diffuse floor which will materially contribute to both ceiling brightness, general diffusion, and elimination of excessive contrasts. See Fig. 21.7*e*. Surface mounted luminous fixtures, as well as certain pendant units may be subsumed under this category. This system of lighting is applicable whenever high efficiency is important and some shadowing is acceptable.

(*e*) *Direct Lighting.* Inasmuch as practically all of the light is directed downward, ceiling illumination results from reflection of light from the floor and furnishings. This system then, more than any other, requires a light, high reflectance, diffuse floor unless a dark ceiling is desired from an architectural or decorative viewpoint. Occasionally the ceilings are deliberately painted a dark color and direct fixtures used in order to lower the apparent ceiling of a poorly proportioned room or to hide unsightly piping, ductwork, etc. As with semi-indirect, direct glare and shadows present a real problem which may be treated as mentioned above. Diffusion is low, resulting in low vertical surface illumination. Therefore, if wall lighting is required or desired, fixtures must be specifically located with this purpose in mind. Direct glare is readily controllable by use of proper baffling, refracting and reflecting materials. (See Figs. 21.7*f* and 21.12.)

All ceiling recessed lighting fixtures fall into the direct lighting system category. When these fixtures are designed with black cones or baffles or other devices which are nonreflecting at the viewing angle, the fixture appears dark. It is this writers opinion that installations which give high horizontal surface illumination with no apparent source of brightness such as an installation using black cone downlights, is disturbing to the eye and to our normal bright-sun-and-sky orientation and should therefore be used cautiously and only in limited areas.

If the area of a direct lighting fixture becomes sufficiently large it will cover the entire ceiling. These units are therefore quite logically called "luminous ceilings." Such a system is a natural outgrowth of the attempt to provide ever-increasing levels of illumination while maintaining acceptable glare conditions by the use of larger area lower brightness sources. The result is similar to that obtained by indirect lighting which is, in effect, a luminous ceiling. The difference is of course that the one case uses reflected light and the other transmitted light. The actual luminous ceiling installation com-

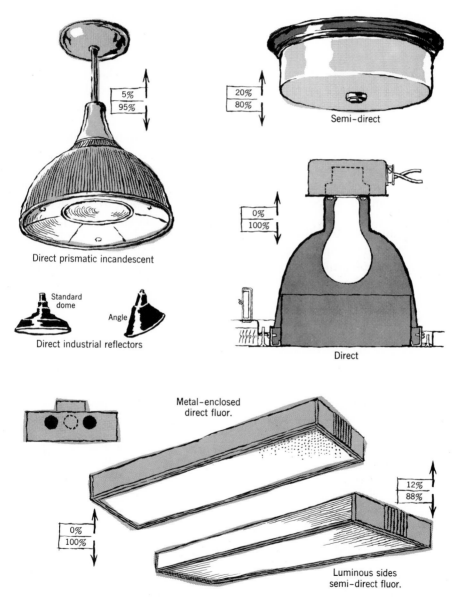

Fig. 21.12   Typical semi-direct and direct fixtures.

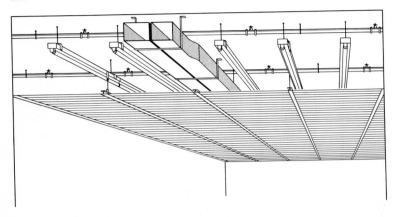

Fig. 21.13 Luminous ceiling installation. Note that in properly designed installation piping and ductwork do not affect the light distribution.

prises a ceiling cavity covered with a light transmitting element such as translucent plastic or glass sheets, or louvers. The principal disadvantage to the luminous ceiling installation is its high initial cost, limited efficiency and severe monotony. The use of colored, shaped, or otherwise treated panels has been attempted to ameliorate this latter condition, with limited success. (See Fig. 21.13.)

8. Lighting Fixture Distribution Characteristics. Having decided upon the lighting method (general, supplemental) and system (e.g., direct, diffuse) the designer is faced with a choice of quite literally hundreds of fixtures, most of which purport to be ideal for the purpose intended. Efficiency and economics will be discussed in the next section, a brightness test was covered in Section 5; distribution will be our concern in this section.

The 2 distribution curves shown in Fig. 21.14a and b are actual test results of two 2-lamp, 1-ft wide by 4-ft long, semidirect fluorescent fixtures, with prismatic enclosures. The flat bottom of curve (a) indicates even illumination over a wide area and therefore a high spacing to mounting height ratio (1.5) whereas the rounded bottom of curve (b) indicates uneven illumination and

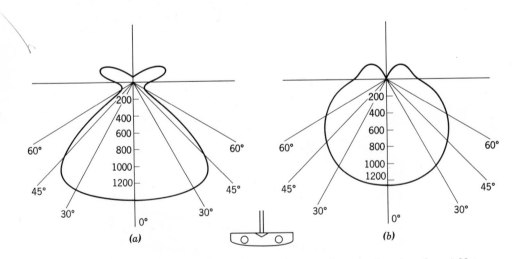

Fig. 21.14 Semi-direct fluorescent fixture distribution (2-lamp 40-watt, prismatic enclosure). Note the sharp cut-off and wide horizontally even distribution of (a) in contrast to the diffuse, broad and horizontally uneven distribution of (b).

closer required spacing for uniformity (1.2 ratio of spacing to mounting height above working plane for a maximum of 20 percent illumination variation).

The straight sides of curve a show a fairly sharp cutoff and the small amount of light above 45° means high efficiency, sufficient wall lighting, low diffuseness, and very little direct glare problem. Conversely, curve b shows a large amount of horizontal illumination (above 45°) with resultant direct glare, diffuseness, and relative inefficiency since horizontal light is attenuated by multiple reflections before reaching the horizontal working plane.

The uplight component of fixture a is directed outward to cover the ceiling and will not cause hot-spots; the corresponding light from fixture b is concentrated above the fixture and will give uneven illumination of the ceiling.

Thus we see then that even a cursory inspection of a fixture curve performed by an informed person can yield a large amount of data on the fixture's performance.

9. **Uniformity of Illumination.** In any illuminated space utilizing multiple, discreet light sources (rather than a luminous ceiling) it is necessary to decide upon a fixture spacing that will give acceptable uniformity of illumination. It has been found experimentally that a ratio of maximum to minimum illumination on the working plane of 1.2 is the maximum acceptable. This assumes that the seeing task is constant over the working plane. In an office with a fixed furniture arrangement this would mean that the 1.2 ratio applies to the desk top, but not to the horizontal working plane in the entire room. Illumination around the desk should yield the 3 to 1 maximum brightness ratio requirement. The data given by manufacturers are generally based on this 1.2 figure, which should not be exceeded in a quality design, where over-all uniformity is required. (See Fig. 21.15.)

We mentioned above that the fixture of Fig. 21.14a had a high spacing to mounting height ratio due to its flat bottomed curve. This ratio, when not given by the manufacturer, may be approximated from the figures in Table 21.6.

The distribution types shown in Table 21.6 are generic and therefore may not be readily applicable in some cases. The curves of Fig. 21.16 are applicable to direct distribution incandescent fixtures. For fixture distributions other than those shown, interpolation will be necessary.

It is well known that illumination levels near walls drop off at least 20 to 30 percent even in a well-designed installation. To

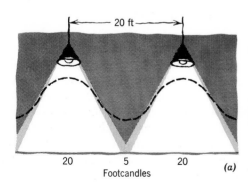

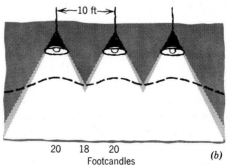

(a) Roller coaster lighting results when spacings are too great.

(b) Closer spacings result in uniform lighting by overlapping the distributions from individual luminaire.

Fig. 21.15   Uniformity of illumination. The ratio of maximum to minimum illumination should not exceed 1.20 in areas requiring uniform illumination.

Table 21.6   **Spacing—Mounting Height of Luminaires** *

Ceiling Height	Indirect		Semi-Indirect	General Diffusing	Semi-Direct	Direct		Semiconcentrating Direct	Concentrating Direct
	Distance† from Walls	Length of Suspension	Maximum‡ Spacing of Luminaires	Mounting** Height of Luminaires	Distance† from Walls	Maximum‡ Spacing of Luminaires	Maximum‡ Spacing of Luminaires	Maximum‡ Spacing of Luminaires	
8	3	§	9	8	3	$7\frac{1}{2}$	$5\frac{1}{2}$	$2\frac{1}{2}$
9	3		$10\frac{1}{2}$	9	3	9	6	3
10	$3\frac{1}{2}$		$12\frac{1}{2}$	10	$3\frac{1}{2}$	$10\frac{1}{2}$	7	4
11	$3\frac{1}{2}$		$13\frac{1}{2}$	11	$3\frac{1}{2}$	12	8	$4\frac{1}{2}$
12	4		15	12	4	$13\frac{1}{2}$	9	5
13	4		17	13	4	15	10	$5\frac{1}{2}$
14	5		19	14	5	$16\frac{1}{2}$	11	6
15	5		20	15	5	18	12	$6\frac{1}{2}$
16	6		22	16	6	20	13	7
18	6		24	18	6	22	$15\frac{1}{2}$	8
20 or more	7		28	20 or more	7	25	$17\frac{1}{2}$	9

* All dimensions in feet.
† These spacings apply where desks and benches are next to wall, otherwise one-half the spacing between units is satisfactory.
‡ The actual spacing of luminaires is usually less than the maximum spacing to suit bay or room dimensions.
§ See Table 21.7.
** For mounting height of general diffusing and direct-indirect fixtures, see Table 21.7.

counteract this effect, particularly when placement of furniture is such that seeing tasks will occur near walls, the designer should arrange to provide additional illumination in these areas. This may readily be accomplished by additional fixtures, higher output units, perimeter lighting or some type of wall-washing arrangement. Particular stress should be placed on this type of local lighting where wall reflectances are low such as at walls covered with book shelves, equipment racks, low-reflectance paint or dark wood paneling.

The foregoing discussion of illumination uniformity concerned itself with uniformity on a horizontal plane. Occasionally, it is necessary to know the degree of uniformity vertically (on horizontal planes at different elevations). Four different lighting situations are normally encountered, viz., point sources such as incandescent downlights, line sources such as continuous row fluorescent fixtures, infinite sources such as luminous ceilings—whether direct trans-

*Table 21.7   Practical Hanger Lengths for Suspended Luminaires in Offices and Schools**

Ceiling Height (Feet)	Room Width (Feet)	Hanger Length (Inches)		Ceiling Height (Feet)	Room Width (Feet)	Hanger Length (Inches)	
		† Offices and Classrooms	Drafting Rooms			† Offices and Classrooms	Drafting Rooms
7	7	‡	‡	13	13	21 or 24	24
	14	‡	‡		26	21 or 24	24
	28 and up	‡	‡		52 and up	21 or 24	24
8	8	‡	6	14	14	30	30
	16	‡	6		28	24	24
	32 and up	‡	6		56 and up	24	24
9	9	6	12	15	15	36	36
	18	6	12		30	30	30
	36 and up	‡	6		60 and up	24	24
10	10	18	21	16	16	42	42
	20	12	18		32	36	36
	40 and up	6	12		64 and up	30	30
11	11	21	21	18	18	42	42
	22	18	21		36	36	36
	44 and up	12	18		72 and up	30	30
12	12	21	21 or 24	20	20	54	54
	24	21	21 or 24		40	42	42
	48 and up	21	21 or 24		80 and up	36	36

* Indirect and semi-indirect luminaires provide low utilization when suspended less than 18 in. If mounted too close to the ceiling, luminaires having a substantial upward component may cause excessively high ceiling brightness. Two-lamp fluorescent units normally should be suspended at least 12 in.; 4-lamp units, 24 in. Indirect incandescent luminaires with 500-watt lamps should be suspended at least 20 in.; 750-watt units at least 24 in.
† Also for libraries, reception rooms, etc.
‡ Luminaires should be surface-mounted or hung very near the ceiling.
From *Westinghouse Lighting Handbook,* 1961.

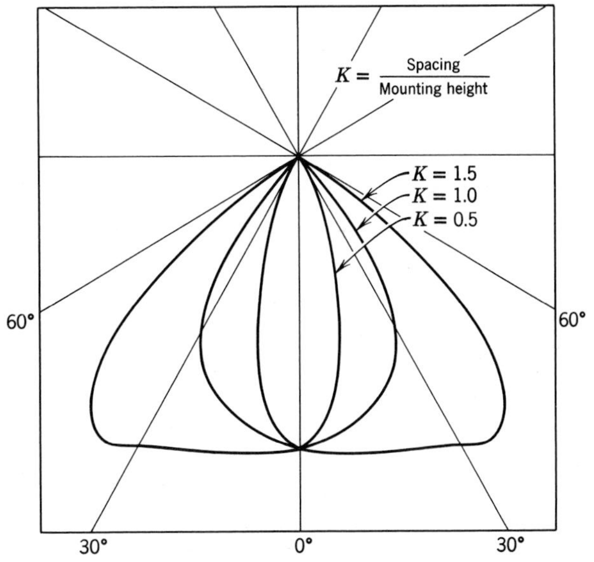

Fig. 21.16 Determination of spacing to mounting height ratio for direct incandescent souces of differing distribution. *Illuminating Engineering Journal,* January 1963. Odle and Smith.

illuminated or indirect—and parabolic reflector beams such as from PAR lamps. The vertical uniformity of each type is shown graphically in Fig. 21.17.

10. Mounting Height of Luminaires. The mounting height of luminaires is normally established before spacing, and uniformity requirements govern spacing as explained above. In arriving at a mounting height for fixtures with an upward component, a balance must be struck between the requirement of low-ceiling brightness and good utilization of light on the one hand (low mounting) and the reticence to dominate an area, particularly a large room by using such a low mounting height that the apparent ceiling height is affected. The overriding consideration however must always be that sufficient illumination be provided for the seeing task involved. If general light-

ing to supply this level would result in too low a mounting height, then local or supplemental lighting must be employed.

11. Luminaire Efficiency. A luminaire, variously called a fixture, lighting unit, or reflector, comprises a device for physically supporting the light source and usually for directing or controlling the light output of this source. Due to internal reflections, some of the generated lumen output of the lamp is lost within the fixture. The ratio of output lumens to lamp (input) lumens, expressed as a percentage, represents the luminous efficiency of the fixture. Though this data is normally available from the manufacturer it is readily calculated from the fixture distribution curve by application of the zonal factors (given in Table 19.4) to the fixture curve. However, this characteristic has little meaning in of itself since the

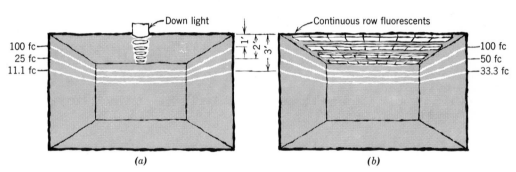

(a), (b). Illumination varies inversely with square of distance for a point source and inversely as distance for a line source.

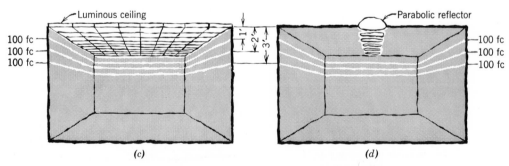

(c), (d). Illumination remains constant at all distances from either an infinite (or nearly) source or a parabolic reflector.

Fig. 21.17 Variation of illumination intensity, vertically, from different sources.

Fig. 21.18   Mounting height of fixtures may be lower in a small room than in a large room because of the illusion of lowness created in a large room.

actual over-all efficiency of a luminaire depends upon the space in which it is used.

To illustrate, let us consider the case of a large high ceiling room in which the ceiling is dark and is covered with dirty piping and ductwork. If we were to use a high efficiency (say 80 percent) indirect lighting unit in such a room, most of the light directed upward would be lost (absorbed) and the actual lighting on the working plane 30 inches above the floor would be very low. If, however, such a room were illuminated with low-efficiency direct lighting units (e.g., 50 percent) utilizing the same wattage, the illumination on the working plane would be considerably higher than in the first case.

Similarly, if we consider a small room with dark walls and ceiling lighted alternatively by diffuse lighting and by direct lighting units of the same wattage and unit efficiency, the horizontal plane illumination will be higher in the case of the direct units because of the large loss of the horizontal and upward components of the diffuse lighting on the walls and ceiling. It should be obvious then that the fixture efficiency alone is not a meaningful factor but that *the overall luminous efficiency of a particular unit in a particular space* is the figure which merits our attention. This figure, since it describes the utilization of the fixture output in a specific space, is known as the *coefficient of utilization*. It is defined as the ratio between the lumens reaching the working horizontal plane to the generated lumens. Since each

luminaire will have a different coefficient for every different space in which it is used, a system of standardization has been evolved utilizing rooms of certain proportions and various surface reflectances. The fixture coefficients are then computed and tabulated as shown in Table 21.9. It should be emphasized that the figures given in Table 21.9 are for the generic fixture type only; in an actual job, actual fixture data should be used. To utilize these tables it is necessary to understand the concept of room index and room reflectance factors.

12. Room Index and Reflectances. The coefficient of utilization is a factor which combines fixture efficiency and distribution with room proportions, mounting height, and surface reflectances. The smaller a room, the greater the proportion of wall surface present to absorb light and the lower the room index. Similarly, the higher the mounting height, the more reflections occur before light, other than that directed downward, reaches the working plane, and therefore the lower the room index. Conversely, the larger the room and the lower the mounting height (ceiling height in the case of indirect units), the less absorption by walls and the better the room index. Various combinations of room proportions are divided into 10 classifications, and each is assigned an index letter, from *A* to *J*, *A* being best and *J* worst. These indexes and the room proportions from which they are derived, are tabulated in Table 21.8.

Table 21.8   Room Index

Ceiling height—feet

Mounting height above floor—feet

Room width Feet	Room length Feet	7 and 7½	8 and 8½	9 and 9½	10 to 11½	12 to 13½	14 to 16½	17 to 20	21 to 24	25 to 30	31 to 36	37 to 50
For semi-indirect and indirect lighting (ceiling height)		9 and 9½	10 to 11½	12 to 13½	14 to 16½	17 to 20	21 to 24	25 to 30	31 to 36	37 to 50		
							Room index					
9 (8½–9)	8–10	H	I	J	J							
	10–14	H	I	I	J							
	14–20	G	H	I	J	J						
	20–30	G	G	H	I	J	J					
	30–42	F	G	H	I	J	J	J				
	42-up	E	F	G	H	I	J	J				
10 (9½–10½)	10–14	G	H	I	J	J						
	14–20	G	H	I	J	J	J					
	20–30	F	G	H	I	J	J					
	30–42	F	G	G	H	I	J	J				
	42–60	E	F	G	H	I	J	J				
	60-up	E	F	F	H	H	I	J				
12 (11–12½)	10–14	G	H	I	I	J	J					
	14–20	F	G	H	I	J	J					
	20–30	F	G	G	H	I	J	J				
	30–42	E	F	G	H	I	J	J				
	42–60	E	F	F	G	H	I	J				
	60-up	E	E	F	G	H	I	J				
14 (13–15½)	14–20	F	G	H	H	I	J	J				
	20–30	E	F	G	H	I	J	J				
	30–42	E	F	F	G	H	I	J	J			
	42–60	E	E	F	F	H	I	J	J	J		
	60–90	D	E	E	F	G	H	J	J	J		
	90-up	D	E	E	F	F	G	I	J	J		
17 (16–18½)	14–20	E	F	G	H	I	J	J				
	20–30	E	F	F	G	H	I	J				
	30–42	D	E	F	G	H	H	J	J	J		
	42–60	D	E	E	F	G	G	I	J	J	J	
	60–110	D	E	E	F	G	G	I	J	J	J	
	110-up	C	D	E	E	F	G	H	I	J	J	
20 (19–21½)	20–30	D	E	F	G	H	I	J	J			
	30–42	D	E	E	F	G	H	I	J	J		
	42–60	D	D	E	E	F	G	I	J	J	J	
	60–90	C	D	E	E	F	G	H	J	J	J	
	90–140	C	D	D	E	F	F	H	I	I	J	J
	140-up	C	D	D	E	F	F	H	H	I	J	J

Table 21.8 Room Index (Continued)

Ceiling height—feet

Mounting height above floor—feet

For semi-indirect and indirect lighting		9 and 9½	10 to 11½	12 to 13½	14 to 16½	17 to 20	21 to 24	25 to 30	31 to 36	37 to 50		
For direct and semi-direct lighting		7 and 7½	8 and 8½	9 and 9½	10 to 11½	12 to 13½	14 to 16½	17 to 20	21 to 24	25 to 30	31 to 36	37 to 50
Room width Feet	Room length Feet						Room index					
24 (22–26)	20–30	D	E	E	F	G	H	I	J	J		
	30–42	C	D	E	F	G	G	I	J	J		
	42–60	C	D	D	E	F	G	H	I	J	J	
	60–90	C	D	D	E	F	F	H	I	J	J	J
	90–140	C	C	D	E	E	F	G	H	I	J	J
	140–up	C	C	D	E	E	F	G	H	I	I	J
30 (27–33)	30–42	C	D	D	E	F	G	H	I	J	J	
	42–60	C	C	D	D	F	F	H	H	I	J	
	60–90	B	C	C	D	E	F	G	H	I	J	J
	90–140	B	C	C	D	E	E	F	G	H	I	J
	140–180	B	C	C	D	E	E	F	G	H	I	J
	180–up	B	C	C	D	E	E	F	G	H	I	J
36 (34–39)	30–42	B	C	D	E	F	F	H	I	I	J	
	42–60	B	C	C	D	E	F	G	H	I	J	J
	60–90	A	C	C	C	E	E	F	H	H	J	J
	90–140	A	B	C	C	D	E	F	G	H	I	J
	140–200	A	B	C	C	D	E	F	F	G	H	I
	200–up	A	B	C	C	D	E	F	F	G	H	I
42 (40–45)	42–60	A	B	C	C	E	F	G	H	I	I	J
	60–90	A	B	B	C	D	E	F	G	H	I	J
	90–140	A	B	B	C	D	D	E	F	G	H	J
	140–200	A	A	B	C	D	D	E	F	G	H	I
	200–up	A	A	B	C	D	D	E	F	F	G	I
50 (46–55)	42–60	A	A	B	C	D	E	F	G	H	I	J
	60–90	A	A	B	C	C	D	F	F	G	H	J
	90–140	A	A	A	C	C	D	E	F	F	G	I
	140–200	A	A	A	C	C	D	E	E	F	G	I
	200–up	A	A	A	C	C	D	E	E	F	G	H
60 (56–67)	60–90	A	A	A	B	C	D	E	F	G	H	I
	90–140	A	A	A	B	C	C	D	E	F	G	H
	140–200	A	A	A	B	C	C	D	E	E	F	H
	200–up	A	A	A	B	C	C	D	E	E	F	H
75 (68–90)	60–90	A	A	A	A	B	C	D	E	F	G	I
	90–140	A	A	A	A	B	C	D	E	F	F	H
	140–200	A	A	A	A	B	B	C	D	E	F	G
	200–up	A	A	A	A	B	B	C	D	E	F	G

Room index is the classification of a room according to its proportions; large and small rooms of the same proportion have the same index. Hence, for large rooms of dimensions greater than those shown, divide each dimension by the same number and use the index determined for the smaller room.

Table 21.9   Coefficients of Utilization for Typical Luminaires with Suggested Maximum Spacing Ratios and Maintenance Factors

Typical Distribution and Maximum Spacing*	Ceiling (%)	80			70			50			30		0	Typical Luminaire and Estimated Maintenance Factors
	Walls (%)	50	30	10	50	30	10	50	30	10	30	10	0	
	Room Ratio (Index)	Coefficients of utilization (Zonal Method) For 10% Floor Reflectance (See end for 30% Floor Multipliers)												

Recessed Direct Fluorescent

1 — 0% / 60% — Max. Spacing 0.8×MH

Room Ratio	80-50	80-30	80-10	70-50	70-30	70-10	50-50	50-30	50-10	30-30	30-10	0
0.6 (J)	.30	.26	.25	.29	.26	.23	.29	.26	.23	.25	.23	.22
0.8 (I)	.36	.32	.29	.35	.32	.29	.35	.31	.29	.31	.29	.27
1.0 (H)	.43	.40	.37	.43	.40	.37	.42	.39	.37	.39	.37	.36
1.25(G)	.47	.44	.42	.47	.44	.41	.46	.43	.41	.43	.41	.40
1.5 (F)	.50	.47	.44	.50	.47	.44	.49	.46	.44	.46	.44	.43
2.0 (E)	.53	.50	.49	.53	.50	.48	.51	.50	.48	.49	.47	.46
2.5 (D)	.55	.53	.51	.55	.53	.51	.54	.52	.50	.51	.50	.49
3.0 (C)	.57	.54	.53	.56	.54	.52	.55	.53	.51	.52	.51	.50
4.0 (B)	.59	.57	.55	.58	.56	.55	.56	.55	.54	.54	.53	.52
5.0 (A)	.60	.58	.57	.59	.57	.56	.57	.56	.56	.56	.54	.53

Single lamp aluminum troffer with baffles
Maint. Factor Good .75 Med. .70 Poor .65

2 — 0% / 50% — Max. Spacing 0.8×MH

Room Ratio	80-50	80-30	80-10	70-50	70-30	70-10	50-50	50-30	50-10	30-30	30-10	0
0.6 (J)	.27	.24	.21	.27	.23	.21	.27	.23	.21	.23	.21	.20
0.8 (I)	.33	.29	.26	.32	.29	.26	.32	.28	.26	.28	.26	.25
1.0 (H)	.36	.33	.30	.36	.33	.30	.35	.32	.30	.32	.30	.29
1.25(G)	.40	.36	.34	.39	.36	.34	.38	.36	.34	.36	.34	.33
1.5 (F)	.42	.39	.37	.42	.39	.37	.41	.38	.36	.38	.36	.35
2.0 (E)	.45	.42	.40	.44	.42	.40	.44	.42	.40	.41	.40	.39
2.5 (D)	.47	.44	.43	.46	.44	.42	.45	.44	.42	.43	.42	.41
3.0 (C)	.48	.46	.44	.47	.46	.44	.47	.45	.44	.44	.43	.42
4.0 (B)	.50	.48	.46	.49	.48	.46	.48	.47	.46	.46	.45	.44
5.0 (A)	.50	.49	.48	.50	.49	.48	.49	.48	.47	.47	.46	.45

Two lamp aluminum troffer with louvers
Maint. Factor Good .75 Med. .70 Poor .65

3 — 0% / 55% — Max. Spacing 0.9×MH

Room Ratio	80-50	80-30	80-10	70-50	70-30	70-10	50-50	50-30	50-10	30-30	30-10	0
0.6 (J)	.26	.23	.20	.26	.22	.20	.25	.22	.20	.22	.20	.19
0.8 (I)	.32	.29	.26	.32	.29	.26	.31	.29	.26	.28	.26	.25
1.0 (H)	.37	.34	.31	.37	.33	.30	.36	.32	.30	.32	.30	.29
1.25(G)	.41	.37	.35	.41	.37	.35	.40	.37	.34	.36	.34	.33
1.5 (F)	.44	.40	.37	.43	.40	.37	.42	.40	.37	.39	.37	.36
2.0 (E)	.47	.44	.42	.47	.44	.41	.46	.43	.41	.42	.41	.40
2.5 (D)	.50	.47	.45	.49	.47	.45	.48	.46	.44	.45	.43	.42
3.0 (C)	.51	.49	.47	.51	.48	.46	.50	.47	.46	.47	.45	.44
4.0 (B)	.53	.51	.49	.53	.51	.49	.51	.50	.48	.49	.47	.46
5.0 (A)	.55	.53	.52	.54	.53	.51	.53	.52	.51	.51	.50	.48

Two lamp 12″-wide troffer glass, plastic, or 30° louver
Maint. Factor (Louver / Enclosed) Good .75 / .70 Med. .70 / .65 Poor .65 / .55

4 — 0% / 45% — Max. Spacing 0.6×MH

Room Ratio	80-50	80-30	80-10	70-50	70-30	70-10	50-50	50-30	50-10	30-30	30-10	0
0.6 (J)	.24	.21	.19	.24	.21	.19	.23	.21	.19	.20	.19	.18
0.8 (I)	.29	.26	.24	.29	.26	.24	.28	.26	.24	.26	.24	.23
1.0 (H)	.32	.29	.27	.32	.29	.27	.32	.29	.27	.29	.27	.26
1.25(G)	.36	.32	.31	.35	.32	.31	.34	.32	.30	.32	.30	.29
1.5 (F)	.38	.35	.33	.38	.35	.33	.37	.34	.32	.34	.32	.32
2.0 (E)	.41	.38	.37	.40	.38	.36	.39	.38	.36	.37	.36	.35
2.5 (D)	.43	.40	.38	.42	.40	.38	.41	.39	.38	.39	.38	.37
3.0 (C)	.44	.42	.40	.43	.42	.40	.42	.41	.39	.40	.39	.38
4.0 (B)	.45	.44	.42	.45	.43	.42	.44	.43	.42	.42	.41	.40
5.0 (A)	.47	.45	.44	.46	.45	.44	.45	.44	.43	.43	.42	.41

Two lamp 12″ wide troffer with 45° metal louver
Maint. Factor Good .75 Med. .70 Poor .65

* Maximum Spacing between luminaire centers for uniform illumination.   MH—Mounting Height above floor.
CH—Ceiling Height above floor.
NOTE: All reflectances are effective values.

Table 21.9 (Continued)

Typical Distribution and Maximum Spacing*	Ceiling (%)	80			70			50			30		0	Typical Luminaire and Estimated Maintenance Factors
	Walls (%)	50	30	10	50	30	10	50	30	10	30	10	0	
	Room Ratio (Index)	Coefficients of Utilization (Zonal Method) For 10% Floor Reflectance (See end for 30% Floor Multipliers)												

Recessed Direct Fluorescent

5 — 0% / 65%

Room Ratio	80 / 50	30	10	70 / 50	30	10	50 / 50	30	10	30 / 30	10	0 / 0
0.6 (J)	.31	.27	.24	.31	.27	.24	.30	.27	.24	.27	.24	.23
0.8 (I)	.39	.34	.31	.38	.34	.31	.38	.34	.31	.34	.31	.30
1.0 (H)	.44	.40	.37	.44	.40	.36	.43	.39	.36	.39	.36	.35
1.25 (G)	.49	.45	.41	.49	.44	.41	.47	.43	.41	.43	.41	.39
1.5 (F)	.52	.49	.45	.52	.48	.45	.51	.47	.45	.47	.45	.43
2.0 (E)	.56	.53	.51	.56	.52	.50	.54	.52	.50	.51	.49	.48
2.5 (D)	.59	.56	.53	.58	.56	.53	.57	.54	.52	.54	.52	.51
3.0 (C)	.61	.58	.56	.60	.58	.55	.58	.56	.54	.56	.54	.53
4.0 (B)	.63	.61	.58	.62	.60	.58	.61	.59	.58	.58	.56	.55
5.0 (A)	.65	.63	.61	.63	.62	.60	.62	.61	.60	.60	.58	.57

Max. Spacing 0.9xMH

Two lamp 24"-wide troffer with prismatic lens
Maint. Good .70
Factor Med. .65
Poor .55

6 — 0% / 60%

Room Ratio	80 / 50	30	10	70 / 50	30	10	50 / 50	30	10	30 / 30	10	0 / 0
0.6 (J)	.26	.20	.17	.26	.20	.17	.25	.20	.17	.20	.17	.15
0.8 (I)	.32	.26	.22	.32	.26	.22	.31	.26	.22	.25	.22	.21
1.0 (H)	.37	.31	.27	.36	.31	.27	.35	.30	.27	.30	.27	.26
1.25 (G)	.42	.36	.32	.41	.36	.32	.40	.35	.32	.35	.32	.30
1.5 (F)	.45	.40	.36	.44	.39	.36	.43	.38	.35	.38	.35	.34
2.0 (E)	.49	.44	.41	.48	.44	.41	.47	.43	.40	.42	.40	.38
2.5 (D)	.52	.48	.44	.51	.47	.44	.49	.46	.43	.45	.43	.42
3.0 (C)	.54	.50	.47	.53	.50	.47	.51	.49	.46	.48	.46	.44
4.0 (B)	.56	.54	.51	.56	.53	.51	.54	.52	.50	.51	.49	.48
5.0 (A)	.58	.56	.54	.58	.56	.54	.56	.54	.53	.53	.53	.50

Max. Spacing 0.9xMH

Three lamp 24"-wide troffer with diffusing plastic
Maint. Good .70
Factor Med. .65
Poor .55

Recessed Direct General Service Incandescent

7 — 0% / 65%

Room Ratio	80 / 50	30	10	70 / 50	30	10	50 / 50	30	10	30 / 30	10	0 / 0
0.6 (J)	.40	.35	.32	.39	.35	.32	.39	.35	.32	.35	.32	.31
0.8 (I)	.46	.42	.39	.46	.42	.39	.45	.41	.39	.41	.39	.38
1.0 (H)	.50	.46	.44	.50	.46	.44	.49	.46	.45	.46	.45	.42
1.25 (G)	.54	.51	.48	.54	.50	.48	.53	.50	.48	.50	.47	.46
1.5 (F)	.57	.54	.51	.56	.53	.51	.55	.53	.50	.52	.50	.49
2.0 (E)	.60	.58	.55	.60	.57	.55	.59	.56	.54	.56	.54	.53
2.5 (D)	.62	.60	.58	.62	.60	.58	.60	.59	.57	.58	.56	.55
3.0 (C)	.64	.62	.60	.63	.61	.59	.62	.60	.59	.59	.58	.57
4.0 (B)	.65	.63	.62	.65	.63	.62	.63	.62	.61	.61	.60	.58
5.0 (A)	.66	.65	.63	.66	.64	.63	.64	.63	.62	.62	.61	.60

Max. Spacing 0.8xMH

Medium distribution reflector and lens
Maint. Good .75
Factor Med. .65
Poor .55

8 — 0% / 50%

Room Ratio	80 / 50	30	10	70 / 50	30	10	50 / 50	30	10	30 / 30	10	0 / 0
0.6 (J)	.28	.24	.21	.27	.24	.21	.27	.24	.21	.23	.21	.20
0.8 (I)	.33	.29	.26	.32	.29	.26	.32	.29	.26	.28	.26	.26
1.0 (H)	.36	.33	.30	.36	.33	.30	.36	.32	.30	.32	.30	.29
1.25 (G)	.40	.37	.34	.40	.36	.34	.39	.36	.34	.36	.34	.33
1.5 (F)	.42	.39	.37	.42	.39	.37	.41	.39	.36	.38	.36	.35
2.0 (E)	.45	.43	.40	.44	.42	.40	.44	.42	.40	.41	.40	.39
2.5 (D)	.47	.45	.43	.46	.44	.43	.45	.44	.42	.43	.42	.41
3.0 (C)	.48	.46	.44	.48	.46	.44	.47	.45	.44	.44	.43	.42
4.0 (B)	.50	.48	.48	.49	.48	.46	.48	.47	.46	.46	.45	.44
5.0 (A)	.50	.49	.48	.50	.49	.48	.49	.48	.47	.47	.46	.45

Max. Spacing 0.8xMH

Wide distribution reflector lens or louver

	Louver	Lens
Maint. Good	.80	.75
Factor Med.	.70	.65
Poor	.65	.55

*Maximum Spacing between luminaire centeis for uniform illumination. MH—Mounting Height above floor CH—Ceiling Height above floor.
Note: All reflectances are effective values.

Table 21.9 (Continued)

Left margin (vertical): Recessed Direct Reflectorized Incandescent

TYPICAL DISTRIBUTION AND MAXIMUM SPACING*	ROOM RATIO (Index)	80			70			50			30		0	TYPICAL LUMINAIRE AND ESTIMATED MAINTENANCE FACTORS
	WALLS (%)	50	30	10	50	30	10	50	30	10	30	10	0	
		COEFFICIENTS OF UTILIZATION (ZONAL METHOD) FOR 10% FLOOR REFLECTANCE (See end for 30% Floor Multipliers)												

9   0% / 60%   Max. Spacing 0.9xMH

Room Ratio	50	30	10	50	30	10	50	30	10	30	10	0
0.6 (J)	.29	.24	.21	.29	.24	.21	.29	.24	.21	.24	.21	.20
0.8 (I)	.36	.31	.27	.36	.31	.27	.35	.30	.27	.30	.27	.26
1.0 (H)	.41	.36	.32	.40	.35	.32	.39	.35	.32	.35	.32	.31
1.25 (G)	.45	.40	.37	.44	.40	.37	.43	.40	.37	.39	.36	.35
1.5 (F)	.48	.44	.41	.47	.44	.40	.46	.43	.40	.42	.40	.39
2.0 (E)	.52	.48	.45	.51	.48	.45	.50	.47	.45	.46	.44	.43
2.5 (D)	.54	.51	.48	.54	.51	.48	.52	.50	.48	.49	.47	.46
3.0 (C)	.56	.53	.51	.55	.53	.51	.54	.52	.50	.51	.50	.48
4.0 (B)	.58	.56	.54	.58	.56	.54	.56	.55	.53	.54	.52	.51
5.0 (A)	.60	.58	.56	.59	.58	.56	.58	.57	.55	.56	.54	.53

Louvered coffer with silvered-bowl lamp. Maint. Factor: Good .70, Med. .60, Poor .55

10   0% / 70%   Max. Spacing 0.5xMH

Room Ratio	50	30	10	50	30	10	50	30	10	30	10	0
0.6 (J)	.53	.50	.48	.53	.50	.48	.52	.50	.48	.49	.48	.47
0.8 (I)	.57	.55	.53	.57	.55	.53	.57	.55	.53	.54	.53	.52
1.0 (H)	.60	.57	.55	.60	.57	.55	.60	.57	.55	.57	.55	.54
1.25 (G)	.63	.60	.58	.62	.60	.58	.62	.60	.58	.59	.57	.56
1.5 (F)	.65	.63	.61	.65	.62	.60	.64	.62	.60	.61	.60	.59
2.0 (E)	.68	.66	.64	.67	.65	.64	.66	.65	.63	.64	.63	.62
2.5 (D)	.69	.67	.66	.68	.67	.65	.67	.66	.65	.65	.64	.63
3.0 (C)	.70	.69	.67	.69	.68	.67	.68	.67	.66	.66	.65	.64
4.0 (B)	.71	.70	.68	.70	.69	.68	.69	.68	.67	.67	.66	.65
5.0 (A)	.72	.71	.70	.70	.70	.69	.70	.69	.68	.68	.67	.66

PAR-38 flood with metal louvers. Maint. Factor: Good .65, Med. .60, Poor .55

11   0% / 35%   Max. Spacing 0.5xMH

Room Ratio	50	30	10	50	30	10	50	30	10	30	10	0
0.6 (J)	.27	.25	.24	.27	.25	.24	.27	.25	.24	.25	.24	.24
0.8 (I)	.29	.28	.27	.29	.28	.27	.29	.28	.27	.28	.27	.27
1.0 (H)	.31	.30	.29	.31	.30	.29	.30	.29	.28	.29	.28	.29
1.25 (G)	.32	.31	.30	.32	.31	.30	.32	.31	.30	.30	.30	.30
1.5 (F)	.33	.32	.31	.33	.32	.31	.32	.32	.31	.31	.31	.30
2.0 (E)	.34	.33	.32	.34	.33	.32	.34	.33	.32	.32	.32	.31
2.5 (D)	.35	.34	.33	.35	.34	.33	.34	.34	.33	.33	.33	.32
3.0 (C)	.36	.35	.34	.35	.35	.34	.35	.34	.34	.34	.33	.33
4.0 (B)	.36	.36	.35	.36	.35	.35	.35	.35	.34	.34	.34	.33
5.0 (A)	.36	.36	.35	.36	.35	.35	.36	.35	.35	.34	.34	.33

R-40 flood in baffled cylinder. Maint. Factor: Good .70, Med. .65, Poor .60

12   0% / 65%   Max. Spacing 0.5xMH

Room Ratio	50	30	10	50	30	10	50	30	10	30	10	0
0.6 (J)	.54	.52	.50	.54	.52	.50	.53	.51	.50	.51	.50	.50
0.8 (I)	.58	.56	.54	.58	.55	.54	.57	.55	.54	.55	.54	.53
1.0 (H)	.60	.58	.56	.60	.58	.56	.59	.57	.56	.57	.56	.56
1.25 (G)	.62	.60	.58	.61	.59	.58	.61	.59	.58	.59	.58	.57
1.5 (F)	.63	.61	.60	.63	.61	.60	.62	.60	.59	.60	.59	.58
2.0 (E)	.65	.63	.62	.64	.63	.62	.63	.62	.61	.61	.61	.60
2.5 (D)	.66	.65	.63	.65	.64	.63	.64	.63	.62	.63	.62	.61
3.0 (C)	.67	.66	.64	.66	.65	.64	.65	.64	.63	.63	.63	.62
4.0 (B)	.68	.67	.66	.67	.66	.65	.66	.65	.64	.64	.64	.62
5.0 (A)	.68	.67	.66	.68	.67	.66	.66	.66	.66	.65	.64	.63

PAR-38 flood in baffled cylinder. Maint. Factor: Good .70, Med. .65, Poor .60

*Maximum Spacing between luminaire centers for uniform illumination. MH—Mounting Height above floor. CH—Ceiling Height above floor.
NOTE: All reflectances are effective values.

Table 21.9 (Continued)

Left margin (vertical): **Surface Mounted Semi-Direct Fluorescent**

Typical Distribution and Maximum Spacing*	Room Ratio (Index)	Ceiling 80 / Walls 50	30	10	Ceiling 70 / Walls 50	30	10	Ceiling 50 / Walls 50	30	10	Ceiling 30 / Walls 30	10	Ceiling 0 / Walls 0	Typical Luminaire and Estimated Maintenance Factors
		Coefficients of utilization (Zonal Method) For 10% Floor Reflectance (See end for 30% Floor Multipliers)												
13 10% / 50%	0.6 (J)	.18	.14	.11	.17	.14	.11	.17	.13	.11	.13	.11	.09	
	0.8 (I)	.23	.19	.16	.22	.19	.16	.21	.18	.15	.17	.15	.13	
	1.0 (H)	.27	.23	.20	.26	.22	.20	.25	.21	.19	.20	.18	.16	
	1.25(G)	.31	.27	.24	.30	.26	.23	.28	.25	.22	.23	.21	.19	
	1.5 (F)	.34	.30	.27	.33	.29	.26	.30	.27	.25	.26	.23	.21	Diffusing plastic enclosed 2 & 4 lamp
	2.0 (E)	.38	.34	.31	.37	.33	.31	.34	.31	.29	.29	.27	.24	
	2.5 (D)	.40	.37	.34	.39	.36	.33	.36	.34	.32	.31	.30	.26	
Max.	3.0 (C)	.42	.39	.36	.40	.38	.35	.37	.35	.34	.33	.31	.28	Maint. Good .70
Spacing	4.0 (B)	.45	.41	.39	.43	.40	.38	.40	.37	.36	.35	.34	.30	Factor Med. .65
1.0xMH	5.0 (A)	.46	.44	.42	.45	.43	.40	.42	.40	.38	.37	.36	.32	Poor .55
14 10% / 55%	0.6 (J)	.28	.23	.20	.27	.23	.20	.26	.23	.19	.22	.19	.18	
	0.8 (I)	.34	.31	.26	.34	.29	.26	.32	.29	.26	.28	.25	.24	
	1.0 (H)	.39	.34	.31	.38	.34	.31	.37	.32	.29	.32	.29	.27	
	1.25(G)	.45	.38	.36	.44	.38	.36	.41	.37	.34	.36	.34	.32	Prismatic glass enclosed or diffusing side & louver bottom
	1.5 (F)	.47	.43	.40	.46	.42	.39	.44	.41	.38	.40	.39	.35	
	2.0 (E)	.52	.47	.45	.50	.47	.44	.48	.45	.43	.43	.41	.39	Enclosed Louver
	2.5 (D)	.54	.51	.47	.53	.50	.47	.50	.48	.46	.47	.44	.42	
Max.	3.0 (C)	.57	.53	.51	.55	.51	.49	.52	.50	.48	.48	.46	.44	Maint. Good .70 .75
Spacing	4.0 (B)	.59	.55	.53	.58	.55	.53	.55	.53	.50	.50	.49	.46	Factor Med. .65 .70
1.0xMH	5.0 (A)	.61	.58	.56	.59	.57	.55	.57	.55	.54	.52	.51	.48	Poor .55 .65
15 10% / 60%	0.6 (J)	.28	.24	.20	.27	.24	.20	.27	.24	.20	.24	.19	.17	
	0.8 (I)	.35	.31	.29	.35	.31	.29	.34	.31	.28	.30	.27	.25	
	1.0 (H)	.41	.37	.34	.40	.37	.34	.40	.36	.34	.35	.33	.31	
	1.25(G)	.46	.41	.39	.46	.41	.39	.45	.40	.38	.39	.37	.35	
	1.5 (F)	.50	.46	.43	.49	.45	.42	.48	.45	.41	.43	.40	.38	
	2.0 (E)	.56	.51	.49	.55	.51	.48	.54	.50	.47	.48	.46	.43	Diffusing sides and prismatic bottom
	2.5 (D)	.59	.55	.51	.58	.54	.51	.55	.52	.50	.51	.48	.45	
Max.	3.0 (C)	.62	.58	.55	.60	.57	.54	.58	.55	.53	.54	.51	.48	Maint. Good .70
Spacing	4.0 (B)	.65	.61	.59	.63	.60	.58	.60	.58	.56	.56	.54	.50	Factor Med. .65
1.1xMH	5.0 (A)	.66	.63	.61	.64	.62	.60	.63	.60	.59	.58	.57	.53	Poor .55
16 10% / 80%	0.6 (J)	.30	.24	.19	.29	.24	.19	.29	.23	.19	.22	.18	.17	
	0.8 (I)	.39	.32	.27	.38	.31	.26	.37	.31	.25	.29	.25	.23	
	1.0 (H)	.46	.38	.34	.46	.38	.33	.42	.37	.33	.35	.31	.28	
	1.25(G)	.53	.46	.40	.52	.45	.39	.49	.43	.38	.41	.36	.34	
	1.5 (F)	.58	.51	.46	.56	.50	.44	.53	.48	.44	.45	.41	.38	
	2.0 (E)	.65	.57	.53	.63	.57	.52	.60	.54	.50	.52	.47	.45	Bare lamp unit
	2.5 (D)	.69	.63	.58	.67	.62	.57	.64	.59	.55	.56	.53	.49	
Max.	3.0 (C)	.73	.67	.62	.71	.65	.61	.67	.62	.58	.60	.57	.52	Maint. Good .80
Spacing	4.0 (B)	.77	.72	.67	.75	.70	.66	.71	.67	.64	.64	.62	.57	Factor Med. .75
1.0xMH	5.0 (A)	.81	.76	.73	.78	.74	.71	.74	.71	.68	.68	.66	.61	Poor .70

* Maximum Spacing between luminaire centers for uniform illumination. MH—Mounting Height above floor. CH—Ceiling Height above floor.
NOTE: All reflectances are effective values.

Table 21.9 (Continued)

Left vertical label: Suspended Industrial Incandescent and Mercury

Typical Distribution and Maximum Spacing*	Ceiling (%)	80			70			50			30		0	Typical Luminaire and Estimated Maintenance Factors
	Walls (%)	50	30	10	50	30	10	50	30	10	30	10	0	
	Room Ratio (Index)	Coefficients of Utilization (Zonal Method) For 10% Floor Reflectance (See end for 30% Floor Multipliers)												

17 (0%, 85%)

Room Ratio	50	30	10	50	30	10	50	30	10	30	10	0
0.6 (J)	.34	.30	.26	.33	.30	.26	.33	.29	.25	.29	.25	.23
0.8 (I)	.42	.38	.34	.42	.37	.34	.42	.37	.34	.37	.34	.31
1.0 (H)	.50	.44	.40	.49	.44	.40	.48	.44	.40	.43	.40	.36
1.25(G)	.56	.51	.48	.56	.51	.47	.55	.50	.47	.50	.47	.42
1.5 (F)	.61	.56	.53	.61	.56	.52	.60	.55	.52	.55	.52	.47
2.0 (E)	.69	.63	.60	.68	.63	.60	.67	.63	.59	.62	.59	.54
2.5 (D)	.72	.68	.64	.72	.68	.64	.70	.67	.64	.66	.63	.59
3.0 (C)	.75	.71	.68	.75	.71	.68	.73	.70	.67	.69	.67	.63
4.0 (B)	.79	.75	.73	.79	.75	.73	.77	.74	.72	.73	.71	.68
5.0 (A)	.80	.78	.77	.80	.78	.76	.79	.77	.75	.75	.74	.70

Max. Spacing 1.0xMH

Porcelain-enameled standard dome—incandescent

	Vent.	Non-Vent
Maint. Good	.80	.75
Factor Med.	.75	.65
Poor	.65	.55

18 (0%, 70%)

Room Ratio	50	30	10	50	30	10	50	30	10	30	10	0
0.6 (J)	.39	.35	.32	.38	.34	.32	.38	.34	.32	.34	.32	.31
0.8 (I)	.48	.43	.40	.47	.43	.40	.46	.43	.40	.42	.40	.39
1.0 (H)	.53	.49	.46	.52	.48	.46	.52	.48	.45	.48	.45	.44
1.25(G)	.58	.54	.51	.57	.53	.50	.56	.53	.50	.52	.50	.49
1.5 (F)	.61	.57	.54	.60	.56	.54	.59	.56	.54	.56	.53	.52
2.0 (E)	.65	.62	.59	.64	.61	.59	.63	.61	.59	.60	.58	.57
2.5 (D)	.68	.65	.62	.67	.64	.62	.66	.63	.61	.63	.61	.59
3.0 (C)	.69	.67	.65	.68	.66	.64	.67	.65	.64	.64	.63	.61
4.0 (B)	.72	.69	.68	.71	.68	.67	.69	.68	.66	.67	.66	.64
5.0 (A)	.73	.71	.69	.72	.70	.69	.70	.69	.68	.68	.67	.65

Max. Spacing 1.0xMH

Enclosed reflector with incandescent lamp

Maint. Good	.80
Factor Med.	.75
Poor	.70

19 (0%, 70%)

Room Ratio	50	30	10	50	30	10	50	30	10	30	10	0
0.6 (J)	.35	.32	.30	.35	.32	.30	.35	.32	.30	.32	.30	.29
0.8 (I)	.43	.39	.37	.43	.39	.37	.42	.39	.37	.39	.37	.36
1.0 (H)	.48	.45	.42	.48	.44	.42	.47	.44	.42	.43	.41	.41
1.25(G)	.53	.50	.47	.52	.50	.47	.52	.49	.47	.48	.46	.46
1.5 (F)	.57	.53	.50	.56	.53	.50	.55	.52	.50	.52	.50	.49
2.0 (E)	.61	.57	.55	.60	.57	.55	.59	.57	.54	.56	.54	.53
2.5 (D)	.64	.61	.59	.63	.60	.58	.62	.60	.58	.59	.57	.56
3.0 (C)	.66	.63	.61	.65	.62	.60	.63	.61	.60	.61	.59	.58
4.0 (B)	.68	.66	.63	.67	.65	.63	.66	.64	.63	.63	.62	.61
5.0 (A)	.69	.67	.66	.68	.67	.65	.67	.66	.64	.65	.63	.62

Max. Spacing 0.9xMH

Improved-color mercury aluminum or glass medium distribution high bay (ventilated)

	400W	1000W
Maint. Good	.65	.60
Factor Med.	.60	.55
Poor	.55	.50

20 (0%, 75%)

Room Ratio	50	30	10	50	30	10	50	30	10	30	10	0
0.6 (J)	.36	.32	.29	.35	.32	.29	.35	.31	.29	.31	.29	.28
0.8 (I)	.43	.39	.36	.43	.39	.37	.43	.39	.37	.39	.37	.35
1.0 (H)	.50	.46	.43	.49	.45	.42	.49	.45	.42	.45	.42	.41
1.25(G)	.55	.51	.47	.55	.51	.47	.54	.50	.47	.50	.47	.46
1.5 (F)	.59	.55	.53	.59	.55	.52	.58	.54	.52	.54	.51	.50
2.0 (E)	.64	.61	.58	.64	.60	.58	.63	.60	.57	.59	.57	.55
2.5 (D)	.67	.64	.62	.67	.64	.61	.66	.63	.61	.62	.60	.58
3.0 (C)	.70	.67	.64	.69	.66	.64	.68	.66	.63	.65	.63	.61
4.0 (B)	.74	.70	.68	.73	.70	.68	.71	.69	.67	.68	.67	.64
5.0 (A)	.75	.72	.71	.74	.72	.70	.73	.71	.69	.70	.68	.66

Max. Spacing 1.0xMH

Improved-color mercury porcelain enameled wide distribution high bay (ventilated)

	400W	1000W
Maint. Good	.65	.60
Factor Med.	.60	.55
Poor	.55	.50

* Maximum Spacing between luminaire centers for uniform illumination. MH—Mounting Height above floor. CH—Ceiling Height above floor.

NOTE: All reflectances are effective values.

Table 21.9 (Continued)

Left margin (vertical): **Suspended Industrial Incandescent and Mercury**

TYPICAL DISTRIBUTION AND MAXIMUM SPACING*	Ceiling (%)	80	80	80	70	70	70	50	50	50	30	30	0	TYPICAL LUMINAIRE AND ESTIMATED MAINTENANCE FACTORS
	Walls (%)	50	30	10	50	30	10	50	30	10	30	10	0	
	Room Ratio (Index)	Coefficients of utilization (Zonal Method) for 10% Floor Reflectance (See end for 30% Floor Multipliers)												

21 (0% / 70%)

Room Ratio (Index)	50	30	10	50	30	10	50	30	10	30	10	0
0.6 (J)	.36	.32	.28	.36	.32	.28	.36	.31	.28	.31	.28	.28
0.8 (I)	.44	.39	.36	.44	.39	.36	.43	.39	.36	.39	.36	.35
1.0 (H)	.50	.45	.42	.49	.45	.41	.48	.44	.41	.44	.41	.39
1.25 (G)	.54	.50	.47	.54	.50	.47	.53	.49	.46	.49	.46	.43
1.5 (F)	.58	.54	.50	.57	.53	.50	.56	.53	.50	.52	.50	.46
2.0 (E)	.62	.59	.56	.62	.58	.56	.60	.58	.55	.57	.55	.51
2.5 (D)	.65	.62	.59	.64	.61	.59	.63	.60	.58	.60	.58	.53
3.0 (C)	.67	.64	.62	.66	.63	.62	.64	.62	.60	.62	.60	.55
4.0 (B)	.69	.67	.65	.68	.66	.64	.67	.65	.63	.64	.63	.58
5.0 (A)	.70	.68	.67	.70	.68	.66	.68	.67	.65	.66	.65	.59

Max. Spacing 1.0xMH

3-kw mercury in aluminum reflector
Maint. Good .60
Factor Med. .55
Poor .50

22 (0% / 100%)

Room Ratio (Index)	50	30	10	50	30	10	50	30	10	30	10	0
0.6 (J)	.51	.45	.42	.51	.45	.41	.50	.45	.41	.45	.41	.40
0.8 (I)	.62	.56	.52	.61	.56	.52	.60	.55	.51	.55	.51	.50
1.0 (H)	.69	.63	.59	.68	.63	.59	.67	.62	.59	.62	.59	.57
1.25 (G)	.75	.70	.66	.75	.70	.66	.73	.69	.66	.68	.66	.64
1.5 (F)	.80	.75	.71	.79	.75	.71	.78	.74	.70	.73	.70	.68
2.0 (E)	.86	.81	.78	.85	.80	.77	.83	.80	.77	.79	.76	.75
2.5 (D)	.89	.85	.82	.88	.85	.82	.87	.83	.81	.83	.80	.78
3.0 (C)	.92	.88	.85	.90	.87	.85	.89	.86	.84	.85	.83	.81
4.0 (B)	.95	.92	.89	.94	.91	.88	.92	.90	.88	.88	.86	.85
5.0 (A)	.97	.94	.92	.95	.93	.91	.94	.92	.90	.91	.89	.87

Max. Spacing 1.0xMH

Wide distribution including reflector lamp in protective reflector (based on 0.4 S/MH ratio)
Maint. Good .80
Factor Med. .75
Poor .70

23 (0% / 100%)

Room Ratio (Index)	50	30	10	50	30	10	50	30	10	30	10	0
0.6 (J)	.56	.51	.47	.56	.51	.47	.56	.50	.47	.50	.47	.46
0.8 (I)	.66	.60	.57	.66	.60	.57	.65	.60	.57	.60	.57	.56
1.0 (H)	.73	.67	.64	.73	.67	.64	.72	.67	.64	.67	.64	.62
1.25 (G)	.78	.73	.70	.78	.73	.70	.77	.73	.69	.72	.69	.68
1.5 (F)	.82	.78	.74	.82	.77	.74	.80	.76	.74	.76	.73	.72
2.0 (E)	.88	.83	.80	.87	.83	.80	.85	.82	.79	.81	.79	.77
2.5 (D)	.90	.87	.84	.90	.86	.83	.88	.85	.83	.84	.82	.81
3.0 (C)	.93	.89	.87	.92	.89	.86	.90	.88	.86	.87	.85	.83
4.0 (B)	.96	.93	.90	.95	.92	.90	.93	.91	.89	.90	.88	.86
5.0 (A)	.97	.95	.93	.97	.94	.92	.95	.93	.91	.92	.90	.88

Max. Spacing 1.0xMH

Wide distribution including reflector lamp in protective reflector (based on 1.0 S/MH ratio)
Maint. Good .80
Factor Med. .75
Poor .70

24 (0% / 70%)

Room Ratio (Index)	50	30	10	50	30	10	50	30	10	30	10	0
0.6 (J)	.57	.54	.51	.56	.53	.51	.56	.53	.51	.52	.51	.49
0.8 (I)	.63	.60	.57	.62	.59	.57	.61	.58	.56	.58	.56	.54
1.0 (H)	.67	.63	.61	.66	.62	.61	.64	.62	.60	.60	.59	.57
1.25 (G)	.71	.67	.65	.70	.66	.64	.67	.65	.63	.63	.62	.60
1.5 (F)	.73	.70	.67	.72	.69	.67	.69	.67	.65	.65	.64	.62
2.0 (E)	.76	.73	.71	.75	.72	.70	.72	.70	.68	.67	.66	.64
2.5 (D)	.78	.75	.73	.77	.74	.72	.74	.72	.70	.69	.68	.65
3.0 (C)	.79	.77	.75	.78	.76	.74	.75	.73	.72	.70	.69	.66
4.0 (B)	.81	.79	.77	.79	.78	.76	.76	.75	.74	.72	.71	.67
5.0 (A)	.82	.80	.79	.80	.78	.77	.77	.75	.75	.72	.71	.68

Max. Spacing 0.6xMH

Mercury high bay reflector
Maint. Good .65
Factor Med. .60
Poor .55

Maximum Spacing between luminaire centers for uniform illumination. MH—Mounting Height above floor. CH—Ceiling Height above floor.
NOTE: All reflectances are effective values.

Table 21.9 (Continued)

Suspended Industrial Incandescent and Mercury

TYPICAL DISTRIBUTION AND MAXIMUM SPACING*	CEILING (%)	80			70			50			30		0	TYPICAL LUMINAIRE AND ESTIMATED MAINTENANCE FACTORS
	WALLS (%)	50	30	10	50	30	10	50	30	10	30	10	0	
	ROOM RATIO (Index)	COEFFICIENTS OF UTILIZATION (ZONAL METHOD) FOR 10% FLOOR REFLECTANCE (See end for 30% Floor Multipliers)												

25 — 10% / 60%, Max. Spacing 1.0xMH

Room Ratio	50	30	10	50	30	10	50	30	10	30	10	0
0.6 (J)	.39	.35	.32	.38	.34	.32	.38	.34	.31	.33	.31	.30
0.8 (I)	.48	.43	.40	.47	.42	.40	.46	.42	.39	.41	.38	.37
1.0 (H)	.53	.49	.46	.52	.48	.45	.51	.47	.45	.46	.44	.41
1.25(G)	.58	.54	.51	.57	.53	.50	.55	.51	.49	.50	.48	.45
1.5 (F)	.62	.58	.54	.61	.57	.54	.58	.55	.52	.53	.51	.48
2.0 (E)	.66	.62	.59	.64	.61	.58	.61	.59	.57	.56	.55	.52
2.5 (D)	.68	.65	.63	.67	.64	.62	.64	.61	.60	.59	.57	.54
3.0 (C)	.70	.67	.65	.69	.66	.64	.65	.63	.61	.60	.59	.56
4.0 (B)	.72	.70	.68	.70	.69	.67	.67	.66	.64	.63	.61	.58
5.0 (A)	.73	.71	.70	.71	.70	.68	.68	.67	.66	.64	.63	.59

Improved-color mercury in low bay reflector. Maint. Factor — Good .65, Med. .60, Poor .55

26 — 0% / 100%, Max. Spacing 0.7xMH

Room Ratio	50	30	10	50	30	10	50	30	10	30	10	0
0.6 (J)	.66	.62	.60	.66	.62	.60	.65	.62	.59	.62	.59	.58
0.8 (I)	.75	.71	.68	.75	.71	.68	.74	.71	.68	.70	.68	.67
1.0 (H)	.80	.76	.73	.80	.76	.73	.79	.76	.73	.76	.73	.72
1.25(G)	.85	.81	.80	.85	.81	.80	.84	.81	.78	.80	.78	.77
1.5 (F)	.88	.86	.82	.88	.85	.82	.88	.84	.82	.84	.82	.81
2.0 (E)	.94	.90	.88	.93	.90	.88	.92	.89	.87	.88	.87	.85
2.5 (D)	.96	.93	.92	.96	.93	.91	.94	.92	.90	.91	.89	.88
3.0 (C)	.99	.95	.94	.98	.95	.93	.96	.94	.92	.93	.91	.89
4.0 (B)	1.01	.99	.96	1.00	.98	.96	.98	.97	.95	.95	.94	.92
5.0 (A)	1.02	1.01	.99	1.01	1.00	.98	1.00	.98	.97	.97	.96	.94

Narrow distribution including reflector lamp in protective reflector. Maint. Factor — Good .80, Med. .75, Poor .70

27 — 0% / 85%, Max. Spacing 1.1xMH

Room Ratio	50	30	10	50	30	10	50	30	10	30	10	0
0.6 (J)	.37	.32	.29	.37	.32	.29	.37	.32	.29	.32	.29	.28
0.8 (I)	.47	.42	.38	.46	.42	.38	.46	.41	.38	.41	.38	.37
1.0 (H)	.54	.48	.45	.54	.48	.45	.53	.48	.45	.48	.45	.43
1.25(G)	.60	.56	.52	.60	.55	.52	.60	.55	.52	.54	.52	.50
1.5 (F)	.66	.61	.57	.65	.60	.57	.64	.60	.57	.59	.56	.55
2.0 (E)	.72	.67	.64	.71	.67	.64	.70	.66	.63	.66	.63	.62
2.5 (D)	.76	.71	.68	.75	.71	.68	.73	.71	.68	.70	.67	.65
3.0 (C)	.79	.75	.72	.78	.75	.71	.77	.73	.71	.72	.71	.69
4.0 (B)	.82	.79	.77	.81	.79	.76	.80	.77	.75	.76	.75	.73
5.0 (A)	.84	.82	.79	.83	.81	.78	.82	.79	.77	.78	.77	.75

Improved-color mercury semi-reflector lamp in porcelain-enameled ventilated reflector.

Maint. Factor —   400W / 1000W — Good .65 / .60, Med. .60 / .55, Poor .55 / .50

28 — 15% / 70%, Max. Spacing 1.0xMH

Room Ratio	50	30	10	50	30	10	50	30	10	30	10	0
0.6 (J)	.41	.37	.34	.40	.36	.34	.40	.36	.34	.36	.33	.32
0.8 (I)	.49	.44	.42	.49	.44	.42	.47	.44	.41	.43	.41	.40
1.0 (H)	.55	.51	.48	.54	.51	.47	.53	.49	.47	.46	.45	.44
1.25(G)	.59	.56	.53	.59	.56	.53	.57	.54	.52	.53	.50	.48
1.5 (F)	.64	.60	.57	.64	.59	.57	.61	.57	.56	.56	.55	.52
2.0 (E)	.69	.65	.64	.68	.64	.62	.65	.62	.59	.60	.58	.55
2.5 (D)	.72	.68	.65	.70	.67	.65	.67	.64	.62	.63	.60	.57
3.0 (C)	.74	.71	.69	.73	.70	.67	.70	.67	.64	.64	.62	.59
4.0 (B)	.76	.74	.71	.75	.72	.70	.71	.70	.67	.65	.64	.60
5.0 (A)	.79	.76	.74	.76	.75	.72	.72	.71	.70	.67	.65	.62

Improved-color mercury semi-reflector lamp in open top aluminum reflector.

Maint. Factor —   400W / 1000W — Good .65 / .60, Med. .60 / .55, Poor .55 / .50

* Maximum Spacing between luminaire centers for uniform illumination. MH—Mounting Height above floor CH—Ceiling Height above floor.

NOTE: All reflectances are effective values.

Table 21.9 (Continued)

TYPICAL DISTRIBUTION AND MAXIMUM SPACING*	CEILING (%)	80			70			50			30		0	TYPICAL LUMINAIRE AND ESTIMATED MAINTENANCE FACTORS
	WALLS (%)	50	30	10	50	30	10	50	30	10	30	10	0	
	ROOM RATIO (Index)	COEFFICIENTS OF UTILIZATION (ZONAL METHOD) FOR 10% FLOOR REFLECTANCE (See end for 30% Floor Multipliers)												

29

15% / 45%

Max. Spacing 1.0xMH

Room Ratio	50	30	10	50	30	10	50	30	10	30	10	0
0.6 (J)	.18	.14	.11	.17	.14	.11	.17	.14	.11	.14	.11	.10
0.8 (I)	.23	.19	.16	.23	.19	.16	.22	.18	.16	.18	.15	.14
1.0 (H)	.28	.24	.20	.27	.23	.19	.26	.23	.19	.21	.19	.18
1.25(G)	.33	.28	.24	.31	.27	.24	.30	.26	.24	.25	.23	.21
1.5 (F)	.36	.31	.28	.35	.31	.28	.33	.30	.26	.28	.27	.23
2.0 (E)	.41	.36	.32	.40	.36	.32	.37	.33	.31	.32	.29	.27
2.5 (D)	.44	.39	.36	.43	.38	.35	.40	.36	.34	.34	.32	.29
3.0 (C)	.46	.43	.39	.45	.41	.38	.42	.39	.37	.37	.34	.32
4.0 (B)	.50	.46	.43	.48	.45	.42	.45	.42	.41	.39	.38	.34
5.0 (A)	.52	.49	.46	.50	.48	.45	.47	.44	.43	.41	.40	.36

Plastic enclosed with apertured top
Maint. Good .70
Factor Med. .60
Poor .50

30

10% / 70%

Max. Spacing 1.0xMH

Room Ratio	50	30	10	50	30	10	50	30	10	30	10	0
0.6 (J)	.31	.25	.23	.31	.25	.23	.29	.25	.21	.25	.21	.20
0.8 (I)	.40	.34	.30	.39	.34	.30	.38	.33	.30	.33	.30	.28
1.0 (H)	.47	.41	.37	.47	.40	.37	.45	.40	.36	.39	.36	.34
1.25(G)	.54	.48	.44	.54	.48	.43	.52	.46	.43	.45	.42	.40
1.5 (F)	.60	.54	.49	.58	.53	.49	.56	.51	.48	.50	.47	.45
2.0 (E)	.67	.61	.57	.65	.60	.56	.62	.58	.54	.56	.54	.50
2.5 (D)	.71	.65	.61	.69	.64	.60	.66	.62	.59	.60	.58	.54
3.0 (C)	.74	.69	.65	.72	.67	.65	.69	.66	.62	.62	.61	.57
4.0 (B)	.78	.74	.70	.75	.73	.69	.73	.69	.67	.67	.64	.61
5.0 (A)	.81	.77	.75	.79	.76	.74	.76	.72	.70	.70	.67	.64

Porcelain-enameled industrial with 13° crosswise shielding
Maint. Good .75
Factor Med. .70
Poor .65

31

20% / 70%

Max. Spacing 1.0xMH

Room Ratio	50	30	10	50	30	10	50	30	10	30	10	0
0.6 (J)	.32	.27	.24	.31	.26	.23	.30	.25	.22	.25	.22	.21
0.8 (I)	.41	.36	.32	.40	.35	.31	.38	.34	.30	.33	.30	.27
1.0 (H)	.49	.43	.39	.47	.42	.38	.45	.40	.37	.38	.36	.32
1.25(G)	.56	.50	.45	.54	.48	.44	.51	.46	.43	.44	.41	.36
1.5 (F)	.61	.55	.50	.59	.53	.49	.55	.51	.47	.48	.45	.40
2.0 (E)	.68	.62	.58	.65	.60	.56	.61	.57	.53	.54	.51	.44
2.5 (D)	.72	.67	.63	.69	.65	.61	.65	.61	.58	.57	.55	.47
3.0 (C)	.75	.71	.67	.72	.68	.65	.67	.64	.61	.60	.58	.49
4.0 (B)	.79	.75	.72	.76	.73	.70	.71	.68	.66	.63	.62	.54
5.0 (A)	.82	.79	.76	.78	.76	.73	.73	.71	.69	.66	.64	.53

Porcelain-enameled industrial with 30° crosswise shielding
Maint. Good .75
Factor Med. .70
Poor .65

32

20% / 60%

Max. Spacing 0.9xMH

Room Ratio	50	30	10	50	30	10	50	30	10	30	10	0
0.6 (J)	.31	.26	.23	.30	.25	.22	.28	.24	.22	.24	.22	.20
0.8 (I)	.39	.34	.31	.38	.33	.28	.36	.32	.28	.31	.27	.25
1.0 (H)	.45	.40	.37	.44	.39	.36	.41	.38	.35	.36	.34	.31
1.25(G)	.52	.46	.42	.49	.45	.41	.46	.43	.40	.41	.38	.35
1.5 (F)	.55	.50	.46	.54	.49	.46	.50	.47	.44	.44	.41	.39
2.0 (E)	.61	.56	.52	.59	.55	.51	.55	.52	.49	.49	.47	.43
2.5 (D)	.65	.60	.57	.62	.59	.56	.58	.55	.53	.52	.50	.45
3.0 (C)	.68	.64	.60	.65	.62	.59	.61	.58	.56	.54	.52	.47
4.0 (B)	.71	.68	.65	.68	.65	.63	.63	.61	.57	.57	.55	.49
5.0 (A)	.73	.70	.68	.70	.68	.66	.65	.63	.62	.59	.57	.51

Porcelain-enameled industrial with 30° crosswise & lengthwise shielding
Maint. Good .75
Factor Med. .70
Poor .60

(left margin: Suspended Semi-Direct Fluorescent)

* Maximum Spacing between luminaire centers for uniform illumination. MH—Mounting Height above floor CH—Ceiling Height above floor.
NOTE: All reflectances are effective values.

Table 21.9 (Continued)

Ceiling (%)		80			70			50			30		0
Walls (%)		50	30	10	50	30	10	50	30	10	30	10	0
Room Ratio (Index)		Coefficients of Utilization (Zonal Method) for 10% Floor Reflectance (See end for 30% Floor Multipliers)											

Left margin label: Suspended General Diffuse & Direct-Indirect

33 — Direct-indirect with opaque side panels & louver bottom
Distribution: 30% / 35%. Max. Spacing 1.1×MH.
Maint. Factor: Good .75, Med. .70, Poor .65

Room Ratio	80 / 50	30	10	70 / 50	30	10	50 / 50	30	10	30 / 30	10	0
0.6 (J)	.20	.16	.13	.20	.16	.13	.19	.16	.13	.15	.13	.12
0.8 (I)	.25	.22	.18	.25	.20	.18	.23	.19	.17	.19	.17	.16
1.0 (H)	.31	.27	.24	.30	.26	.23	.28	.24	.22	.22	.21	.18
1.25 (G)	.35	.31	.28	.34	.30	.28	.30	.28	.26	.26	.24	.21
1.5 (F)	.37	.33	.30	.36	.32	.29	.32	.30	.27	.27	.25	.23
2.0 (E)	.42	.38	.35	.40	.37	.34	.37	.33	.31	.31	.29	.25
2.5 (D)	.44	.41	.39	.42	.40	.37	.39	.36	.34	.33	.32	.27
3.0 (C)	.47	.44	.41	.45	.42	.40	.40	.38	.36	.34	.33	.28
4.0 (B)	.50	.47	.45	.47	.45	.43	.42	.40	.39	.36	.35	.29
5.0 (A)	.51	.49	.47	.49	.47	.46	.43	.42	.40	.39	.36	.30

34 — Direct-indirect with metal or dense diffusing sides and 40° louver shielding
Distribution: 30% / 40%. Max. Spacing 1.0×MH.
Maint. Factor: Good .75, Med. .70, Poor .65

Room Ratio	80 / 50	30	10	70 / 50	30	10	50 / 50	30	10	30 / 30	10	0
0.6 (J)	.22	.18	.16	.21	.18	.16	.20	.17	.15	.16	.15	.13
0.8 (I)	.29	.24	.21	.27	.24	.21	.25	.23	.20	.22	.19	.18
1.0 (H)	.33	.29	.26	.33	.29	.25	.31	.27	.24	.26	.23	.21
1.25 (G)	.39	.34	.31	.37	.33	.31	.35	.31	.29	.29	.28	.24
1.5 (F)	.43	.38	.35	.41	.36	.34	.38	.34	.32	.32	.30	.26
2.0 (E)	.48	.44	.40	.46	.42	.39	.41	.39	.35	.34	.33	.28
2.5 (D)	.51	.47	.44	.49	.45	.43	.44	.40	.39	.37	.35	.30
3.0 (C)	.53	.50	.48	.51	.47	.45	.46	.44	.41	.40	.38	.32
4.0 (B)	.57	.53	.51	.53	.51	.49	.48	.46	.45	.41	.40	.34
5.0 (A)	.59	.56	.54	.55	.53	.51	.49	.47	.46	.42	.41	.35

35 — Direct-indirect with metal or dense diffusing sides and 35°C x 45°L louver shielding
Distribution: 45% / 35%. Max. Spacing 1.2×MH.
Maint. Factor: Good .75, Med. .70, Poor .65

Room Ratio	80 / 50	30	10	70 / 50	30	10	50 / 50	30	10	30 / 30	10	0
0.6 (J)	.24	.19	.16	.23	.19	.16	.22	.18	.15	.17	.14	.13
0.8 (I)	.31	.26	.22	.30	.25	.21	.27	.24	.20	.22	.19	.17
1.0 (H)	.37	.30	.27	.34	.29	.26	.32	.27	.24	.25	.23	.19
1.25 (G)	.42	.36	.32	.40	.35	.32	.36	.32	.29	.29	.26	.22
1.5 (F)	.46	.40	.35	.44	.39	.34	.38	.35	.31	.31	.28	.23
2.0 (E)	.53	.46	.42	.49	.44	.40	.43	.39	.36	.34	.33	.26
2.5 (D)	.57	.51	.47	.52	.48	.45	.47	.43	.40	.37	.34	.28
3.0 (C)	.60	.55	.50	.56	.51	.48	.49	.45	.43	.39	.37	.29
4.0 (B)	.63	.59	.55	.59	.56	.53	.51	.49	.45	.41	.40	.30
5.0 (A)	.66	.63	.60	.62	.58	.57	.53	.51	.49	.43	.42	.32

36 — 4 Bare lamps in-a-line
Distribution: 36% / 58%. Max. Spacing 1.0×MH.
Maint. Factor: Good .80, Med. .75, Poor .70

Room Ratio	80 / 50	30	10	70 / 50	30	10	50 / 50	30	10	30 / 30	10	0
0.6 (J)	.25	.18	.15	.24	.18	.15	.23	.18	.14	.17	.14	.12
0.8 (I)	.32	.26	.21	.31	.25	.21	.29	.24	.20	.23	.19	.17
1.0 (H)	.40	.32	.27	.38	.31	.26	.36	.30	.25	.27	.24	.21
1.25 (G)	.46	.39	.33	.45	.38	.32	.40	.35	.30	.33	.29	.25
1.5 (F)	.51	.43	.41	.49	.41	.37	.45	.39	.34	.35	.32	.28
2.0 (E)	.58	.52	.45	.56	.50	.44	.51	.46	.41	.41	.38	.33
2.5 (D)	.63	.57	.51	.62	.55	.50	.56	.50	.46	.45	.42	.36
3.0 (C)	.69	.62	.56	.65	.60	.55	.59	.57	.50	.48	.45	.38
4.0 (B)	.74	.69	.63	.70	.65	.60	.63	.59	.56	.53	.51	.42
5.0 (A)	.77	.74	.68	.74	.69	.66	.67	.63	.61	.56	.54	.45

* Maximum Spacing between luminaire centers for uniform illumination. MH—Mounting Height above floor.
CH—Ceiling Height above floor.
Note: All reflectances are effective values.

Table 21.9 (Continued)

Typical Distribution and Maximum Spacing*	Room Ratio (Index)	Ceiling 80 · Walls 50	80 · 30	80 · 10	70 · 50	70 · 30	70 · 10	50 · 50	50 · 30	50 · 10	30 · 30	30 · 10	0 · 0	Typical Luminaire and Estimated Maintenance Factors
		\multicolumn{12}{} Coefficients of Utilization (Zonal Method) for 10% Floor Reflectance (See end for 30% Floor Multipliers)												

37 — 35% / 25% — Max. Spacing 1.0xCH — Suspended Direct-Indirect

Room Ratio	80·50	80·30	80·10	70·50	70·30	70·10	50·50	50·30	50·10	30·30	30·10	0·0
0.6 (J)	.17	.13	.11	.16	.13	.11	.15	.12	.10	.12	.10	.08
0.8 (I)	.23	.18	.16	.21	.18	.15	.19	.17	.14	.15	.14	.11
1.0 (H)	.27	.22	.20	.25	.22	.19	.23	.20	.18	.18	.16	.13
1.25(G)	.31	.27	.24	.30	.26	.23	.27	.23	.21	.21	.19	.15
1.5 (F)	.34	.30	.26	.32	.29	.25	.29	.25	.23	.22	.20	.17
2.0 (E)	.39	.35	.32	.37	.34	.31	.32	.29	.27	.25	.23	.19
2.5 (D)	.43	.41	.35	.39	.36	.34	.35	.32	.30	.28	.26	.20
3.0 (C)	.45	.42	.38	.42	.39	.36	.36	.34	.32	.29	.28	.21
4.0 (B)	.48	.45	.42	.44	.42	.40	.39	.36	.34	.31	.30	.23
5.0 (A)	.49	.47	.44	.46	.44	.42	.39	.38	.36	.32	.31	.23

Chandelier with opaque or dense diffusing shades. Maint. Good .80 Factor Med. .75 Poor .70

38 — 60% / 15% — Max. Spacing 1.2xCH — Semi-Indirect

Room Ratio	80·50	80·30	80·10	70·50	70·30	70·10	50·50	50·30	50·10	30·30	30·10	0·0
0.6 (J)	.16	.11	.07	.15	.10	.06	.12	.08	.06	.07	.06	.03
0.8 (I)	.21	.15	.12	.19	.15	.12	.16	.12	.08	.09	.07	.04
1.0 (H)	.26	.20	.16	.23	.19	.15	.19	.15	.12	.12	.10	.05
1.25(G)	.32	.25	.20	.28	.23	.19	.23	.18	.15	.14	.12	.06
1.5 (F)	.36	.30	.24	.33	.26	.22	.25	.21	.18	.16	.13	.07
2.0 (E)	.42	.36	.31	.38	.33	.27	.29	.25	.22	.18	.16	.08
2.5 (D)	.46	.40	.36	.41	.36	.33	.32	.29	.25	.20	.19	.09
3.0 (C)	.50	.44	.40	.44	.40	.36	.34	.31	.28	.22	.20	.09
4.0 (B)	.54	.50	.45	.48	.44	.41	.37	.34	.32	.25	.22	.10
5.0 (A)	.57	.53	.50	.51	.48	.44	.39	.36	.34	.25	.25	.10

4 LAMP. Translucent bottom and sides. Maint. Good .70 Factor Med. .60 Poor .50

39 — 65% / 10% — Max. Spacing 1.2xCH — Semi-Indirect

Room Ratio	80·50	80·30	80·10	70·50	70·30	70·10	50·50	50·30	50·10	30·30	30·10	0·0
0.6 (J)	.16	.11	.08	.15	.10	.07	.13	.09	.06	.08	.06	.03
0.8 (I)	.22	.16	.12	.20	.15	.11	.17	.13	.10	.10	.08	.04
1.0 (H)	.27	.21	.17	.25	.19	.15	.20	.16	.13	.12	.10	.05
1.25(G)	.32	.26	.21	.29	.24	.19	.23	.19	.16	.15	.12	.06
1.5 (F)	.37	.30	.26	.33	.28	.23	.26	.22	.19	.16	.14	.07
2.0 (E)	.43	.37	.32	.39	.34	.29	.30	.26	.23	.19	.16	.08
2.5 (D)	.48	.42	.36	.43	.38	.34	.33	.29	.26	.21	.19	.09
3.0 (C)	.51	.46	.39	.46	.41	.38	.35	.32	.29	.22	.21	.09
4.0 (B)	.56	.51	.43	.49	.46	.43	.38	.35	.33	.25	.24	.10
5.0 (A)	.58	.55	.51	.52	.49	.46	.39	.37	.35	.26	.25	.10

Luminous-indirect fluorescent grid. Maint. Good .70 Factor Med. .60 Poor .50

40 — 65% / 5% — Max. Spacing 1.2xCH — Suspended Indirect

Room Ratio	80·50	80·30	80·10	70·50	70·30	70·10	50·50	50·30	50·10	30·30	30·10	0·0
0.6 (J)	.11	.07	.04	.10	.07	.04	.08	.06	.03	.05	.03	
0.8 (I)	.14	.10	.07	.13	.09	.07	.10	.07	.06	.06	.04	
1.0 (H)	.19	.14	.10	.17	.13	.09	.13	.10	.07	.08	.05	
1.25(G)	.23	.18	.15	.21	.16	.14	.15	.13	.10	.09	.07	
1.5 (F)	.26	.20	.17	.24	.19	.16	.18	.14	.12	.10	.08	
2.0 (E)	.31	.26	.23	.28	.24	.20	.20	.18	.16	.12	.11	
2.5 (D)	.35	.30	.26	.31	.26	.24	.24	.20	.18	.13	.12	
3.0 (C)	.37	.34	.29	.33	.30	.26	.25	.21	.20	.14	.13	
4.0 (B)	.39	.37	.34	.36	.33	.30	.27	.25	.23	.16	.16	
5.0 (A)	.44	.40	.37	.37	.35	.33	.28	.26	.25	.17	.17	

Luminous-indirect fluorescent. Maint. Good .70 Factor Med. .60 Poor .50

* Maximum Spacing between luminaire centers for uniform illumination. MH—Mounting Height above floor.
CH—Ceiling Height above floor.
Note: All reflectances are effective values.

Table 21.9 (Continued)

	CEILING (%)	80			70			50			30		0	
TYPICAL DISTRIBUTION AND MAXIMUM SPACING*	WALLS (%)	50	30	10	50	30	10	50	30	10	30	10	0	TYPICAL LUMINAIRE AND ESTIMATED MAINTENANCE FACTORS
	ROOM RATIO (Index)	COEFFICIENTS OF UTILIZATION (ZONAL METHOD) FOR 10% FLOOR REFLECTANCE (See end for 30% Floor Multipliers)												

41 — Suspended Indirect — 80% / 5% — Max. Spacing 1.2xCH

Room Ratio	80:50	80:30	80:10	70:50	70:30	70:10	50:50	50:30	50:10	30:30	30:10	0:0
0.6 (J)	.15	.09	.06	.13	.08	.05	.10	.07	.04	.05	.03	.01
0.8 (I)	.20	.13	.09	.19	.12	.08	.15	.09	.07	.07	.04	.01
1.0 (H)	.25	.18	.13	.23	.17	.12	.17	.13	.09	.09	.06	.01
1.25(G)	.30	.23	.19	.27	.22	.17	.20	.16	.12	.11	.08	.02
1.5 (F)	.35	.28	.23	.31	.25	.20	.23	.19	.15	.12	.10	.02
2.0 (E)	.42	.35	.30	.38	.31	.26	.28	.23	.19	.14	.12	.02
2.5 (D)	.47	.41	.35	.41	.36	.31	.31	.26	.23	.15	.14	.02
3.0 (C)	.51	.46	.41	.45	.40	.36	.32	.29	.27	.18	.15	.02
4.0 (B)	.56	.51	.46	.49	.45	.41	.35	.32	.31	.20	.19	.03
5.0 (A)	.59	.55	.50	.51	.48	.45	.37	.35	.32	.21	.20	.03

Luminous-indirect incandescent
Maint. Good .70
Factor Med. .60
　Poor .50

42 — 85% / 0% — Max. Spacing 1.2xCH

Room Ratio	80:50	80:30	80:10	70:50	70:30	70:10	50:50	50:30	50:10	30:30	30:10	0:0
0.6 (J)	.14	.08	.04	.13	.07	.04	.11	.06	.03	.05	.02	0
0.8 (I)	.19	.12	.07	.17	.11	.07	.14	.09	.05	.07	.04	0
1.0 (H)	.24	.16	.11	.22	.15	.11	.17	.12	.08	.09	.05	0
1.25(G)	.30	.22	.16	.27	.20	.14	.21	.15	.10	.10	.06	.01
1.5 (F)	.35	.26	.20	.31	.24	.18	.23	.17	.13	.11	.08	.01
2.0 (E)	.42	.34	.28	.37	.30	.24	.27	.22	.17	.14	.11	.01
2.5 (D)	.48	.40	.34	.41	.35	.31	.29	.25	.21	.16	.13	.01
3.0 (C)	.52	.45	.38	.45	.39	.34	.32	.27	.25	.17	.15	.01
4.0 (B)	.57	.52	.46	.50	.45	.41	.36	.32	.29	.20	.18	.01
5.0 (A)	.61	.56	.51	.52	.49	.45	.40	.35	.32	.21	.20	.01

Silvered-bowl indirect
Maint. Good .75
Factor Med. .70
　Poor .65

43 — Cove 12" to 18" below ceiling. Reflectors with fluorescent lamps will increase coefficients 5 to 10%

Room Ratio	80:50	80:30	80:10	70:50	70:30	70:10	50:50	50:30	50:10
0.6 (J)	.11	.09	.06	.09	.07	.06	.07	.05	.04
0.8 (I)	.15	.12	.10	.13	.10	.08	.09	.07	.06
1.0 (H)	.18	.15	.12	.16	.13	.10	.10	.09	.07
1.25(G)	.22	.18	.16	.20	.16	.14	.13	.11	.10
1.5 (F)	.25	.21	.19	.21	.19	.17	.15	.13	.11
2.0 (E)	.29	.26	.22	.25	.22	.20	.17	.15	.14
2.5 (D)	.33	.30	.28	.28	.26	.24	.20	.19	.17
3.0 (C)	.35	.32	.30	.31	.28	.26	.21	.20	.19
4.0 (B)	.36	.34	.32	.32	.30	.28	.22	.21	.20
5.0 (A)	.39	.38	.36	.35	.34	.32	.24	.23	.23

Fluorescent cove without reflector
Maint. Good .70
Factor Med. .60
　Poor .50

44

Ceiling cavity reflectance 75%

Plastic or glass reflectance 45%

Plastic or glass transmittance 45%

Room Ratio	80:50	80:30	80:10
0.6 (J)	.19	.15	.13
0.8 (I)	.25	.22	.19
1.0 (H)	.31	.26	.23
1.25(G)	.35	.32	.29
1.5 (F)	.40	.35	.33
2.0 (E)	.45	.42	.38
2.5 (D)	.49	.46	.42
3.0 (C)	.52	.49	.46
4.0 (B)	.56	.54	.52
5.0 (A)	.58	.57	.55

In the use of these tables consideration must be given to the fact that the coefficients of utilization shown are based on a single set of representative conditions. The efficiency of wall-to-wall lighting sys-

* Maximum Spacing between luminaire centers for uniform illumination. MH—Mounting Height above floor CH—Ceiling Height above floor.
NOTE: All reflectances are effective values.

Table 21.9 (Continued)

TYPICAL DISTRIBUTION AND MAXIMUM SPACING*	CEILING (%)	80			70			50			30		0	TYPICAL LUMINAIRE AND ESTIMATED MAINTENANCE FACTORS
	WALLS (%)	50	30	10	50	30	10	50	30	10	30	10	0	
	ROOM RATIO (Index)	COEFFICIENTS OF UTILIZATION (ZONAL METHOD) FOR 10% FLOOR REFLECTANCE (See end for 30% Floor Multipliers)												

44 Continued		tems varies greatly with cavity proportion and reflectances, the type of lighting equipment used, and with the reflection and transmission characteristics of the shielding medium.	Diffusing glass or plastic extended area system Maint. Good .65 Factor Med. .55 Poor .45

45									Ceiling cavity reflectance 75% Louver surface reflectance 75% In the use of these tables consideration must be given to the fact that the coefficients of utilization shown are based on a single set of representative conditions. The efficiency of wall-to-wall lighting systems varies greatly with cavity proportion and reflectances, the type of lighting equipment used, and with the reflection and transmission characteristics of the shielding medium.	Opaque louver (white) extended area system Maint. Good .70 Factor Med. .65 Poor .55
	0.6 (J)	.19	.16	.15						
	0.8 (I)	.23	.20	.19						
	1.0 (H)	.25	.22	.21						
	1.25(G)	.27	.25	.24						
	1.5 (F)	.30	.26	.25						
	2.0 (E)	.32	.30	.29						
	2.5 (D)	.33	.31	.30						
	3.0 (C)	.34	.32	.32						
	4.0 (B)	.35	.34	.33						
	5.0 (A)	.36	.35	.34						

The above tabulations are based on floors of 10 per cent effective reflectance and take into account reflectances and obstructions below the work plane (machinery, furniture, etc.). Higher effective reflectances, naturally, will tend to increase utilization, especially in high ratio rooms. Below is a table giving approximate correction factors for floors of 30 per cent reflectance.

APPROXIMATE MULTIPLYING FACTORS FOR 30 PER CENT REFLECTANCE FLOORS
(10 Per Cent Reflectance Floor = 1.00)

CEILING	80%			70%			50%			30%		
WALLS	50%	30%	10%	50%	30%	10%	50%	30%	10%	50%	30%	10%
ROOM RATIO												
0.6 (J)	1.03	1.02	1.01	1.03	1.02	1.01	1.02	1.02	1.00	1.02	1.01	1.00
0.8 (I)	1.04	1.02	1.01	1.04	1.02	1.01	1.03	1.02	1.01	1.02	1.01	1.01
1.0 (H)	1.05	1.03	1.02	1.04	1.03	1.02	1.04	1.02	1.01	1.03	1.02	1.01
1.25(G)	1.06	1.04	1.02	1.05	1.04	1.02	1.04	1.03	1.02	1.03	1.02	1.01
1.5 (F)	1.07	1.06	1.03	1.07	1.05	1.03	1.05	1.04	1.02	1.03	1.02	1.02
2.0 (E)	1.09	1.07	1.05	1.08	1.06	1.04	1.05	1.04	1.03	1.04	1.03	1.02
2.5 (D)	1.10	1.08	1.06	1.09	1.08	1.06	1.07	1.05	1.04	1.04	1.04	1.03
3.0 (C)	1.12	1.10	1.08	1.10	1.09	1.07	1.08	1.06	1.04	1.05	1.04	1.03
4.0 (B)	1.14	1.12	1.10	1.12	1.10	1.08	1.08	1.07	1.06	1.05	1.04	1.04
5.0 (A)	1.15	1.13	1.11	1.13	1.11	1.10	1.09	1.08	1.07	1.05	1.05	1.04

* Maximum Spacing between luminaire centers for uniform illumination. MH—Mounting Height above floor. CH—Ceiling Height above floor.

NOTE: All reflectances are effective values

IES Handbook, 3rd Ed.

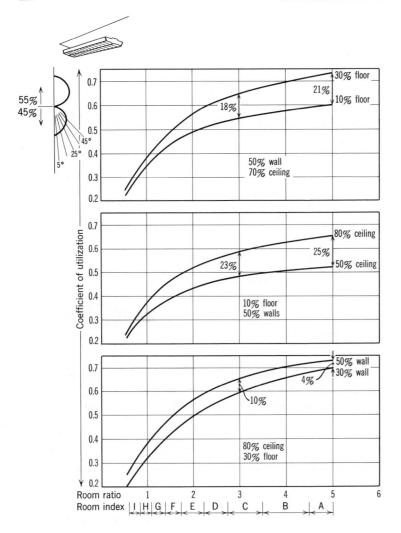

Fig. 21.19 Effect of room finishes on illumination for a direct-indirect louvered fluorescent.

It must be obvious at this stage of our discussion that much of the light from a fixture is reflected from the various room surfaces and that therefore the reflectance factors of these surfaces is of prime importance in determining the coefficient of utilization of a particular luminaire.

This is graphically illustrated by the curves of Figs. 21.19, 21.20, and 21.21.

The light from the direct-indirect fixture of Fig. 21.19 is cast principally on the ceiling and floor. The difference between a low grade floor (10 percent) and a good reflectance floor (30 percent) in a large *A* room is

21 percent. Since lighting cost accounts for some 2 percent to 5 percent of *total construction cost* a 21 percent differential may amount to as much as 1 percent of total cost. This differential would not only pay for the increased cost of the better floor material but would simultaneously pay for a portion of the lighting, improve the lighting, or go to reduce total cost. A similar situation is encountered with the ceiling reflectance. Due to the distribution of this particular unit, wall color and reflectance are the least important elements.

Less dramatic but equally impressive dif-

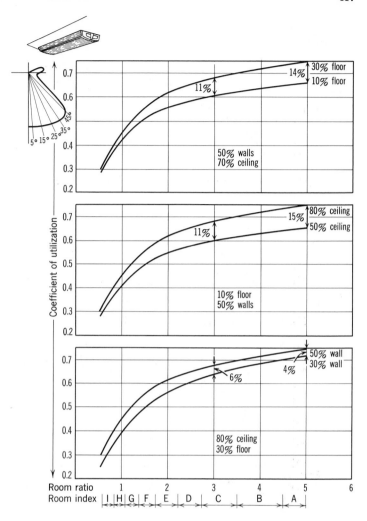

Fig. 21.20 Effect of room finishes on illumination for a prismatic wrap-around fluorescent.

ferences in illumination are shown in the comparative curves of Figs. 21.20 and 21.21 for the prismatic fixture and the troffer. All of this data indicates clearly that the lighting designer must have considerable say in selection of the room finishes in order to be able to best utilize his working medium—lighting.

13. Economics of Luminaire Selection. The problem facing the designer at this point is to select a luminaire of the many available that will most economically meet all the various requirements of brightness, appearance, maintenance, and lighting. In con-

sidering the cost of an installation, it is necessary to consider not only the cost of the lighting installation, but also the operating cost *and* the cost of the wiring installation. Figure 21.22 gives approximate average values of "watts per square foot" for various lighting systems with illumination as the variable. Since wiring cost is directly proportional to load, the "watts per square foot" figure is an indication of cost of the installation.

When a space is air-conditioned, the watts per sq ft figures of Fig. 21.22, are effectively increased approximately 40 to 50

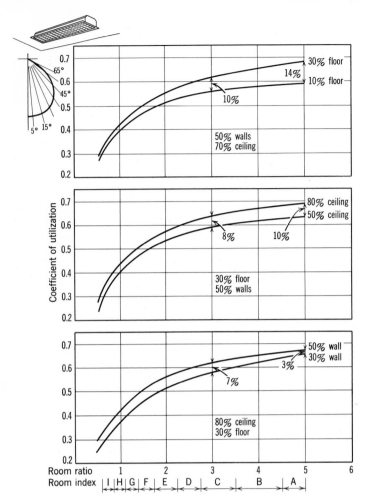

Fig. 21.21 Effect of room fin-nishes on illumination for a lou-vered fluorescent troffer.

percent due to the required air-conditioning equipment. This increases the wiring cost, cost of air-conditioning equipment, and operating cost. A typical lighting cost study is shown in Table 20.6, which accounts for all the above factors except initial and op-erating cost of air-conditioning equipment. Studies of this type are generally made by consulting engineers rather than architects, and then only after initial, operating, and total costs have been set in proper perspec-tive for the particular job, by the architect and client. This is necessary because often, as in the case of speculative construction, the client's overriding consideration is first cost, thus rendering a complete cost analysis unnecessary.

14. Diffusing Elements. The diffusing ele-ments usually considered include white plastic, striped and prismatic glass, pris-matic plastic, high reflectance aluminum (alzac) baffles, and miniature eggcrate lou-vers. In addition to these types there are various sizes and shapes of metal and plas-tic louvers and baffles, white glass, ribbed glass, etc. Each of these diffusers must be considered on its merits, and a decision arrived at. Recently, a good deal of publicity has been given to the so-called "polarizing panel" diffusers. These elements provide

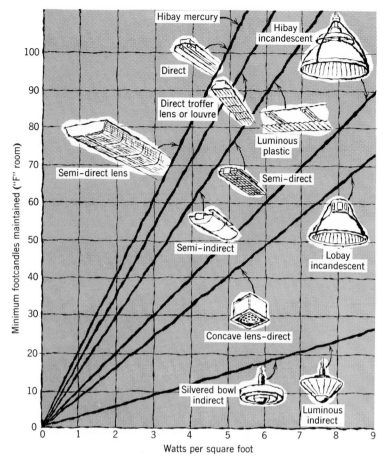

Fig. 21.22   Approximate luminous efficiency of various fixture types in terms of power consumption.

varying percentages of vertically polarized light depending upon manufacturer and type. It has been shown that vertically polarized light increases seeing efficiency, by decreasing veiling reflections. An alternate method of decreasing reflected glare, as discussed in Section 14, Chap. 19, is to increase overall illumination. The two methods thus achieve their purpose by changing the lighting quality and quantity respectively. That the former method is the more desirable is obvious from the data presented in Fig. 19.22, i.e., that a 300 percent increase in lighting quantity is required to achieve a 15 percent increase in visual performance.

Unfortunately, the lack of agreement in the lighting field as to the useful polarizing efficiacy of the commercially available materials, coupled with the lowered efficiency and high surface brightness demonstrated by certain of.these panels, prevent our making a clear recommendation at this writing.

15. Daylighting.   Although fenestration is often not within the control of the lighting designer, control of daylighting generally is, to the extent that control elements can be introduced. With this in mind the designer should provide brightness control to prevent excessive brightness ratios, and should make such suggestions to the person

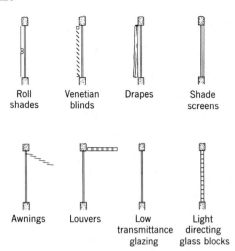

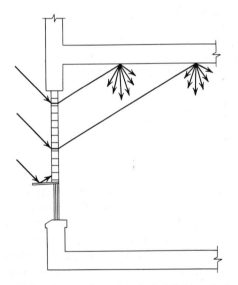

Fig. 21.23 Daylight control devices. Uncomfortably high brightness from daylighting may be prevented by any of several types of fenestration control devices. *IES Recommended Practice for Office Lighting.*

Fig. 21.24 Arrows illustrate principal light paths into room with light-directing prism glass blocks above visor and clear glass below. Clear section permits unobstructed view outdoors. When light-directing glass or glass block panels are used, they should begin approximately six feet above floor level. They are particularly effective in lower-ceilinged rooms, since the lower band of blocks near the six-foot sill delivers most of the light to the deeper portions of the room. *IES Recommended Practice of Office Lighting.*

designing the fenestration as will benefit the lighting. Avoidance of direct sunlight, use of light reflected from the ground outside (ground light) rather than sky brightness, provision of daylighting from more than one wall (and ceiling if possible); use of high windows with clear glazing for deeper room illumination and use of various types of light-controlling glass are all principles which should be borne in mind by the lighting and (or) fenestration designer.

Normally a room which may be assured of daylighting on all occasions of use is rare, and even when such is the case, the amount of daylighting is not predictable due to weather conditions. For this reason, the only cognizance which is normally taken of daylighting is in switching of lights in order to conserve power and lamp life in areas which are adequately illuminated by daylight. For a detailed discussion of daylighting, and design procedures, the reader is referred to the IES standard "Recommended Practice of Daylighting."

Figure 21.25 shows daylighting spacing factors and room illumination levels with one side fenestration. If windows are furnished on both sides of the spaces, the resultant illuminations are additive.

16. Calculation of Lighting Requirements. Having selected a luminaire on the basis of all the foregoing criteria, it remains only to calculate the number of such units required in each space for *general* illumination, and to properly arrange them. Although a number of calculation methods are available, the "lumen method" is simplest and most applicable to our needs for area lighting calculations. Intensity calculation from point, line, or area sources, or indirect systems are beyond the scope of this book and are left to the lighting engineer or designer.

17. Lumen Method. This method relates the total light flux (lumens) generated by the sources to the light flux (illumination) incident on the working plane, by means of the space efficiency (coefficient of utilization). Thus:

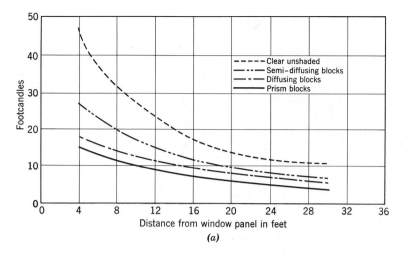

(a)

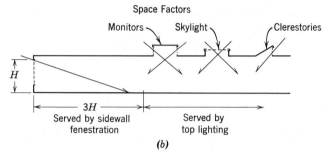

(b)

Fig. 21.25 (*a*) Interior illumination on a typical horizontal work plane with 700 footcandles of skylight outdoors. The window area of this test room was 25 percent of the floor area. (*b*) Space factors for daylighting. *IES Recommended Practice of Office Lighting.*

(*a*) Lumens generated × system efficiency = lumens utilized or

(*b*) Lamp lumens × Coefficient of Utilization = F.C. × Area and

(*c*) Lamp lumens

$$= \frac{\text{Footcandles} \times \text{Area}}{\text{Coefficient of utilization}}$$

Since fixtures are subject to light deterioration due to decrease in lamp output, dirt on lamps and within the fixture, and dirt on walls, floors, and ceilings, the system efficiency must be reduced by a "maintenance factor," abbreviated M.F. This factor is usually suggested by the manufacturer for a particular luminaire and varies between 0.5 and 0.8. The levels calculated using a M.F. are maintained, in service illumination; those calculated without using a M.F. are initial levels. Thus, our over-all formula becomes:

$$\text{Lamp lumens} = \frac{\text{F.C.} \times \text{Area}}{\text{C.U.} \times \text{M.F.}}$$

but

$$\text{Number of lamps} = \frac{\text{Total lumens}}{\text{Lumens per lamp}}$$

and

Number of luminaires

$$= \frac{\text{Number of lamps}}{\text{Lamps per luminaire}}$$

Therefore, we find our **final form:**

Number of luminaires

$$= \frac{\text{F.C.} \times \text{Area}}{\text{Lamps/luminaire} \times \text{lumens/lamp} \times \text{C.U.} \times \text{M.F.}}$$

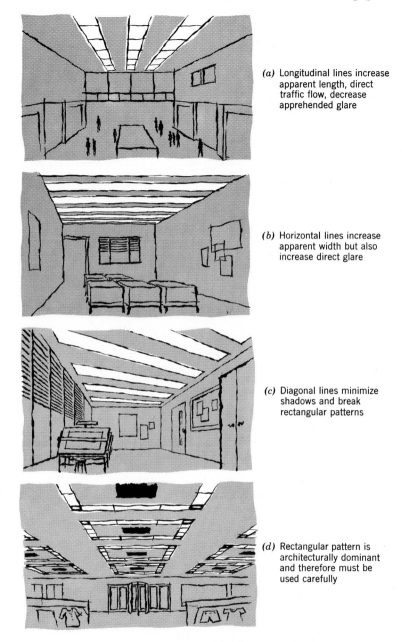

(a) Longitudinal lines increase apparent length, direct traffic flow, decrease apprehended glare

(b) Horizontal lines increase apparent width but also increase direct glare

(c) Diagonal lines minimize shadows and break rectangular patterns

(d) Rectangular pattern is architecturally dominant and therefore must be used carefully

Fig. 21.26   Architectural effects of various lighting systems.

18. Fixture Pattern. In order to achieve the uniformity of illumination necessary for general lighting, regular spacing is desirable. However, various effects may be obtained within the regularity, to accomplish an architectural purpose, as shown in Fig. 21.26. The pattern of the lights must never be at cross purpose with any dominant architectural pattern; rather it should either reinforce an architectural form or be neutral. If a strong architectural element is absent, a dominant lighting pattern may be desirable.

Generally, continuous row installations

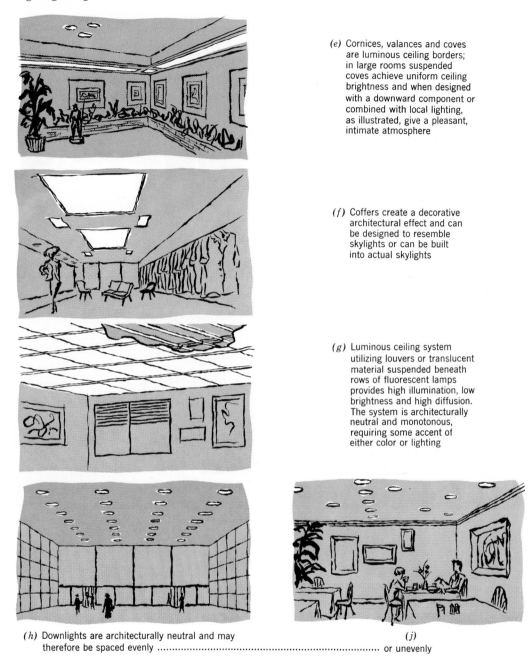

(e) Cornices, valances and coves are luminous ceiling borders; in large rooms suspended coves achieve uniform ceiling brightness and when designed with a downward component or combined with local lighting, as illustrated, give a pleasant, intimate atmosphere

(f) Coffers create a decorative architectural effect and can be designed to resemble skylights or can be built into actual skylights

(g) Luminous ceiling system utilizing louvers or translucent material suspended beneath rows of fluorescent lamps provides high illumination, low brightness and high diffusion. The system is architecturally neutral and monotonous, requiring some accent of either color or lighting

(h) Downlights are architecturally neutral and may therefore be spaced evenly .... or unevenly

(j)

Fig. 21.26   (Continued)

are more attractive than individual units, and eliminate the checkerboard effect of the latter. Coves and cornices give the ceiling a floating or light effect. Geometric patterns can be used to add interest or break monotony of large areas, such as depart-ment stores. Generally, incandescent down-lights are not dominant, and regularity of placement is not essential. Thus in Figure 21.1, (a) is a neutral pattern, (b) is a harmo-nizing dominant arrangement, and (c) is a reinforcement of the architectural pattern.

(k) That patterns of lighting are plainly visible even during
the daytime is apparent from this photo. The attractive-
ness of uniformity of fixture pattern can readily be seen.
—Photo B. Stein

(l) Since fixtures are readily visible even when unlit during
daylight hours, their outline can be accentuated and the
resultant pattern utilized as an architectural motif.
—Welton Becket & Assoc.

(m) The prominence of daylighting, the
strong geometry of the structure, and
the minimal seeing tasks involved
dictated the choice of an unobtrusive
and harmonizing decorative lighting
fixture.
Architect: Minoro Yamasaki
Photo by Baltazar Korab

(n) Lighting can be utilized as a medium to connect the inside and outside
of a building. The simple expedient of continuing the lighting pattern
beyond the window or wall glass provides visibility from inside out as
well as outside in. Care must be exercised to avoid fixture placement
which will reflect in the glass.

Fig. 21.26   (Continued)

19. Illustrative examples. To illustrate the foregoing design principles, we will pose two typical lighting problems—a school and an office—and offer at least 2 solutions each.

EXAMPLE 21.1. Design the lighting installation for a school laboratory 30′ × 36′ × 12′
in height. The room utilizes wall and island

benches. The room finishes are in accordance with recommended practice. Assume
daylighting to be controlled; artificial lighting only to be calculated.
SOLUTION.
a. In order to control reflected glare which
may be a problem with glossy table tops
and specular equipment, a semi-indirect
or direct-indirect system is preferable.

b. General level should be 70 F.C. (Table 21.2) which dictates the use of fluorescent rather than incandescent. This level of illumination is approximately the maximum obtainable with indirect lighting without exceeding ceiling brightness limits. Since color rendering may be important, warm white or white tubes should be used. Supplementary lighting should be provided over one table which will be used for demonstrations.

c. (1) For the direct-indirect system, we have selected fixture No. 34, Table 21.9. This unit provides good distribution, low area brightness, good ceiling coverage, and fair spacing ratio. Mounting height will be 10′ (24″ hanger) to avoid excessive ceiling brightness. See Table 21.7.

M.F. = 0.7 (Table 21.9)
Room index = E (Table 21.8)
Coefficient of Utilization = 0.48 (Table 21.9)
30 percent floor multiplier = 1.09 (Table 21.9)
Ceiling R.F. = 80%
Wall R.F. = 50%
Floor R.F. = 30%
Room area = 30 × 36 = 1080 sq ft
Lamp lumens = 3200 lumens/tube

Number of luminaires

$$= \frac{70 \text{ F.C.} \times 1080 \text{ sq ft}}{3200 \text{ lumens per lamp} \times 2 \text{ lamp per unit} \times 0.7 \text{ M.F.} \times (0.48 \times 1.09) \text{ C.U.}}$$

Number of luminaires = 32
The arrangement of the fixtures is shown in Fig. 21.27a. The additional row at the front of the room serves the demonstration table and the blackboard.

(2) For a semi-indirect system, we choose fixture No. 39 Table 21.9.

M.F. = 0.6
C.U. = 0.48
Room Index = D

Correction factor for 30 percent floor = 1.10

We will utilize a 1500 ma. 96 in. Very High Output lamp, white, rated at 15000

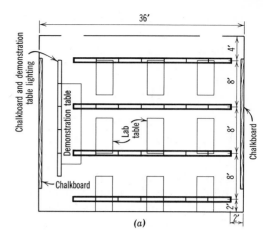

(a)

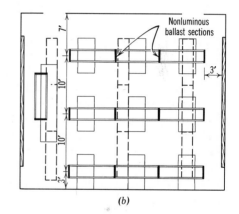

(b)

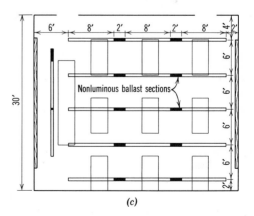

(c)

Fig. 21.27 (a) Direct-indirect lighting scheme and (b) semi-indirect lighting system. (c) Design utilizing single semi-indirect high output fluorescent strips yields high level of illumination with acceptable ceiling brightness, excellent diffusion, and good vertical surface illumination.

lumens per lamp. Units are to be mounted at 10'6". We have chosen a plastic panel bottom giving a maximum brightness of 400 F.L. at 0° and 370 F.L. at 45°.

Number of luminaires

$$= \frac{70 \times 1080}{15000 \times 2 \times 0.6 \times 0.48 \times 1.1}$$
$$= 8 \text{ units}$$

Since 8 units cannot readily be arranged, 10 units were used. An alternative would be to turn the units 90° as shown dotted, on Fig. 21.27b. A third possibility would be to use single strips (not shown in Table 21.9) rather than the double grid of fixture No. 39 in Table 21.9. This would not only decrease ceiling brightness (approx. 400 F.L. directly above the fixture) but would be more readily adaptable to the room. (See Fig. 21.27c). To compare the solutions we utilize a short comparative table, (See Table 21.10) on the basis of which we would choose the single strip semi-indirect solution because it offers the best combination of economy, uniformity, and vertical surface illumination with minimum direct and reflected glare.

EXAMPLE 21.2. Design a lighting system for a general accounting office 40' × 58' × 8'6". The ceiling is acoustic tile and the floor vinyl-asbestos tile. Desks are placed as shown in Fig. 21.28. Daylight is assumed to be absent, this being an interior space. SOLUTION. Due to the low ceiling height which is typical of modern office building design, the ceiling lighting treatment resolves itself into either recessed troffers or surface mounted units. We choose the recessed unit because the low ceiling would be excessively cluttered by a surface unit and sufficient ceiling brightness can be supplied by reflection from a light color floor. In order to reduce direct glare, prismatic lens units are selected, arranged in rows at right angles to the desks. Visual Comfort Factor from Table 21.4 is 95 crosswise and 95 lengthwise, indicating that direct glare will not be a problem in any arrangement. An alternate solution would be to reduce the apparent room length by running the fixtures across the room or at a 45° angle (shown dotted). Since over-all cost of 2' × 4' units is *usually* less than the corresponding 1' × 4' units and fixture brightness is lower, this size unit will be utilized. The following recommendations are made

Table 21.10   Fixture Comparison

Item	Fixture #34 Direct-Indirect	Fixture #39 Semi-Indirect	Single Strips Semi-Indirect
First Cost	Lowest	Highest	Intermediate
Wattage	3200	4100	3485
Watts/sq ft	2.96	3.8	3.22
Operating Cost	Lowest	Highest	Intermediate
Maintenance Cost	Highest	Lowest	Intermediate
Direct Glare	Highest	Intermediate	Lowest
Reflected Glare	Highest	Intermediate	Lowest
Ceiling Brightness	Lowest (approx. 150 F.L.)	Highest (approx. 400 F.L.)	Intermediate (approx. 300 F.L.)
Ceiling Brightness Pattern	Good	Very good	Excellent
Maintained F.C. (horizontal surface)	72	80	75
Diffusion	Good	Very good	Excellent
Foot candles/watt/sq ft	24.3	21.1	23.3

to the persons responsible for painting, tile and furnishing:

Ceiling tile—light, 70% R.F.
Floor tile —buff, 30% R.F.
Walls   —light green, 50% R.F.
Desk tops —tan, or grey—35% R.F.

Since fenestration is absent, a valance is recommended around the room. This will remove the wall-ceiling line, in an attempt to compensate for the lack of windows. It will also brighten the walls and increase illumination on desks placed adjacent to the walls.

Calculations:
General office 40′ × 58′ × 8′6″
Illumination level = 150 F.C. = Table 21.2
Room index = B   Table 21.8
Select fixture No. 6, for 4 tubes   Table 21.9
M.F. = 0.65   Table 21.9
Coefficient of Utilization = 0.56
               Table 21.9
Correction for 30 percent floor = 1.14
               Table 21.9
Spacing to Mounting Height Ratio = 0.9
               Table 21.9
Room area = 40 × 58 = 2320 sq ft
Lamp lumens = 3100 (using cool white lamps) 4 lamps per fixture

No. of luminaires

$$= \frac{40′ \times 58′ \times 150 \text{ F.C.}}{3100 \times 4 \times 0.65 \times 0.59 \times 1.14} = 67.8$$

Maximum spacing between units should be 8′6″. The units are spaced on 8′ × 6′ centers, with continuous rows at the back wall to compensate for wall losses. Side walls are compensated by the valance utilizing continuous 800 ma. 96″ tubes. The supervisors' offices Nos. 1, 2, 3, are treated with a double 2′ × 4′ unit above the desk yielding approximately 180 F.C. on the desk, and wall washer units on the facing wall to reduce brightness contrasts. The ceiling units should be arranged for 2 level illumination by switching alternate tubes.

Office No. 4 is that of the Office Manager and is treated with a dimmer controlled luminous ceiling. Utilizing the data in Table 21.9, Fixture No. 44, with the listed transmittance and reflectances;

Room area = 10 × 10 = 100 sq ft
Room index = H   Table 21.8
Coefficient = 0.31   Table 21.9
Floor multiplier = 1.05

Lamp lumens

$$= \frac{200 \text{ F.C.} \times 100 \text{ sq ft}}{0.32 \text{ C.U.} \times 0.60 \text{ M.F.}} = 104{,}000$$

Utilizing 6 ft (6000 lumens) and 4 ft (4000

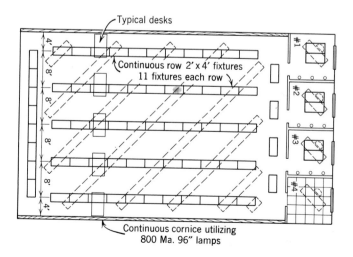

Fig. 21.28 Alternate office lighting solutions (see text).

lumens) H.O. lamps operating at 800 ma, placed 12″ on center, and mounted no less than 12″ above the ceiling track system, we obtain the necessary illumination.

20. Modular Design. An increasingly large number of buildings are being designed on a modular system resulting in a need for flexible lighting to fit the module utilized. In such buildings, having established the general lighting scheme and the fixture involved, it is convenient to draw a family of curves for the fixture chosen, thus facilitating the utilization of the modular unit in various spaces. The square foot per fixture ordinate may readily be replaced with multiples of modular areas, as shown in Fig. 21.29.

The sq ft per fixture is arrived at thus:

Sq ft per fixture

$$= \frac{\text{Lumens/lamp} \times \text{lamp/fixt.} \times \text{M.F.} \times \text{C.U.}}{\text{Footcandle level}}$$

21. Supplementary Lighting. Supplementary lighting has 2 basic functions: to provide local illumination, and to add directivity, controlled shadows, and highlights, where required. Local illumination may be desired to provide for a localized difficult seeing task (above 200 F.C.) or to provide vertical illumination, where such is not present in sufficient quantity from the general lighting. Figure 21.30 illustrates several types and uses of supplementary lighting. In using local lighting, care should be taken to design the general lighting so that rec-

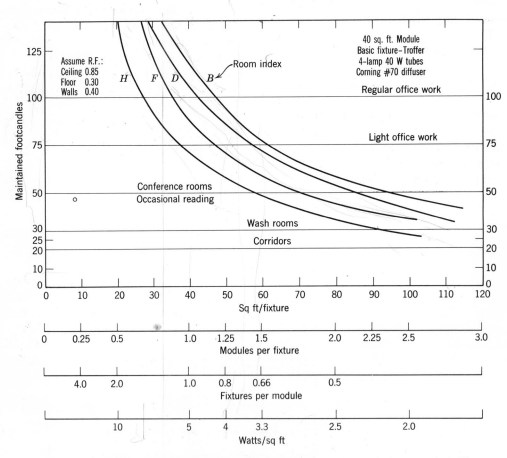

Fig. 21.29   Modular design. Use of families of curves for the various room indexes greatly facilitates lighting calculations, and lends itself readily to modular design.

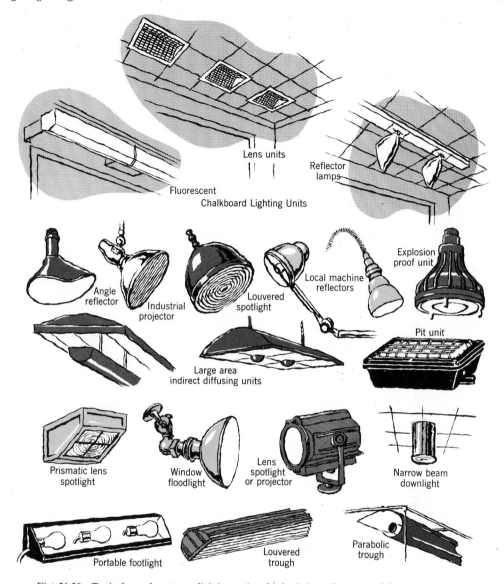

Lens units

Reflector lamps

Fluorescent
Chalkboard Lighting Units

Angle reflector

Industrial projector

Louvered spotlight

Local machine reflectors

Explosion proof unit

Pit unit

Large area indirect diffusing units

Prismatic lens spotlight

Window floodlight

Lens spotlight or projector

Narrow beam downlight

Portable footlight

Louvered trough

Parabolic trough

Fig. 21.30 Typical supplementary lighting units: for both incandescent and fluorescent lamps.

ommended maximum brightness ratios are not exceeded.

22. Architectural Lighting Elements. Reference to architectural lighting elements is usually made when dealing with coves, cornices, valances, coffers, skylights, or other luminous surfaces not normally comprising a lighting fixture. Although such units are inherently relatively inefficient, their use is often indicated by architectural

consideration since they generally create an attractive indirect lighting source. Data is provided for one such design in Table 21.9, Fixt. 43; additional empirical design data is given in the sketches comprising Fig. 21.31.

Using fluorescent tubes, it is possible to avoid dark spots between lamps by placing lamps at a slight angle rather than end-to-end, thus enabling ends to overlap. Reflec-

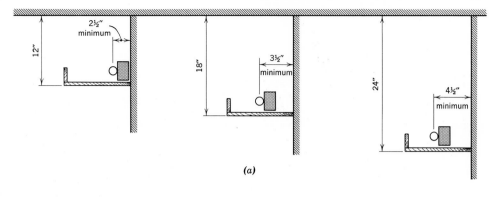

(a)

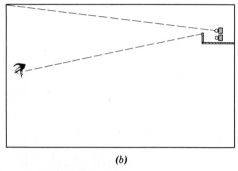

(b)

Fig. 21.31   Cove installations. Proper cove proportions: Height of front lip of cove should shield cove from the eye yet expose entire ceiling to the lamp. Orientation of fluorescent strip as shown is preferable to upright arrangement. *Westinghouse Lighting Handbook.*

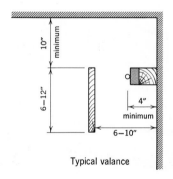

Typical valance

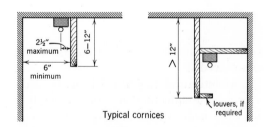

Typical cornices

Fig. 21.32   Wall washing equipment mounted in valances and cornices provide improved brightness ratios and may be used for lighting desks against walls, or vertical illumination of walls and objects mounted thereon. *Westinghouse Lighting Handbook.*

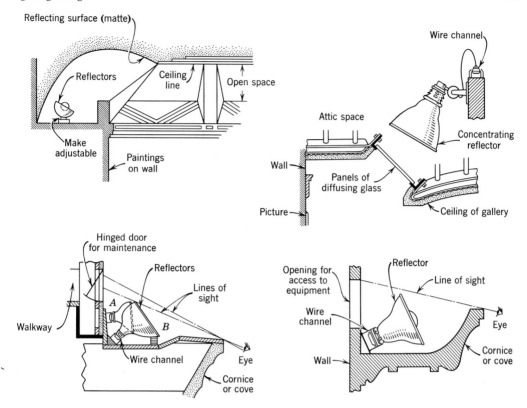

Fig. 21.33 Typical arrangement of equipment for cove lighting and panel lighting. All wire channels and individual lamp sockets should be made adjustable for ease in obtaining final focus.

tors, when used, should be aimed 15° to 25° above the horizontal and field adjusted for best ceiling coverage. When using double strips they should be stacked vertically as shown in Fig. 21.31. Coefficients for double lamp installation rarely exceed 0.75 times the single lamp coefficient. Interiors of cove surfaces should be painted with a high reflectance white paint with diffuse (flat) rather than specular (gloss) finish.

Figure 21.32 gives dimensions of typical effective wall washing cornices and valance. Reflectors, though not required, increase the efficiency of the installation. As in the case of coves, finish of the valance interior should be flat white of approximately 30 to 40 percent R.F. Incandescent fixtures may also be effectively employed in architectural lighting as shown in Fig. 21.33.

23. Floodlighting. Floodlighting, both in-terior and exterior, is extensively used for such diverse locations as are listed in Table 21.12, in addition to the more common sports lighting, which is not listed. The ad-dition of quartz lamps to the incandescent, mercury, and fluorescent sources long in use provides the designer with a variety of sources with respect to output, color, life, efficiency, and wattage. Table 21.11 provides a tabulation of the comparative character-istics of these 4 major sources from which the designer may select one or more.

Although a detailed floodlighting design involves complex calculations beyond the scope of this work, it is often sufficient for the designer to utilize a watts per sq ft table such as Table 21.12 in order to determine the approximate floodlighting requirements.

Thus, if one is concerned with lighting a self-parking lot at a neighborhood shopping

Table 21.11   Floodlight Source Selector

Type	Incandescent (General Service)	Quartz (Quartz-Iodine)	Mercury	Fluorescent
Initial cost	Low	Low	Higher	Highest
Power consumption	Medium or high	Medium or high	Low	Low
Annual operating cost	Medium	Medium	Low	Low
Fixture size	Medium	Small	Medium	Large
Average lamp life (hours)	1000	2000	9000 to 12,000	12,000
Long burning hrs—per-year (over 1000)	Fair	Fair	Good	Good
Short burning hrs—per-year (under 1000)	Good	Good	No	Fair
Color definition	Good	Good	Fair	Fair
Location considerations*	Fair	Fair	Good	Good
Beam control	Very good	Very good	Fair	Fair
Cold weather operation	Very good	Very good	Good	Fair
Long range projection (narrow beam)	Best	Fair	Fair	No
Medium range projection	Good	Good	Good	Fair

* Fixtures difficult or expensive to relamp and service.

center, and mercury is selected, Table 21.12 tells us that approximately 0.09 watts per sq ft will suffice. If the lot is 200′ by 500′ or 100,000 sq ft, then 0.09 × 100,000 = 9000 watts are required.

Arrangement and choice of equipment remains then, before the problem can be considered solved. Considerable assistance on this score can be obtained from either the lighting engineer involved or from representatives of the equipment manufacturers.

Although most floodlights have fixed beam patterns, some types are available with variable patterns which facilitates the design considerably. One such type is utilized to effect the rather spectacular lighting shown in Fig. 21.35 and 21.36.

Detailed recommendations for floodlighting of sports may be obtained from the publication "NEMA Standard Floodlighting Layouts for Floodlighting Sports Areas" obtainable through NEMA and IES.

24. Emergency Lighting. Under this heading is subsumed the types of lighting required by the various fire and safety codes to provide safe egress from areas and structures. This includes exit, aisle, corridor, and lobby lighting normally fed from a source of supply other than the normal service. Often, battery operated lights are strategically located in a building to provide lighting in the event of power failure. These units may be individually self-contained or fed from a central battery; in all cases they are arranged to operate only on failure of normal lighting.

25. Future Trends. Lighting in all its facets from production to utilization is making greater strides today than ever before. New sources are being tested daily, higher efficiency, better control, and more economy are the products of today's lighting laboratories. As levels are pushed beyond 200 F.C., serious consideration is being given to the utilization of the waste heat produced by

Table 21.12 Lighting Application Guide

Application	Minimum Footcandles Maintained	Watts Per sq ft Generally Required							
		Incandescent PS-Lamp Units		Quartz Units		Mercury Units		Fluorescent Units	
AIRPORT APRONS									
Hanger aprons	1	.15–.22		.13–.15		.06–.08		.06–.12	
Terminal bldg. aprons	2	.3–.44		.26–.38		.3–.55		.12–.24	
Service aprons	1‡	.15–.22		.13–.15		.06–.08		.06–.12	
Aprons—parking only	0.5	.08–.11		.07–.1		.03–.04		.03–.06	
AUTOMOBILE PARKING									
Attendant parking	2	.44		.38		.22		.24	
Industrial lots	1	.15–.22		.13–.15		.06–.11		.06–.08	
Self-parking lots	1	.15–.22		.13–.15		.06–.11		.06–.08	
SHOPPING CENTERS									
Neighborhood	1	.15–.22		.13–.19		.06–.11		.06–.12	
Average commercial	2	.3–.36		.26–.3		.12–.16		.12–.16	
Heavy traffic	5	.75		.65		.3		.3	
AUTOMOBILE SALES LOTS									
Front row (Front 20′)	50	12.		10.		8.		*	
Remainder	10	1.8–2.1		1.5–1.8		.8–1.1		*	
BUILDING									
Construction	10	1.8–2.1		1.5–1.8		.8–1.1		*	
Excavation	2	.3–.44		.26–.3		.12–.16		*	
BUILDINGS UP TO 50′ HIGH	Adj. Area LT. DARK								
Light surfaces	15 5	3.8	1.4	3.3	1.2	2.4	.8	3.15	1.05
Medium light	20 10	5.	2.6	4.3	2.2	3.2	1.6	4.2	2.1
Dark surfaces	50 20	12.	5.	10.	4.3	8.	3.2	10.5	4.2
BILLBOARDS AND SIGNS	Adj. Area LT. DARK								
Good contrast	50 20	12.	5.	10.	4.3	8.	3.2	10.5	4.2
Poor contrast	100 50	24.	12.	20.	10.	16.	8.	21	10.5
FLAGS	50	*		*		†		†	
INDUSTRIAL AREAS									
Coal storage	0.1	.015–.018		.013–.015		.008–.006		†	
Car loading and unloading	5	1.1–1.4		.95–1.2		.55–.8		.6–1.05	
Freight docks	20	4.2–5.0		3.6–4.3		2.2–3.2		2.4–4.2	
PROTECTIVE LIGHTING									
Gates and vital area	5	1.4		1.2		.8		1.5	
Building surrounds	1	.18–.22		.15–.19		.08–.11		.08–.12	
ROADWAYS									
Along buildings	1	.28		.24		.16		.21	
Open areas	0.5	.09–.11		.08–.1		.04–.06		.04–.06	
Storage tanks	1	.28		.24		.16		.21	
Storage yards (active)	20	4.2–5.0		3.6–4.3		2.2–3.2		2.4–4.2	
Storage yards (inactive)	1	.18–.22		.15–.19		.08–.11		.08–.12	
Sub stations	2	.44		.38		.22		.24	

Table 21.12 (Continued)

Application	Minimum Footcandles Maintained	Watts Per sq ft Generally Required			
		Incandescent PS-Lamp Units	Quartz Units	Mercury Units	Fluorescent Units
SMOKE STACKS					
Obstruction	15 (top ⅓)	*	†	*	†
Advertising	20–50	*	†	*	†
Watertank advertising	20–50	*	*	*	*
LUMBER YARDS	1	.18–.22	.15–.19	.08–.11	.08–.12
MONUMENTS					
Light surfaces	15	*	*	*	†
Medium light	20	*	*	*	†
Dark surfaces	50	*	*	*	†
PARKING AREAS		(See Automobile Sales Lots)			
PRISON YARDS	5	.75–.9	.65–.75	.4–.55	.3–.4
RAILROAD YARDS					
Classification yards					
Head end	5	.75–.9	.65–.75	.4–.55	.3–.4
Body of yard	1	.15	.13	.06	.06
Pull-out end	2	.3–.36	.26–.3	.12–.16	.12–.16
Hump area	20 (vert.)	*	*	*	†
Receiving yard	1	.15	.13	.06	.06
RECREATIONAL AND SPORTS					
Bathing beaches					
On land	1	.15–.18	.13–.15	.06–.08	.06–.08
150′ from shore	3 (vert.)	*	*	*	†
Drag strips	20	*	*	*	†
GOLF COURSES					
Fairways	3	.54–.66	.45–.57	.24–.33	†
Greens	10 §	2.1–2.6	1.8–2.2	1.1–1.6	†
Miniature golf	10	2.1–2.6	1.8–2.2	1.1–1.6	1.2–2.1
Putting greens	10 §	2.1–2.6	1.8–2.2	1.1–1.6	1.2–2.1
Tee area	10	2.6	2.2	1.6	†
KART RACE TRACKS					
Recreational	10	2.1–2.6	1.8–2.2	1.1–1.6	†
Competition	20	4.2–5.0	3.6–4.3	2.2–3.2	†
PLAYGROUNDS	5	3.5–4.2	.75–.95	.4–.55	.4–.6
SKATING AREAS					
Recreational	1	.22–.28	.15–.19	.08–.11	.08–.12
SKI SLOPES					
Practice	3	.45–.54	.39–.45	.18–.24	†
SERVICE STATIONS					
Pump Island	100	†	†	8.	10.
Approach ramps	10	2.6	2.2	1.6	2.1
Building faces	20	5.0	4.3	3.2	4.2
General area	5	1.1–1.4	.95–1.2	.55–.8	.6–1.05

Table 21.12 (Continued)

Application	Minimum Footcandles Maintained	Watts Per sq ft Generally Required			
		Incandescent PS-Lamp Units	Quartz Units	Mercury Units	Fluorescent Units
SHIP YARDS					
Docks	5	.9–1.1	.75–.95	.4–.55	.4–.6
Fabrication area	30	5.2–6.3	4.5–5.4	2.4–3.3	2.4–3.6
General	5	.75–.9	.65–.75	.3–.4	.3–.4
Ways	10	1.5–1.8	1.3–1.5	.6–.8	.6–.8
SHOPPING CENTERS					
Parking areas (Attraction)	5	.75	.65	.3	.3
Buildings (Attraction)		(See Buildings)			
USED CAR LOTS		(See Automobile parking)			

All footcandle levels for ground area applications are *horizontal* values.   Table adapted from Crouse-Hinds.
* Requires Individual Calculation.
† Not Normally Used.
‡ 1.0 F.C. horizontal on area; 2.0 F.C. on vertical at center of service area.
§ Should be lighted from at least 2 directions.

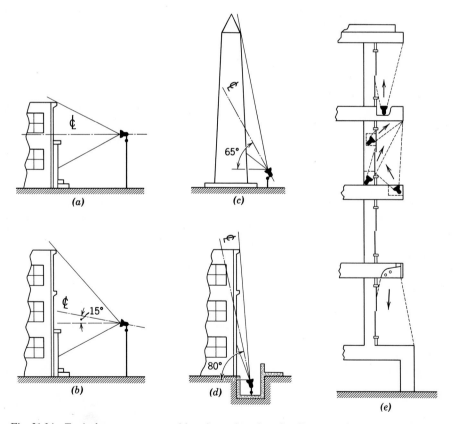

Fig. 21.34   Typical arrangements and locations of outdoor floodlamps (*a, b, c, d*); and suggested arrangements (*e*) of incandescent mercury, quartz, or fluorescent lamps for lighting exterior building surfaces and cantilever floor extensions.

Fig. 21.35   Monumental monument floodlighting. 170 floodlights illuminate the 985-ft high Eiffel tower, from the ground. Courtesy of Infranor.

Fig. 21.36   Spectacular floodlighting of the Palace at Versailles. Courtesy of Infranor.

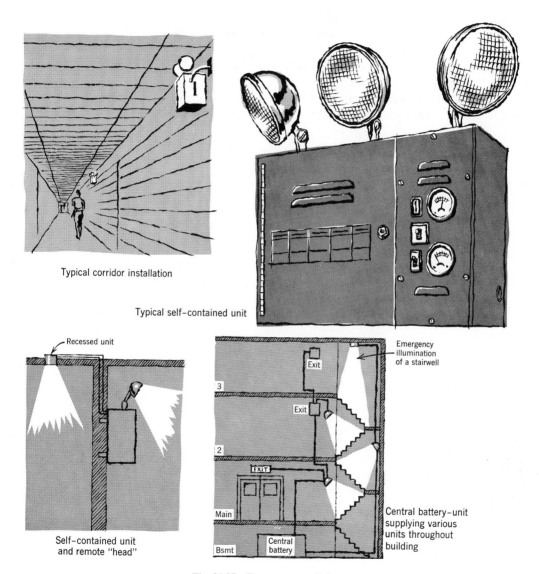

Typical corridor installation

Typical self-contained unit

Recessed unit

Self-contained unit and remote "head"

Emergency illumination of a stairwell

Exit

3

Exit

2

EXIT

Main

Bsmt

Central battery

Central battery–unit supplying various units throughout building

Fig. 21.37 D-c emergency lights.

the lighting, to heat the building spaces. At this writing several such buildings are completed or under construction and many more are being designed. Conversely, higher efficiency light sources and improved means of disposing of waste heat are being developed, to reduce the high cost of cooling (air-conditioning) such well lighted spaces, as well as to reduce operating costs.

Hi-cycle (high frequency) and high-voltage lighting are coming into ever greater use due to these economic and efficiency considerations. The lighting designer who seeks new approaches, new materials, and new techniques while simultaneously fully utilizing the established materials and techniques is the man to whom the preceding lighting chapters are dedicated.

References and Bibliography

Published by the *Illuminating Engineering Society:*
  Lighting Handbook, 3rd Edition.
  Recommended Practice for Office Lighting.
  Recommended Practice for Daylighting.
  American Standard Guide for School Lighting.

22

Electricity

and Electric Circuits

1. Electric Generators and Batteries. The common sources of electricity are alternating-current (a-c) generators, direct-current (d-c) generators, and storage batteries. Alternating-current generators, abbreviated to alternators, provide the bulk of electrical energy used today. The d-c generator, however, furnishes energy in a few important building applications, including passenger elevators, intercommunicating telephone systems, control of signal systems, clock systems, special business machines, and the recharging of storage batteries. The storage battery often supplies emergency lighting circuits for hallways, stairways, exits, and exit signs and the operation of automatic switchgear and switchgear control devices, clocks, police and fire alarms, automatic locks, certain types of automatic calculating machines, and signal systems.

2. Electricity. Scientists now believe that all matter is made up principally of two kinds of extremely small particles of matter called electrons and protons. These particles are electricity. Electrons are negatively charged particles, and protons are positively charged particles of matter. Particles of unlike charge (+ and −) attract each other; like charges (+ and +) or (− and −) repel each other. Each *chemical element,* such as copper, tin, iron, hydrogen, and nitrogen, is composed of atoms made up of these two kinds of particles. For instance, a hydrogen atom (Fig. 22.1*a*) is made up of a nucleus of 1 proton about which 1 electron rotates. The atoms of other elements, such as copper (Fig. 22.1*b*), have various combinations of protons and electrons welded into a small particle (the positive nucleus) about which a definite number of negative electrons (planetary electrons) rotate. Molecules are closely related groups of these atoms. The outermost planetary electrons in some types of atoms are rather weakly attracted to the nucleus. Elements composed of these atoms therefore contain many electrons which are not bound to one atom but which move about continually from one to another. These are called free electrons. Although the free electrons constitute only a small percentage of the total number of electrons present in matter, still they are very numerous—a cubic centimeter of copper, for instance, contains about one sextillion free

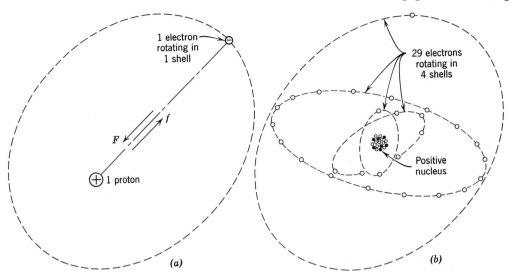

Fig. 22.1 Hydrogen atom (*a*): centrifugal force (*f*), and the centripetal force (*F*) due to attraction between the charges on the proton (+) and on the electron (−) counterbalance each other. Copper atom (*b*): this is a much more complicated atomic structure than the hydrogen atom; however, the same centrifugal and centripetal forces are reacting on the free electrons rotating in their orbits.

electrons (10^{21}) or 1,000,000,000,000,000,-000,000 electrons. It is the motion of these electrons which constitutes an *electric current* in a solid conductor.

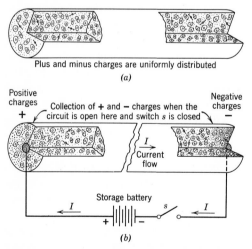

Fig. 22.2 (*a*) The relatively even distribution of atoms and electrons in a deenergized copper conductor. (*b*) The collection of positive charges at the left end and negative charges at the right end of the copper conductor due to the influence of the storage battery. Under such conditions when a circuit is completed from the left end to the right end and the switch *s* is closed, current will flow as indicated.

Figure 22.2*a* is a model of a round conductor in its normal state, not electrified, giving some idea of the uniform distribution of atoms and free electrons. Figure 22.2*b* shows the migration of charges to the ends of the conductor, due to the action of some external magnetic field, or to chemical reactions in a battery. When the switch *s* is closed, a continuous flow of current (*I*) will take place; i.e., by convention the electrons will travel around the circuit in a clockwise direction from the positive battery terminal to the negative terminal.

3. Unit of Current: the Ampere. When electric current flows in a wire, a certain number of electrons pass through the cross section of the wire in 1 sec. The practical unit of measurement of this current is the ampere. One ampere (amp) of current flows in a conductor when 6.251×10^{18} electrons pass a given cross section in 1 sec. In the home and office, on 120-volt service, the ordinary 100-watt lamp filament carries about 0.833 amp; the motor for an office desk fan, about 1.00 amp.

Experiment shows that electric current travels with the speed of light; i.e., 186,000

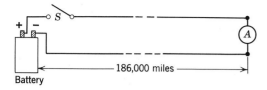

Fig. 22.3 Speed of propagation of electric current: 186,000 miles per second.

miles per sec. For example, if the terminals of a battery (Fig. 22.3) should be connected by a switch S to a 2-wire line 186,000 mi. in length, a current would be noted in an ammeter A in 1 sec. after closing the switch. The rate of conduction of electric current may therefore be considered instantaneous.

It is convenient to establish an analogy between electric systems and mechanical systems as an aid to comprehension. Current is a measure of flow of electrons and as such would correspond to water flow in a hydraulic system. (See Fig. 22.4.) In the hydraulic system the velocity of water flow varies; in the electric system the velocity of propagation is constant at 186,000 mi. per sec.

4. Unit of Electrical Potential: the Volt. Free electrons are caused to move along a given conducting material, such as a wire, by creating a higher positive electric charge

at one end than at the other. In the ordinary dry cell or the storage battery, chemical action causes positive charges (+) to collect on the positive terminal and electrons or

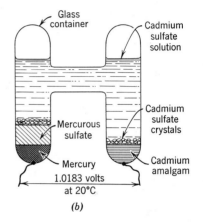

(a)

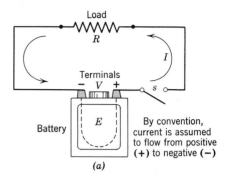

(b)

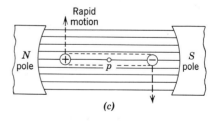

(c)

Fig. 22.5 (a) Flow of conventional electric current around a conducting circuit, electrons flowing as the result of the emf of the battery. (b) Weston standard cell used as the international standard for the measurement of volts. This standard is easily reproduced in the testing laboratory. (c) A coil rapidly revolving in a clockwise direction (about point p) and at the same time cutting a magnetic field extending from the N-pole to the S-pole. This rapid cutting of the lines of magnetic force induces voltage in the coil in the directions shown by the + and − signs. When 10^8 lines are cut in 1 sec by 1 conductor, 1 volt is induced.

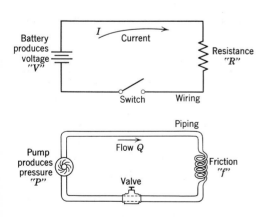

Fig. 22.4 Electric-hydraulic analogy. The circuits show that voltage is analogous to pressure, current to flow, friction to resistance, wire to piping, and switches to valves.

negative charges ($-$) to collect on the negative terminal. It is here assumed that nothing is connected to the battery terminals. There is a definite force-attraction, or tendency to flow, between the electrified particles concentrated at the positive and negative terminals. *Potential difference* or *voltage* is the name given to this *electromotive* force (emf) which exists between the terminals. This force is analagous to pressure in a hydraulic or pneumatic system. Just as the pressure produced by a pump or blower cause water or air to flow, so too the potential (emf, voltage) produced by a battery or generator causes current to flow. The higher the voltage (pressure) the higher the current (flow), for a given resistance (friction).

5. Unit of Resistance: the Ohm. The flow of fluid in a hydraulic system is impeded by friction; the flow of current in an electric circuit is impeded (resisted) by *resistance,* which is the electrical term for friction. In a direct-current circuit (d-c) this unit is called resistance; in an alternating-current circuit (a-c) it is called impedance. The unit of measurement is called the *ohm.*

Materials display different resistance to the flow of electric current. Metals generally have the least resistance and are therefore called conductors in that they readily conduct electricity through them. The best conductors are the precious metals such as silver, gold, and platinum with copper and aluminum only slightly inferior. Conversely, materials which prevent (resist) the flow of current, displaying high resistance to electricity are called *insulators.* Glass, mica, rubber, oil, distilled water, porcelain, and certain synthetics such as phenolic compounds exhibit this insulating property and are therefore used to insulate electric conductors. Common examples are rubber covering on wire, porcelain cable supports, porcelain lamp sockets, glass pole-line insulators, and oil-immersed electric switches.

6. Ohm's Law. The current I which will flow through a given resistance R is directly proportional to the voltage V impressed on it. This is known as *Ohm's law.* It is expressed by the equation.

$$I = \frac{V}{R}$$

where I is the current in amperes, V the voltage in volts, and R the resistance in ohms. The letter V is used to indicate the voltage at the terminals of the resistance R or the power-consuming device. A few examples will illustrate the practical application of Ohm's law.

EXAMPLE 22.1. An incandescent lamp having a hot resistance of 66 ohms is put into a socket which is connected to a 115-volt supply. What is the current?

SOLUTION. $I = \dfrac{V}{R} = \dfrac{115}{66} = 1.74$ amp

It is apparent that if any two factors of the formula are given the third factor may be determined.

EXAMPLE 22.2. A bathroom heating unit draws 10 amp. at 115 volts. What is its hot resistance?

SOLUTION. $R = \dfrac{V}{I} = \dfrac{115}{10} = 11.5$ ohms

EXAMPLE 22.3. If a fuse is protecting the circuit of a 15-ohm percolator, and it is designed to blow out at a current exceeding 10 amps, what is the maximum voltage that should be applied across the terminals of the percolator?

SOLUTION. $V = RI = 15 \times 10 = 150$
volts

In the above examples it should be remembered that some resistances are higher when they are hot, i.e., at operating temperatures. When cold, at room temperatures, their resistances are lower. Clear evidence of this is the fact that when a tungsten filament lamp (cold) is first turned on it takes for a fraction of a second, perhaps 10 to 15 times the current that flows when the filament is hot.

7. Power and Energy. The unit of electric power is the watt (w). A larger unit is 1000 watts, called the kilowatt (kw). The power input in watts to any electrical device in which the element has a resistance R and in which the current is I, is given by the equation:

$$W = I^2 R$$

But by Ohm's law $V = RI$; hence

$$W = VI$$

where W is in watts, R in ohms, I in amperes, and V in volts.

EXAMPLE 22.4. An electric ironer is rated at 1000 watts. (a) What is its hot resistance, and (b) what is the current through it if it is connected to a 115-volt outlet?

SOLUTION.

$W = I^2 R$ or $W = VI$. Therefore:

$$I = \frac{W}{V} = \frac{1000}{115} = 8.7 \text{ amps}$$

$$R = \frac{W}{I^2} = \frac{1000}{(8.7)^2} = 13.2 \text{ ohms}$$

The energy delivered is equal to the power input times the elapsed time. This is usually expressed in watthours or in kilowatthours. A watthour (whr) is 1 watt delivered for 1 hour; a kilowatthour (kwhr) is 1000 watts delivered for 1 hour.

The *national averages* of costs per kilo- watthour for these classifications of customers of public utilities in the United States are approximately as follows:

For residences, 2.94 cents per kwhr
For commercial users, 2.72 cents per kwhr
For industrial users, 1.52 cents per kwhr

The variation from these would depend upon: variations in cost of coal or water power; density of business, industrial, and domestic population; variations in load factors (hours of use); changes in kw demands; changes in load power factors. (This information is indicated by reports of the Edison Electric Institute.)

The meters installed by the electric utility company measure energy consumption (kwhr) and in installations other than residences, a quantity called "kw demand." The consumption of electricity varies in most installations from moment to moment and from hour to hour; the actual load at any given time being the "demand" at that time. Thus a factory might have a demand chart as shown in Fig. 22.6.

The electric bill would include both total energy charge and a maximum demand charge. In a typical private residence, although loads vary from 0 to 10 kw, the

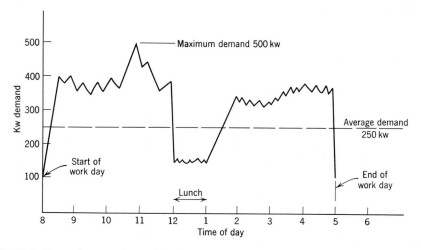

Fig. 22.6 Demand curve of a small industrial installation. Total electric bill would reflect both total actual energy consumption and maximum demand charge.

average daytime demand load is approximately 750 watts.

When t is the time in hours,

whr $= I^2Rt$
whr $= VIt$

and

$$\text{kwhr} = \frac{I^2R}{1000}$$

$$\text{kwhr} = \frac{VIt}{1000}$$

Most electrical devices used in the home, office and factory are required by the National Board of Fire Underwriters (NBFU) and by the National Electrical Code (NEC), to be marked with name plates which identify the electrical rating in volts, amperes, and watts. Such ratings are necessary in order to aid in the determination of the electrical capacity of the service and

the sizes of circuit breakers, fuses, cables, wires, switchboards, and panelboards. The name plates of rotating electrical machinery also include the speed in rpm, type of design, the allowable temperature rise in degrees centigrade at rated horsepower or kilowatts output, and the manufacturer and the manufacturer's type and serial number. These name plates are also helpful to NEC inspectors who are engaged to approve and certify the safety of all installations, as specified by the NEC. As will be discussed in Chapter 23, lists are available which identify tested and approved equipment for installation under the NEC regulations.

8. Direct Current and Alternating Current (D-C and A-C). Whenever the flow of electric current takes place at a constant time rate, practically unvarying and in the same direction around the circuit, it is called direct current. The curve (straight line) of Fig. 22.7a indicates such a current of 10 amperes.

Whenever the flow of current is periodically varying in time rate and in direction, as indicated by the symmetrical positive and negative loops or sine waves in Fig. 22.7b, it is called an *alternating current*. The distance along the time axis spanned by a positive and a negative a-c loop is called 1 cycle of time. Present-day a-c systems are usually 60-cycle. This means that current at 60 cycles per second (cps) is delivered to the consumer. The d-c generator, the dry battery, and the storage battery produce direct voltages and currents. The a-c generator delivers alternating voltages and currents.

When alternating current is rectified (changed to direct current), it appears as in Fig. 22.7c. This current is called fully rectified in contradistinction to that of Fig. 22.7d which is half-rectified.

9. Simple D-C Series Circuits. In general, an *electric circuit* may be defined as a complete conducting path carrying current from a source of electricity to and through some electrical device (or load) and back to

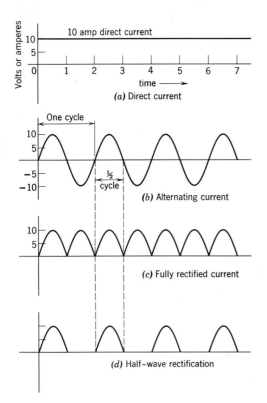

Fig. 22.7   Direct, alternating and pulsating current.

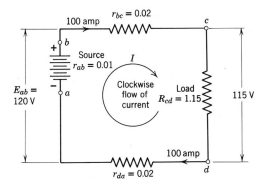

Fig. 22.8   A simple series circuit.

SOLUTION . The current flowing is

(a) $I = \dfrac{E}{R} = \dfrac{E_{ab}}{r_{ab} + r_{bc} + r_{cd} + r_{da}}$

$= \dfrac{120}{0.01 + 0.02 + 1.15 + 0.02}$

$= 100$ amp

The total line loss is

(b) $W = I^2R = I^2(r_{bc} + r_{da})$
$= (100)^2 \times 0.04 = 400$ watts

The power input to the load is

(c) $W = I^2R = I^2R_{cd} = (100)^2 \times 1.15$
$= 11,500$ watts or 11.5 kilowatts

The voltage drop across the load is

(d) $V_{cd} = IR_{cd} = 100 \times 1.15 = 115$ volts

the source. A current can never flow unless there is such a complete (closed) circuit. The simple *series* circuit is represented by the wiring diagram (Fig. 22.8), in which *all separate parts of the circuit carry the same current*. In any series circuit the total resistance R is the sum of the resistances around the circuit. The general equation for resistances in series is

Total resistance $R = r_{ab} + r_{bc} + r_{cd} + r_{da}$

where $r_{ab} + r_{bc} + r_{cd} + r_{da}$ are the resistances of each part of the series circuit. Hence the total circuit resistance is

$0.01 + 0.02 + 1.15 + 0.02 = 1.20$ ohms

It is customary to refer to certain connection points on such wiring diagrams by letters a, b, c, d, etc. Then the battery voltage may be called $E_{ab} = 120V$; the voltage across the load resistance, $V_{cd} = 115V$; the resistance of the two wires $r_{bc} + r_{da} = 0.04$ ohms. The positive and negative terminals of the battery are shown.

EXAMPLE 22.5. The battery in Fig. 22.8 is rated at 120 volts, the line resistance (both wires) is 0.04 ohms, the battery internal resistance is 0.01 ohms, and the load resistance is 1.15 ohms. Determine (a) current flowing in the circuit, (b) the power loss in the line, (c) power input to the load, (d) the voltage across the load (V_{bc}).

An example of the use of the series circuit is a simple battery-operated doorbell (Fig. 22.9), in which the battery supplies current over the resistance of the wires to and through the resistance of the bell.

10. Simple D-C Parallel Circuits.   When more than 1 branch of a circuit is connected between the same 2 points, they are said to be connected in parallel. Such an arrangement is shown in Fig. 22.10 in which the three resistances r_1, r_2, and r_3 are connected between points b and c. The total current I_T, which flows through the battery, will divide into 3 parts I_1, I_2, and I_3 at point b and will recombine at point c into I_T. Thus, we have the fundamental current equation of parallel circuits, viz. the total current is equal to the sum of the branch currents, or

$$I_T = I_1 + I_2 + I_3$$

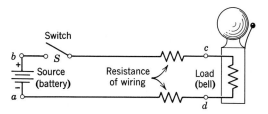

Fig. 22.9   This series circuit which is similar to Fig. 22.8 indicates connections for the operation of a bell by means of switch S.

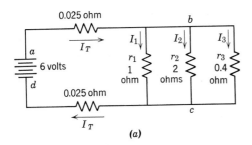

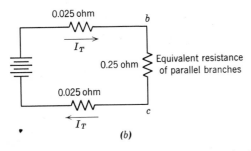

(b)

Fig. 22.10 Typical series-parallel circuit. The circuit of (a) must be reduced, by combining parallel resistances, into a simple series circuit as in (b) before currents can be calculated.

Each of these individual currents may be calculated from Ohm's Law, i.e.,

$$I_1 = \frac{V_{bc}}{r_1} \qquad I_2 = \frac{V_{bc}}{r_2} \qquad I_3 = \frac{V_{bc}}{r_3}$$

The voltage V_{bc} is the same across all of the individual resistances.

In order to calculate the total current I_T which flows in the circuit, it is necessary to combine all of the parallel resistances into a single resistance. This resistance is equal to the reciprocal of the sum of the reciprocals, or

$$R_{\text{Total}} = \frac{1}{\dfrac{1}{r_1} + \dfrac{1}{r_2} + \dfrac{1}{r_3}}$$

To demonstrate the application of these formulas we will apply them to a specific problem.

EXAMPLE 22.6. Given the circuit of Fig. 22.10a, find the total current flowing, the voltage across the parallel resistances, the

current in each branch, and the total power dissipated in the circuit.

(a) To find the total current, we must reduce the parallel branches to a single resistance and combine this with the line resistance.
Thus,

$$
\begin{aligned}
R_{\text{Parallel branches}} &= \frac{1}{\dfrac{1}{r_1} + \dfrac{1}{r_2} + \dfrac{1}{r_3}} \\[6pt]
&= \frac{1}{\frac{1}{1} + \frac{1}{2} + \frac{1}{.4}} \\[6pt]
&= \frac{1}{1 + .5 + 2.5} \\[6pt]
&= \frac{1}{4} \\[6pt]
&= .25 \text{ ohm}
\end{aligned}
$$

We can then draw the circuit as in Fig. 22.10b. Combining the parallel resistances with the line resistances, we find

$$
\begin{aligned}
R_{\text{Total circuit}} &= .025 + .25 + .025 \\
&= .3 \text{ ohm}
\end{aligned}
$$

Total current is then

$$I_T = \frac{6 \text{ volts}}{.3 \text{ ohms}} = 20 \text{ amperes}$$

(b) To find the voltage across the parallel branches, we multiply r_{bc} by the total current, or

$$V_{bc} = .25(20) = 5 \text{ volts}$$

(c) To find the current in each branch, we apply Ohm's Law once again;
Thus,

$$I_{r_1} = \frac{V_{bc}}{r_1} = \frac{5}{1} = 5 \text{ amperes}$$

$$I_{r_2} = \frac{V_{bc}}{r_2} = \frac{5}{2} = 2.5 \text{ amperes}$$

$$I_{r_3} = \frac{V_{bc}}{r_3} = \frac{5}{.4} = 12.5 \text{ amperes}$$

These currents must add up to the total current

$$I_T = I_{r_1} + I_{r_2} + I_{r_3}$$
$$= 5 + 2.5 + 12.5$$
$$= 20 \text{ amps}$$

which checks the figure arrived at in step (a).

(d) To find the power dissipated in each branch, we recall that $P = I^2R$, thus,

$$P_{r_1} = (5)^2 \times 1 = 25 \times 1 = 25 \text{ watts}$$
$$P_{r_2} = (2.5)^2 \times 2 = 6.25 \times 2$$
$$= 12.5 \text{ watts}$$
$$P_{r_3} = (12.5)^2 \times .4 = 156.25 \times .4$$
$$= 62.5 \text{ watts}$$

A very common application of the parallel circuit is given in Fig. 22.11 showing the wiring diagram for a lamp circuit in a long room. There are 5 lamps connected in parallel across a given circuit operated by a switch at the door. If each lamp takes 1 amp, the total current in the branch circuit will be 5 amps. It is quite probable that another connection, shown by the dotted lines, would be run to a convenience outlet near the baseboard. If a toaster taking 7 amps should be plugged in, the branch circuit supplying the room would carry $5 + 7 = 12$ amps. The convenience outlet would at all times be alive, but the lamps in this room would be controlled by a switch. Note that the lamps are in parallel with one another and that the convenience outlet (toaster) is in parallel with this group of lamps. The various branch circuits feeding parallel connected outlets are themselves connected in parallel to the panelboard bus.

11. Terminology and Definitions. Since much of the succeeding discussions will utilize terms common in the electrical field, a short list of these terms and definitions is being included here. This list is taken from the National Electric Code, 1961 edition.

ACCESSIBLE. (As applied to wiring methods). Not permanently closed in by the structure or finish of the building; capable of being removed without disturbing the building structure or finish. (See CONCEALED and EXPOSED.)

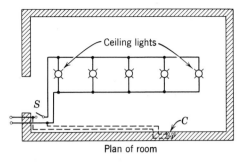

Fig. 22.11 Schematic wiring plan of a single circuit to supply lamps in parallel, and connections to a plug outlet. Switch S controls the lamps. The plug outlet C is energized at all times.

ACCESSIBLE (As applied to equipment). Admitting close approach because not guarded by locked doors, elevation, or other effective means.

APPLIANCE. Appliances are current-consuming equipment, fixed or portable; for example, heating, cooking, and small motor-operated equipment.

ASKAREL. A synthetic nonflammable insulating liquid which, when decomposed by the electric arc, evolves only nonflammable gaseous mixtures.

BRANCH CIRCUIT. A branch circuit is that portion of a wiring system extending beyond the final overcurrent device protecting the circuit.

NOTE. A device not approved for branch circuit protection such as a thermal cutout or motor overload protective device is not considered to be the overcurrent device protecting the circuit.

BRANCH CIRCUIT (General Purpose). A branch circuit that supplies a number of outlets for lighting and appliances.

BRANCH CIRCUIT (Individual). A branch circuit that supplies only one item of utilization equipment.

CABINET. An enclosure designed either for surface or flush mounting, and provided with a frame, mat, or trim in which swinging doors are hung.

CIRCUIT BREAKER. A device designed to

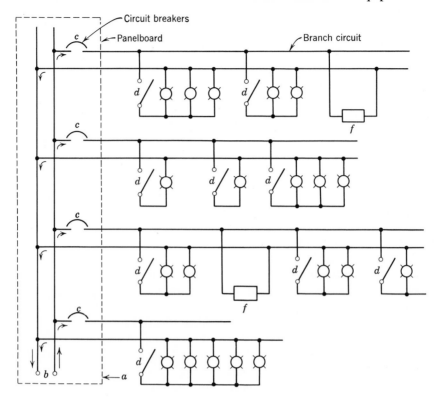

Fig. 22.12 Schematic a-c 2-wire panelboard on which are mounted the bus bars *b* and the single-pole circuit breakers *c*. The four circuits shown indicate how the 2-wire branch circuits are supplied from the panelboard bus bars when the breakers are closed. The switches *d* indicate local switches near the respective loads on the branch circuits. Receptacle outlets are designated by *f* and all lamps by circles.

open under abnormal conditions a current-carrying circuit without injury to itself. The term as used in the Code applies only to the automatic type designed to trip on a predetermined overload of current.

CONCEALED. Rendered inaccessible by the structure or finish of the building. Wires in concealed raceways are considered concealed, even though they may become accessible by withdrawing them.

CONNECTOR, PRESSURE (SOLDERLESS). A pressure-wire connector is a device which establishes the connection between 2 or more conductors or between 1 or more conductors and a terminal by means of mechanical pressure and without the use of solder.

CONTROLLER. A device, or group of devices, which serves to govern, in some predetermined manner, the electric power delivered to the apparatus to which it is connected.

DEMAND FACTOR. The demand factor of any system, or part of a system, is the ratio of the maximum demand of the system, or part of a system, to the total connected load of the system, or of the part of the system under consideration.

DISCONNECTING MEANS. A device, or group of devices, or other means whereby the conductors of a circuit can be disconnected from their source of supply.

EXPOSED. Exposed means that a live part can be inadvertently touched or approached nearer than a safe distance by a person.

GROUNDED. Grounded means connected to earth or to some conducting body which serves in place of the earth.

GROUNDED CONDUCTOR. A conductor which is intentionally grounded, either solidly or through a current limiting device.

GROUNDING CONDUCTOR. A conductor used to connect an equipment, device, or wiring system with a grounding electrode or electrodes.

GUARDED. Covered, shielded, fenced, enclosed, or otherwise protected, by means of suitable covers or casings, barriers, rails, or screens, mats, or platforms, to remove the liability of dangerous contact or approach by persons or objects to a point of danger.

PANELBOARD. A single panel or a group of panel units designed for assembly in the form of a single panel; including buses, and with or without switches and/(or) automatic overcurrent protective devices for the control of light, heat, or power circuits of small individual as well as aggregate capacity; designed to be placed in a cabinet or cutout box placed in or against a wall or partition and accessible only from the front.

RACEWAY. Any channel for holding wires, cables, or busbars, which is designed expressly for, and used solely for, this purpose. Raceways may be of metal or insulating material and the term includes rigid metal conduit, flexible metal conduit, electrical metallic tubing, underfloor raceways, cellular metal floor raceways, surface metal raceways, wireways, busways, and auxiliary gutters.

SERVICE ENTRANCE CONDUCTORS, OVERHEAD SYSTEM. The service conductors between the terminals of the service equipment and a point usually outside the building, clear of building walls, where joined by tap or splice to the service drop.

SERVICE ENTRANCE CONDUCTORS, UNDERGROUND SYSTEM. The service conductors between the terminals of the service equipment and the point of connection to the service lateral. Where service equipment is located outside the building walls, there may be no service-entrance conductors, or they may be entirely outside the building.

SERVICE EQUIPMENT. The necessary equipment, usually consisting of circuit-breaker or switch and fuses, and their accessories, located near the point of entrance of supply conductors to a building and intended to constitute the main control and means of cutoff for the supply to that building.

SERVICE CONDUCTORS. The supply conductors which extend from the street main, or from transformers to the service equipment of the premises supplied.

SERVICE DROP. The overhead service conductors between the last pole or other aerial support and the first point of attachment to the building.

12. A-C Circuits; definitions and terminology. A-C circuits differ from d-c circuits in a number of important respects, and since normal current supply is 60 cps, a-c, it is important to understand a-c terminology and usage. Instead of resistance, an a-c circuit deals with impedance which is also measured in ohms, but which, depending upon the device being considered, can be markedly different from resistance. Impedance which is comprised of resistance and reactance (a-c resistance of inductance and capacitance) causes a phase difference between voltage and current. This phase difference is represented by an angle; the cosine of this angle is called the *power factor*.

This quantity is extremely important, in that it enables us to know the power drawn by a circuit, as follows:

$$KW = \text{Voltage} \times \text{Current}$$
$$\text{(in a d-c circuit)}$$

$$KW = \text{Voltage} \times \text{Current}$$
$$\times \text{Power factor (in an a-c circuit)}$$

If power factor is not applied to the product of VI, we obtain volt-amperes, not watts.

EXAMPLE 22.7. A room air conditioner contains a $\frac{1}{2}$ hp motor, which draws 10.0

Fig. 22.13   (continued on p. 451).

(c)

Fig. 22.13   Typical electrical meters and instruments. (a) 30-amp 240-volt socket-type watthour meter with kw demand register; (b) a-c and d-c switchboard instruments; (c) typical portable instruments.

amperes at 120 volts and at 60 percent power factor. Find

(a) Apparent motor impedance
(b) Power consumption
(c) Volt-amperes of the circuit
(d) Efficiency of the motor.

SOLUTION:

a. Impedance $Z = \dfrac{V}{I} = \dfrac{120}{10} = 12$ ohms

b. Power consumption
$$\text{watts} = VI \,(\text{PF})$$
$$= 120 \times 10 \times .60$$
$$= 720 \text{ watts}$$
$$= .72 \text{ kw}$$

c. Volt amperes (va)
$$= 120 \times 10 = 1200 \text{ va}$$
$$= 1.2 \text{ kva}$$

d. Efficiency $= \dfrac{\text{output}}{\text{input}}$

$= \dfrac{(\frac{1}{2} \text{ H.P.} \times 746 \text{ watts/hp})}{720.0 \text{ watts}} = 52$ percent

13. Measurements. Every reader has undoubtedly seen at one time or another the type of meter installed in an electrified residence by the local utility. These meters serve a particular function: to measure energy consumption, on the basis of which bills are prepared. Also as mentioned earlier, the power companies make a demand charge to other than small residential customers on the basis of the readings of the demand meter, which records the maximum 15 min or $\frac{1}{2}$ hr demand kw drawn by the customer between billings. This charge is levied because sharp peak loads (see Fig. 22.6; 10:45 A.M.) tie up a large amount of power generating capacity with but little revenue return to the utility since the peak nature of the load (short time) does not utilize much energy (kwhr) though drawing large amounts of power (kw).

Other meters are readily available for measuring all the parameters in electric circuits: voltmeter (volts), ammeter (amperes), wattmeter, power factor meter, frequency meter and various meters for measuring resistance and impedance.

14. Generation of Electricity. D-C. With respect to generation of sizable amounts of power, photoelectric, piezoelectric, and thermoelectric effects can be ignored, leaving the battery and the d-c generator as the principal sources of d-c current. Since the

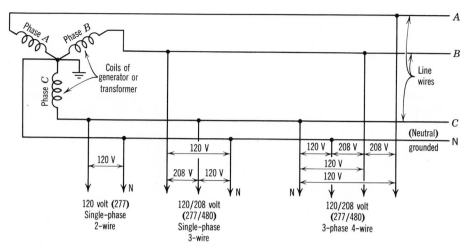

Fig. 22.14*a*   Three-phase 4-wire 'WYE' connection 120/208 volts, giving 120 volts between phases and neutral, 208 volts between phases. Numbers in parentheses are the voltages of a similar 277/480-volt system; 277 volts phase to neutral, 480 volts phase to phase. Neutral 'N' is normally grounded.

d-c generator is in reality an a-c generator with a device (commutator) attached which rectifies the a-c to d-c, the battery is still the only major direct source of d-c. (There are some special types of generators which produce d-c directly, but their use to date has been extremely limited.)

Batteries are available in various designs and sizes with the lead-acid type (similar to the one used in the automobile) being the most common. The more expensive and more reliable nickel-cadmium cell has gained considerable popularity in recent years. Batteries are used most often as sources of control power, standby emergency power, instrument power, and other applications requiring smooth, ripple-free power in either small quantities or on an intermittent basis.

D-C Generators are used where accurate motor speed control is desired, e.g., elevators or where d-c is required on a larger and

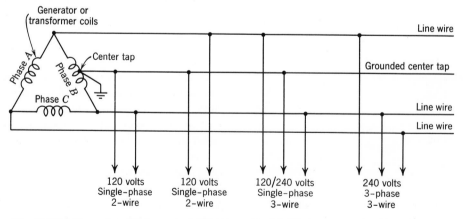

Fig. 22.14*b*   Three-phase Delta system, 240 volts, with grounded center tap on phase *B* giving 120 volts on that phase only.

more sustained basis than would be economical for batteries. Of course, a rotating d-c generator, unlike a battery, must be driven to produce power. The prime mover can be a motor, engine, water wheel, or any other device which will provide the required input power.

Another source of direct-current power is rectification of a-c which can be done on any scale to provide as much d-c as there is available a-c. Various types of rectifiers are in commercial use, including selenium, silicon, and copper-oxide types.

A.-C. Alternating current is produced commercially by an a-c generator, generally called an alternator. The prime mover as in the case of the d-c units mentioned above may be any type of engine or turbine which will provide the necessary motive energy. The frequency of the voltage generated (cps) is a function of the machine design (number of poles) and the speed at which it is driven. Normal generator frequency in this country is 60 cps.

15. Systems of A-C Voltage. Electricity is normally generated 3-phase, that is, the coils of the generator are so arranged that 3 distinct voltages are produced, 120° out of phase with each other. The coils are connected in "wye" or "delta" arrangement (see Fig. 22.14). The commonest voltages are 120/208 volts, 277/480 volts, 240-volt 3-phase, and 480-volt 3-phase. Three-phase power is normally utilized for motors larger than $\frac{1}{2}$ hp and for other industrial devices utilizing large amounts of power. Single-phase 120 volts or 277 volts are used for lighting and single phase 240 volts for electric cooking, heaters, and the like. The common 3-wire 120/240 volts residential service is either taken from a center-tapped delta connection, as shown in Fig. 22.14b or from a single-phase transformer as in Fig. 22.15. Recently some utility companies have been using 120/208 volt systems extensively, supplying 120/208 volt single-phase 3-wire to small consumers (see Fig. 22.14a). The 120/208 volt system has the advantage

of being able to supply power loads and machinery at 208 volts 3-phase and lighting and small appliances at 120 volts, single phase. The delta connection is used extensively for industrial installations where the 120-volt lighting and appliance load is small.

16. Grounding. Most secondary wiring systems are grounded in order to provide protection against dangerous shocks and the possibility of fires due to insulation ruptures from overvoltage conditions. These overvoltage conditions may be the result of lightning, short circuits within stepdown transformers, or other unusual circumstances. Primary systems are always grounded because a ground provides a fixed potential which is necessary for the proper operation of such systems.

Figure 22.15 shows what the effect of an accidental overvoltage (short within the transformer) would be in an ungrounded house-wiring system. The fault is shown by the dotted line connecting the primary and secondary transformer coils. Such a condition would result if the coil insulation were to break down. The full 2400 volts from the primary is impressed on wire L1 and via the secondary of the transformer, on to L2 and N. Since the secondary system is not insulated for more than 600 volts, current will leak through the weakened insulation to ground, through various high resistance paths, since grounds are always present near the wiring in the form of piping, conduit, machine casings, etc. Such leaks on high-resistance paths produce considerable heat (I^2R) and may easily cause a fire. Also, if by any mischance a person were to contact any of the wiring while grounded (e.g., a person repairing an appliance), he would receive the full 2400 volts shock (See Fig. 22.15a), which is more than enough to be lethal.

If the neutral conductor of the system is solidly grounded as in Fig. 22.15b, the situation is markedly altered. The current from the primary will flow through the low-resistance ground path which is generally less than 1 ohm, thus elevating the secondary system potential only slightly. If the current becomes large, the primary fuses will open the circuit. Therefore no great strain is put on the secondary system insulation and the person touching the wiring will receive a shock only slightly higher than the normal 120 volts.

Universal acceptance and use of grounded secondary 120-volt systems introduces another shock hazard while eliminating the dangers described above. This is shown in Fig. 22.15c. An accidental fault within an appliance can connect the metal case of the appliance to the line. This may readily occur with such common devices as an electric drill, clothes washer, dryer, food mixer, etc. A person contacting the appli-

ance housing and simultaneously a ground, such as a water pipe, will receive a nasty 120-volt shock. If the hands were wet the shock could be fatal. Until such an incident occurred, however, the internal fault would remain an unnoticed but constant source of danger.

To eliminate this hazard, appliance manufacturers have always recommended that appliance housings be grounded to a cold-water pipe, and have in recent years been supplying their appliances with 3-wire plugs; 2 wires connected to the appliance and the third wire to the housing. To accommodate such plugs and to provide a ground path, the National Electric Code requires all receptacles to be of the ground-

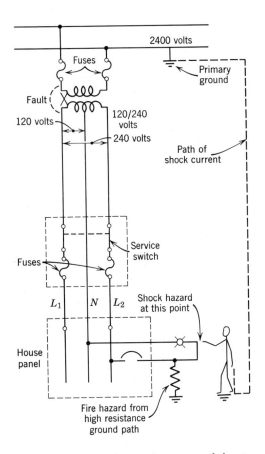

Fig. 22.15a Inherent danger of an ungrounded system is indicated by the fire and shock hazard which are present when faults occur with the system.

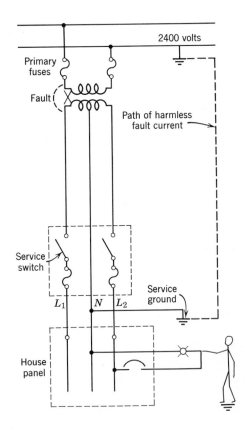

Fig. 22.15b Inherent safety of a grounded system. Building service ground, normally made to the cold water service, removes the fire and shock hazard by providing a ready-made ground path for fault currents.

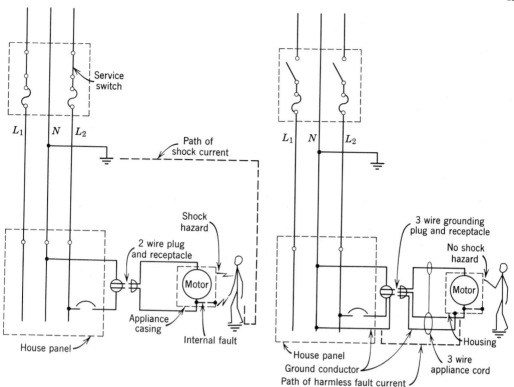

Fig. 22.15c Inherent danger of utilizing 2-wire connections with a grounded system. Shock hazard is great and internal faults of the type shown are common.

Fig. 22.15d Inherent safety of enclosure grounding; showing necessity for use of 3 wire grounding plugs and receptacles connected to the system raceway ground or the special grounding conductor.

ing type and all wiring systems to provide a ground path, separate and distinct from the neutral conductor. The result of such wiring is shown in Fig. 22.15d, where the ground current passes harmlessly through the internal fault, along the ground path and back to the panel. No shock hazard is encountered by a person contacting the appliance housing. If the ground current is high the branch circuit breaker or fuse will open, disconnecting the circuit.

When wiring systems are installed in metallic conduit, the conduit itself or the conduit plus a separate insulated or uninsulated conductor within the conduit may be used as the grounding path. (This latter method is preferable.)

When nonmetallic or flexible metallic wiring is used ('Romex' or BX), a separate grounding conductor run with the regular circuit conductors *must* be used. All insulated ground conductors must have their covering colored green for identification as a grounding conductor. Many industrial installations have in recent years installed complete "green-ground" systems in a largely successful attempt to eliminate shock hazard and to reduce insulation failures. Although there still exist many industrial facilities utilizing ungrounded 480-volt, 3-phase, 3-wire delta systems, the number is decreasing as they gradually change over to the safer and more reliable grounded systems.

23

Electrical Materials and Installation Methods

1. Components of Electrical Systems. Electric wiring of buildings requires a varied assortment of equipment and auxiliaries for adequate, safe, and efficient operation. These may be classified according to the functions that they perform: the service switch for main service control, protection, and metering; the main switchboard for control and protection of main feeders; the panelboards (near the load end of feeders) for control and protection of branch circuits; the outlets for local connections to lamps, motors, and other devices; the starting switches and (or) control devices for power-consuming equipment; and the conduit and wiring system which interconnects all the preceding apparatus. Each of these parts must be carefully designed to operate safely and economically under normal and abnormal conditions. It is the work of the engineer and architect to anticipate the type of electric services desired or needed, and then to provide the necessary plans and specifications covering the proper equipment. The qualities of electrical products and the effectiveness, economy, and efficiency of the various systems that may be specified vary widely. Experience in electrical applications and design is therefore essential to adequate planning.

2. National Electric Code. The National Electric Code (NEC) of the National Board of Fire Underwriters and the National Fire Protection Association (NFPA) defines the fundamental safety measures which must be followed in the selection, construction, and installation of all electrical equipment. This code is used by all inspectors, electrical designers, engineers, contractors, and the operating personnel charged with the responsibility for safe operation. The reader of this book should obtain and review the latest edition of the NEC, from the NFPA at 80 Batterymarch Street, Boston 10, Massachusetts, the National Board of Fire Underwriters, in any large city, or at 85

456

John Street, New York 38, New York. Frequent references will be made to this code.

In addition to the National Code, many large cities such as New York, Boston, and Washington, D.C., have their own electrical codes which, though similar to the NEC, contain numerous special requirements. For this reason it behooves the designer to ascertain all of the applicable codes before commencing the design work.

In order to assure a minimum standard for manufacture of electrical equipment the need was recognized for a single agency to establish standards for, and to actually test and inspect electrical equipment. Such an organization exists in the Underwriters Laboratories, Incorporated, which publishes lists of inspected and approved electrical equipment. These listings are universally accepted and many local codes state that only electrical materials bearing the Underwriters Laboratories (UL) label (of approval) will be acceptable. Since these requirements apply, of course, only to materials inspected by the UL, the listings should be consulted for any specific piece of equipment in question.

3. Equipment Ratings. All electrical equipment is rated for the normal service it is intended to perform. These ratings may be in voltage, current, duty, horsepower, temperature, enclosure, etc., depending upon the type of equipment. Ratings will be discussed in detail in the sections below related to the specific equipment.

4. System Components. The major components of a typical electrical system are shown in block diagram form in Fig. 23.1. These items will be discussed individually in the sections that follow and the salient relevant NEC requirements adduced. It must be emphasized that this text is not intended to be a substitute for the National Electrical Code, and therefore, in any actual design the detailed NEC requirements should be ascertained.

5. Conductors. (NEC Article 320) Electrical conductors (wiring) are the means by which the current is conducted through the wiring system, corresponding to the piping in our hydraulic analogy. Although conductors are selected for current capacity, insulation and jacket type, voltage drop, voltage class, and mechanical strength as major characteristics, the usual method of specifying a wire or cable is by number and size of conductor, insulation type, and voltage class, e.g., single conductor (1/c) No. 10, RHW, 600V. or 3/c No. 2 TW 600V., or 1/c No. 4 VCL, 5000V. (The "L" in VCL represents an outer lead sheath.) By convention, a single insulated conductor No. 6 AWG (American Wire Gauge) or larger, or several conductors of any size assembled into a single unit is referred to as a *cable;* single conductors No. 8 AWG and smaller are called *wire.*

(a) Current-Carrying Capacity of a wire is determined by its maximum safe operating temperature. Since, for any given cur-

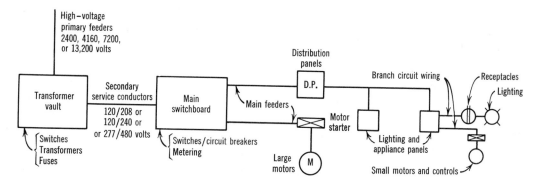

Fig. 23.1   Block diagram of a typical electrical system showing the major components.

Table 23.1 Allowable Current-Carrying Capacities of Insulated Copper Conductors in Amperes

Not More than Three Conductors in Raceway or Cable or Direct Burial
(Based on Room Temperature of 30 C 86 F)

Size AWG MCM	Rubber Type R, Type RW, Type RU, Type RUW (14–2), Type RH-RW*, Thermoplastic Type T, Type TW	Rubber Type RH, RUH (14–2), Type RH-RW*, Type RHW, Thermoplastic Type THW, THWN	Paper, Thermoplastic Asbestos Type TA, Thermoplastic Type TBS, Silicone Type SA, Var-Cam Type V, Asbestos Var-Cam Type AVB, MI Cable, RHH†	Asbestos Var-Cam Type AVA, Type AVL	Impregnated Asbestos Type AI (14–8), Type AIA	Asbestos Type A (14–8), Type AA
14	15	15	25	30	30	30
12	20	20	30	35	40	40
10	30	30	40	45	50	55
8	40	45	50	60	65	70
6	55	65	70	80	85	95
4	70	85	90	105	115	120
3	80	100	105	120	130	145
2	95	115	120	135	145	165
1	110	130	140	160	170	190
0	125	150	155	190	200	225
00	145	175	185	215	230	250
000	165	200	210	245	265	285
0000	195	230	235	275	310	340
250	215	255	270	315	335	. . . .
300	240	285	300	345	380	. . . .
350	260	310	325	390	420	. . . .
400	280	335	360	420	450	. . . .
500	320	380	405	470	500	. . . .
600	355	420	455	525	545	. . . .
700	385	460	490	560	600	. . . .
750	400	475	500	580	620	. . . .
800	410	490	515	600	640	. . . .
900	435	520	555	. . . .	. . . .	. . . .
1000	455	545	585	680	780	. . . .
1250	495	590	645	. . . .	. . . .	. . . .
1500	520	625	700	785	. . . .	. . . .
1750	545	650	735	. . . .	. . . .	. . . .
2000	560	665	775	840	. . . .	. . . .

Correction Factors, Room Temps. Over 30 C 86 F

C.	F.						
40	104	.82	.88	.90	.94	.95	. . . .
45	113	.71	.82	.85	.90	.92	. . . .
50	122	.58	.75	.80	.87	.89	. . . .
55	131	.41	.67	.74	.83	.86	. . . .
60	140	. . . .	.58	.67	.79	.83	.91
70	158	. . . .	.35	.52	.71	.76	.87
75	167	. . . .	. . . .	.43	.66	.72	.86
80	176	. . . .	. . . .	.30	.61	.69	.84
90	194	. . . .	. . . .	. . . .	.50	.61	.80
100	212	. . . .	. . . .	. . . .	. . . .	.51	.77
120	248	. . . .	. . . .	. . . .	. . . .	. . . .	.69
140	284	. . . .	. . . .	. . . .	. . . .	. . . .	.59

* The current-carrying capacity for Type RH-RW conductors is the same as Type RH in dry locations and the same as Type RW in wet locations.

† The current-carrying capacities for Type RHH conductors for sizes AWG 14, 12, and 10 shall be the same as designated for Type RH conductors in this Table.

National Electric Code, Article 310.

rent being carried by a cable, its operating temperature depends upon the insulation, the material of which the conductor is made and the environment, tables are available which list the various current ratings for these different parameters.

The heat which produces the conductor temperature rise is caused by the I^2R wattage loss in the conductor. Since aluminum has greater electrical resistance than copper, aluminum wire will have a lower current rating than copper wire of the same size because its higher resistance generates more heat and therefore the maximum operating temperature is reached with lower current. This is clearly demonstrated by the figures of Tables 23.1, 23.2, 23.3, and 23.4.

Thus, from Tables 23.1 and 23.3 we see

Table 23.2   Allowable Current-Carrying Capacities of Insulated Copper Conductors in Amperes

Single Conductor in Free Air
(Based on Room Temperature of 30 C 86 F)

Size AWG MCM	Rubber Type R Type RW Type RU Type RUW (14-2) Type RH-RW Thermoplastic Type T Type TW	Rubber Type RH RUH (14-2) Type RH-RW* Type RHW Thermoplastic Type THW THWN	Paper Thermoplastic Asbestos Type TA Thermoplastic Type TBS Silicone Type SA Var-Cam Type V Asbestos Var-Cam Type AVB MI Cable RHH†	Asbestos Var-Cam Type AVA Type AVL	Impregnated Asbestos Type AI (14-8) Type AIA	Asbestos Type A (14-8) Type AA	Bare and Covered Conductors
14	20	20	30	40	40	45	30
12	25	25	40	50	50	55	40
10	40	40	55	65	70	75	55
8	55	65	70	85	90	100	70
6	80	95	100	120	125	135	100
4	105	125	135	160	170	180	130
3	120	145	155	180	195	210	150
2	140	170	180	210	225	240	175
1	165	195	210	245	265	280	205
0	195	230	245	285	305	325	235
00	225	265	285	330	355	370	275
000	260	310	330	385	410	430	320
0000	300	360	385	445	475	510	370
250	340	405	425	495	530	....	410
300	375	445	480	555	590	....	460
350	420	505	530	610	655	....	510
400	455	545	575	665	710	....	555
500	515	620	660	765	815	....	630
600	575	690	740	855	910	....	710
700	630	755	815	940	1005	....	780
750	655	785	845	980	1045	....	810
800	680	815	880	1020	1085	....	845
900	730	870	940	....	....	....	905
1000	780	935	1000	1165	1240	....	965
1250	890	1065	1130	....	....	....	....
1500	980	1175	1260	1450	....	....	1215
1750	1070	1280	1370	....	....	....	....
2000	1155	1385	1470	1715	....	....	1405

For correction factors and notes, see Table 23.1.
National Electric Code, Article 310.

that No. 4 Copper, RW type insulation will carry 70 amps, whereas No. 4 Aluminum RW is only allowed 55 amps. The figures given in Table 23.1 differ markedly from those of Table 23.2, the change being entirely due to the environment of the conductors. When conductors are placed in conduit the heat generated is not as easily dissipated as it would be if the conductor were in free air (Tables 23.2 and 23.4) and the temperature rises more rapidly. Thus the current rating in free air is much higher than for the same wire in conduit. Conversely, if the ambient temperature is above 40 C the current capacity must be reduced by the factors given below Table 23.1.

Table 23.3   Allowable Current-Carrying Capacities of Insulated Aluminum Conductors in Amperes

Not More than Three Conductors in Raceway or Cable or Direct Burial (Based on Room Temperature of 30 C 86 F)

Size AWG MCM	Rubber Type R, RW, RU, RUW (12-2) Type RH-RW Thermoplastic Type T TW	Rubber Type RH RUH (14-2) Type RH-RW Type RHW Thermoplastic Type THW THWN	Paper Thermoplastic Asbestos Type TA Thermoplastic Type TBS Silicone Type SA Var-Cam Type V Asbestos Var-Cam Type AVB MI Cable RHH†	Asbestos Var-Cam Type AVA Type AVL	Impregnated Asbestos Type AI (14-8) Type AIA	Asbestos Type A (14-8) Type AA
12	15	15	25	25	30	30
10	25	25	30	35	40	45
8	30	40	40	45	50	55
6	40	50	55	60	65	75
4	55	65	70	80	90	95
3	65	75	80	95	100	115
**2	75	90	95	105	115	130
**1	85	100	110	125	135	150
**0	100	120	125	150	160	180
**00	115	135	145	170	180	200
**000	130	155	165	195	210	225
**0000	155	180	185	215	245	270
250	170	205	215	250	270	....
300	190	230	240	275	305	....
350	210	250	260	310	335	....
400	225	270	290	335	360	....
500	260	310	330	380	405	....
600	285	340	370	425	440	....
700	310	375	395	455	485	....
750	320	385	405	470	500	....
800	330	395	415	485	520	....
900	355	425	455	....	....	....
1000	375	445	480	560	600	....
1250	405	485	530	....	....	....
1500	435	520	580	650	....	....
1750	455	545	615	....	....	....
2000	470	560	650	705	....	....

For correction factors and other notes, see Table 23.1.

** For three-wire, single-phase service and subservice circuits, the allowable current-carrying capacity of RH, RH-RW, RHH, RHW, and THW aluminum conductors shall be for sizes #2-100 amp, #1-110 amp, #1/0-125 amp, #2/0-150 amp, #3/0-170 amp, and #4/0-200 amp.

National Electric Code, Article 310.

Table 23.4   Allowable Current-Carrying Capacities of Insulated Aluminum Conductors in Amperes

Single Conductor in Free Air
(Based on Room Temperature of 30 C 86 F)

Size AWG MCM	Rubber Type R, RW, RU, RUW (12-2) Type RH-RW Thermo-plastic Type T, TW	Rubber Type RH RUH (14-2) Type RH-RW* Type RHW Thermo-plastic Type THW THWN	Paper Thermo-plastic Asbestos Type TA Thermo-plastic Type TBS Silicone Type SA Var-Cam Type V Asbestos Var-Cam Type AVB MI Cable RHH†	Asbestos Var-Cam Type AVA Type AVL	Impreg-nated Asbestos Type AI (14-8) Type AIA	Asbestos Type A (14-8) Type AA	Bare and Covered Conductors
12	20	20	30	40	40	45	30
10	30	30	45	50	55	60	45
8	45	55	55	65	70	80	55
6	60	75	80	95	100	105	80
4	80	100	105	125	135	140	100
3	95	115	120	140	150	165	115
2	110	135	140	165	175	185	135
1	130	155	165	190	205	220	160
0	150	180	190	220	240	255	185
00	175	210	220	255	275	290	215
000	200	240	255	300	320	335	250
0000	230	280	300	345	370	400	290
250	265	315	330	385	415	. . . .	320
300	290	350	375	435	460	. . . .	360
350	330	395	415	475	510	. . . .	400
400	355	425	450	520	555	. . . .	435
500	405	485	515	595	635	. . . .	490
600	455	545	585	675	720	. . . .	560
700	500	595	645	745	795	. . . .	615
750	515	620	670	775	825	. . . .	640
800	535	645	695	805	855	. . . .	670
900	580	700	750	. . . .	. . . .	. . . .	725
1000	625	750	800	930	990	. . . .	770
1250	710	855	905	. . . .	. . . .	. . . .	. . . .
1500	795	950	1020	1175	. . . .	. . . .	985
1750	875	1050	1125	. . . .	. . . .	. . . .	. . . .
2000	960	1150	1220	1425	. . . .	. . . .	1165

For correction factors and notes, see Table 23.1.
National Electric Code, Article 310.

These factors apply to Tables 23.1 through 23.4. Similarly, if more than 3 conductors are placed in a conduit the temperature will increase proportionally and the conductors must be derated by the amount shown in Table 23.5.

(b) *Insulation.* Most conductors are covered with some type of insulation that prevents the metallic conductor from con-

Table 23.5   Current-Carrying Capacity Derating Factors

Number of Conductors in Raceway	Derating Factor
4 to 6	0.80
7 to 24	0.70
25 to 42	0.60
43 and above	0.50

Table 23.6 *Conductor Insulation Types*

Trade Name	Type Letter	Max. Operating Temp.	Application Provisions
Code Rubber	R	60 C 140 F	Dry locations.
Heat-Resistant Rubber	RH	75 C 167 F	Dry locations.
Heat-Resistant Rubber	RHH	90 C 194 F	Dry locations.
Moisture-Resistant Rubber	RW	60 C 140 F	Dry and wet locations. For over 2000 volts, insulation shall be ozone-resistant.
Moisture and Heat-Resistant Rubber	RH-RW	60 C 140 F	Dry and wet locations. For over 2000 volts, insulation shall be ozone-resistant.
		75 C 167 F	Dry locations. For over 2000 volts, insulation shall be ozone-resistant.
Moisture and Heat-Resistant Rubber	RHW	75 C 167 F	Dry and wet locations. For over 2000 volts, insulation shall be ozone-resistant.
Latex Rubber	RU	60 C 140 F	Dry locations.
Heat-Resistant Latex Rubber	RUH	75 C	Dry locations.
Moisture-Resistant Latex Rubber	RUW	60 C 140 F	Dry and wet locations.
Thermoplastic	T	60 C 140 F	Dry locations.
Moisture-Resistant Thermoplastic	TW	60 C 140 F	Dry and wet locations.
Moisture and Heat-Resistant Thermoplastic	THW	75 C 167 F	Dry and wet locations.
Moisture and Heat-Resistant Thermoplastic	THWN	75 C 167 F	Dry and wet locations.
Thermoplastic and Asbestos	TA	90 C 194 F	Switchboard wiring only.
Thermoplastic and Fibrous Outer Braid	TBS	90 C 194 F	Switchboard wiring only.
Mineral Insulation (Metal Sheathed)	MI	85 C 185 F	Dry and wet locations with Type O termination fittings. Max. operating temperature for special applications 250 C.

Table 23.6 (Continued)

Trade Name	Type Letter	Max. Operating Temp.	Application Provisions
Silicone-Asbestos	SA	90 C	Dry locations—max. operating temperature for special application 125 C.
Varnished Cambric	V	85 C 185 F	Dry locations only. Smaller than No. 6 by special permission.
Asbestos and Varnished Cambric	AVA	110 C 230 F	Dry locations only.
Asbestos and Varnished Cambric	AVL	110 C 230 F	Dry and wet locations.

tacting other wiring or the grounded raceway, piping or other conductors at earth potential, and also prevents accidental contact with the wiring. Insulation also serves as a physical shield to the conductor against heat, corrosive liquids, water, etc., although outer jackets are often placed over the insulation to accomplish this protective function.

Returning to our hydraulic analogy: conductors are analogous to pipes; when pressure is high, pipes are heavier; when voltage is high, insulation must be thicker. Therefore insulation is rated by voltage, e.g., 300, 600, 1000, 3000, 5000, and 15,000 volts. Insulation may be used on any circuit up to its rated voltage but not higher. If insulation is used above its rating it may break down or puncture, causing short circuits, tripping of breakers, blowing of fuses, and arcing, with the possibility of fire. Ordinary building wiring is usually rated 300 volts for control wiring and 600 volts for lighting, feeders and power work.

As explained in (a) above, the current-carrying rating of a conductor depends upon its maximum permissible operating temperature. It is therefore apparent that an insulation which can withstand high temperatures, such as asbestos, will allow higher current capacity for a given wire size. That this is indeed the case may be seen from Tables 23.1 through 23.4 where, for No. 2 AWG Type RW cable the capacity

is 95 amps (Table 23.1) while 165 amps is permitted for Type A insulation. The common types of insulation are listed in Table 23.6 with the associated trade names, code letters, maximum temperatures, and special provisions.

(c) **Voltage Drop** becomes a consideration of major importance in long circuits since by NEC rule total voltage drop from the service points to the final panelboard before the current-utilizing device must be held to 1 percent for lighting or combination light and power loads and 3 percent for power and heating loads. Since the impedance of the wiring causes a voltage drop ($V = IZ$) the size of the conductors is of paramount importance. Very often, feeders are sized much larger than the size required for current carrying capacity in order to keep the voltage drop in the wiring within the specified limits. This item will be discussed quantitatively in the following chapter.

(d) **Mechanical Strength** of a cable becomes a factor in pulling the cables through raceways. In order to minimize the stresses placed on cables, it is wise not to exceed 3 right angle bends in any single cable pull (2 bends with lead covered cable).

(e) **Protective Coverings.** As mentioned above various materials are utilized for outer coverings on wire and cable. Lead provides moisture protection, neoprene protects against moisture and general corrosion, braid against abrasion and steel wire or tape guards cable from physical damage. These materials and many more are available in almost countless combinations to provide the specific construction best applicable to any particular installation.

(*f*) *Conductor Gauge.* The standard of the American wire and cable industry is the "American Wire Gauge," abbreviated AWG. All wire sizes up to No. 0000 (also written No. 4/0) are expressed in AWG; the smaller the AWG number, the larger the size. (This designation applies only to round conductors; other shapes will be discussed later.) Thus No. 10 is a heavier wire than No. 12 and lighter (thinner) than No. 8. The No. 4/0 size is the largest AWG designation, beyond which MCM is used (thousand circular mil). In this designation wire diameter increases with number; thus 500 MCM is a heavier wire (double the area) than 250 MCM. Table 23.7 lists the circular mil equivalents of the various

Table 23.7 Physical Properties of Bare Conductors

Size	Area	Diameter	
AWG or MCM	Circular Mils	Solid	Stranded
18	1624	.0403	....
16	2583	.0508	....
14	4107	.0641	....
12	6530	.0808	....
10	10,380	.1019	....
8	16,510	.1285	....
6	26,250	.162	.184
4	41,740	.205	.232
2	66,370	.258	.292
1	83,690	.290	.332
0	105,500	.325	.373
00	133,100	.365	.418
000	167,800	.409	.470
0000	211,600	.460	.528
250 MCM	250,000	.500	.575
300 MCM	300,000	.547	.630
400 MCM	400,000	.633	.728
500 MCM	500,000	.707	.814
600 MCM	600,000	.775	.893
750 MCM	750,000	.866	.998
1000 MCM	1,000,000	1.000	1.152

designations. A circular mil is an artificial area measurement, representing the square of the cable diameter when the diameter is expressed in mils (thousandths of an inch). Thus a solid conductor $\frac{1}{2}$ in. in diameter is 500 mils in diameter, or 250,000 circular mils in area, or 250 MCM:

$$MCM = \frac{CM}{1000} = \frac{Diam.^2}{1000} = \frac{(500)^2}{1000}$$
$$= \frac{250,000}{1000} = 250$$

6. Special Cable Types. Although most building wiring is accomplished with rubber- and plastic-insulated 300-volt and 600-volt conductors of the types listed in Table 23.6 with a few special high-temperature asbestos types, applications often indicate the use of some of the special cables in the following list.

High-voltage cables, from 3 kv to 15 kv, are usually insulated with layers of varnished cambric or oil-impregnated paper and covered with a lead sheath. These cables, designated VCL and PILC respectively may be installed in conduit or duct. Some local electrical codes require that all high-voltage cable runs within a building be put in concrete encased conduit or duct. Splicing of high voltage cables is a highly specialized skill which should not be attempted by an electrician not specifically trained for the purpose. Rubber-insulated cable is also available for high voltages but is not as extensively used as VCL and PILC. Generally, at 5 kv varnish cambric insulated cable with braid covering is chosen in dry locations, and VCL in wet locations. At 15 kv and higher PILC is most often used.

Type MI mineral-insulated wire and cable is an assembly of bare copper conductors in a copper sheath with highly compressed insulating material filling the space between wires. It is used exposed or concealed in wet or dry locations, hazardous or nonhazardous areas, interior, exterior, or underground. It is particularly useful where conduit work would be expensive due to tortuous runs, or in hazardous areas such as oil refineries.

Type ALS aluminum cable is an assembly of *insulated* conductors in a close-fitting watertight aluminum sheath. Application is similar to type MI except that use in hazardous areas is not permitted and usage depends upon the characteristics of the wire insulation type.

Type AC armored wire and cable commonly known by the trade name 'BX' is an assembly of wires, normally rubber-insulated, bound together with a tape or braid and then wrapped with a spiral wound interlocking strip of steel tape. Similar cables are available with varnish and thermoplastic insulated conductors, and with lead covered conductors for use in wet locations. Such cable must have an internal bonding strip of copper or aluminum in contact with the armor for its entire length. The wire and the interlocking armor are installed as a unit, usually by simple U-clamps or staples holding it against beams, walls, ceilings, and columns. This type of installation is frequently used in residences, summer cottages, garages, and barns. It also finds frequent application in wiring or rewiring of existing buildings. Such armored cable can be pulled into place through existing spaces back of plastered surfaces, under floor joists, or behind studding in the walls. Special couplings, box connectors, and other fittings are made to complete such armored cable installations or to interconnect them with rigid conduit systems. A similar type of armored cable, oval instead of round in cross section, is available for installation under plaster, or where the round armored cable would be too thick for the space. Use of type AC cable is restricted to dry locations and for under-plaster extensions except that use in wet locations is permitted where conductors are lead-covered or the armor is covered with a

moisture-resistant jacket. This type cable, generally, may *not* be used in theatres, movie-houses, hazardous locations, battery rooms, hoistways or garages except in very special conditions as detailed in the applicable NEC sections.

Types NM and NMC nonmetallic sheathed cable comprises an assembly of rubber or plastic insulated cable covered with a fibrous flame retardant braid (NM) or flame-retardant moisture retardant braid (type NMC). Both types usually carry a bare copper grounding wire throughout the length, and are referred to in the trade as "Romex." This type of wiring is similar in application to type AC, but less expensive and easier to handle.

Type NM is restricted to dry locations; NMC may be used in wet locations and under plaster provided it is protected from accidental nail puncture by a strip of $\frac{1}{16}''$ thick steel. Neither type may be embedded in concrete or cement. Nonmetallic outlet boxes approved for the purpose may be used with this type of wiring.

Service entrance cable, (NEC Art. 338) types ASE, SE and USE, are assemblies of conductors, one of which may be uninsulated (neutral), intended for service entrance use. Type SE is the basic cable with moisture and flame resisting covering; when armored to prevent physical damage the designation is SE style A or ASE; when provided with moisture proofing for underground use the designation is SE style U or simply, USE. Type USE cable may not be buried directly in the earth unless equipped with an outer moisture-resistant jacket such as neoprene, designated for direct burial use. Type ASE and USE may be used as overhead service conductors and for interior wiring, generally, where all conductors are insulated. See the appropriate articles of the NEC for special provisions.

Type UF underground cables comprise one or more rubber or plastic insulated

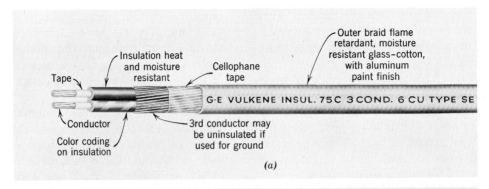

Outer braid flame retardant, moisture resistant glass–cotton, with aluminum paint finish

Insulation heat and moisture resistant

Cellophane tape

Tape

Conductor

Color coding on insulation

3rd conductor may be uninsulated if used for ground

G-E VULKENE INSUL. 75C 3 COND. 6 CU TYPE SE

(a)

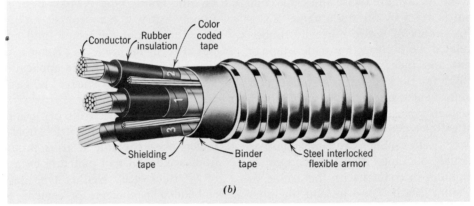

Conductor   Rubber insulation

Color coded tape

Shielding tape

Binder tape

Steel interlocked flexible armor

(b)

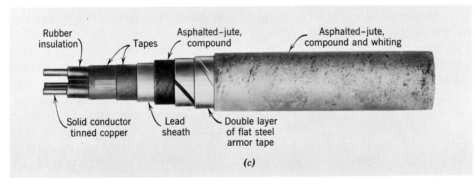

Rubber insulation

Tapes

Asphalted–jute, compound

Asphalted–jute, compound and whiting

Solid conductor tinned copper

Lead sheath

Double layer of flat steel armor tape

(c)

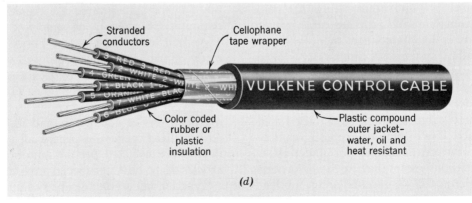

Stranded conductors

Cellophane tape wrapper

VULKENE CONTROL CABLE

Color coded rubber or plastic insulation

Plastic compound outer jacket– water, oil and heat resistant

(d)

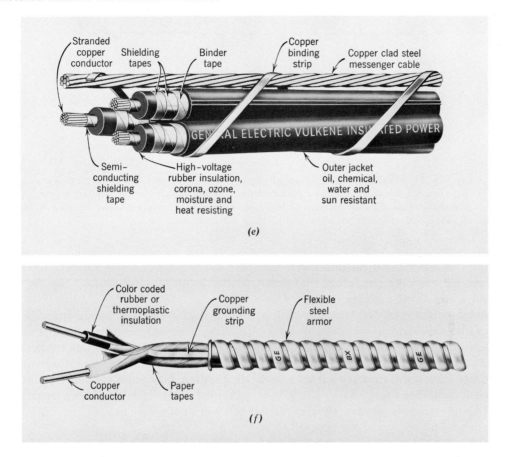

Fig. 23.2 Insulated wire and cable: (*a*) three conductor underground service entrance cable, type USE; (*b*) high voltage 3 conductor interlocked steel armored cable; (*c*) 3 conductor 600 volt steel tape armored parkway cable, suitable for direct burial; (*d*) multi-conductor 300 volt control cable; (*e*) 3 conductor 5 KV. pre-assembled aerial cable; (*f*) type A-C flexible armored cable (BX). Courtesy of General Electric Wire and Cable Dep't.

conductors with an outer jacket which is designed to protect the cables from moisture and corrosion when buried directly in the earth. These cables are available up to No. 4/0 AWG and with various types of insulation, as listed in Table 23.6. The cable may be used for interior wiring if all conductors are insulated although an uninsulated conductor is permissible if used for grounding only. When installed direct burial it is good practice to cover the cable with a protecting board (as illustrated in Fig. 23.3) and to bury it a minimum of 18 in.

below the ground. Type UF cable shall not be used as SE cable, in garages, theaters, movie houses, storage battery rooms, hazardous locations, hoistways, embedded in cement, or concrete or exposed to direct sunlight.

Overhead cables are of several types; bare, weatherproof, or preassembled aerial cable. Bare copper cable supported on porcelain or glass insulators on crossarms is normally used for high voltage (2.4 kv and higher) lines. Secondary circuits at 600 volts and below are generally run on porcelain spool secondary racks

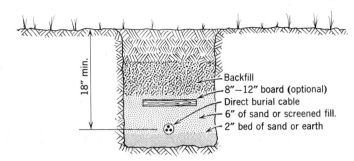

Fig. 23.3   Direct burial cable installation. All phase conductors of a circuit should be installed in a single trench. Cable shall be unreeled into trench (not dragged) after all coarse stones have been removed from base of trench and sand fill laid down. Cable should be snaked slightly to allow for movement and settlement. Minimum burial for high voltage cables is 24".

with 1/c double or triple-braid weatherproof cable as the conductor. Preassembled aerial cable consists of 3 or 4 insulated cables wrapped together with a metallic tape and suspended by hooks from the poles. This type of construction may be used up to 5 kv. It often proves to be less economical than crossarm or rack installation. (See Fig. 23.2)

Aerial runs are always cheaper than underground ducts and are generally less costly than direct burial installation unless a large number of cables are being installed in a single trench.

7. Busways. When large conductors are not circular in cross-section, they are usually made solid and are referred to as busbars. Busbars are described by dimensions; thus a bar may be $\frac{1}{4}'' \times 2''$, $\frac{1}{4}'' \times 4''$, $\frac{5}{16}'' \times 6''$, etc. As a rule of thumb, the current carrying capacity of copper bus is 1000 amperes per square inch of cross-section. Thus, a $\frac{1}{4}'' \times 2''$ copper bar is $\frac{1}{2}$ sq in. in area and will safely carry 500 amp. Bus is normally constructed of solid copper or aluminum and when assembled with other bars in a metal housing is referred to as bus duct or busway.

The bars in bus duct whether bare or insulated, are rigidly assembled by bolting to insulating supports which in turn connect to the steel housing (see Fig. 23.4). The insulators are normally porcelain, micarta, or other material which serves to separate the bars. A wide variety of fittings and joints

are available, to enable buswork to be installed with angles, bends, tapoffs, and curves.

Bus duct is specified by material, number of buses, current capacity (since it carries its own enclosure its operating temperature can be predetermined), type, and voltage. In addition, maximum voltage drop is often specified. Thus, a typical brief description of a bus duct would be:

Copper bus duct, 4-wire, 1000-amp, low-impedance type, 600V, or aluminum bus duct, 3-wire, 2000-amp plug-in type, 600V.; both with a maximum full load voltage drop of 2.5 volts per 100 ft at 90 percent power factor.

"Plug-in" refers to a design which allows devices such as switches, controllers, circuit breakers, etc., to be directly plugged into the bus duct in similar fashion to a common plug being inserted into a receptacle. Low impedance refers to a design which is specifically intended to give minimum voltage drop.

Bus duct is available in current ratings of 100 to 4000 amp and voltages up to 5 kv, with other ratings available on special order. Although housings are normally ventilated and intended for indoor use, designs are available in weatherproof housings for outdoor application.

Busways, whether factory preassembled as bus duct or field assembled, are most

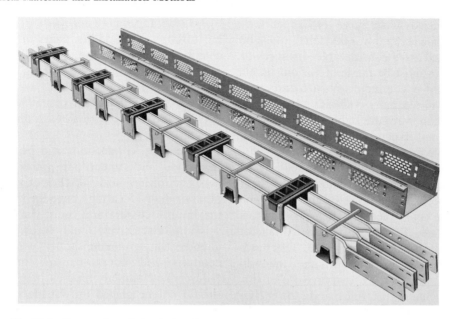

Fig. 23.4   Construction of plug-in bus duct. Plug-ins are spaced every 12″ on alternate sides to facilitate connection of plug-in breakers, switches, transformers or cable taps. Note that bars are insulated over their entire length and are clamped rigidly at plug-ins with spacer blocks of insulating material. Housing is of sheet steel with openings for ventilation. Cover plate is not shown. (Federal Pacific Electric)

Fig. 23.5   Typical bus duct installation showing different types of ducts emanating from a main switchboard.

often utilized when large blocks of low-voltage power (below 600 volts) must be transmitted over considerable distances or where taps must be made at various points along a power conductor. In such cases busway provides a more compact and efficient system than wire and cable, since taps are difficult and expensive to make on paralleled cable feeders.

8. Wiring Methods—(NEC Art. 300).

a. Conductors of light and power system of 600 volts or less may occupy the same enclosure (box, raceway) if all conductors are insulated for the maximum voltage of any conductor in the enclosure. This holds true without regard as to whether the individual conductors are carrying a-c or d-c.

b. Conductors of light and power systems of over 600 volts may not occupy the same enclosure as conductors of systems less than 600 volts.

c. Conductors of signal or radio systems shall not occupy the same enclosure as conductors of light and power systems except as *specifically permitted* for elevators, recording, remote control, and communication. Reference should be made to the appropriate Code sections for such wiring.

d. Conductors of emergency wiring systems shall not occupy the same enclosure as any other wiring except in transfer switches or exit and emergency lights fed from both normal and emergency sources.

e. All metal raceways, cable armor, metal enclosures, fittings, and boxes shall be metallically joined, either mechanically or by bonding jumpers, so as to provide effective electrical continuity.

f. Conductors in vertical raceways shall be supported at intervals as specified in the NEC by means of insulated wedges or other approved devices.

g. When installed in ferrous enclosures (iron, steel), circuits shall have all phases run together. When feeders are paralleled and run in more than one steel conduit, each conduit shall contain all phases and neutral, in order to minimize induced eddy current heating effects.

h. Generally, where necessary to run wiring through air-handling ducts or plenum chambers, the wiring method shall be rigid conduit, electric metallic tubing (EMT), Type ACL, MI, or ALS cable.

i. No bare conductors or earth returns may be used for the wiring of any temporary circuit.

j. Electrical connections and pull boxes, raceways, and underfloor ducts should never be located near very hot or very cold pipes or ducts. Heating above the allowable maximum temperatures may damage insulation. Excessively cold locations frequently cause condensation within the conduits and ducts, causing insulation failure. For similar reasons, riser shafts should not be placed on outside walls exposed to direct sunlight.

9. Knob and Tube Wiring. In small, low-cost installations wiring may be supported on porcelain knobs and tubes, shown in Fig. 23.9. The most common applications are in older buildings although since this type of installation is generally obsolete, some city building codes prohibit its use. Some disadvantages, as compared to rigid metallic conduit, are that conductors are not protected from mechanical injury; burning insulation may ignite timbers; warping or settling of the building structure may slacken the wires; porcelain tubes or insulators may break or loosen owing to vibration, and replacement or change of wires is difficult. Flexible, nonmetallic, fire-resisting tubing known as loom must be placed around adjacent wires if they are closer together than 3 in. on centers. Wherever it enters an outlet box each wire must have this additional tubing.

10. Copper vs Aluminum Wiring. With the development of satisfactory splicing and connecting techniques, the use of aluminum wiring increased due to its inherent weight advantage over copper, with concomitant lower installation costs. Both copper and aluminum posses the requisite properties of good electrical conductors, copper being more conductive and aluminum lighter.

Economy usually lies with copper in the smaller and medium-size cable since weight is not a problem and the smaller conduit required for the smaller copper conductors is cheaper. In the larger sizes of cable the aluminum weight advantage offsets the economy of smaller copper size and smaller conduit and may prove less expensive, particularly in areas of high labor cost, such as urban areas.

11. Connections. In the installation of electrical conductors it is necessary to make joints, splices, and branch-circuit connections or taps. Such electrical conductor connections must be made on round wire, on rectangular busbars, and on busbars made of pipes. Figure 23.6 shows a few of the most common methods and materials for making such connections.

The solderless connector has almost universally replaced the older soldered type of joint by providing a quick and simple method of effecting a good splice by pressure. Various types of solderless connectors are available; the wire nut which is widely used on branch circuit wiring; the tool applied crimp connector and the lug terminal which is applied to a wire and then bolted to a similar connector on another wire.

Soldering is still employed on large cable joined with splicing sleeves and with solder-type lug connectors. Another very effective splicing means is in actuality a welding process, the heat being generated by a chemical reaction involving certain chemicals added to the splicing chamber. The resultant splice is a permanent welding of the 2 or more conductors (see Fig. 23.6g).

In any type of connection, large or small, the resistance of the connection should be not greater than a corresponding length of the adjacent smallest conductor.

Whenever an insulated conductor is spliced, tapped, or connected by any of these types of joints to another insulated conductor the connection should be covered with insulation and protective wrappings which are in all respects equal in electrical and mechanical characteristics to the insulation on the conductors themselves. In order to provide such adequate insulation and protection, various types of adhesive-rubber, varnished-cambric, and friction tapes, and insulating compounds and varnishes are available.

Whenever splices are made in lead-sheath cables the connection and insulation must first be made and then a lead-wiping sleeve of larger diameter must be slipped back over the joint and soldered to the lead sheath on either side of the joint. Skilled workmen are required to neatly and effectively make these splices.

On large uninsulated rectangular or tubular bus bars, the connections are usually made with bolts and nuts and with threaded or clampjoint connectors. The portions of the bars held in contact by the bolts are often silver-plated to provide permanent low-resistance contacts.

12. Conduits and Raceways. The purpose of conduit is to protect the enclosed wires from mechanical and chemical injury, to protect persons from shock hazard by providing a grounded enclosure, to protect surroundings against fire hazard due to overheating or arcing of the conductors and to support the conductors. For these reasons the NEC requires that all conductors be enclosed in a rigid metallic conduit or otherwise properly protected.

Generally, all metal raceways and associated fittings must be protected inside and out by corrosion resistant material unless the raceway is inherently corrosion resistant. To this end, steel conduit is manufactured in several ways, among which are:

1. Hot dip galvanized (dipped into molten zinc).
2. Sherardized (coated with zinc dust).
3. Enameled (coated with a corrosion resistant enamel).
4. Plastic or asphaltum covered.

Inherently corrosion resistant materials of which conduit is manufactured include wrought iron, aluminum and copper.

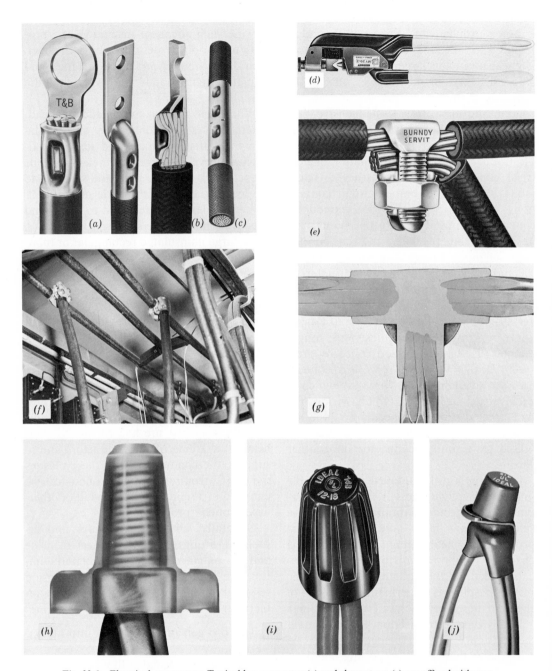

Fig. 23.6   Electrical connectors: Typical lug connector (*a*) and sleeve type (*c*) are affixed with pressure indenting tool (*d*). High quality of splice is shown in cutaway (*b*). "Burndy Servit" screw type pressure connector (*e*) can be used for straight through or 'T' taps; larger cables require special bolted connectors (*f*). Thermal welding process actually welds the conductors together (*g*). Branch circuit wiring is usually spliced by use of small screw-on pressure connectors (wire nuts) of various design (*h*) (*i*) (*j*). Photos courtesy of Thomas and Betts Co., Burndy Co. and Ideal Industries.

(*a*) *Heavy Wall Steel Conduit* comprises the major portion of all conduit in use, and is manufactured with all of the various coatings listed above. Enameled conduit may only be used indoors and in location which are not, by Code, classified as severely corrosive.

Generally, no conduit smaller than $\frac{1}{2}''$ nominal trade diameter is used. The nominal trade sizes are $\frac{1}{2}$, $\frac{3}{4}$, 1, $1\frac{1}{4}$, $1\frac{1}{2}$, 2, $2\frac{1}{2}$, 3, 4, 5, and 6 in., although the last two sizes are not often encountered. Conduit is made in standard lengths of 10 ft and includes one coupling per length.

Steel conduit may be bent provided that the conduit is not injured, the radius is not less than required by NEC, and that no more than 4-90° bends or equivalent occur between any 2 outlets. Ordinary steel pipe may not be used for electric purposes, and all electric steel conduit is distinctively marked as such. Where conduits enter boxes a bushing or other means must be provided to prevent abrasion of the wire insulation against the box.

When steel conduit is installed in direct contact with the earth it is advisable to use hot-dip galvanized type and to coat the joints with asphaltum. If the earth is very wet, the complete conduit system should be coated with an asphalt compound.

Rigid steel conduits may be supported in exposed locations or within structural walls, and may be carried in or across the flanges of steel columns and beams, or embedded in slabs, columns, or beams of concrete. Figure 23.7 illustrates some typical methods of installing conduits and raceways.

For all the conduit systems, rigid, flexible, etc., the range of conduit fittings is wide. Such fittings include straight and angle couplings, elbows, T- and cross-connec-

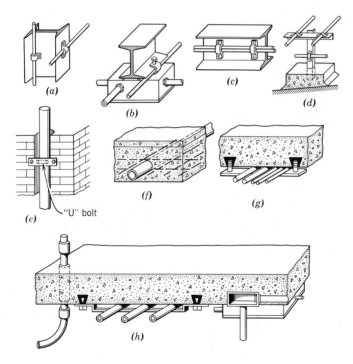

Fig. 23.7 Typical conduit installations: (*a*), (*b*), and (*c*) mounted on structural-steel members; (*d*) angle bracket supported by a concrete block and supporting brackets holding conduits; (*e*) in wall chase; (*f*) cast in concrete slab; (*g*) supported by steel strap and inserts (trapeze); (*h*) miscellaneous slab details showing support of conduits, outlet box and pull box beneath the slab.

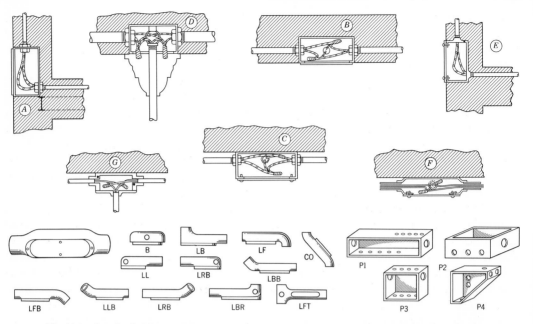

Fig. 23.8   Standard outlet and junction boxes A, B, C, D, E, F, and G showing some typical conduit connections and wiring details. Four designs of sheet metal pull and junction boxes (P1, P2, P3, and P4) are shown. These come in a variety of standard sizes (covers not shown) and may be made up to fit any number of conduit connections and conduit sizes. The holes represent the desired locations and sizes. Thirteen of many types of standard conduit fittings are shown with their symbols, at the lower left of the figure.

tions, and many forms of outlet boxes. A number of these fittings and outlet boxes for the rigid conduit system are shown in Fig. 23.8.

The selection of size depends upon the number and diameter of the wires which may be drawn into the conduit without undue abrasion or cutting of the insulation, and without stretching the wire. The number and radius of bends in the conduit, as well as the total length, affect the degree of abrasion of insulation when the wire is pulled in. Long straight pulls may be made through as much as 150 to 200 ft of continuous conduit without bends. The above comments represent conservative practice, but many field conditions arise to alter practical rules of this kind.

To frequently exceed a total of 6 or 8 power conductors in a given conduit is not good practice. In general the service requirements in any one portion of a build-

ing are such that circuits of only perhaps 2 or 3 conductors are installed in 1 conduit. In running branch circuits from the panel board to local lamp or plug outlets, 3 or 4 circuits may run in 1 large conduit to a given pull box in the system, and then branched off in smaller conduits to the final outlet points.

The NEC states that no wire shall be spliced, connected, or tapped and then drawn into the conduit so that the connection is within the conduit itself. All such splices, connections, and taps shall be made within connection or pull boxes. Also, no wires should be installed until the conduit system has been inspected and approved by the NBFU.

When conduits are to be cast in concrete slabs and prior to pouring, the boxes and conduits are installed and held in position by blocks and iron wire fastened to the reinforcing bars. The concrete is then poured and tamped. For structural reasons these runs of conduit are usually close to the bottom surface or near the central portion of a floor slab. If a great number of conduits must be embedded it may be necessary to increase the slab thickness. This refers, of course, to conduits being installed in a structural slab. In many instances the structural slab is covered with a concrete topping or fill in which the conduit may be installed without affecting the integrity of the slab. In all cases, local building codes should be consulted for limitations on imbedded conduits. In any event the top of any conduit should be at least 1 in. below the finished floor surface in order to prevent possible cracking. When heavy trucking is to be expected this allowance should be increased to $1\frac{1}{2}$ inch or 2 in.

(*b*) *Electrical Metallic Tubing* is similar in use and application to rigid steel conduit except that having a thinner wall its use is restricted to areas where severe physical abuse is absent. Too, EMT may not be used in hazardous areas or for wiring operating above 600 volts.

Most EMT installations use compression type fittings rather than threaded joints. EMT finds its principal application in the smaller size conduits ($\frac{1}{2}''$, $\frac{3}{4}''$) although it is manufactured up to 2″ in diameter.

(*c*) *Flexible Metal Conduit.* This type of conduit construction which comprises an empty spirally wound interlocked armor raceway is known to the trade as "Greenfield." It is used principally for motor connections or other locations where vibration is present, movement is encountered, or where physical obstructions make its use practical. It may not be used in wet locations unless the enclosed wire is approved for such use, in hoistways, battery rooms, hazardous areas or in atmospheres injurious to rubber insulated conductors.

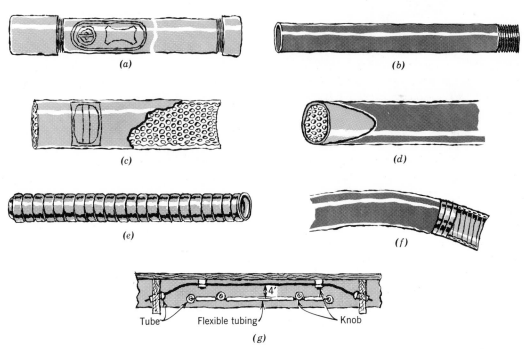

Fig. 23.9 Conduits and Raceways: (*a*) galvanized, heavy wall, rigid steel conduit; (*b*) black enameled steel conduit; (*c*) EMT thin wall steel conduit; (*d*) plastic coated EMT for use in corrosive atmospheres; (*e*) flexible steel conduit ("Greenfield"); (*f*) jacketed flexible steel conduit ("Sealtite") for moisture-proofing; (*g*) knob-and-tube wiring.

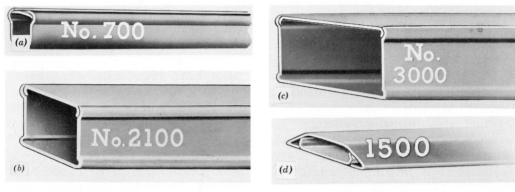

Flexible conduit is available in galvanized steel, brass, bronze, and aluminum, in all standard trade diameters and with requisite fittings.

(d) *Liquid-Tight Flexible Metal Conduit* is of the same construction as flexible conduit except covered with a liquid-tight jacket. It is not intended as a general purpose conduit, its use being restricted to motor connections where flexibility and imperviousness to liquid is required

This type of conduit, available in diameters up to 3 in., may not be used where subject to physical abuse, in contact with rapidly moving parts or at temperatures above 140 F. (See Fig. 23.9.)

(e) *Surface-Metal-Raceways and Multi-Outlet Assemblies* may be utilized only in dry, nonhazardous, noncorrosive locations, and may generally contain only wiring operating below 300 volts. Such raceways are normally installed exposed and where not

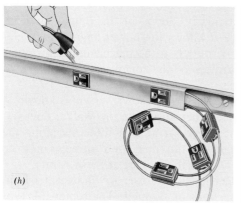

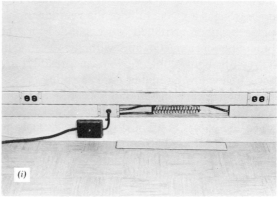

Fig. 23.10 Surface Raceways. Figures (a), (b), (c) are typical wall and ceiling surface raceways; type (d) is for floor use as shown in (e). Typical applications of the large raceway (c) are shown in (f) and (g). A special usage of the smaller (b) duct is shown in (h) utilizing prewired snap-in receptacles. When two of the longer (c) raceways are installed adjacent to each other as in (i) they form a convenient power and communications baseboard arrangement of large enough size to accommodate almost any wiring device. Courtesy of Wiremold Co.

subject to physical injury. Conductors not larger than No. 6 AWG may be so installed.

The principal application of this product is for rewiring existing installations where wall cutting for conduit is to be avoided; in areas where outlets are required at frequent intervals such as laboratories or business machine areas; and in new work where economy is the governing factor in the choice of a wiring system. Multisection units are available for running power and signal conductors; where used the wiring must be segregated and the compartments color coded and maintained in the same relative position throughout the installation.

(f) *Wireways, Troughs, and Cable Trays.* Sheet metal enclosures with hinged or removable covers may be utilized to carry up to 30 conductors rated 600 volts maximum, in dry nonhazardous noncorrosive locations and where not subject to physical abuse. If properly gasketed such troughs or wireways may also be used outdoors. Splices and taps are permitted in such raceways, making them particularly useful for feeding groups of starters, switches, and other equipment which may be nippled into the trough and its wiring spliced at that point. Another advantage of this type of raceway is that the hinged or removable cover exposes all the conductors to full view and access for replacement, inspection, addition of other wiring, etc. Although available in such standard sizes as $2\frac{1}{2}$ by $2\frac{1}{2}$, 4 by 4, 4 by 6, 6 by 6, 6 by 8, and 8 by 8 in. and 1, 2, 3, 4, 5, and 10 ft lengths, any special size is readily available. All troughs are limited to a maximum cable fill of 20 percent of cross sectional area.

A special type of wireway known simply as cable tray although not intended as a general use raceway is sometimes used where large numbers of power and control cables must be installed in limited spaces. These open troughs are generally of the ventilated type, being constructed of expanded or otherwise open metal and with no cover. Trays are light, cool, flexible and readily accessible allowing higher current rating of conductors, easy installation of both tray and wiring and over-all economy. However, since the cables contained (see Fig. 23.11) are not protected from heat, moisture, fumes, or other harmful influences as they would be in a completely enclosed raceway, the types of cables used should be of the self-protected type such as MI, ALS, USE, UF, neoprene jacketed rubber cable, or similar types. Factory assembled multiple-conductor control and power cables specifi-cally intended for tray installation may also be used.

(g) *Underfloor Raceways.* Underfloor raceways of metallic or nonmetallic construction may be installed in any area except corrosive or hazardous areas, commercial garages or storage battery rooms. Nonmetallic raceways in rectangular, oval, or open-bottom types are used in concrete construction, most often in single-cell units, although multicell fiber duct systems are available which are similar to the metal duct systems. (See Fig. 23.12.)

The use of underfloor duct systems is particularly prevalent in office buildings since it allows for power, signal, and telephone outlets to be placed under furniture regardless of the location of partitions or desks.

One such well known system is known as Walker duct. Inserts in the Walker duct system are preset at 2 ft intervals along the length of the duct and outlets may be brought to the surface at these points.

The junction boxes are shown at the intersections of all ducts. The removable tops of the boxes are flush with the floor and finished with the same material as the floor. For example, a linoleum floor covering would be matched by the circular piece of

Fig. 23.11 Typical installations utilizing cable tray. Note the open ventilated construction and the method of fastening the cables.

linoleum set in the depression provided in the cover. The boxes and ducts are placed on the concrete subfloor and leveled with vertical adjusting clamps. Then the top pouring of concrete comes almost level with the top of the box rim, lacking only the thickness of the linoleum or other floor covering. These systems may likewise be installed in monolithic or steel deck floors.

One-, two-, or three-duct systems are available using the appropriate junction boxes. Two sizes of ducts may be used:

No. 2, with outside dimensions $3\frac{1}{8}$ in. by $1\frac{1}{4}$ in. and inside area 3.313 sq in.; and No. 4, with outside dimensions of $6\frac{1}{2}$ in. by $1\frac{1}{2}$ in.; and inside area 8.58 sq in.

A single No. 2 duct is normally used for high tension (120 volt), a single No. 2 or No. 4 for signals and proprietary intercom, and in view of the increasing use of call-

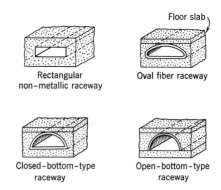

Fig. 23.12 Typical single cell nonmetallic underfloor raceways.

director phones, a No. 4 duct should be used for telephones.

Standard duct of the above sizes comes in lengths of 5 ft, 0 in.; 6 ft, 8 in.; 7 ft, 6 in.; and full length, 10 ft, 0 in.

With desks averaging 48 to 60 in. in

Fig. 23.13 A typical layout of the Walker underfloor duct system: (a) three separate ducts; (b) with preset inserts for outlet fittings spaced 24 in. apart; (c) a 3-duct junction box; (d) a typical duct spacing of 7 ft on centers (can be varied); (e) duct inserts (spacing changed on special order), exact center location of each of which can be identified by a magnetic pointer instrument; (f) locations of special floor outlets for telephone and signal circuits, for 120/240 volt appliances, and for desk-top machines.

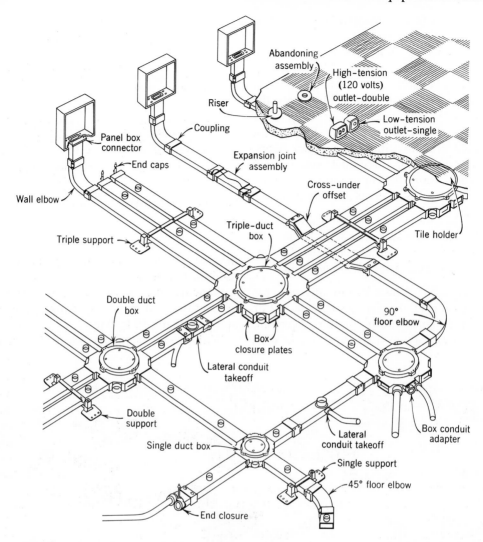

Fig. 23.14   With all ducts mounted at same elevation, junction boxes may be obtained to accommodate either one, two, or three ducts on each side, closure plates sealing unused openings. Duct supports are available for one or more cells, while wide variety of accessory components promotes flexibility in layout and variety in service facilities. Courtesy of Electrical Construction and Maintenance—May, 1960.

width a convenient spacing of duct runs is from 6 to 8 ft on centers with cross-connecting ducts spaced as required. (See Fig. 23.13.) The room walls should be 3 to 4 ft from the center lines of the adjacent parallel duct run. The inserts for the attachment of service fittings along each duct are furnished spaced on 24-in. centers although they may be available at other intervals on special order. The service connections to the duct system from the various cabinets and panelboards can either be made by means of round conduits entering the corner of the junction box (Fig. 23.15) or with a single-cell duct and elbow fittings as in Fig. 23.14.

Many fittings are available for connecting underfloor ducts of the two standard sizes to the junction boxes; or for connecting any size conduit (up to 2 in.) to the corners of the junction boxes. A typical layout of

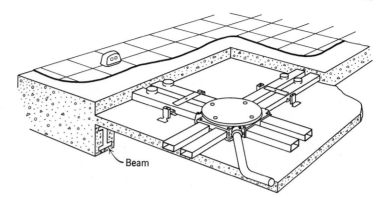

Fig. 23.15 Detail of duct installation in slab. Note that entire duct system may be placed in cement fill on top of structural slab.

Beam

underfloor duct is shown in Fig. 23.17 for a large office area.

The largest size cable which can be run in any underfloor duct system is 500 MCM. As in the case of rigid conduit, the combined cross sectional area of all conductors in a duct may not exceed 40 percent of the duct's interior area.

The methods of installation for all underfloor systems are quite similar. In general, the procedure for installing an outlet (where one does not exist) is to cut away the floor finish and the surface thickness of concrete or wood floor until the desired duct is exposed. Then the conduit (fiber or metal) is cut and threaded to fit the threads of the desired outlet fitting. Patching cement and pieces of the linoleum or other floor covering are then applied. One, two, or three ducts may be installed in any of the systems mentioned. Special tools and instruments are provided by underfloor duct manufacturers to facilitate installation and operation. Among these are junction-box and conduit-leveling screws; a magnetic instrument for locating the centers of junction boxes and separate conduit runs; braces, drills, and threading tools for inserting additional outlet fittings at any place along any of the ducts.

(h) *Cellular Metal Floor Raceways.* Where a structural floor is composed of hollow metal cells, these cells may be utilized for running utilities to feed the spaces above and below the floor. When utilized for electrical wiring, such con-struction is known by the trade name of "Q" flooring. If the Q-floor system contains large cells for carrying conditioned air, the system is called a Q-air-floor system. A section of such a system is shown in Fig. 23.18.

Note that the Q floor is part of the structural system and is designed accordingly. The electrical wiring is fed into the cells from header ducts which run perpendicular to the Q floor cells and constitute a system of underfloor duct in themselves. The header ducts in turn feed from lighting panels, signal and telephone cabinets in much the same manner as normal underfloor ducts.

All Q floor cell sections and the crosswise header ducts (for feeder and branch circuits) are tack-welded to the main floor beams and to each other. These welds assure electrical grounding of the raceways. The following 3 types of wiring systems must run in separate Q floor cells and header ducts: general lighting and appliances, telephones, and low-voltage signal systems. A complete range of outlets and fittings is available, together with installation tools and accessories.

Although the same 40 percent wire occupancy rule applies to the floor cells as to underfloor ducts, the wire size is limited to No. 0. The use of Q floor construction for wiring is restricted to noncorrosive, nonhazardous areas. In commercial garages such cells may feed devices below but not above the floor. No electric conductors may be installed in any cell or header which contains any service other than electric.

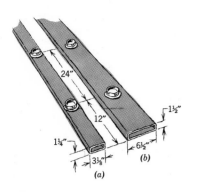

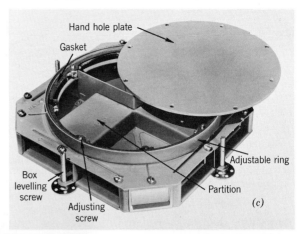

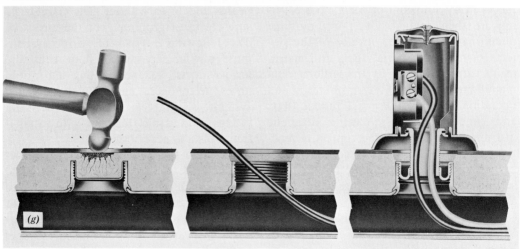

Fig. 23.16   Underfloor duct system: the basic components are (*a*) the #2 duct, (*b*) the #4 duct, and (*c*) the junction box, of which a typical 2 way unit is illustrated. Note in the installation photo (*d*) the duct supports, the cabinet connections and the conduit connection fitting in the left fore-

(i) Underground Duct Banks. When wiring must be run underground and exterior to a building there are 3 wiring methods available:

1. Direct burial.
2. Buried conduit or duct.
3. Concrete encased duct bank.

The first of these methods was discussed in the section on direct burial wiring above, although even direct burial cable when passing under paved areas should be run in some type of raceway. Steel conduit may be direct buried if galvanized or painted with asphaltum, but due to high cost should only be used where the cable may be subjected to severe physical abuse. Since this is not often the case with underground wiring, nonmetallic ducts are often used. These ducts, available in thin wall for concrete encasement, and thick wall for burial without concrete, have a number of advantages over metallic raceways including freedom from corrosion and rust. Both fiber ("Orangeburg") and asbestos-cement ("Transite") offer reasonable strength, are readily installed with or without encasement, and form excellent raceways for telephone cable, high voltage cable, secondary cables and control wiring. Several other types of raceways including square clay tile and the newer plastic pipe are also in use.

(j) Steel vs Aluminum Conduit. Aluminum conduit should not be used buried in the earth or concrete or where galvanic action with other metals may occur. Where large conduits are encountered and in high labor cost areas, aluminum conduit may prove more economical than steel due to its weight advantage. Each case should be considered separately and a conclusion drawn individually.

13. Pull Boxes, Connection Boxes, and Outlet Boxes. In order to provide access to the conduits for installing the necessary wires and for making connections to them, the continuous conduit runs are interrupted at frequent intervals by sheet-metal or cast-metal boxes. These boxes are usually of a rectangular, octagonal or round form having punched or knock-out holes to fit the conduits which terminate in them. "Knock-outs" are partially punched holes that are easily knocked out with a hammer. The threaded ends of the conduit are held rigid in the holes by means of a locknut and bushing on the inside and a locknut on the outside of the box. The bushing is tapered and rounded to provide a smooth entrance to the inside of the conduit. On certain sizes of conduit the NEC requires bushings covered with or made of solid insulation. This reduces the possibility of abrasion of conductor insulation where the conductor leaves the end of the conduit. Such pull, connection, and outlet boxes are manufactured in a number of small standard sizes punched with holes for $\frac{1}{2}$, $\frac{3}{4}$, and 1-in. conduits. The holes are located on the sides and in the bottom at positions which provide easy manipulation of the wrenches in tightening the locknuts and bushings. Figure 23.8 shows a few typical standard fittings and boxes.

In many conduit systems the number and size of conduits terminating at a given location require boxes much larger and, in many systems, much different in design from any standard box. Such boxes may be rectangular, L-shaped, or T-shaped, or may have rounded sections or other odd contours to fit into corners of the building structure or to avoid interference with other electrical or mechanical equipment. All boxes, whether standard or specially designed, are fitted with removable or hinged covers which are screwed on after the wires are pulled in and the connections are made.

ground. Typical high and low tension floor outlets are shown in (*e*) and (*f*) respectively. Installation of a new outlet at any preset insert is a 3 step operation (*g*). Courtesy of Walker/Parkersburg (*a, b, c, e, f*) H. K. Porter Co. (*d, g*)

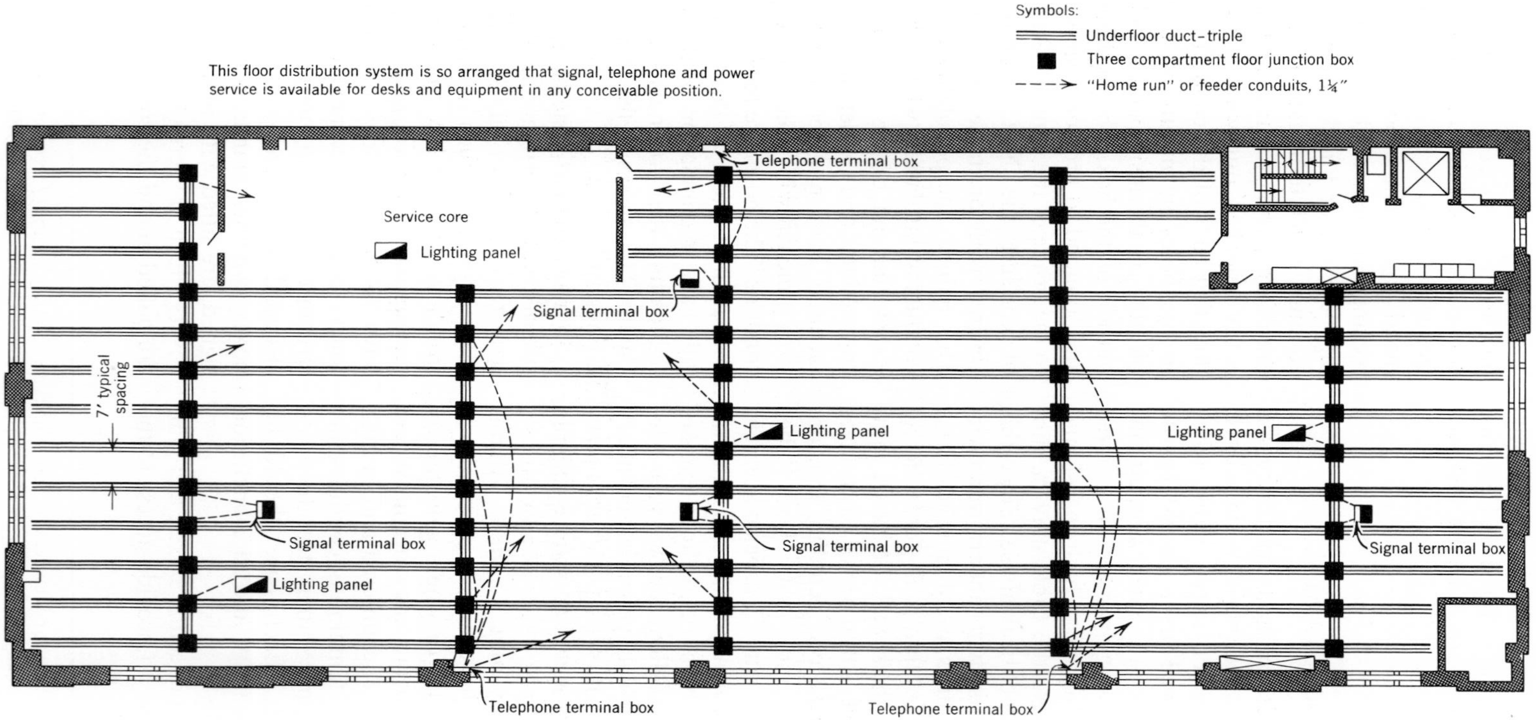

Symbols:

══════ Underfloor duct–triple

■ Three compartment floor junction box

–– ––► "Home run" or feeder conduits, 1¼"

This floor distribution system is so arranged that signal, telephone and power service is available for desks and equipment in any conceivable position.

Service core

Lighting panel

Signal terminal box

Lighting panel

Telephone terminal box

Lighting panel

Signal terminal box

Telephone terminal box

Signal terminal box

Lighting panel

Signal terminal box

Telephone terminal box

7' typical spacing

Fig. 23.17   Typical underfloor duct plan using 3 cells, comprising power, signal and telephone service.

484

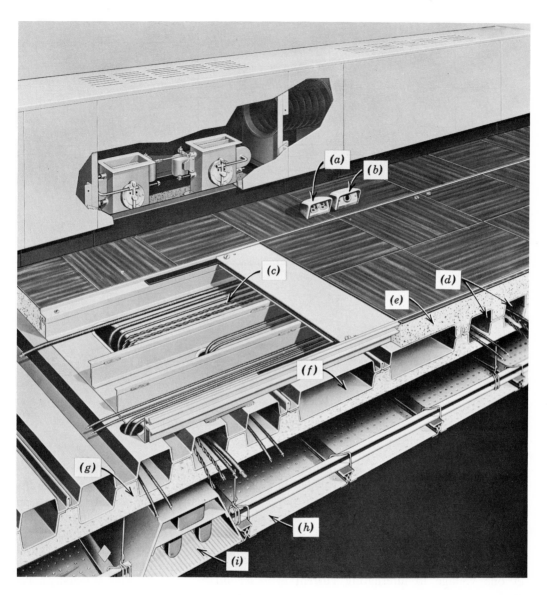

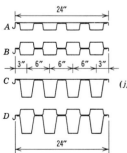

Fig. 23.18 Section through a typical Q floor construction: (a) High tension receptacle; (b) low tension receptacle; (c) header for wiring between cells and for main feeds; (d) wiring cells; (e) $2\frac{1}{2}''$ concrete fill; (f) air cell; (g) sprayed-on fireproofing; (h) suspended ceiling; (i) lighting fixture on ceiling below; (j) available duct cross-sections. (H. H. Robertson Co.)

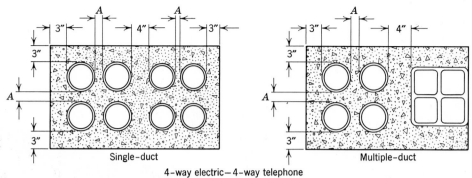

Single-duct   Multiple-duct

4-way electric—4-way telephone

Notes: $A = 1\frac{1}{2}''$ for clay and soapstone duct and $2''$ for fiber or asbestos cement.
All dimensions are minimum from outside surface of ducts.
Concrete not required between horizontal faces of clay duct.

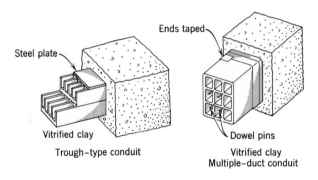

Trough-type conduit   Vitrified clay
Multiple-duct conduit

Fig. 23.19   Some types of raceways cast in concrete.

Boxes are rigidly fastened in position by screws or bolts through holes provided in the box or drilled on the job. When they are fastened to concrete, stone, or brick, expansion bolts or inserts are used.

14. Transformers. A transformer is a device which transforms alternating current of one voltage to alternating current of another voltage. A transformer would typically be used to step down an incoming 4160-volt service to 480 volts for distribution within a building and another transformer used in a local electric closet to step down the 480 volts to 120 for use on receptacle circuits. Thus one of the ratings of a transformer is its voltages. A transformer rated 4160/120 transforms (steps-down) 4160 volts to 120 volts; a transformer rated 120/480 volts transforms

(steps-up) 120-volt a-c to 480 volts a-c. A transformer cannot be used on d-c. A transformer usually has 2 sets of terminals; an input set called the primary terminals and an output set called the secondary terminals. Unfortunately, there is some ambiguity in the use of the terms "primary" and "secondary." High voltage is usually called primary voltage and low voltage, secondary; in a step-down transformer, say 4160/120, this is fine, in a step-up transformer, e.g. 480/4160, this is confusing since the primary of the transformer is connected to secondary voltage and the secondary of the transformer yields primary voltage. It is well to remember that ordinarily 120, 208, 240, 277, and 480 volts are called secondary voltages, and 2400, 4160, 4200, 12,470, and 13,200 are primary voltages. Since power is often distributed by the local utility company at these latter voltages, they are also referred to as distribution voltages in contradistinction to 22 kv, 44 kv, 69 kv and 138 kv which are transmission voltages.

Transformers are available in single-phase or 3-phase construction. If desired a 3-phase bank can be assembled by interconnecting 3 single-phase units in either delta or wye. The advantage of this system is that if one transformer of a 3-phase bank fails, limited service (57 percent capacity) can still be maintained and replacement of a single-phase unit is cheaper than replacing a 3-phase unit. The disadvantage lies in the higher initial cost and larger space requirement of the 3 single units.

Transformers, in addition to voltage and phase ratings, are also rated in kva (kilovolt-amperes). This figure is the product of the full load current and the voltage; since the voltages are different on primary and secondary so are the currents, *but the kva remains constant.* Thus a 100 kva 2400/120 volt transformer will carry at full load:

Primary current $= \dfrac{100,000 \text{ va}}{2400 \text{ v}}$

$= 41.6$ amp

Secondary current $= \dfrac{100,000 \text{ va}}{120 \text{ v}}$

$= 832.$ amp

Two other characteristics by which transformers are specified are cooling medium and noise level. The transformer coils are either oil immersed, askarel immersed or dry. Askarel is a synthetic non-inflammable liquid commonly utilized for indoor transformers. Some pertinent transformer rating data is contained in Table 23.8.

Due to the extensive indoor use of transformers, the generated noise or hum becomes a problem in normally quiet areas such as school and office buildings, libraries, etc. To combat this problem, the National Electrical Manufacturers Association, abbreviated NEMA, established some years

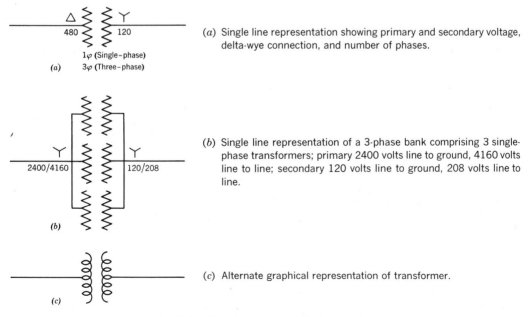

(a) Single line representation showing primary and secondary voltage, delta-wye connection, and number of phases.

(b) Single line representation of a 3-phase bank comprising 3 single-phase transformers; primary 2400 volts line to ground, 4160 volts line to line; secondary 120 volts line to ground, 208 volts line to line.

(c) Alternate graphical representation of transformer.

Fig. 23.20   Transformer graphical representation.

Table 23.8 Transformer Data

Transformer Type	Cooling and insulating medium	Voltage*		Max. Capacity† of 3-Phase bank	Usage
		Primary	Secondary		
General Purpose Dry	Air	120, 208, 240 480, 600	120, 208, 240 480, 600	750 kva	General purpose, light and power circuits, indoor.
Load Center	Air Askarel Oil	2400 4160 7200 11000 13200 13800	120 208 240 480 600	2000 kva	Building Service, Unit Substations, Load Center Indoor and Outdoor.
Distribution	Askarel Oil	2400 4160 7600 13200 13800	120 208 240 480 600	750 kva	Pole, Pole Platform, or concrete pad outdoors.
Substation	Oil	2400 4160 7200 11000 13200 15000 22000 44000 62000	480 600 2400 4160 7200 13200	Above 500 kva	Outdoor substations for groups of buildings or large single buildings.

* These are nominal voltages. Taps are often available to change the voltage ± 5 percent.
† Larger ratings are available on special order.

ago a standard of noise rating to which all reputable manufacturers adhere. These levels are tabulated in Table 23.9 along with reference levels to enable the designer to appreciate the sound levels which are expressed in decibels (db). Since location in empty closets and switchgear rooms tend to amplify sound, it merits the designer's attention to select both the proper transformer and the proper location. Transformers are available with lower sound rating on special order, at a cost increase of approximately 1 percent for each 1 db reduction. Often, an acceptable situation can be created without the additional expense of special quiet transformers by adherence to a few guiding principles of installation:

a. Attempt to avoid the quiet areas of buildings when locating transformers.
b. Utilize flexible conduit connections.
c. Employ proper mounting method— rigid connection to large masses which dampen vibration and vibration pad or other flexible mounting to bodies which will carry sound, such as steel columns or masonry walls.
d. Select by trial the optimum mounting position in each room.
e. Treat transformers rooms acoustically to increase sound absorption.

The physical size of a transformer of given kva rating and voltage depends upon the type of insulation used. In order of decreasing physical size and increasing operating temperature we have, for dry transformers, class A, B, and H insulations which represent organic, inorganic, and silicone insulating materials respectively. Before availing oneself of the size advantage of the type H insulated units, it must be pointed out that at full load in an ambient of 104 F, the windings of A, B, and H insulated transformers will run about 235, 280, and 442 F, respectively. Thus the smaller units run much hotter and their locations must be carefully chosen.

In summary then, a transformer is specified by type, phase, voltages, kva rating,

Table 23.9 Transformer Sound Levels

Sound Level in decibels (db)	Transformer Size	Reference Situation
0		Threshhold of hearing
10		Rustle of leaves
20		Quiet conversation
30		Quiet office
40	0–10 kva	Ordinary speech
45	15–50 kva	
50	75–150 kva	Average office
55	200–300 kva	
60	350–500 kva	Noisy office
70		Street with traffic
80		
90		Shooting at 5 feet
100		Pnematic drill
110		75 piece orchestra
120		Airplane engine
130		Jet engine
140		Threshhold of pain
190		Rocket engine

sound level and insulation type. Thus "100-kva 3-phase 480/120–208V air-cooled indoor dry type transformer with class B insulation and NEMA sound rated" is a brief but adequate transformer description.

15. Transformer Installation Indoors. When transformers are installed indoors they are subject to stringent NEC regulations designed to make the installation intrinsically safe.

Dry-type transformers rated 600 volts or less, of any kva rating may be installed anywhere in the building provided they are completely enclosed except for ventilating openings.

Dry-type transformers rated $112\frac{1}{2}$ kva or less and 601 to 35,000 volts may be installed anywhere provided a fire barrier of 12″ space or adequate thickness of fire resistant heat-insulating material separates the unit from combustible material.

Dry-type transformers rated more than $112\frac{1}{2}$ kva and 601 to 35,000 volts with class A insulation must be installed in a

Table 23.10 Typical Dry-Type Transformer Dimensions and Weights

SINGLE PHASE

Kva Output Continuous 80 C Rise	Approx Dimensions (Inches)			Approx Weight (Pounds)
	Height	Width	Depth	

Primary 2400/4160Y Volts with (4) 2½% Taps Below Normal—Secondary 120/240 Volts

3	$15\frac{1}{4}$	$8\frac{5}{8}$	$7\frac{3}{4}$	97
5	$15\frac{5}{8}$	$11\frac{1}{4}$	$9\frac{7}{8}$	135
10	$19\frac{1}{8}$	$11\frac{1}{4}$	$9\frac{7}{8}$	235
15	$30\frac{1}{8}$	$22\frac{3}{8}$	$18\frac{1}{8}$	325
25	$34\frac{1}{8}$	$25\frac{7}{8}$	$20\frac{1}{8}$	375
37.5	$36\frac{1}{8}$	$30\frac{1}{8}$	$22\frac{1}{8}$	500
50	$36\frac{1}{8}$	$30\frac{1}{8}$	$22\frac{1}{8}$	600
75	$40\frac{1}{8}$	$36\frac{1}{8}$	$25\frac{3}{8}$	900
100	$40\frac{1}{8}$	$36\frac{1}{8}$	$25\frac{3}{8}$	1100
167	$46\frac{7}{8}$	$38\frac{3}{4}$	$25\frac{1}{2}$	1400
250	$51\frac{7}{8}$	$44\frac{3}{4}$	35	2050

THREE-PHASE

Primary 480 Volts with (4) 2½% Taps Below Normal—Secondary 208Y/120 Volts

45*	$34\frac{1}{8}$	$28\frac{3}{4}$	$15\frac{3}{8}$	680
45	$34\frac{1}{8}$	$33\frac{1}{4}$	$20\frac{3}{8}$	580
75*	$34\frac{1}{8}$	$32\frac{3}{4}$	$15\frac{3}{8}$	960
75	$36\frac{1}{8}$	$41\frac{1}{4}$	$22\frac{3}{8}$	820
112.5*	$34\frac{1}{8}$	$34\frac{1}{2}$	$15\frac{3}{8}$	1120
112.5	$40\frac{1}{8}$	$45\frac{7}{8}$	$25\frac{3}{4}$	1175
150*	$34\frac{1}{8}$	$36\frac{1}{2}$	$15\frac{3}{8}$	1260
150	$40\frac{1}{8}$	$50\frac{7}{8}$	$25\frac{3}{4}$	1500
225	$58\frac{3}{4}$	$62\frac{1}{4}$	35	2630
300	$58\frac{3}{4}$	$62\frac{1}{4}$	35	3100
500	$70\frac{1}{2}$	69	$39\frac{1}{4}$	4100

* Quiet type

transformer room of fire resistant construction due to fire hazard of combustible insulation. If class B or H insulation is used, a fire barrier of 6 ft horizontal and 12 ft vertical space or adequate insulating material may be used to separate the unit from combustible material, and units need not be installed in a special room or vault.

Dry type or askarel transformers of any kva rating and voltage rating above 35,000 volts shall be installed in a vault.

Askarel transformers may be installed anywhere in the building but must be provided with the proper ventilation and a relief vent.

Oil-insulated transformers rated 600 volts or less, may be installed in a combustible area if 10 kva or less and in a fire resistant area if rated from 11 kva to 75 kva. In either case, means shall be provided to prevent the spread of a transformer oil fire. All other oil filled transformers *must* be installed in a vault.

16. Transformer Vaults shall be located, if practicable, where they can be ventilated to the outside air without flues or ducts. The combined net area of all ventilating openings (gross area less screens, louvers, etc.) shall be not less than 3 sq in. per kva of transformer, but in no case less than 1 sq ft. This is best accomplished by the use of louvered doors and fixed louvers in walls leading to areaways or courts.

Vault construction of walls and ceiling shall be reinforced concrete, brick, load-bearing tile, concrete block or other material which will give a 2½ hour fire rating. Nominal figures are 6 in. reinforced concrete, 8 in. brick or plastered 12 in. block. Each vault must have a locked class A fire door with a 3-hour rating. If total transformer capacity is 112½ kva or less, the vault may be constructed entirely of 4 in reinforced concrete. All slabs in contact with the earth may be 4″ concrete. Each vault shall have a door sill of sufficient height to contain all the oil in the event of tank rupture, but in no case less than 4 in.

If practicable, vaults shall have a pitched floor and drain to carry off accumulated water and oil.

No pipes, ducts, or other equipment foreign to the electrical installation shall enter the vault unless absolutely necessary. Drip pans shall be installed so that any moisture condensation or leak from such equipment will not strike the transformers.

Sufficient clearance around transformers must be supplied to allow for easy maintenance and removal. This would normally mean 3–4 ft around units and 2–3 ft between units.

17. Switches. An electrical switch is a device intended for ON-OFF control of circuits and for electrical isolation of equipment. Switches are rated by current, poles and throw, voltage, duty, fusibility, and enclosure.

(*a*) *Current Rating.* Every switch has an ampere rating which for all switches other than isolating types indicates the amount of current which can be carried continuously and *interrupted* repeatedly without overheating or injuring the switch in any way. Certain switches are rated in horsepower in addition to being current rated, indicating the maximum horsepower motor which the switch can control. All such switches are capable of interrupting the locked rotor current of a motor of the horsepower indicated.

Switches which can carry rated load continuously but cannot interrupt full load without injuring the switch are called *isolating* switches. These switches may be used in certain high-voltage applications, for control of motors larger than 50 horsepower and if of knife switch construction, for use at more than 1200 amp, 0–250 volts or more than 600 amp, 251–600 volts. Such switches should always be clearly labeled *Do not open under load.* When a load-interrupting switch is required for these high currents, a bolted pressure switch should be used. Normal 3-pole switch current ratings in amperes are 30, 60, 100, 200, 400, 600, 800, 1200, 1600, and 2000 amp.

A manually operated circuit breaker may serve as a switch if it has the required number of poles.

(*b*) *Poles and Throw.* An examination of Fig. 23.21 should clarify what is meant by the number of poles and the throws of a switch. Since the NEC states generally that the grounded conductor of a circuit (neutral) should not be broken except in special arrangements, most switches carry the neutral through unbroken by means of solid link within the switch. This gives rise to the term *solid neutral* switch.

Double-throw switches are often used to transfer a load from one source to another as for example from normal to emergency supply or from one feeder to an alternate. Switches are generally available in 1, 2, 3, 4, and 5 pole construction.

(*c*) *Voltage.* Switches, like most other electrical apparatus, are voltage rated. Nominal switch ratings are 250, 600, 5 kv, and 15 kv, the prior 2 ratings being for normal building equipment and the latter 2 for switchgear and special switches.

(*d*) *Duty.* Switches intended for varied use in general light and power circuits are called *general-use* or safety switches and are classified by duty as Heavy Duty (HD), Normal Duty (ND), or Light Duty (LD). Type HD is designed for hard, severe, and repeated use while ND is intended for normal industrial and commercial use. Both are available up to 1200 amps and 600 volts. Type LD is designed for infrequent use and is available up to 600 amps and 250 volts. It is well applied as a service switch since such switches are rarely operated. General use switches are also normally horsepower rated for use as motor circuit switches.

(*e*) *Fusibility.* A switch may be constructed with or without provision for fusing; if provided, the switch is fusible, if not, the switch is nonfusible.

(*f*) *Enclosure.* All switches, except snap or knife switches mounted on a switchboard must be enclosed in an appropriate cabinet. The NEMA has standardized the nomenclature and application of such cabinets, which are tabulated in Table 23.11.

Many special types of switches are available such as magnetically operated remote control types (contactors), mercury arc switches, float and pressure switches, automatic transfer switches and a host of outdoor types used with pole line and substation equipment. Most of these types are beyond the scope of this book except for the magnetic switch which we will discuss briefly.

(g) **Magnetic Switches.** A magnetic switch is one in which the switch is operated by an electromagnet rather than by an operating handle. In small sizes such devices are called *relays,* in larger sizes (above 10 amp) they are called *contactors.* Instead of a movable blade and a fixed blade or grip, such devices usually utilize blocks of silver coated copper, called contacts, which are moved together and separated by magnetic force, thus "making" (closing) or "breaking" (opening) the circuit. The number of poles of a relay or contactor has the same significance as for a switch. Such devices are controlled by push-button or automatic devices such as float switches, thermostats, pressure switches, etc. Since control can be both remote and automatic, the application of relays and contactors becomes enormous in remote control of lighting, heating, air-conditioning, all motor control, sequence switching, automatic load transfer, etc.

18. Circuit Protective Devices. In order to protect insulation, wiring, bus, switches, and other apparatus from overload (load currents beyond their ratings) and from fault or short circuit currents, it is necessary to provide automatic means for opening the circuit. The 2 commonest devices employed

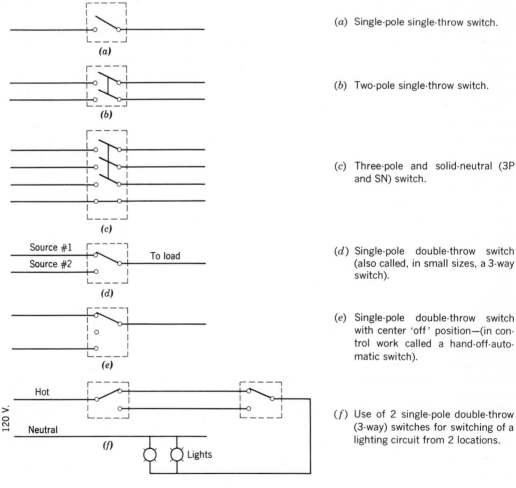

(a) Single-pole single-throw switch.

(b) Two-pole single-throw switch.

(c) Three-pole and solid-neutral (3P and SN) switch.

(d) Single-pole double-throw switch (also called, in small sizes, a 3-way switch).

(e) Single-pole double-throw switch with center 'off' position—(in control work called a hand-off-automatic switch).

(f) Use of 2 single-pole double-throw (3-way) switches for switching of a lighting circuit from 2 locations.

Fig. 23.21 Typical switch configurations.

to fulfill this function are the fuse and the circuit breaker, abbreviated c/b.

(*a*) *Fuses:* The fuse is a simple device consisting of an alloy link or wire of relatively low melting temperature which when enclosed in an insulating fiber tube is called a cartridge fuse, and when in a porcelain cup is known as a plug fuse. Figure 23.23 shows common types of fuses. Plug fuses, such as those normally used in a dwelling, are obtainable in capacities of 5 to 30 amp. Cartridge fuses with ferrule contacts are made in sizes from approximately 5 to 60 amp, and with knife-blade contacts from 61 to 600 amp. In larger sizes, fuses are available in ratings from 601 to 6000 amp. Table 23.12 lists the standard fuse sizes. When a fuse is subjected to an excess current the energy loss in the link (I^2R loss) generates heat and eventually melts it. In cases of very high current, such as those which result from short circuits, the melting of the fuse is followed by the creation of a large volume of vapor, which in turn creates pressure within the fuse housing. These explosive pressures must be temporarily sustained within the tube by the excellence of its mechanical construction. Small holes are placed in the ends of the fuse to allow the pressure to be released gradually and without the expulsion of flames.

The 2 principal types are the renewable link fuse (Fig. 23.23*d*, *f* and *g*) and the one-time fuse (Fig. 23.23*a*, *b*, *c*, *e*). As the name implies, the renewable fuse may be disassembled and a new fuse link put in to replace the one blown. In the one-time fuse the fuse link is permanently soldered to the contacts at each end of the fuse, and this link is then surrounded by an arc-quenching powder. By far the greater number of fuses used at present are the renewable type.

Fuses are applied not by current rating alone but also by interrupting capacity, i.e., its capacity to safely interrupt a short circuit current of given magnitude, since such fault current if not quickly interrupted can cause explosive damage, fire, and loss of life and property. This is particularly true

Fig. 23.22 Typical heavy duty (type H.D.) 3 pole 30 amp fusible switch in general purpose type NEMA I enclosure. Note the handle and door interlock which prevents opening the cover while the switch is in the "closed" position. (Federal Pacific Electric)

in urban areas where the large power systems make the careful application of fuses imperative. The NEC specifies the exact rating of fuses which should be used for the protection of each type circuit. It also states the exact ratings for fuses which may be used in the main feeder, subfeeders, and

Table 23.11 NEMA Enclosure—Designations

Type	Description	Application
1A	General purpose Dust resistant	Dry indoor locations.
2	Drip-proof	Indoor, subject to dripping
3R	Raintight, Weatherproof	Exterior, vertical rain, sleet, and snow
4	Watertight	Driving rain and sleet
5	Dust tight	Nonhazardous dust-filled areas
6	Submersible	Self-explanatory
7–11	Hazardous	In hazardous and corrosive areas
12	Industrial	Indoor, dust, lint, oil, and moisture resistant; used in place of Type 1 in industrial interiors.

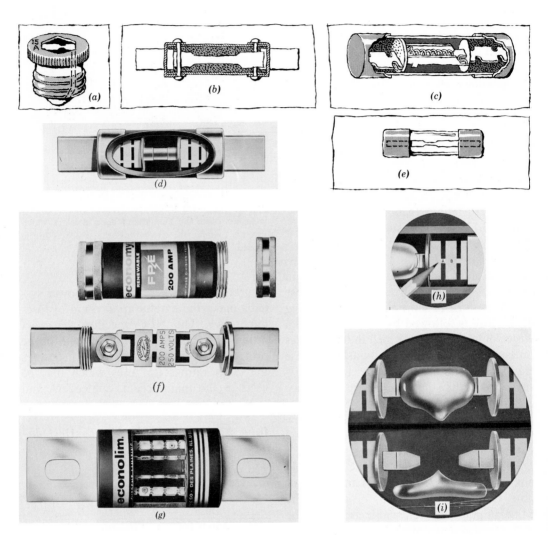

Fig. 23.23   Standard types of fuses are: (*a*) non-renewable plug fuse, (*b*) non-renewable knife blade
fuse, (*c*) non-renewable dual-element time delay ferrule cartridge fuse, (*d*) renewable dual-element
time delay knife-blade cartridge fuse, (*e*) non-renewable miniature fuse (electronic and instrument
applications), (*f*) renewable single-element knife blade cartridge fuse, (*g*) current limiting fuse.
Since fuses are inherently very fast acting devices, time delay must be built into a fuse to prevent
"blowing" on short-time overloads such as are caused by motor starting. Referring to (*h*) above, a
dual-element fuse such as type (*e*) or (*d*) allows the heat generated by temporary overloads to be
dissipated in the large metal element B, preventing fuse blowing. If the overload reaches dangerous
proportions the metal at A will melt, opening the circuit. On continuous overload the second element
shown in (*i*) will melt out, opening the circuit. The time to clear (blow) for both elements, as for fuses
generally, is inversely proportional to the amount of current. (Federal Pacific Electric)

branch circuits. When fuses are being specified this code should always be consulted.

The NEC also specifies that a disconnecting means (switch) must be provided on the line side of all fuses in circuits operating at more than 150 volts, and where fuses are accessible to other than qualified persons.

(b) *Circuit Breakers.* A circuit breaker is an electro-mechanical device which performs the same protective function as a fuse and in addition acts as a switch. Thus it can be used in lieu of a switch and fuse combination to both protect and disconnect a circuit. The functioning of a circuit breaker is either thermal, magnetic, or a combination, depending upon the type of breaker. The thermal action, unlike the melting of a fuse, is similar to that of a thermostat. The heat generated by the excessive current flowing in the breaker causes a bimetallic element to move and trip the latching mechanism of the breaker, thus opening the breaker contacts and thereby, the circuit. The magnetic trip comprises a coil with a movable damped core. On heavy overloads or short circuits, magnetic forces actuate the core which trips the circuit breaker latch. Both the thermal and the magnetic action have inverse time characteristics, i.e., the heavier the overload the faster the trip action.

The great inherent advantage of the breaker lies in the fact that it can be reset after tripping by merely operating its handle; it is not self-destructive on operation, as the fuse is. Whereas the fuses are single-pole devices, requiring a separate fuse for each ungrounded line, circuit breakers are available in multipole construction with a common trip so that an overload in any leg of a 3-phase circuit protected by a 3-pole breaker will cause disconnection of the entire circuit. The relative merits of this arrangement will be discussed below.

Like the fuse, the circuit breaker is also rated in interrupting capacity. In circuits where the available short circuit current exceeds the rating of the normal circuit

Table 23.12 Fuse Ratings and Construction

Current Rating	Remarks
0–10 15, 20, 25, 30	Plug fuse construction; max. 150 volts to ground
0–10 15 20 25 30 35 40 45 50 60	Cartridge-type with ferrules; single and dual element; 250 and 600 volts
70 80 90 100 110 125 150 175 200 225 250 300 350 400 450 500 600	Cartridge-type, knife blade contacts; 250 and 600 volts
800 1000 1200 1600 2000 2500 3000 4000 5000 6000	Cartridge-type, bolted knife blade contacts; 600 volts

breaker, special fused breakers can be used which combine the advantages of a circuit breaker with the high interrupting capacity (I.C.) of the fuses.

Air circuit breakers are available in 2 general types, the molded case breaker and the "large air breaker." Molded case breakers consist of a complete mechanism encased in a molded phenolic case. In the smaller sizes (frames) the trips are neither adjustable nor interchangeable; in the larger sizes the trips are both interchangeable within a frame size and adjustable. The large air circuit breaker is a more complicated and widely adjustable mechanism than the molded case and can be used in many circuits and operations which preclude use of molded case breakers. They are readily available with electric operation (i.e., closing and tripping) whereas the molded case breaker is normally manually operated, although motor operators are available for remote operation. Other features available on large air breakers are relay control, undervoltage trip and suitability for contactor operation. All breakers

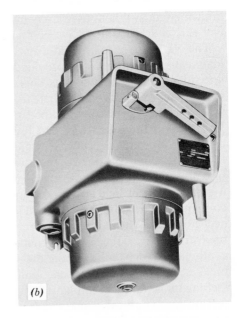

Fig. 23.24 Circuit breakers are available in all NEMA enclosures to meet service requirements: (a) Type 1A is a semi-dust tight general purpose enclosure which utilizes gaskets on doors and other openings; (b) illustrates an explosion proof enclosure, NEMA Type VII, for a molded case circuit breaker. (Federal Pacific Electric)

Table 23.13   Molded Case Circuit Breaker Characteristics

Frame size (amp) Type, Rating	Trip setting amps				Voltage Volts	Remarks
Q 50 A 70 A	15, 20, 30, 40, 50 15 20				120 240	1–3 poles 1 pole
'E' 100 A	15 20 30 40 50 60 70 100				240	1–3 poles
J 225 A	15 20 30 40 50 60 70 100 125 150 175 200 225				600	1–3 poles
K 400 A	50 70 100 125 150 175 200 225 250 300 350 400				600	1–3 poles
L-M 800 A	100 125 150 175 200 225 250 300 350 400 500 600 800				600	1–3 poles
Special 1200 A 1600 A	400 600 800 1000 1200 400 600 800 1000 1200 1600				600	2–3 poles 3 poles

can be equipped with remote trip and auxiliary contacts and all good breakers have trip indicating handles and are "trip-free," (i.e., will trip out harmlessly if closed in on a short-circuited line).

(c) Fuses vs Circuit Breakers:

Fuses—(Switch and Fuse Combination)

Advantages	Disadvantages
Simple and foolproof	Single pole only
Constant characteristics	Requires switch
Initial economy	Necessity for storage of replacements
Very high I.C.	Cannot be reset
No maintenance	Nonadjustable
	Nonindicating
	No electric or remote control
	Not trip free

Circuit Breakers

Advantages	Disadvantages
Usable as switch	Low to medium I.C.
Multipole	Periodic maintenance
Small, convenient	High initial cost
No replacement	Complex construction
Resettable	
Indicates trip	
Trip-free	
Remote control	
Adjustable	
Auxiliary contacts	

The above tabulation demonstrates that there is no all inclusive answer to the oft-posed question "which is preferable—fuses or breakers?" The answer depends on the specific situation involved. Generally, breakers are indicated for all lighting and appliance panels and for main panels and switchboards where the I.C. requirement is not excessively high. Fuses are utilized in high capacity main switchboards and panels and where required for coordination with other fuses or where the economics warrant.

The question as to whether "single phasing" is harmful, that is, loss of one fuse of a 3-fuse bank, and consequent operation of a 3-phase circuit on single phase, has been debated but no conclusion reached. Proponents state that this prevents loss of *all* power to a facility and that if motors are properly protected they will not be damaged; opponents demonstrate that damage to motors is possible even with "proper" protection. The argument is not crucial however and the choice of circuit breakers or fuses is generally made on the basis of other considerations.

19. Switchboards and Switchgear. Switchboards and switchgear are free-standing assemblies of switches, fuses, and (or) circuit breakers whose function it is normally to provide switching and feeder protection to a number of circuits connected to a main source. The main switchboard of Fig. 23.1, is represented in a single-line diagram in Fig. 23.25.

Switchboards are so called because originally switches and fuses were mounted on a large ebony or slate board supported by pipe or steel frames. Owing to the hazards of operating switchboards with energized bare copper on the front, live-front switchboards should never be used today in modern buildings, designed for public or private use or for commercial or industrial purposes, though certain laboratory facilities may require the use of open copper switches, contacts, etc. When replacements are to be made to open-front switchboards the new panels should be of the dead-front type.

Dead-front switchboards (Figs. 23.26, 23.27, 23.28) are those that have all circuit breakers (commonly referred to as breakers) and all other live parts installed behind steel face panels. The operator controls switches, circuit breakers, and other devices by means of insulated handles, extending through holes in the front panel. Main service, main distribution switchboards and load-center switchboards should be of the dead-front metalclad type, i.e., totally enclosed with steel plates on the top and all sides of the structures and with important units within them (circuit breakers, fuses, instrument transformers, bus bars, and cable entrance terminals) enclosed in separate metal compartments. When a load-center switchboard

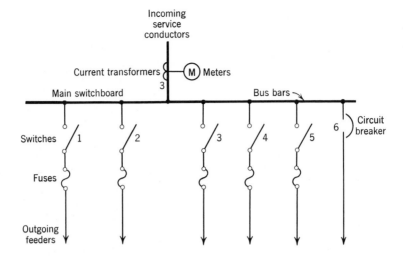

Fig. 23.25 Typical switchboard. Switches are normally shown in the open position. The NEC allows up to 6 switches in parallel as service entrance equipment. Switches must be on the line (supply) side of fuses. Metering is normally placed on the service conductors and the metering equipment built into the main switchboard. Each line in a single-line diagram represents a 3-phase circuit. If circuit breakers were used, the entire board would be comprised of units as illustrated in circuit 6.

has circuit breakers with bayonet-type contacts mounted in a movable drawer (like the drawers of a standard letter file), these are designated as switchboards of the draw-out type. This draw-out arrangement facilitates emergency replacements, inspection and repairs.

There is no clear distinction made between the terms "switchboard" and "switchgear" although often high voltage equipment is referred to as switchgear (above 600 volts) as is equipment which comprises individual units rather than an assembly.

When molded case circuit breakers are utilized in a switchboard it is often known as a "building type switchboard." The advantage of such equipment over a switchboard employing large air circuit breakers lies in its economy and compactness. Low-voltage drawout gear should not be used unless the service will require frequent breaker inspection, since this construction is more expensive and bulky. Space requirements are shown in Fig. 23.29.

Main metalclad switchgear for commercial, industrial, and public buildings are almost invariably located in the basement,

and housed in separate well-ventilated electrical switchgear rooms. Access to such rooms must provide for the entrance and exit of an individual removable section of the metalclad switchgear which can be lifted by a truck crane on the street, skidded within the building, and lowered into the building by a fixed-position crane or chain-hoist mounted over the hatchway to floors below (or above). The designer will realize that adequate lifting hooks, exits, hallways, and hatches should always be provided for the entrance and exit of the equipment of largest dimensions and (or) weight to be moved. Therefore, the specifications for switchgear should state the maximum number and over-all maximum dimensions of operating panels to be bolted together as one portable section. Two, three, or four panels form the usual practical section. These sections may vary in length from about 8 to 12 ft.

20. Unit Substations (Transformer Load Centers). An assembly of primary incoming switch, fuse or breaker, step-down transformer, meters, controls, buswork, and secondary switchgear is often called a unit

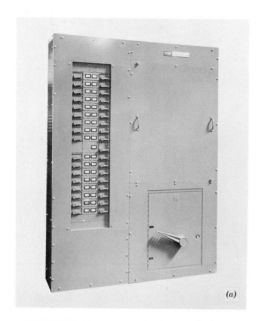

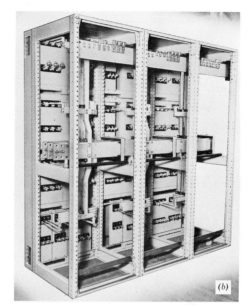

Fig. 23.26   Low voltage switchboards are available in various designs to meet all requirements. (a) Illustrates a light duty NEMA class I circuit breaker switchboard, with main breaker. Such a unit is free standing, completely front accessible and 14″ to 20″ deep. Fig. (b) shows a rear view of a heavy duty NEMA class III switchboard utilizing molded case breakers. Note the heavy copper busbars behind the breakers. Such units average 30″ deep and 16 to 26 inches wide per section. Large air circuit breakers of the drawout type are shown in figures (c) and (d). These units are heavy duty, manually or electrically operated. They are utilized where heavy duty service will require frequent breaker inspection and where molded case breaker-tripping characteristics are not suitable for the application. These units vary from 42″ to 60″ in depth and 16 to 30 inches wide per section. (Federal Pacific Electric)

(a)

(b)

(c)

Fig. 23.27   Typical high voltage metal-clad switchgear is 90 inches high, 50″ to 80″ deep and 20″ to 36″ wide per section depending upon the contained equipment. A 15 kv 3 section assembly is shown in (a) with the breaker removed from the middle cubicle. Each breaker is equipped with wheels and its method of removal is shown in (b). The section above the breaker compartment contains a 15 kv non-load break disconnect switch, operated by an external bar. The devices on the door are, top to bottom, meters, relays, indicating lights and breaker operating handles. Figure (c) illustrates a duplex control board which contains remote controls, relays and indicating lights for circuit breakers and other devices located elsewhere. The door at the end gives access to the inside so that the devices located on the back of the front panel as well as those illustrated can be wired and adjusted. These front panels are fixed in position and are not hinged or removable. (Federal Pacific Electric)

substation, or, a load-center substation. It is available for indoor or outdoor use, to supply power from a primary voltage line to any large facility.

Load-center switchboards (Fig. 23.26, (a), (b), (c), and (d) are supplied by feeders from the unit substation main switchboard in the building. They are located at approximate centers of load distribution. For example, closely located groups of motors and furnaces, lighting loads, welding machines, large office accounting machines, etc., would be economically served by a load-center switchboard of several panels. Large loads such as air-conditioning compressors, house pumps, fire pumps etc. are fed directly from the unit substation main switchgear. The front aisles per Fig. 23.29 provide for the removal and replacement of heavy truck-type breakers if drawout gear is used.

21. Metering. All service equipment must be arranged for Utility Company metering unless the metering is done at the service drop point outside the building. Generally, for a single use building or a building where electric energy is included in the rental charge only a single meter is necessary. Provision for such metering in the form of current transformers and wiring is made in the main switchboard and the meter is furnished and installed by the Utility Company. Where submetering is required, such as in most apartment houses, banks of meter sockets and wiring troughs are installed to

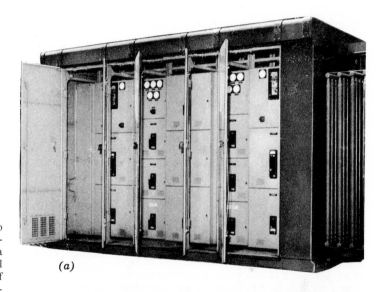

(a)

Fig. 23.28 When switchgear is to be installed outdoors three methods may be employed; build a small "shack" to house normal indoor gear, utilize weatherproof outdoor gear (a) or utilize switchgear which is built into its own metal house (b). Such integral housings are equipped with heat and light and often prove the most economical choice. (Federal Pacific Electric)

(b)

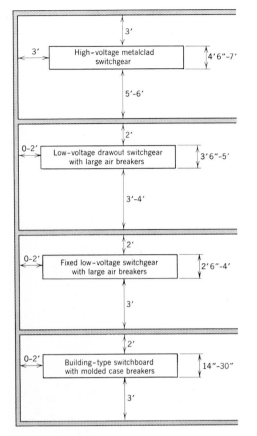

Fig. 23.29 Switchgear space requirements. Clearance to ceiling should not be less than 3 ft. Each room should have 2 doors where switchgear is connected to high capacity systems. If all wiring and equipment is accessible from the front, the board may be placed against the wall.

accommodate the multiple meters. A typical assembly of such socket meters is shown in Fig. 23.31.

22. Panelboards and Cabinets. A panelboard is an insulating panel on which are mounted various fuses, switches, and (or) circuit breakers. (See Fig. 23.32.) The circuit protection may be either by automatic circuit breakers or fuses. One terminal of each switch in the case of a switch and fuse panelboard is connected to the bus bars of the panelboard; the other terminal of the switch is connected to the fuse, which in turn is connected to an outgoing branch circuit. With circuit breakers no switch is

used since the breaker itself acts as a switch. The return wire from the branch circuit device (lamp, receptacle, motor) connects to the panel neutral bus. The bus bars of the panelboard are energized by a feeder or subfeeder which brings service to the panel from some main switchboard or loadcenter in another part of the building.

Panelboards may be classified as flush-type or surface-type. Flush-type panelboards used in most buildings are those which have the trim and doors practically flush with the finished surface of the wall. Surface-type panelboards project into the room, the cabinets being bolted to wall surfaces or columns. The latter type is frequently used in industrial plants. A further classification of panelboards has to do with the number of wires in the feeder and branch-circuit systems. For instance, if a 3-wire feeder serves a number of 2-wire branch circuits, the panelboard will be classified as having "3-wire mains and 2-wire branches." Such specifications as these depend upon the types of wiring systems adopted for the building, as described in Chapter 22.

Panelboards may be designed to serve branch circuits to lamps, motors, heating devices, or other electrical equipment. In general, however, a panelboard is designed to serve a group of somewhat similar branch circuits, feeding the same type of power-consuming devices. They are then designated as lighting panelboards, motor or power panelboards, etc.

It is common practice to install in large buildings, as separate units, lighting panelboards and power panelboards. Deadfront panelboards (with insulated manually operated main and branch breaker handles) should always be used for safety reasons. Such panelboards are enclosed in metal boxes, with hinged covers, called panelboard cabinets. The cabinets are set in the walls and connected to the conduit system before the panelboards and trims are installed. The panelboards are then bolted into place in the cabinets, and the wires are pulled in through the conduits to make connections to the terminals of the panelboard bus bars and the outgoing branch circuits. The space between the edges of the panelboard and the sides, top, and bottom of the cabinet is called the wire gutter. Wire gutters must provide adequate space between the cabinet and the panelboard for making connections to branch circuits, the feeder, and the bus bars, for pulling in additional wires, or for replacement of defective wires.

On engineering drawings the power and lighting panelboards are numbered systematically. For example, PP1 generally means power panelboard number 1; LP2 means lighting panelboard number 2. A combination panelboard might be numbered PL1, meaning power and lighting

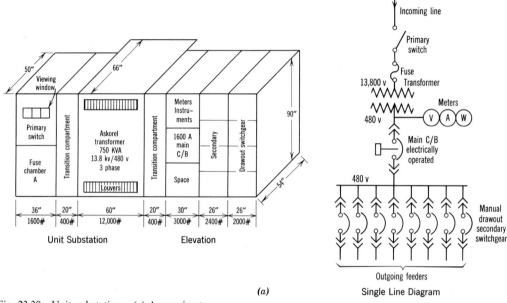

Unit Substation   Elevation

(a)   Single Line Diagram

Fig. 23.30 Unit substations: (*a*) Approximate sizes and weights of a single ended unit substation. Such a unit would supply a building with a maximum demand of 750 KVA. When two such units are placed end to end and connected electrically by a tie circuit breaker, the assembly is known as a double ended substation. The incoming 13,800 volt cables enter cubicle A and connect to the switch and fuses. The load side of the fuses connects to the transformer which in turn connects to the secondary switchgear. This main secondary switchgear in turn feeds various switchboard and panelboards distributed through the building. (*b*) Small unit substations, called power centers and designed for pad mounting comprise a compact assembly of incoming H.V. section, dry transformer and secondary switchgear. Dry transformers and molded case breakers are used for compactness. The pictured unit shows the high voltage switch and fuses and the L.V. breakers. The transformer is behind the breakers. The entire unit is approximately 78″ high, 80″ long and 48″ deep.

(b)

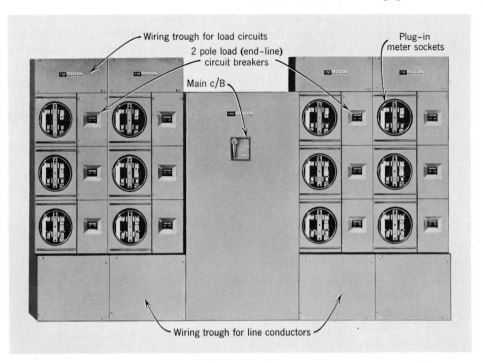

Fig. 23.31   Typical assembly of socket-type watt-hour meters for multiple metering. Banks of meter sockets and load circuit breakers can be readily assembled from prefabricated subassemblies, as illustrated. Such assemblies are mounted in meter rooms with access available to all building tenants. Approximate dimensions of illustrated unit are 60″ high, 96″ wide and 10″ deep. (Federal Pacific Electric)

panelboard number 1. Some engineering drawings include numbering to identify the floor location; thus LP3A means lighting panelboard 'A' on the third floor. Such code numbers aid operators, electricians, and maintenance men in checking and maintaining defective circuits and equipment. These code numbers should be lettered on the outside of panelboard doors.

Panelboards are generally referred to as Main Distribution, Power Distribution, and Lighting and Appliance. Main distribution panels (MDP) may serve as service entrance equipment if equipped with 6 or less fused switches or breakers. Current rating may be up to 800 amp.

Power panels may contain any size switch fuse or breaker and are utilized to feed specific pieces of apparatus such as motors, heaters, ranges, etc. Lighting and appliance panels contain devices up to 30

amp in size, 1, 2, or 3 poles and are used to feed lighting, small motors, business machinery, and similar loads. Such panels may not contain devices which total more than 42 poles, and mains are usually sized at no more than 200 amp. These panels are rated for 250-volt or 600-volt service.

Panelboards are rated by type, bus arrangement, branch breakers, main breaker, voltage and mounting, though not necessarily in that order. A typical description would be:

Lighting and appliance panel, 3-phase 4-wire, 20-SP 15 A, 2-2P 20 A and 4-3P 30 A branch breakers 225 A Frame Main c/b, 175 amp trip, for 120/208-volt service and for flush mounting.

23. Motors. Motors are selected by the manufacturer of the driven equipment and therefore are not within the scope of our discussion except for a brief description of the various types.

(a) Direct Current Motors. Because of high cost and the relative rarity of d-c these motors are not frequently used unless continuous fine speed control is required, as in the case of elevator drives.

(b) Alternating Current Motors fall into 3 general classifications: induction motors, synchronous motors, and universal motors.

1. By far, the most frequently utilized integral horsepower motor is the squirrel cage induction motor which is used to drive pumps, compressors, fans, blowers, and almost every type of mechanical equipment. The motor is available in various designs which provide different characteristics of starting current and torque, and breakdown

torque. The most commonly used machine is Design B which provides low-starting current and medium-starting and breakdown torque. Induction motors operate slightly below synchronous speeds (1720, 1140, 860 rpm), the speed varying with the load. If speed control is required, a wound rotor induction motor is utilized which, when equipped with the proper controller, allows control over approximately a 2:1 speed range. Despite the low efficiency of this type of operation, the speed and torque control make this machine the choice of manufacturers of certain types of compressors and crushing machinery.

Another way of obtaining multispeed operation is the use of a 2-winding machine which, using the proper controller, allows

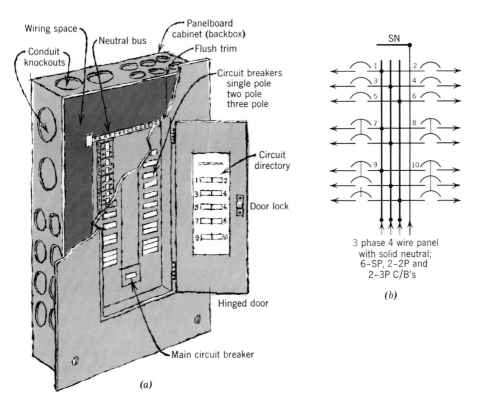

Fig. 23.32   Panelboards may be of the circuit breaker or fuse type. The illustrated panel contains 1, 2 and 3 pole branch circuits and a main circuit breaker. Panels are provided with a minimum 4″ gutter space to allow routing of circuit wiring and any feed-through conductors. Splices may also be made if space is sufficient. Lighting panels average 4½″ deep by 16″ to 20″ wide; power panels are 5″ to 6″ deep and 20″ to 30″ wide. Panels are mounted with the top circuit device no higher than 78″ A.F.F. and the bottom device no lower than 18″ A.F.F.

2-speed operation (full speed and half speed).

2. The synchronous motor, so called due to its constant speed operation is frequently utilized for generator and compressor drives. Due to its high (and variable) power factor, it is often used for power factor correction. The principal disadvantages lie in its high initial cost, complex control equipment and the need for a source of d-c excitation.

3. *Universal Motors* are small, d-c series motors which operate on both a-c and d-c. They are used primarily in small portable appliances.

All integral horsepower machines are available in the various NEMA enclosures which are required for the duty imposed on the machines. The 2 major classifications of enclosure are *open* and *enclosed.* Under the former heading there are general purpose, dripproof, splashproof, and weatherproof; under the latter are subsumed nonventilated, fan-cooled, pipe-ventilated, explosion-proof, and dust-proof.

Motors are rated by horsepower, type, enclosure, voltage, frequency, speed, and insulation type. Thus, a brief description might read:

> Squirrel cage induction motor, 3-phase 220/440 volts, 10 hp, 60 cps, 1140 rpm, open drip-proof with Class B insulation.

24. Motor Controllers. Since d-c controllers are highly specialized and infrequently encountered, we will confine our remarks to a-c motor controllers. The function of an a-c motor controller is 2-fold: to start and stop the motor and to protect the machine from overload. These 2 separate and distinct functions are accomplished by a set of contacts for on-off control and by a set of thermal overload elements for overload protection, combined in a single unit constituting a normal motor controller.

When the contacts are operated by hand, the controller is called a manual starter; when the contacts are operated by a magnetic coil controlled by push buttons, ther-mostats, or other pilot devices, the unit is known as a magnetic controller or starter.

Motor overload protection, required by the NEC for all motors larger than 1 hp, normally comprises thermal relays which interrupt the magnetic coil circuit thus opening the starter contacts. Motors 1 hp or less which require overload protection are controlled by a manual switch which contains an overload relay. It is advisable, though not required, to utilize such a device, for all fractional hp motors. Similarly, although only 2 overload relays are required for a 3-phase motor, it is advisable to specify that 3 relays be supplied.

Certain motors are provided with integral overload protectors; in such case only a switch or simple contactor is required for motor starting. Motor control circuits are normally arranged so that the motor controller must be manually reset and the motor restarted after an interruption due to overload, in order to avoid the hazard of a stopped motor suddenly starting.

Starters are available in various sizes, voltages and NEMA enclosures (see Table 23.11). Table 23.14 lists some typical starters with the physical dimensions of a unit in an open NEMA type I general purpose enclosure.

Most starters are of the full-voltage across-the-line type, i.e., the contacts place the motor directly onto the line and the motor starts up immediately. Where such a procedure is undesirable because of voltage dip and flicker or Utility Company limitations, a reduced voltage starter, sometimes called a compensator, is used. These units, which are either of resistor, reactor or autotransformer design, apply reduced voltage to the motor and thus while reducing starting inrush current also reduce starting torque.

Every motor controller is required by Code to have a disconnecting means within sight of the controller. Where convenient this disconnect switch may be combined with the starter into a single unit, known as a combination starter. A circuit breaker is

Table 23.14   Rating and Approximate Dimensions and Weights of A-C Full-Voltage Single Speed Motor Controllers

NEMA Size Designation	Voltage	Maximum Horsepower	Weight lbs	Width	Height inches	Depth
0	208–220	2	6	$5\frac{1}{2}$	$7\frac{1}{2}$	4
	440	2				
1	208–220	5	8	$6\frac{1}{2}$	$8\frac{1}{2}$	4
	440	$7\frac{1}{2}$				
2	208–220	15	20	9	14	5
	440	25				
3	208–220	30	40	12	18	6
	440	50				
4	208–220	50	90	14	25	8
	440	100				
5	208–220	100	200	20	40	12
	440	200				
*6	208–220	200	400	30	80	20
	440	400				
*7	208–220	300	400	30	80	20
	440	600				

All starters are housed in a NEMA I indoor ventilated enclosure.
* Housing is a free-standing unit.

often used in such an arrangement constituting the branch circuit protection and disconnecting means.

Motor starters, disconnect switches, motor controls, and indicating devices may be combined into a single large assembly, for convenience and economy. Such an assembly is called a motor control center. Typical data for motor control centers are given in Figure 23.33.

A typical brief motor controller description would be similar to the following:

Combination circuit-breaker type across-the-line motor controller, NEMA size 2, with 3 O.L. elements, for a 10 hp 208-volt motor, in a NEMA I general purpose enclosure. Starter shall contain integral on-off push buttons and integral control transformer for 24-volt control circuit.

25. Lighting Fixtures. Since lighting and lighting fixtures are discussed at length in Chapter 21, we will here only review some of the code requirements bearing on the construction and installation of lighting fixtures.

a. All units must be installed in such a manner as to properly dissipate heat. Therefore fixtures recessed into unventilated closed, dead, or insulated spaces should be avoided where possible.

b. Any luminaire exceeding 50 lbs. in weight must be supported independently of its outlet box.

c. Luminaires, lampholders, and rosettes must have no live parts exposed to contact.

d. Luminaires must not be used as raceways for circuits other than the one supplying it, unless specifically designed and approved as a raceway.

e. Sheet-metal enclosures shall be protected against corrosion by galvanizing or other means and shall be not less than No. 22 U.S.S. gauge, commonly called "code gauge."

f. Metal luminaires, transformers, and enclosures operating in circuits at more than 150 volts to ground shall be grounded.

g. The voltage to ground on branch circuits supplying lampholders and lighting fixtures shall not exceed 150 volts except for:

Fig. 23.33   A typical motor control center is shown in (a) and the interior of a single compartment in (b). Note in (a) vertical wiring space, the spare (blank) compartments, the use of a lighting panel built into the control center and the neatness and compactness of this type of installation. Fig. (b) illustrates the easy accessibility of all components of the combination starter including (L to R) breaker, contactor and controls, and pilot light. This unit also utilizes a fused control transformer. The usual control center dimensions are 90″ high, 20″ wide per section and 14″ to 20″ deep. (Federal Pacific Electric)

(1) Mogul base lampholders mounted not less than 8 ft above the floor, and accessible only to authorized personnel.

(2) Fluorescent lamp fixtures, permanently installed with appropriate ballasts, in which case the voltage may be up to 300 volts. Such fixtures may not have integral switching but must use wall switches. This rule allows the use of 277-volt fluorescent and 240-volt mercury lighting. Use of lighting circuits above 150 volts is not permitted in residences.

26. Wiring Devices:

(a) *Receptacles* shall be of the grounding type where installed on 15 or 20 amp circuits. Receptacles connected to different voltages, frequencies, or current-type (a-c or d-c) on the same premises must be polarized so that attachment plugs are not interchangeable. Figure 23.34 shows some of the standard receptacle configurations and their ratings.

Receptacles are regularly available from 10 to 400 amp, 2 to 4 poles and 125 to 600 volts. In addition, special types are made such as locking types and miniature ('interchangeable') types. Many specific usage units are available such as range receptacles, radio and TV types, hazardous area types, weatherproof, and combination receptacle and switch assemblies. All receptacles other than the normal 15-amp 2-wire parallel slot type should be specified to be furnished with the required number of matching caps (plugs).

Receptacles are normally mounted between 12 and 18 in. from the floor except that in shops, labs, and other areas utilizing tables against the walls, 42 in. is the usual mounting height.

(b) *Switches.* Generally, a-c snap switches are preferable to the a-c–d-c type because of better rating, better construction, and quieter operation. Use of the ac-dc switch in control of incandescent lamp loads is limited to $\frac{1}{2}$ of its rating unless the switch is "T" rated.

The common a-c–d-c ratings are 10 amp, 125 volts and 5 amp, 250 volts. The usual a-c switch rating is 15 or 20 amp at 120 or 120/277 volts. Other snap switches are available up to 30 amp at 600 volts. Normal constructions are single-pole, 2-pole, 3-way, 4-way, momentary-contact, 2-circuit, maintained contact SPDT and DPDT. Operating handles are toggle-type, button, key, push, rocker, lighted push and rocker, rotary and tap-plate types. The mercury and a-c quiet types are relatively noiseless; the toggle, tumbler and a-c–d-c types are generally not. The "Despard" or interchangeable devices are miniature types, fully rated, which mount 3 to a strap in a normal outlet box. Other devices available in this construction are pilot lights, push buttons, and receptacles.

(c) *Wall Plates.* Wall plates are commonly used on the plaster or finished surface of a room in a residence, office or factory. Such plates may contain openings for the ordinary toggle or push-button switch, single or double-plug outlets, pilot lamps or radio outlets. Some standard types and sizes of conventional wall plates are shown in Fig. 23.35.

A 1-gang plate is one of standard size ($2\frac{3}{4}$ in. by $4\frac{1}{2}$ in.), which is mounted on a 1-gang outlet box containing a single device such as a switch for controlling the lamp circuit in a room. Two-gang, three-gang plates, etc., are available for several switches, outlets, pilot lamps, or other combinations.

Wall plates are made of metal, rigid insulated compound, or glass, in many plain and ornamental designs. Some of the common finishes include brass, silver, gold, wood veneer, celluloid in various colors, colored enamels, and mother-of-pearl. The most common standard finish is polished or brushed brass, and black or brown shades of phenolic compound (Bakelite).

The height of the center of switch plates is usually specified as 48 or 54 in. above floor level.

(d) *Outlet and Devices Boxes* are generally of galvanized stamped sheet metal with multiple $\frac{1}{2}''$, $\frac{3}{4}''$, and several $1''$ conduit knockouts conveniently placed around the periphery and on the back. The most common sizes are the 4-in. square and 4-in. octagonal boxes used for fixtures, junctions, and devices, and the $4 \times 2\frac{1}{8}$ box used for single devices where no splicing is required. Box depths vary from $1\frac{1}{2}$ to 3 in. Generally, except for interchangeable devices, no more than one single device should be placed in

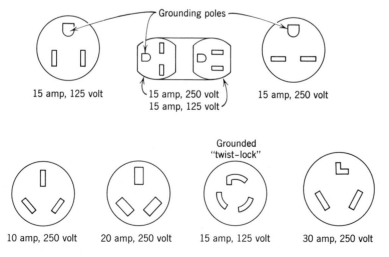

Fig. 23.34   Common receptacle configurations.

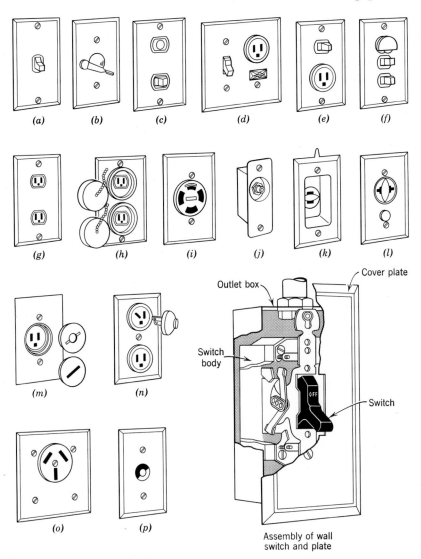

Fig. 23.35 Typical switches and outlets: (*a*) standard wall switch; (*b*) weatherproof switches; (*c*) switch and pilot light; (*d*) switch pilot light and outlet; (*e*) switch and outlet; (*f*) night light; (*g*) duplex outlet; (*h*) weatherproof convenience; (*i*) grounded 4-wire outlet lock type; (*j*) door switch; (*k*) clock hanger; (*l*) fan hanger; (*m*) floor outlet with cover; (*n*) radio outlet; (*o*) range outlet; (*p*) telephone outlet. Item (*f*) demonstrates the miniature interchangeable line of wiring devices.

a single-gang box. The number of wires permissible in various boxes is specified in Article 370 of the NEC.

Nonmetallic boxes may be used with NM and NMC cable and with nonmetallic conduit installations. In wet locations and for outdoor work, cast-iron or cast-aluminum boxes are recommended.

27. Batteries and Battery Rooms. Storage batteries are often installed in buildings as part of an emergency power system, or for supply of d-c control power. The batteries must be mounted in suitable racks as detailed in the NEC. Batteries need not be installed in separate battery rooms unless the units are in *unsealed jars,* and the aggregate capacity at the 8-hour rate exceeds 5 kwhr.

Ventilation must be provided in such rooms to prevent accumulation of gases. Wiring methods shall be open wiring, MI cable, ALS cable or wiring in conduit or EMT. Type V insulated conductors shall not be used.

The principal types of storage battery in use are the lead acid and the nickel cadmium cells. The former is less expensive, has higher efficiency, shorter life, smaller size, and is more easily damaged by overload or lack of maintenance. The nickel cadmium cell is the indicated choice where maintenance is poor and (or) infrequent, such as in standby lighting units. Batteries must be kept fully charged by means of either periodic charging or constant connection to charging equipment.

28. Electric Closets. In the design of a building electric system, particularly in multistory construction, it is often advantageous and convenient to group the electrical equipment in a small room called an electric closet. The shape of this space can be varied to fit the architectural and electrical demands, but it should provide the following:

a. One or more locking doors.
b. Vertically stacking, above and below other electric closets and located so as not to block conduits entering or leaving horizontally.
c. Space free of other utilities such as piping or duct, passing through the closet, either horizontally or vertically.

d. Sufficient wall space to mount all requisite and future panels, switches, transformers, telephone cabinets, and signal equipment.
e. Floor slots or sleeves of sufficient size for all present and future conduit or bus risers.
f. Sufficient floor space so that an electrician can work comfortably on initial installation and repair.
g. Adequate illumination and ventilation since the equipment is temperature sensitive.

29. System Inspection and Design. Each electric wiring system is inspected at least twice by the local inspection authorities; once after raceways (roughing) have been installed and before wiring and closing in of walls, and once after the entire job is complete. The purpose of these inspections is to determine whether design, material, and installation techniques are meeting the national and local code requirements. Excellence of design and equipment selection is the responsibility of the designer; excellence of installation is the responsibility of the contractor. The designer, however, must be completely familiar with installation work and equipment physical characteristics in order to properly design an electrical system, so that it will not present the contractor with difficulties. He must also be ever wary of equipment substitutions by the contractor who, having submitted his bid on the basis of plans and specifications, should be held to them.

24

Electric Wiring Design

1. **General Considerations.** In wiring design, as in lighting design, there are numerous possible solutions to each design problem—some good, some fair, and some bad. Experience guides the designer to a solution which best suits the job, as it is his responsibility to establish a most economical design within the framework of the design criteria. Some of these criteria are discussed below.

(a) *Flexibility.* Every wiring system should incorporate sufficient flexibility of design of branch circuitry, feeders, and switchboard to accommodate all probable patterns, arrangements, and locations of electric loads. In addition, the system must be designed for expansion since it has been conclusively demonstrated that all types of facilities have experienced, and will continue to experience, an expansion of electric load demand. It must be emphasized, however, that over-design in this or other regard is just as bad as under-design since both are wasteful and uneconomical.

(b) *Reliability.* Reliability of the electric wiring system is our concern since the reliability of the incoming utility lines is generally beyond our control. The service record of the Utility must be investigated to determine whether auxiliary (emergency) power equipment is justified, and to what

extent. In most instances an economic balance can be struck between the cost of outages and the cost of standby equipment. Of course, in instances where lives are at stake, as in certain hospital facilities such as surgical lighting, or iron lungs, or for emergency lighting in public areas, no compromise is possible, and adequate standby equipment must be provided. In other cases, however, the duration as well as frequency of outages must be carefully investigated before deciding on standby sources, because such equipment, to be effective, must be properly maintained, and its over-all cost is therefore relatively high.

Another factor affecting reliability is quality of equipment in the wiring system. Economy grade equipment causes outages within a system and the initial economy effected by the use of such equipment must be carefully weighed against the dollar cost of such outages.

Finally, the system must be designed so that the equipment failures which will occur, even with the finest of equipment, can be readily detected and corrected so that the cost of such normal outages is minimized. Where such disruptions cannot be tolerated, duplicate equipment facilities must be provided.

(c) *Safety.* Although rigid adherence to

Table 24.1 Load Estimating

Type of Occupancy	Lighting Load*			Other Loads‡	
	Unit Load Per Sq Ft (Watts)	Load to which Demand Factor Applies (Watts)	Demand Factor	Misc. Power	Air conditioning (Electric)
				Watts per sq. ft.	
Armories and auditoriums	1	Total wattage	100%	$\frac{1}{2}$	7
Banks	2	Total wattage	100%	$\frac{1}{2}$	7
Barber shops and beauty parlors	3	Total wattage	100%	1	7
Churches	1	Total wattage	100%	$\frac{1}{2}$	10
Clubs	2	Total wattage	100%	1	7
Court Rooms	2	Total wattage	100%	$\frac{1}{2}$	7
Dwellings— (Other Than Hotels)	3	3000 or less / Next 117,000 / Over 120,000	100% / 35% / 25%		
Garages—commercial (storage)	$\frac{1}{2}$	Total wattage	100%	$\frac{1}{2}$	
Hospitals	2	50,000 or less / Over 50,000	40%† / 20%	$1\frac{1}{2}$	5
Hotels, including apartment houses without provisions for cooking by tenants	2	20,000 or less / Next 80,000 / Over 100,000	50%† / 40% / 30%	1	$1\frac{1}{2}$ per room
Industrial Commercial (Loft) Buildings	2	Total wattage	100%	2	
Lodge rooms	$1\frac{1}{2}$	Total wattage	100%	$\frac{1}{2}$	7
Office buildings	5	Total wattage	100%	2	5
Restaurants	2	Total wattage	100%	$\frac{1}{2}$	10
Schools	3	Total wattage	100%	$1\frac{1}{2}$	
Stores	3	Total wattage	100%	1	6
Warehouses storage	$\frac{1}{4}$	12,500 or less / Over 12,500	100% / 50%	$\frac{1}{4}$	
In any of above occupancies except single-family dwellings and individual apartments of multi-family dwellings: Assembly halls and auditoriums / Halls, corridors, closets / Storage spaces	1 / $\frac{1}{2}$ / $\frac{1}{4}$	Total wattage as specified for the specific occupancy			

* These figures are taken from the NEC, no future allowance being included.

† For sub-feeders to areas in hospitals and hotels where entire lighting is likely to be used at one time; as in operating rooms, ballrooms, dining rooms, etc., a demand factor of 100 percent shall be used.

‡ These figures are estimates based on experience and must be applied judiciously. Figures are to be used as total demand, i.e. 100% demand factor.

the requirements of the NEC and other applicable NFPA Codes will assure an initially safe electrical installation, the designer must be constantly alert to such factors as electric hazards caused by misuse or abuse of equipment, or by equipment failure. Too, a thorough acquaintance with the size of equipment used will eliminate the oft-encountered physical hazard caused by obstruction of access spaces, passage, closets, and walls with electric equipment.

2. Load Estimating. When initiating the wiring design of a building it is important to be able to estimate the total building load in order to plan such spaces as transformer rooms, chases, and closets. This information is also required by the local power company well in advance of the start of construction. An exact take-off can be made after completing the design but since this is often several months later, a good preliminary estimate is required. Such an estimate can be made from the figures given in Art. 220 of the NEC and reproduced in Table 24.1.

These figures are minimum and where it appears that the building will have heavier load due to high lighting levels, or other factors, the figures should be raised. Table 24.2 gives a tabulation of service entrance sizes in amperes, based on single and 3-phase service for typical occupancies. These figures are for quick estimate purposes and should be checked after the design is completed.

3. System Voltage. As discussed in Chapter 22, the commonest voltage systems are:

(*a*) *120/240 volt, single-phase, 3-wire,* used for residences, small stores, small warehouses, and generally where demand loads do not exceed 10 to 15 kva.

(*b*) *120/208 volts, 3-phase, 4-wire* for loads of all sizes in occupancies of all types. The lighting and receptacle loads are fed at 120 volts and all power loads receive 208 volts, 3-phase. Where buildings are large, either horizontally or vertically, considerable machinery must be fed, lighting is fluorescent, and the 120-volt load is not excessive, a more economical system (c) is available.

(*c*) *277/480 volts, 3-phase, 4-wire,* utilizing 277-volt fluorescent lighting, 480-volt machinery and small (3 to 25 kva) dry-type closet installed transformers to step down from 480 to 120 volts for supplying receptacles and other 120-volt loads. This system is ideally suited to multistory office buildings and large single- or multilevel industrial

Table 24.2 Nominal Service Size in Amperes

Nominal service sizes are 100A, 150A, 200A, 400A, 800A, 1200A, 1600A and 2000A.

| | *Area in Square Feet* | | | | |
Facility	1000	2000	5000	10000	Remarks
Single-Phase 120/240 volts 3 wire					
Residence	100A	100A	200A	. . . .	Minimum 100A
Stores*	100A	150A	. . . .	. . . .	
School	100A	150A	. . . .	. . . .	
Church*	100A	100A	. . . .	. . . .	
3-Phase 120/208 volts 4 wire					
Apartment House	. . . .	. . . .	200A	200A	
Hospital*	. . . .	. . . .	. . . .	400A	
Office*	. . . .	. . . .	200A	400A	
Store*	. . . .	100A	200A	400A	
School	. . . .	100A	200A	400A	

* Fully air conditioned. See Table 24.1.

buildings. Savings are generated by the smaller feeder and conduit sizes and smaller switchgear, which more than offset the additional cost of step-down transformers if the 120-volt load is not more than 25–35 percent of the total building load.

(*d*) *2400/4160 volts, 3-phase, 4-wire* systems are only used in very large commercial buildings or in industrial buildings with machinery requiring these voltages. The cost of running this type of feeder within a building is high due to NEC requirements and the inherent high cost of 5kv equipment, and so a detailed cost and engineering analysis by a competent engineer is required for each such case. Voltages above this level are widely used in large industrial plants and are beyond this volume's consideration.

4. Design Procedure.

(*a*) Locate on the area floor plans all the lighting fixtures, receptacles, switches, wiring devices, motors, and other current consuming devices.

(*b*) Locate the lighting and appliance panelboards.

(*c*) If required, locate power or other special panelboards, including emergency system equipment.

(*d*) Circuit all the devices to the appropriate panels, preparing the while a panel schedule, and computing panel loads.

(*e*) Prepare a panelboard riser diagram.

(*f*) Compute feeder sizes.

(*g*) Design (lay out) the switchboard feeding the panels and other devices.

(*h*) Design the service equipment. (This step may be involved in step (*f*).)

(*i*) Circuit special devices and panels connected ahead of main switches.

(*j*) Check the wiring system, coordinate work with other trades and architectural plans.

5. Layout of Devices.

Wiring devices, under which heading are subsumed receptacles and switches, are located as required by the equipment to be served and by the area usage. The NEC specifies that in dwellings, receptacles shall be so placed in all rooms except bathrooms and closets that no point is more than 6 ft from such an outlet. Such spacing is also good practice in small office areas. All receptacles must be of the 3-pole grounding type, the poles being "hot," neutral, and ground. Switches for control of lighting or receptacles are normally placed on the strike side of the door. Other devices such as plug-in-strip on walls, and special purpose receptacles are shown and identified. Signal outlet locations are often noted but generally remain uncircuited on floor plans, a riser being utilized to show interconnections. These include fire-alarm equipment, telephone and intercom equipment, radio and TV outlets, thermostats, etc. These devices may be identified by a special symbol or note where a standard symbol is not available.

Lighting fixture outlets are normally placed on the same drawing as wiring devices unless the large number of the latter precludes showing the lighting, without undue cluttering of the drawings. In such event, the lighting (and occasionally the signals) are shown on one drawing and receptacles on another. Motors, heaters and other fixed and permanently wired equipment are shown and identified on the receptacle drawings (also called power drawings, in contradistinction to lighting drawings). Similar equipment—portable or fixed—is not shown when furnished with a cord and plug. However, the receptacle intended for supplying the particular device is shown and identified. Standard symbols and a typical device layout are shown in Figs. 24.1 and 24.2 respectively.

6. Panelboard Location and Selection.

The selection and location of the required panelboards depends on the type and quantity, and availability of space. In the research building of which Fig. 24.2 is a part plan, lighting panels are recessed into the corridor wall since the building is only 2 stories high and the panels can be vertically stacked and fed by a single conduit. If this building were 6 or more stories high, an electric closet of the type shown in Fig. 24.3 would be advisable to accommodate

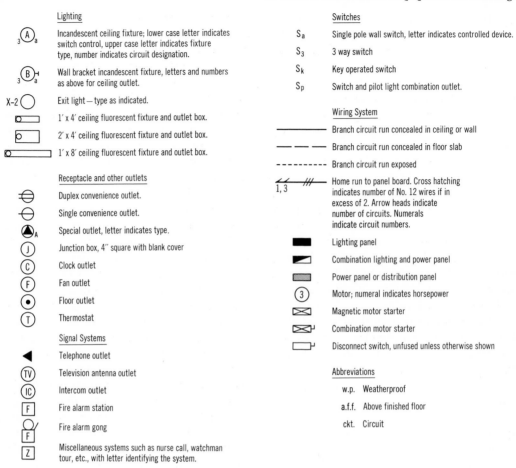

Fig. 24.1   Graphical electrical symbols.

the panel and riser conduits. Of course, when panels are installed in finished areas such as corridors, flush mounting is required.

In order to limit the voltage drop on a branch circuit in accordance with the Code requirements (See Section 5, Chap. 23) panelboards should preferably be located so that no circuit exceeds 75 ft in length. If circuits longer than this are unavoidable, No. 10 AWG wire should be used for runs of 75 to 125 ft, and No. 8 AWG for longer circuits. These wire sizes apply to 15 or 20 amp branch circuits, which are normally wired with No. 12 AWG wire.

The laboratory between the 2 offices of Fig. 24.2 is intended to function as a self-contained unit and is therefore equipped

with its own panel. Multi-outlet assemblies, all wiring within the room and the panel itself are surface mounted to allow ready access to all components for the frequent rewiring encountered in laboratories. A main circuit breaker should be provided in such a panel to act as a main disconnect, whether required by Code or not. Where panels are convenient to the loads controlled, the panel circuit breakers may be used for switching.

Panels supplying large blocks of load simultaneously switched, such as auditorium house lights, lobby lights, large single use office areas, store lighting, etc., can be constructed with built-in contactors to switch the entire panel, with control at any desired remote location. If only part of the panel's circuits are so arranged, a split bus panel is provided, partially contactor controlled (shown graphically in Fig. 24.4).

When lighting and appliance panels require more than 42 poles at a single location, a double panel is utilized comprising 2 panels in a single enclosing cabinet with a steel barrier between the 2 units.

Residence panels are normally placed in the basement, garage, or utility room in private houses and in the kitchen or hallway in apartments. Small offices, stores, and taxpayer buildings have lighting panels mounted in a convenient finished area and utilize the breakers for load-switching. In large buildings, strategically located electric closets are provided to house all elec-

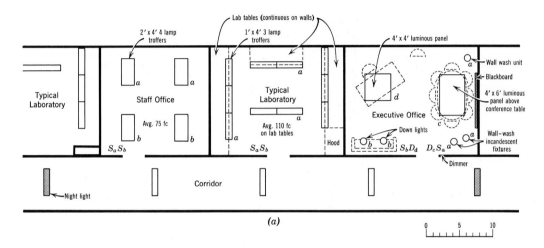

(a)

Notes:
1. All receptacles in staff offices at 42" a.f.f. to c.l.
2. All receptacles in exec. offices at 12" a.f.f. to c.l.
3. Surface raceway in labs mounted at 48" a.f.f. to c.l.

4. Special outlets: A 20 amp. 250 v 2 wire 3 pole grounded outlet (for 208 v ⅓ hp centrifuge)

   B 30 amp. 250 v 2 wire 3 pole grounded outlet (for 208 v 6 kw kiln)

   C 50 amp. 250 v 3 wire 4 pole grounded outlet (for 10 hp M–G set)

   D 15 amp. 125 v/15 amp. 250 v 2 wire 3 pole grounded outlet (for cleaning and general use)

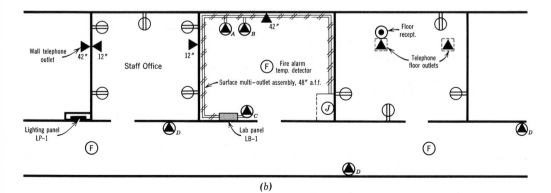

(b)

Fig. 24.2 Typical floor plans for lighting and power for a section of an office-lab building. Separate lighting and power-plans are drawn for the sake of clarity.

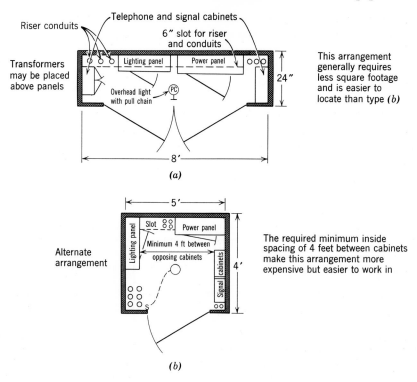

Fig. 24.3   Typical electric closets with some usual equipment. If warranted by amount of equipment, separate closets may be used for signal and telephone conduits and cabinets.

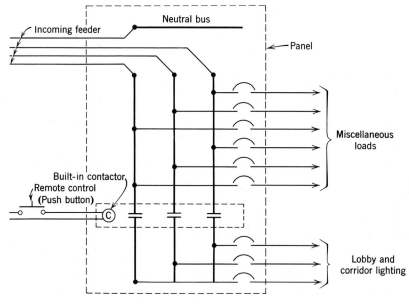

Fig. 24.4   Split bus panel. Lower section of panelboard is contactor operated in order to accomplish simultaneous control of the lobby and corridor lighting. Breakers in this section are kept normally closed.

trical supply equipment. Power panels and distribution panels are located as required by the building loads.

7. Application of Overcurrent Equipment. Before commencing an explanation of circuiting, it is necessary to explain the principles underlying overcurrent protection. As outlined in Chapter 23, the function of an overcurrent device is to open (interrupt) a circuit when the current rating of the equipment being protected is exceeded. These overcurrent devices are placed in circuits to protect wiring, transformers, lights, and all other equipment which can be damaged by excessive current. The following general rules govern the application of overcurrent protection:

(a) Overcurrent devices must be placed on the line, or supply side of the equipment being protected.

(b) Overcurrent devices must be placed in all ungrounded conductors of the protected circuit.

(c) All equipment shall be protected in accordance with its current carrying capacity.

(d) Conductor sizes shall not be reduced in a circuit or tap, unless the smallest size wire is protected by the circuit overcurrent devices.

(e) Overcurrent devices shall be located so as to be readily accessible, protected from physical damage and away from easily ignited material.

8. Branch Circuit Design. As defined in Section 11 of Chapter 22, there are 2 types of branch circuits recognized by the NEC viz., multiple-outlet general purpose branch circuits and individual branch circuits. Although all branch circuits may be 15, 20, 30 or 50 amp in size, the former are intended for serving groups of portable and fixed lighting and appliances, and convenience outlets whereas the latter is designed to serve a specific item of equipment. Therefore, the individual branch circuit may feed any load up to 50 amp whereas the general purpose branch circuit is limited to

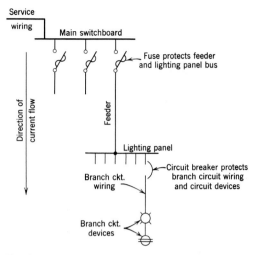

Fig. 24.5 Location of overcurrent protective equipment. Protective equipment should always be located at the point where the conductor receives its source of supply so that when it operates the current supply is cut off.

certain conductors, overcurrent protection and loads, as detailed in Table 24.3.

It is also good practice in all but the smallest installations to circuit lighting and receptacles separately although this is not a Code requirement. Figure 24.10 shows one possible circuiting arrangement of the room layouts shown in Figure 24.2. Although other arrangements are possible, the end result will be the same.

Good practice also dictates:

(a) Use of 20-amp general purpose branch circuits wired with No. 12 AWG wire.

(b) Limiting circuit loading to 10 and 14 amp on 15- and 20-amp circuits respectively.

(c) When wiring residences, supplying at least one 3-wire, 20-amp, 240-volt receptacle in the kitchen and laundry in addition to the Code minimum of two 20-amp branch circuits for receptacles in the kitchen, laundry, pantry, and dining room. In addition to all required outlets, a minimum of 1 branch circuit per 500 sq ft should be provided for general illumination.

(d) In small office spaces (less than 500 sq ft) provide at least 1 outlet for every 50 sq ft, or 1 outlet for every 10 lineal ft of wall

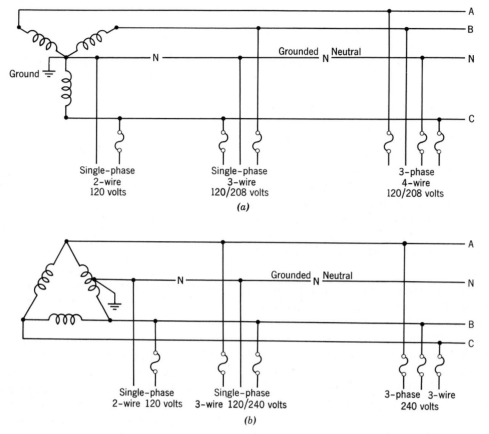

Single-phase
2-wire
120 volts

Single-phase
3-wire
120/208 volts

3-phase
4-wire
120/208 volts

(a)

Single-phase
2-wire 120 volts

Single-phase
3-wire 120/240 volts

3-phase 3-wire
240 volts

(b)

Fig. 24.6 (*a*) Location of overcurrent protective devices in a grounded wye system. Neutral is not normally fused. (*b*) Location of overcurrent devices in a delta 3-phase system. Neutral is not normally fused.

space, whichever is greater. In larger office spaces, provide 1 outlet every 100 to 125 sq ft, beyond the initial 500 sq ft (10 outlets). These should comprise wall outlets spaced

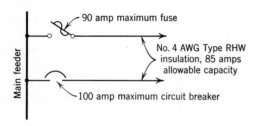

90 amp maximum fuse

No. 4 AWG Type RHW insulation, 85 amps allowable capacity

Main feeder

100 amp maximum circuit breaker

Fig. 24.7   The overcurrent protection shall correspond to the rating of the protected equipment. Where ratings do not correspond exactly, the next larger standard size may be used.

as above plus floor outlets sufficient to make up the required total. In view of the increasingly heavy loads of office machines, these receptacles should be circuited at no more than 6 to a 20-amp branch circuit, and less if the equipment to be fed so dictates.

(*e*) In stores, good practice requires at least 1 convenience outlet receptacle for every 300 sq ft in addition to outlets required for known equipment such as lamps, show windows, and demonstration appliances.

(*f*) The usual practice in wiring of schools is to supply 1 receptacle on each wall of a classroom in addition to the special outlets required for specific equipment such as electric typewriters, photographic projec-

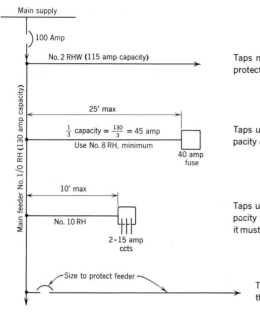

Main supply

100 Amp

No. 2 RHW (115 amp capacity)

Taps may be made if smaller conductor is protected by main feeder protection (100 A C/B protects the No. 2).

Main feeder No. 1/0 RH (130 amp capacity)

25' max

$\frac{1}{3}$ capacity = $\frac{130}{3}$ = 45 amp

Use No. 8 RH, minimum

40 amp fuse

Taps up to 25' long are permitted if tap conductor has min. 1/3 capacity of main and terminates in a single C/B or set of fuses.

10' max

No. 10 RH

2–15 amp ccts

Taps up to 10 ft. long are permitted provided they have sufficient capacity for the circuits they feed; eg, if the wiring feeds 2-15 amp ccts, it must have 30 amp capacity and should be No. 10 AWG, RHW or equal.

Size to protect feeder

Taps of any length may be made if the conductor is protected at the tap point by an approximately sized overcurrent device.

Fig. 24.8   Permissible tap arrangements.

tors, and for laboratory use. Administrative areas in schools are treated in fashion similar to other office spaces. Corridors in all public buildings such as schools, offices, hospitals, etc., should always be equipped with combination 15-amp, 208V/20 amp, 120v receptacles, for supplying current to 120-volt or 208-volt cleaning machines.

Table 24.3   Branch Circuit Requirements

	Branch Circuit Size			
Circuit Rating	*15 amp*	*20 amp*	*30 amp*	*50 amp*
Minimum size conductors	No. 14	12	10	6
Minimum size taps	No. 14	14	14	12
Overcurrent device rating	15 amp	20	30	50
Lampholders permitted	Any type	Any type	Heavy duty	Heavy duty
Receptacle rating permitted	15 amp	15 or 20	30	50 amp
Maximum load (see note 6)	15	20	30	50

NOTES:

1. Wiring shall be types R, RW, RH-RW, RHW, RU, RUH, RUW, RHH, T, THW, TW, THWN in raceway or cable.

2. On 15-amp circuit maximum single appliance shall draw 12 amp. On 20-amp cct. maximum single appliance shall draw 16 amp. If combined with lighting or portable appliances, any fixed appliance shall not draw more than 7.5 amp on a 15-amp circuit, and 10 amp on a 20-amp circuit.

3. On a 30-amp circuit maximum single appliance draw shall be 24 amperes.

4. Heavy duty lamp holders are units rated not less than 750 watts.

5. 30- and 50-amp circuits shall not be used for fixed lighting in residences.

6. When loads are connected long periods, actual load shall not exceed 80% of the branch circuit rating. Conversely, continuous type loads shall be figured at 125% of actual load in all load calculations.

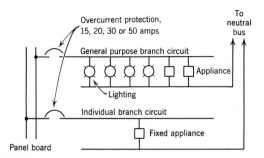

Fig. 24.9 The 2 general types of branch circuit are illustrated. Table 24.3 lists the requirements to which such circuits must adhere.

Having circuited all the loads, a panel schedule is drawn up which lists the circuit numbers, load description and wattage, and number of poles and current rating of the overcurrent devices. Spare circuits are included to the extent that the designer con-

siders necessary, but in no case less than 20 percent of the total active circuits. Such spare circuits should be figured in load calculation at not less than 50 percent of maximum circuit capacity or approximately the same as other branch circuits. A typical panelboard schedule is shown in Fig. 24.11, which includes the laboratory of Fig. 24.10.

In calculating panel loads, the following rules apply:

(1) Each specific appliance is taken at rated load.
(2) Each convenience outlet is counted as 1.5 amp (except in residences).
(3) Loads for special areas and devices such as show windows, dwellings, multi-outlet assemblies, and heavy duty lampholders are covered in the NEC, Article 220.

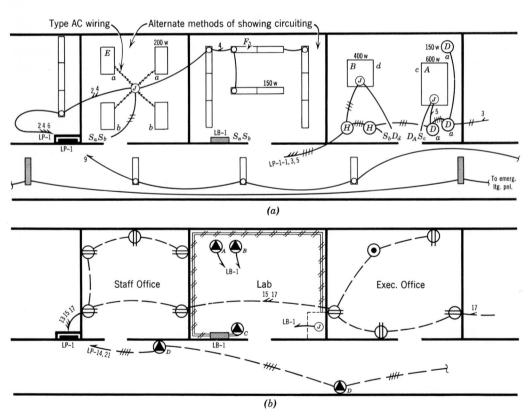

Fig. 24.10 Typical circuiting of several rooms of an office-lab building. Lighting and power (receptacles) are shown on separate plans to avoid crowding. See Fig. 24.1 for symbols and Fig. 24.2 for notes. Lighting in offices is recessed; lighting in labs is surface mounted for flexibility. Note the double circuiting of the ●D receptacles.

ELECT. PANEL—	*LP-1*	120/208 V 3φ 4W					
		LOAD IN WATTS			**BRANCH CIRCUIT**		
No.	SERVES	φ A	φ B	φ C	Poles	Frame	Trip
1	*Lighting*	1150			1	50	20
2	*Lighting*	1250					
3	*Lighting*		1000				
4	*Lighting*		1050				
5	*Lighting*			600			
6	*Lighting*			1500			
7	*Lighting*	800					
8	*Lighting*	1100					
9	*Lighting – Corridor*		700				
10	*Lighting*		1050				
11	*Lighting*			1000			
12	*Lighting*			1200			
13	*Receptacles 5 @ 1.5 amp*	900					
14	*Receptacle – Corridor (Single pole)*	900					
15	*Receptacle*		900				
16	*Spare*		1200				
17	*Receptacle*			900			
18	*Spare*			1200			
19	*Spare*	1200					
20	*Spare*		1200		↓		
21	*Receptacle – Corridor*		1000		2		
	2 pole portion			1000			
22	*Spare*	1200			2	↓	↓
			1200				
	Phase totals	8100	9300	7400			
	Panel total	24,800					
	Max φ current		77.5 a				
	25% spare capacity		20.	(Future loads)			
	Total I		97 Amps				

Main breaker _225A 3 Pole_
Trip _100 A_
Feeder size _4 #2 RHW in 2" C._

Fig. 24.11   Schedule for lighting panel LP-1.

Typical calculations for residences and stores are found in Chapter 9 of the NEC. A typical panel calculation follows.

EXAMPLE 24.1. Assume a single floor of an office building, 100′ x 200′, containing 2 or more lighting panels, located so that branch circuits are not excessively long. Assume further that 15 percent of the area is occupied with corridors and storage.

Minimal requirements:

Office Space: 85% of 100′ x 200′
                                    = 17000 sq ft

Corridor and Storage: 15% of 100′ x 200′
                                    = 3000 sq ft

(By Code, from Table 24.1)

Lighting Load:
  Office Area—17000 sq ft at
                    5 watts/sq ft = 85 kw
  Corridor and Storage—3000 sq ft at
                    $\frac{1}{2}$ watt/sq ft = 1.5 kw
Total Load . . . . 86.5 kw

Due to continuous use, this load must be increased 25% = 108.15 kw. Using an

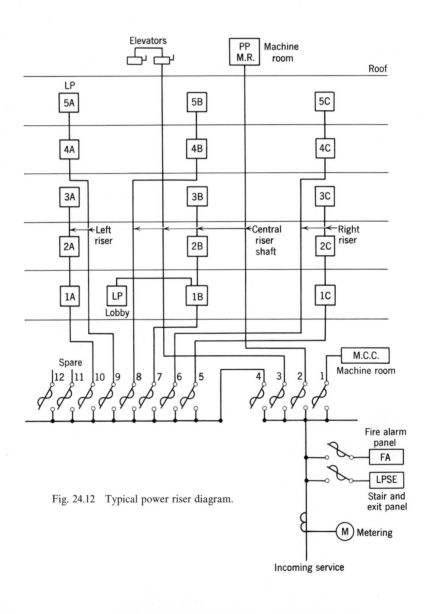

Fig. 24.12 Typical power riser diagram.

average load of approximately 1600 watts (14 amp at 120 volts) per 20-amp circuit.

Minimum No. of Circuits:

$$\frac{108.15 \text{ kw}}{1.6 \text{ kw}} = 68 \text{ circuits}$$

This would then mean 2 lighting panels, each containing 34 circuits.

The actual load should then be evenly circuited over the 68 active circuits, resulting in each circuit carrying an average of

$$\frac{86.5 \text{ kw}}{68} = 1270 \text{ watts}$$

This then indicates that when circuiting the lighting, load should be held to *1200 to 1300* watts per 20-amp lighting circuit.

In actual practice, *though not required by Code,* additional circuits must be allowed for receptacles and spares. Based on the system outlined above, this would be:

Receptacles:
First 500 sq ft,
    1 outlet per 50 sq ft =   10 recept.
Next 16,500 sq ft,
    1 outlet per 100 sq ft = 165 recept.
Total . . . . 175 recept.

Circuit 6 recept. per 20-amp circuit:

$$\frac{175 \text{ receptacles}}{6 \text{ per circuit}} = 30 \text{ circuits}$$

Total Spares—20 percent of 68 lighting circuits + 30 receptacle circuits = 20 circuits

Thus, if 2 panels per floor were used, each panel would contain $\frac{68 + 30 + 20}{2} = 59$ circuits and 2 double panels would be required. An alternate solution would be to select a 3rd-panel location; each panel would then contain $\frac{118}{3} = 39$ circuits, assuming loads were evenly distributed.

Thus, one would initially select 2 or 3 panel locations and proceed to circuit the lighting and receptacles. *If the actual number of circuits is less than 68, then 68 must be provided;* if greater, then of course the actual number required must be used. In either case 20 percent spare should be added.

In calculating the panel load, the actual load as determined by adding the lighting and other loads on the panel is compared to the load by sq ft calculation, and the larger figure used in determining the required panel feeder size. Thus actual load would be compared to $\frac{108.15}{2} = 54.07$ kw per panel for 2 panels

Table 24.4   Current and Wattage Relationships

Load watts	120 v Single-phase	120/240 v 3-Wire	120/208 v 3-Wire	120/208 v 3-phase	277/480 v 3-phase	277 volt Single-phase
100	0.83	0.41	. . . .	. . . .	. . . .	.362
200	1.6	0.8	. . . .	. . . .	. . . .	.72
500	4.2	2.1	. . . .	. . . .	. . . .	1.8
1,000	8.3	4.2	4.8	2.77	1.2	3.6
2,000	16.6	8.3	9.6	5.5	2.4	7.2
5,000	41.7	20.8	24.0	13.9	6.0	18.0
10,000	83.2	41.6	48.0	27.7	12.0	36.0
20,000	. . . .	. . . .	96.0	55.6	24.0	72.0
50,000	. . . .	. . . .	240.0	139.0	60.0	180.0
100,000	. . . .	. . . .	480.0	277.0	120.0	362.0
	$I = \dfrac{W}{120}$	$I = \dfrac{W}{240}$	$I = \dfrac{W}{208}$	$I = \dfrac{W}{360}$	$I = \dfrac{W}{830}$	$I = \dfrac{W}{277}$

Assuming 100% power factor.

or

$$\frac{108.15}{3} = 36.05 \text{ kw per panel for 3 panels.}$$

9. Riser Diagrams and Feeder Calculations.
When all devices are circuited, and panels
are located and scheduled we are ready to
prepare a riser diagram. A typical diagram,
shown in Fig. 24.12, represents a block version of a single line diagram except that, as
the name implies, vertical relationships are
shown. All panels, feeders, switches, switchboards, and major components are shown
up to, but not including, branch circuiting.
This diagram is an electrical version of a
vertical section taken through the building.

*Table 24.5   Anticipated 10-Year Electric
Load Growth in Percent of Initial Load*

Auditoria (convention halls, public halls, etc.)	30–60
Churches and other houses of worship	10–30
Clubs, lodge rooms, game rooms	30–60
Commercial office buildings	30–80
Depots, waiting rooms, ticket offices	30–60
Domestic lighting and apartment lighting	30–80
Hospitals and other medical centers	20–80
Industrial buildings and industries	100–200
Libraries, reading rooms, drafting rooms	30–40
Night clubs and bars	20–50
Post offices	50–150
Public buildings (offices, clerical, general)	40–80
Railway stations, airports and loading platforms	40–80
Schools and other places of study	40–80
Stores and commercial areas (first class)	50–100
Stores and commercial areas (second class)	20–50
Theaters, motion picture, and television auditoria	30–60

NOTE: The above estimates include all lighting, heating,
motor loads, elevators, escalators, air conditioning,
electrified business machines, assortments of new and
improved plug-outlet devices, etc.

The NEC requires that all feeders must be
of sufficient size to supply all the branch circuits connected to it. Thus, in sizing the
feeder for supplying a panel such as outlined above, the panel load in terms of the
3-phase current is calculated.

$$I = \frac{\text{Total load in kva}}{.360} \text{ amp}$$

If we assume that for the example of the
previous section the minimum square foot
wattage requirements are larger than actual
panel loads, and therefore govern, and that
we are using 3 panels per floor, we have
36.05 kw as the panel load.

Thus, for this load, the current drawn
from the feeder is

$$I = \frac{36.05}{.360} = 100 \text{ amp.}$$

As an aid to computing currents, Table
24.4 lists various current, voltage, and wattage relationships and typical values.

Two other considerations enter into
feeder calculations in addition to the load
supplied—future capacity and voltage drop.
Some spare capacity is built into the branch
circuitry by circuiting for no more than 1200
to 1300 watts per 20 amp circuit. This capacity must also be allowed in the feeder,
which is readily done by increasing the calculated panel loads by 25 percent. In addition, spare capacity beyond the panel spares
must be built into the feeder to allow for
future expansion of load and additional
panels. As a guide to estimating such requirements, Table 24.5 lists the average percentage increase which may be expected for
a given occupancy, over a period of 10 years.
These figures are based upon Utility Company statistics.

EXAMPLE 24.2. Feeder F10 of Fig. 24.12
serves lighting panels 1A, 2A, and 3A.

The loads on these panels have been computed in accordance with the above considerations and are

LP–IA—100 amp
LP–2A—120 amp
LP–3A—120 amp
Total Load 340 amp

Demand Factor = 100% from Table 24.1

The 100 percent demand factor is only required by Code for lighting loads calculated by the sq ft method. If actual panel circuit loads are being utilized rather than sq ft loads, the following demand factors may be applied provided that at no time do we reduce our loads below the minimum required by Code.

No. of Panels Fed from a Single Feeder	Demand Factor
1, 2	100%
3, 4	.92
5–7	.85
8–10	.75

In office building work it is customary to utilize the 100% demand factor in all cases.

Table 24.6   Number of Conductors in Conduit or Tubing

Rubber Covered, Types RF-2, RFH-2, R, RH, RHW, RW, RH-RW, RU, RUH, RUW, SF, and SFF

Thermoplastic, Types TF, T, and TW, THW, and THWH

Size AWG MCM	Number of Conductors in 1 Conduit or Tubing								
	1	2	3	4	5	6	7	8	9
18	$\frac{1}{2}$	$\frac{1}{2}$	$\frac{1}{2}$	$\frac{1}{2}$	$\frac{1}{2}$	$\frac{1}{2}$	$\frac{1}{2}$	$\frac{3}{4}$	$\frac{3}{4}$
16	$\frac{1}{2}$	$\frac{1}{2}$	$\frac{1}{2}$	$\frac{1}{2}$	$\frac{1}{2}$	$\frac{1}{2}$	$\frac{3}{4}$	$\frac{3}{4}$	$\frac{3}{4}$
14	$\frac{1}{2}$	$\frac{1}{2}$	$\frac{1}{2}$	$\frac{1}{2}$	$\frac{3}{4}$	$\frac{3}{4}$	1	1	1
12	$\frac{1}{2}$	$\frac{1}{2}$	$\frac{1}{2}$	$\frac{3}{4}$	$\frac{3}{4}$	1	1	1	$1\frac{1}{4}$
10	$\frac{1}{2}$	$\frac{3}{4}$	$\frac{3}{4}$	$\frac{3}{4}$	1	1	1	$1\frac{1}{4}$	$1\frac{1}{4}$
8	$\frac{1}{2}$	$\frac{3}{4}$	$\frac{3}{4}$	1	$1\frac{1}{4}$	$1\frac{1}{4}$	$1\frac{1}{4}$	$1\frac{1}{2}$	$1\frac{1}{2}$
6	$\frac{1}{2}$	1	1	$1\frac{1}{4}$	$1\frac{1}{2}$	$1\frac{1}{2}$	2	2	2
4	$\frac{1}{2}$	$1\frac{1}{4}$	$1\frac{1}{4}$	$1\frac{1}{2}$	$1\frac{1}{2}$	2	2	2	$2\frac{1}{2}$
3	$\frac{3}{4}$	$1\frac{1}{4}$	$1\frac{1}{4}$	$1\frac{1}{2}$	2	2	2	$2\frac{1}{2}$	$2\frac{1}{2}$
2	$\frac{3}{4}$	$1\frac{1}{4}$	$1\frac{1}{4}$	2	2	2	$2\frac{1}{2}$	$2\frac{1}{2}$	$2\frac{1}{2}$
1	$\frac{3}{4}$	$1\frac{1}{2}$	$1\frac{1}{2}$	2	$2\frac{1}{2}$	$2\frac{1}{2}$	$2\frac{1}{2}$	3	3
0	1	$1\frac{1}{2}$	2	2	$2\frac{1}{2}$	$2\frac{1}{2}$	3	3	3
00	1	2	2	$2\frac{1}{2}$	$2\frac{1}{2}$	3	3	3	$3\frac{1}{2}$
000	1	2	2	$2\frac{1}{2}$	3	3	3	$3\frac{1}{2}$	$3\frac{1}{2}$
0000	$1\frac{1}{4}$	2	$2\frac{1}{2}$	3	3	3	$3\frac{1}{2}$	$3\frac{1}{2}$	4
250	$1\frac{1}{4}$	$2\frac{1}{2}$	$2\frac{1}{2}$	3	3	$3\frac{1}{2}$	4	4	5
300	$1\frac{1}{4}$	$2\frac{1}{2}$	$2\frac{1}{2}$	3	$3\frac{1}{2}$	4	4	5	5
350	$1\frac{1}{4}$	3	3	$3\frac{1}{2}$	$3\frac{1}{2}$	4	5	5	5
400	$1\frac{1}{2}$	3	3	$3\frac{1}{2}$	4	4	5	5	5
500	$1\frac{1}{2}$	3	3	$3\frac{1}{2}$	4	5	5	5	6
600	2	$3\frac{1}{2}$	$3\frac{1}{2}$	4	5	5	6	6	6
700	2	$3\frac{1}{2}$	$3\frac{1}{2}$	5	5	5	6	6	..
750	2	$3\frac{1}{2}$	$3\frac{1}{2}$	5	5	6	6	6	..
800	2	$3\frac{1}{2}$	4	5	5	6	6	..	..
900	2	4	4	5	6	6	6	..	..

Demand Load

$$= 100\% \text{ of } 340 \text{ amp} = 340 \text{ amp}$$
$$25\% \text{ Spare capacity} = \underline{85 \text{ amp}}$$
$$425 \text{ amp}$$

From Table 24.5—40% future

$$\text{expansion} = \underline{170 \text{ amp}}$$
$$595 \text{ amp}$$

There are 4 methods of allowing for the 170-amp future expansion load:

1. Provide sufficient capacity initially. This would mean an initial feeder capable of carrying 595 amp, which from Table 23.2 would be 2 parallel sets of 350 MCM or 8–350 MCM in 2-3½″ conduits. This method is the most expensive initially and is wasteful since money is being expended initially for a need which at best will not arise for some years.

2. Provide cable capacity for initial load and space capacity plus oversized conduit so that when the larger loads materialize, new heavier cables can be pulled into the existing conduits. In this case, we would supply 2 sets of No. 4/0 conductors in 3½″ conduits to satisfy the initial 425 amp requirement and if the need arises, we would replace the 8 No. 4/0 with 8–350 MCM in the same two 3½″ conduits. This method requires only a small additional initial expenditure for oversize conduit.

3. The third method exhibits lowest first cost, but highest over-all cost. This method entails initial installation of required conduit only, with sleeves through floors to facilitate future conduit installation. Thus, we would initially install 8 No. 4/0 in two 3″ conduits and leave a sleeve for the future installation of a third parallel set of No. 4/0 cables in a third 3″ conduit.

4. The fourth method is initially the same as (3) above except that when the future load materializes, the existing conduits can be rewired with cables having thinner insulation such as type TW, THW, or THWN, thus increasing capacity. In this case we could rewire the two 3″ conduits with 350 MCM type THW for a capacity of 620 (2 × 310) amp or 500 MCM type

THWN for a total of 760 amp (2 × 380). This last method is desireable because of overall economy.

It must also be borne in mind that this future expansion will not only require additional feeder capacity but panels as well, for which closet space must be left initially.

Table 24.6 lists the conduit sizes required for the various cable sizes and types.

The final consideration in sizing a feeder is *voltage drop*. The NEC specifies, as explained in Section 5 of Chap. 23 that drop from source to final panel should be 1 percent for lighting and combination lighting and power feeders and 3 percent for power and heating load feeders. These figures should be adhered to as closely as possible; however, in instances of long runs where these restrictions will cause excessive cost, lighting feeders up to the branch panel may be run for 2 percent drop and power feeders up to 5 percent voltage drop. Many tables and curves are published by manufacturers from which voltage drop can be obtained. Such a set of curves is shown in Fig. 24.13.

Applying these curves to our last example:

Allowable voltage drop = 1% of 208 volts
$$= 2.08 \text{ volts}$$

Distance—assume 100 ft run

From the curves, 210 amp $\left(\dfrac{425}{2}\right)$ on 350 MCM cable will give a 1 percent drop in 70 ft. Therefore, the allowable 2 percent drop will be reached in 140 ft. Since our run is only 100 ft in length, 350 MCM is adequate.

In summary then, feeders are sized in accordance with load (actual or sq ft, whichever is larger), and voltage drop. Conduit may be oversized for future load expansion.

10. Service Equipment and Switchboard Design. The main switchboard shown in Fig. 24.12 constitutes a combination of service equipment and feeder switchboard. The service equipment portion of the board comprises the metering and the 4 main switches feeding risers, motor control cen-

GENERAL NOTES—Curves are for a 1-volt drop and 90% PF. For any other voltage drop, ratio ordinates. Capacities are for Type RHW 600-volt insulation, 60 cycles, 3 phase in steel conduit.

Typical Example—Required: to carry 70 amp 400 ft with a maximum of 2-volts drop, what is the wire size?

    a. 400 ft for 2-volts drop is the same as 200 ft for 1-volt drop.
    b. Intersection of 70 amp and 200 ft is just below 400MCM.
    c. Use 400MCM conductors to assure best operation of the feeder.

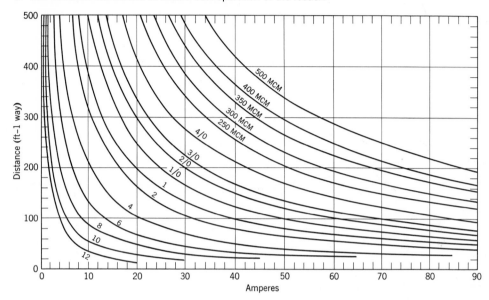

Typical Example—Required: to carry 200 amps 100 ft with a maximum of 2-volts drop, what is the wire size?

    a. 100 ft for 2-volts drop is the same as 50 ft for 1-volt drop.
    b. Intersection of 200 amp and 50 ft is just below 250MCM.
    c. Use 250MCM conductors.

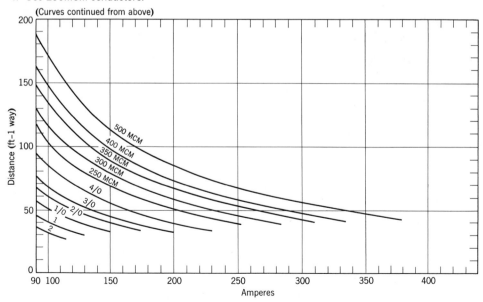

Fig. 24.13 Feeder voltage drop and current capacities for 600-volt, type RHW conductors.

ter (MCC), roof machine room, and elevators. The feeder board comprises switches 5 through 12. Such arrangement is permissible inasmuch as the NEC allows up to 6 fused switches or circuit breakers to serve as the service disconnect means. This arrangement was chosen in order to separate to the largest extent the motor loads (elevators, air conditioning equipment, basement power, etc.) from the lighting. Such a procedure minimizes lighting fluctuations due to motor starting and allows for simpler maintenance. Also, size of the main switch is reduced. This switchboard would be of

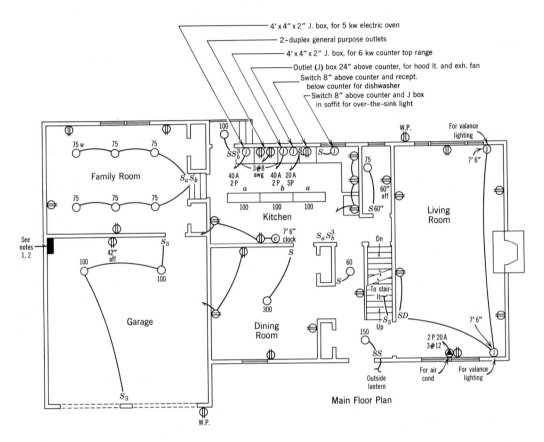

Main Floor Plan

Notes:

1. A residence of this size requires 150 ampere (30 kw) service, with #2/0 service cable. (see table 24.2)

2. Panelboard comprises 2-40A, 2 pole mains for cooking, one 50A, 2 pole main for future air-conditioning and one 70A, 2 pole main feeding a 20 circuit lighting and appliance section, with 20A breakers.

3. All receptacles are of the grounding type and are spaced so that no point on usable wall space is more than 6′ from an outlet.

4. All circuiting is 2 #12 unless otherwise shown.

5. Wiring for 2nd floor (not shown) shall include an air-conditioner receptacle in each B.R. on a separate circuit and a circuit for an attic fan.

6. The electrical contractor should be instructed to wire no more than 6 receptacles to a circuit, to avoid mixing lighting and receptacles on circuits and to have part of at least 2 circuits in each room.

Fig. 24.14 Typical Residential Wiring. Electrical drawings for residences do not normally show wiring beyond switching arrangements and special circuits.

the metalclad dead front type with switches or circuit breakers, as designed. For protection of Feeder F10 designed above, an 800 ampere circuit breaker or switch, with 500 amp trip or fuse respectively would be chosen, assuming the initial installation to be a double set of No. 4/0 cables.

Other considerations and general rules affecting service equipment are:

(*a*) Generally, a building may be supplied from 1 point by either a single set or parallel sets of service conductors.

(*b*) Service drops may generally be not less than No. 8 AWG and service entrance conductors or underground service conductors shall generally be not less than No. 6 AWG.

(*c*) All equipment used for service including cable, switches, meters, etc., shall be approved for that purpose.

(*d*) It is recommended that a minimum of 100 amp, 3-wire, 120/240-volt service be provided for all individual residences.

(*e*) In general no service switch smaller than 60 amp or circuit breaker frame smaller than 50 amp shall be used.

(*f*) In multiple occupancy buildings each tenant must have access to his disconnect means.

(*g*) All building equipment shall be connected on the load side of the service equipment except that service fuses, metering, fire alarm, and signal equipment and equipment serving emergency systems may be connected ahead of the main disconnect. (See Fig. 24.12.)

In computing a size for the service equipment a total is taken of the various feeder loads. Although application of a Diversity Factor to this total is permissible, good practice dictates the use of a unity Diversity Factor in order to provide a measure of space capacity in the service equipment.

The connected loads on the machinery feeders are normally taken at 70–85 percent Demand Factor in comparison to the 90 to 100 percent Demand Factor normally used on lighting feeders.

11. Emergency Systems (NEC Article 700). Emergency equipment includes all devices, wiring, and other electrical equipment intended to supply illumination and power in the event of failure of the normal power system. To such a system should be connected all stair lights, selected corridor lights, exit and directional signs, some lobby lighting, and such signal equipment (e.g., public address and fire alarm) as is required to remain functional during disruption of the building power system. The source of current for such equipment may be an auxiliary source such as batteries or a generator, or the normal source, connected *ahead* of the main service switch. In Fig. 24.12, such a connection is shown going to a fused switch feeding panel LP-SE which in turn feeds stairs, exits, etc. The fire alarm equipment also is shown fed separately ahead of the main switchboard. Circuits beyond panel LP-SE are *not* switched, being of the constant burning type, unless switches are accessible to authorized persons only.

Emergency-system wiring must be kept entirely independent of all other wiring and equipment and shall not occupy the same enclosure or conduit as normal-system wiring except in dual fed units such as transfer switches.

Where battery units are installed in a space to provide emergency lighting they shall be permanently wired and not plug connected. Also, the panel device feeding these outlets shall be capable of being locked or shall be so arranged as to be accessible to authorized personnel only.

25

Passenger Elevators

1. Introduction. Among the many important functional decisions which must be reached by the designer of a multistory building, probably none is more important than the proper selection of the vertical transportation equipment; specifically the passenger elevators, freight elevators, and escalators (moving electric stairways). Not only do these items represent a major building expense, being in the case of a 25-story office building more than 10 percent of the construction cost, but also the quality of elevator service is an important factor in a tenant's choice of space in competing buildings.

Although the final decision as to the type of equipment rests with the architect, the factors affecting it are so numerous that it behooves the building designer to consult with an elevator expert. Such consultation service is normally readily available from the major elevator and escalator manufacturers. It is the function of this chapter to familiarize the architect and engineer with the nature and application of vertical transportation equipment so as to enable him to make preliminary design decisions before consulting manufacturers representatives.

2. Passenger Elevators. Passenger elevators are normally subdivided by application into 4 general classifications, i.e., general-purpose or commercial, apartment, department store and hospital. Our discussion will be principally concerned with the general purpose type although much of the material also is applicable to the other types.

Ideal passenger service from an elevator installation provides immediate access to cars at any floor level, rapid transportation, comfort during the acceleration, steady speed, and deceleration periods, and rapid entrance and exit without discomfort. Also proper and quiet operation of the doors, visual floor indicators, and floor stop-buttons, smooth, quiet, and safe operation of all elevator safety equipment, comfortable and adequate lighting, and ease of passenger control in the absence of an operator, are important factors in the design of high quality elevator service.

B. ELEVATOR EQUIPMENT

3. System Arrangement and Equipment. The principal apparatus and major parts in any elevator installation include the car, the cables, the elevator machine, the control equipment, the counterweights, the shaft or hoistway, the rails, the penthouse, and the pit. Some elementary ideas of the function of these major items and auxiliaries are essential. Figure 25.1 shows these major parts and other auxiliaries.

The cars with their equipment for safety, convenience, and comfort, and their furnishings and finish, are an important unit in the system—the only one with which the average passenger is familiar. Much of the prestige of the architect and engineer depends on proper design of the car. Essentially it is a cage of light metal supported on a structural frame, to the top member of which the cables are fastened. By means of rail shoes on the side members the car is fixed in its vertical travel in the shaft. The car is provided with safety doors, operating control equipment, floor-level indicators, illumination, emergency exit ports, ventilation, kick plates, and hand rails. It is designed for long life, quiet operation, and low maintenance.

The cables lift and lower the car. Usually 3 to 8 cables are placed in parallel, the weight of the car being equally distributed over them. The cables are fastened to the top of the car by cable sockets which provide secure clamping. These cables then pass over a motor-driven cylindrical sheave at the traction machine (grooved for the cables) and pass downward to the counterweight to which they are fastened with cable sockets. Replacement of cables is one of the major costs in elevator operation and maintenance.

The elevator machine turns the sheave and lifts or lowers the car. It consists of a heavy structural frame on which are mounted the sheave and driving motor, the gears (if any), the brakes, the magnetic safety brake, and certain other auxiliaries. The governor which limits the car to safe speeds is mounted on or near the elevator machine. In most modern installations the elevator-driving motor receives its energy from a separate motor-generator set (m-g

set) which is in operation during the period that the particular elevator is available for handling traffic. This m-g set is properly considered a part of the elevator machine, although it may be located some distance from it.

The control equipment, in a general sense, is the combination of push buttons, contacts, relays, cams, and devices which are operated manually or automatically to initiate the door operation, starting, acceleration, retardation, leveling, and stopping of the car. These auxiliaries are interrelated in such a way that the major apparatus functions to produce the maximum of safety, comfort, and convenience. Electrical limit switches automatically stop the car from overrunning at the top and bottom of the hoistway. The well-known floor indicators, floor pilot lights, preset stop panels in the car, call buttons at floor levels, floor leveling devices, and up and down indicating lamps are all parts of the coordinated control equipment.

The counterweights are rectangular blocks of cast iron stacked in a frame which is supported at the opposite ends of the cables to which the car is fastened. The counterweight is related to the weight of the car and its load so that the required energy input to the elevator machine (which moves the car) is relatively low. In fact the energy required is large only during the periods of car acceleration and retardation. The counterweight is guided in its travel up and down the shaft by two guide rails at the back of the shaft. Obviously the counterweight travels in the reverse direction to that of the car.

The shaft is the vertical passageway for the car and counterweights. On its side walls are the guide rails, door frames, and certain mechanical and electrical auxiliaries of the control apparatus. At the bottom of the shaft are the car bumpers. At the top is the structural platform on which the elevator machine rests.

The guide rails are vertical tracks that guide the car and the counterweights. They

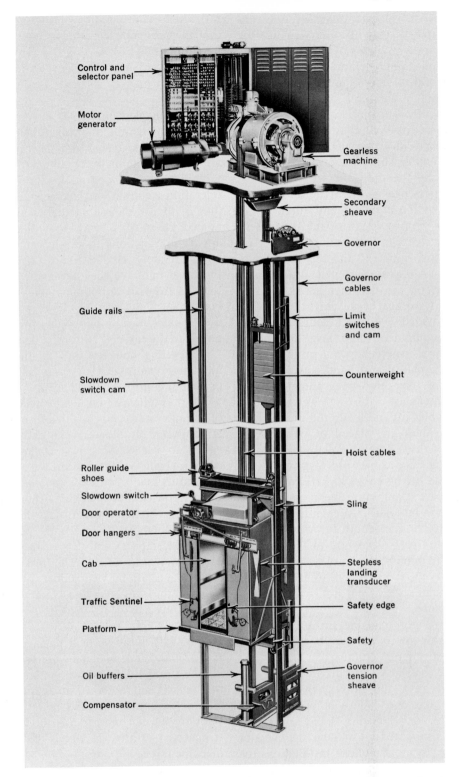

Fig. 25.1 Components of a typical gearless elevator installation. (Westinghouse Electric Corp.)

are of heavy machined steel, dovetailed at the joints and carefully aligned to insure smooth operation. The guide shoes on the side frames of the car fit the projecting web of the guide rail which has a T-cross section. The counterweight rails are somewhat similar in construction but smaller. Guide rails in tall buildings are fastened to the building with sliding rail clips in order to avoid their taking any building load which could result in deflection of the rails. Rails of modern elevators are not lubricated since rubber roller guide shoes are used. Figure 25.2 illustrates the fastening and the guide shoes.

The penthouse is the room directly above the hoistway in which the elevator machine is housed. It contains the m-g set which supplies energy to the elevator machine, the controlboard, and other control equipment. All electrical contractors and other possible sources of noise from machinery and control equipment are designed for quiet operation.

4. Gearless Traction Machines. A gearless traction machine, Fig. 25.3, consists of a d-c motor the shaft of which is directly connected to the brake wheel and driving sheave. The elevator hoist ropes are placed around this sheave. The absence of gears means that the motor must run at the same speed as the driving sheave. Since it is not practical to build d-c motors for operation at very low speeds, this type of machine is limited to medium and high-speed elevators, i.e., speeds from 400 to 1200 feet per minute (fpm). The motors are built in ranges from 20 to 150 hp.

The gearless traction machine is generally considered superior to geared machines. Since there are fewer moving parts, it is more efficient, gives quieter operation, and requires less maintenance. For office buildings and apartment houses of 10 stories or more, where high speeds and smooth high-quality operation are desired, the gearless traction machine is usually chosen.

5. Geared Traction Machines. This type of machine (Fig. 25.4) employs a worm and gear between the driving motor and the hoisting sheave. The driving motor with rheostatic control may therefore run at economical high speeds from 600 to 1800 rpm. Geared machines with rheostatic control use either a-c or d-c motors. Where a-c service only is available and car speeds greater than 100 fpm are desired, it is preferable to use unit multivoltage control, permitting a d-c driving motor on the elevator machine and car speeds up to 350 fpm. Unit multivoltage control (umv) is also preferable since it provides smoother operation than rheostatic control. The geared traction machine is used on both freight

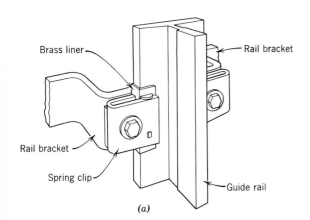

Fig. 25.2 (*a*) Guide rails and sliding clips. (*b*) Roller guide shoes. (Westinghouse Electric Corp., Elevator Division)

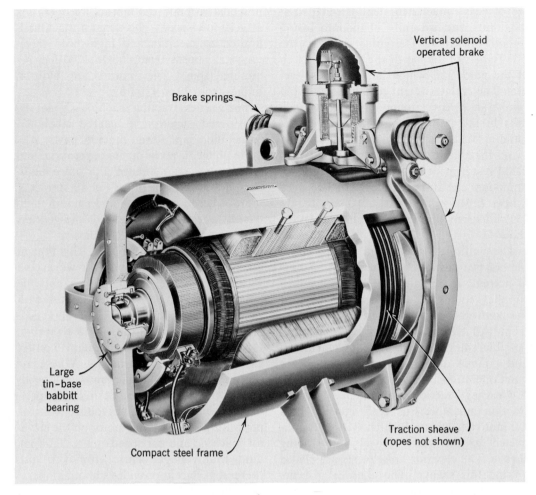

Vertical solenoid
operated brake

Brake springs

Large
tin–base
babbitt
bearing

Compact steel frame

Traction sheave
(ropes not shown)

Fig. 25.3   Cutaway view of a typical high speed gearless traction machine. (Westinghouse Electric
Corp.)

and passenger elevators. The horsepower ratings of these motors range from about 3 to 100 hp.

6. Rheostatic Elevator Control. In installations where economics prevents use of variable-voltage control or where low rise and low speeds (150 to 300 fpm) and traffic conditions do not justify the use of the more costly variable voltage control, the traction machine may be driven either by an a-c or d-c motor whose speed is controlled by rheostat (variable resistance). Such elevators are usually operated by an operator's hand wheel or lever in the car. Figure 25.5 (*a*) is a schematic wiring diagram

of the rheostatic connections of an a-c 3-phase induction motor for a geared traction elevator; and (*b*) for a d-c compound-wound motor on a gearless traction elevator. In (*a*) the contactors (magnetic switches) *A*, *B*, *C*, *D*, and *E* are successively closed as the motor starts and accelerates to full speed. They are opened in the reverse order, *E*, *D*, *C*, *B*, *A*, when the speed is retarded. The opening and closing are automatically timed by relays which are energized by the controller in the car. Within the control panel is a switch (not shown) which changes the internal connections of the motor so that two definite speed ranges may be ob-

Table 25.1 Comparative Table of Geared and Gearless Elevators

	Rise (feet)	Speed (fpm)	Control	Life	Maintenance	Initial Cost	Smoothness
Geared	50–150 50–150	50–200 50–350	Rheostatic, Variable voltage	20–25 years for gear and worm	Medium	Low Medium	Low Medium
Gearless	Above 100	400 and up	Variable voltage	Indefinite	Low	High	High

tained in addition to the intermediate speed steps due to the rheostatic control.

In Fig. 25.5b the d-c motor is accelerated and adjusted in speed by the resistances A, B, C, D, E, which are controlled in the same manner as in the a-c rheostatic drive. Intermediate steps of speed control are obtained by the field rheostat R, which is

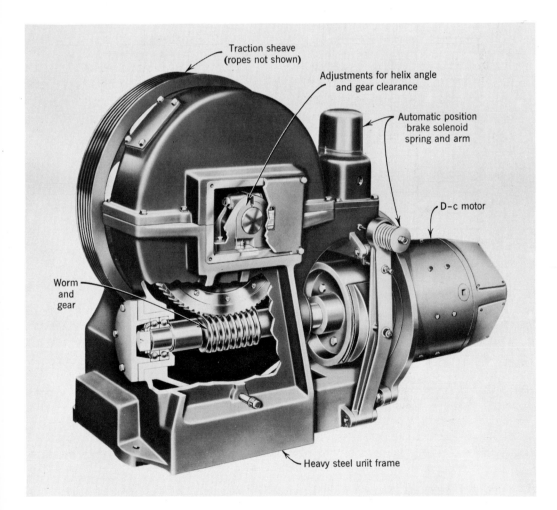

Fig. 25.4   Cutaway view of a typical geared traction machine. (Westinghouse Electric Corp.)

driven automatically by a small motor. Acceleration, retardation, and constant running speeds are initiated in all rheostatic systems by the car operator, but usually he has no control of the rate of acceleration or retardation.

Automatic leveling is available on some a-c 2-speed rheostatically controlled eleva-

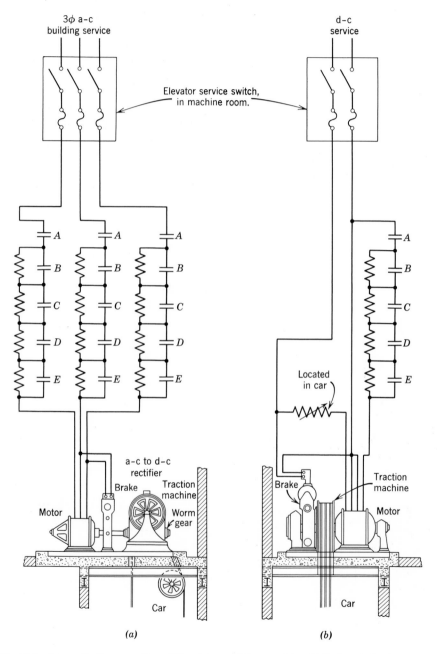

Fig. 25.5 Schematic diagram of two different types of elevator drive. (a) 3-phase induction motor, (b) d-c compound wound motor. The speed of these elevators is varied by rheostatic control. Rheostatic systems are usually associated with geared elevator machines.

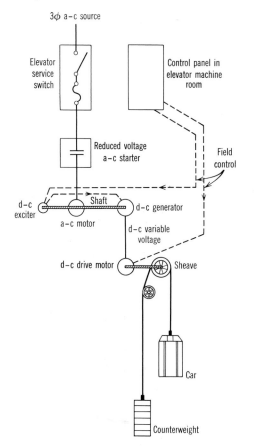

Fig. 25.6 Variable voltage elevator control from an a-c source.

(known as an m-g set) by control of the field of the d-c generator of the set. It is therefore apparent that a separate m-g set is required for each elevator. All gearless elevators and most geared machines utilize this method of control. Since a motor-generator set is interposed between the elevator machine and the building power supply, the motor of the m-g set can readily be matched to building power in voltage and frequency, e.g., 240 volts d-c, 120/208 volts a-c, 480 volts a-c, etc. The generators of the m-g set must be provided with an integral exciter unless the building service is d-c in which case the d-c excitation can be taken directly from the line (see Figs. 25.6 and 25.7).

This system of control provides smooth

tor motors, operating at car speeds up to 100 fpm.

On single speed a-c machines "inching" control is available which will allow a car to park several inches above or below a landing, with the doors open.

Single speed a-c motor installations are least desirable from the smoothness of ride viewpoint. Two-speed motors give a somewhat better ride, but still considerably inferior to installations utilizing adjustable voltage control.

7. Variable Voltage Elevator Control. This system of elevator control requires that a variable voltage be impressed on the d-c traction machine motor, thus varying the speed of the drive. This variable voltage is obtained from a motor-generator set

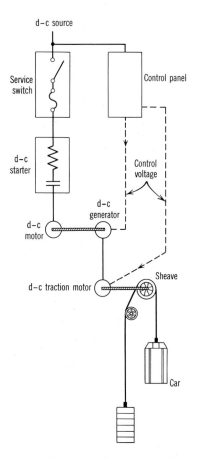

Fig. 25.7 Variable voltage elevator control from a d-c source.

Fig. 25.8   Typical Elevator Control and Selector Panel—note the sliding brushes at the right of the panel. These move in synchronism with the actual elevator car and supply exact car location information. (Westinghouse Electric Corp., Elevator Division)

and accurate speed regulation and efficient operation, in addition to lending itself readily to automatic control systems. Automatic leveling is furnished which compensates for temperature, elevator loading and normal rope stretch.

Leveling is generally accomplished by means of magnetic contactors mounted on the car and so arranged that when the car passes a certain point in the shaft, a fixed ferromagnetic (steel) plate closes the magnetic circuit of the contactor causing it to operate its electric contact. These contacts in turn are connected to circuits in the controller and thus the exact position of the car is established regardless of rope stretch, temperature expansion, etc. The exact position of the car being established, other relays and control devices automatically level the car at the landing. Figure 25.1 shows the positioning of these devices in the hoistway.

Whenever an elevator is to be put into operation, the respective m-g set is started remotely by lobby push button or by corridor call button. The m-g set comes up to speed slowly, through a reduced voltage a-c starter. When the d-c generator has developed full voltage, the elevator control is cut in and the car is ready for operation.

The car operator or automatic signals initiate the automatic sequence for accelerating. The various control devices in the panel release the brake and energize the generator field, thus starting the elevator motor. As voltage comes up to normal the elevator accelerates to its rated speed. Reverse operations are initiated when decelerating and finally stopping (landing) the car. When the car stops, the brake magnet contactor opens, allowing the spring to force the brake band against the brake drum and hold the sheave and elevator stationary.

A signal-control elevator is very largely controlled automatically by a relay panel or selector device which makes the necessary electrical contacts to register the corridor and car calls and actuates the various signals in the lobby, corridors, and car. This automatic equipment allows the waiting passenger to initiate a stop at his floor by means of the "up" or "down" buttons. The system control and selector panel contains a sort of miniature elevator system, with sets of contacts over which small contact brushes move in synchronism with the corresponding car movements in the shaft. These contacts indicate to the controller the points at which specific control

procedures should be initiated. The brushes are moved by mechanical reduction gearing driven by control cables fastened to the car, or by electric motors rotating in synchronism with the car travel. The main controller determines the direction of car travel, the starting acceleration, running, leveling and stopping, and opening and closing of the doors. Figure 25.8 shows a typical controller.

8. Arrangements of Elevator Machines, Sheaves, and Ropes. The simplest method of arranging vertical travel of a car would be to pass a rope over a pulley and to counterbalance the weight of the car by a counterweight. Then, by rotating the pulley, the car would move up or down and require very little energy to move it. This is essentially the scheme which is used on a majority of high-speed passenger elevators and is illustrated in Fig. 25.9a. The pulley referred to above is made in the form of a cylindrical sheave containing grooves for the several ropes which support the weight of the car.

When the supporting ropes merely pass over the sheave (in the grooves) and connect directly to the counterweights, the lifting power is exerted by the sheave through the traction of the ropes in the grooves.

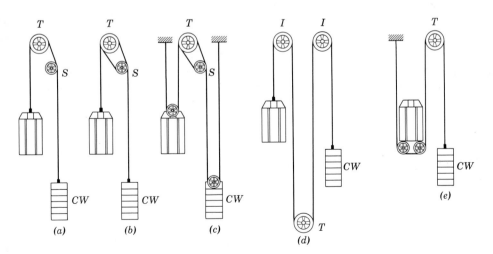

Fig. 25.9 Typical elevator rope and sheave arrangements, (a), (b), and (c) for machine installed above hoistway, (d), (e) machine installed at the bottom of hoistway.

This system is referred to as the single-wrap traction elevator machine. The function of sheave *S* is merely that of a guide pulley; usually it is called the deflector sheave. Each of the three or more supporting ropes lies in a groove cut parallel to all other grooves on the sheave.

In Fig. 25.9*b* the ropes from the car are first wrapped over the traction sheave *T*, then around the secondary or idler sheave *S*, once more around sheave *T*, and back over *S* to the counterweights. This arrangement is characteristic of the *one-to-one, double-wrap traction machine*. It provides greater traction than the single-wrap machine and is used in many automatic hi-speed installations.

In the arrangements of Figs. 25.9*a*, *b*, and *d*, the amount of rope paid out over the support sheave is equal to the distance the elevator travels; hence the one-to-one nomenclature. In Fig. 25.9*c*, however, the amount of rope paid out is double the elevator travel, thus giving such an arrangement the name double-wrap traction, two-to-one roping. Since the sheave travels faster relative to elevator travel with this roping than with the one-to-one type, it provides the economy of high-speed motors. Its principal application is on very heavy, short-travel passenger or freight elevators. Its use is generally limited to elevators rated at speeds not greater than 500 fpm or to freight elevators with heavy loads at speeds less than 500 fpm.

In types *a*, *b*, and *c*, the elevator machines are located at the top of the hoistway. When the elevator machines are placed in the basement a very different arrangement of cables and sheaves must be utilized to secure the same results. Figure 25.9*d* shows such an arrangement. Much more rope is required when elevator machines are located in the basement, and consequently the problems of rope maintenance are increased. These systems however obviate the necessity for a penthouse, and where this is desirable for architectural or other reasons, this arrangement is used.

The roping shown in Fig. 25.9*e* is unusual, being applicable generally to low-speed, low-rise residential or commercial use. Rise does not normally exceed 50 ft nor speed 100 fpm. All the ropings illustrated are used with a full range of car capacities of up to 4000 lbs.

9. Hoisting Ropes and Counterweights. The ropes which are connected to the crosshead (top beam of the elevator) and which carry the weight of the car and its live load are made of groups of traction steel wires especially designed for this application. All cables have a hemp core which serves as a support for the strands. Figure 25.10 shows the general construction of an elevator cable.

The factor of safety is usually taken as 7.0 for passenger elevators and 12.0 for freight elevators.

Frequent inspection of elevator cable is important. Inspection will indicate when it is necessary to shorten the rope because of its natural stretch, to equalize the tension in parallel ropes, to remove the twist from ropes, and finally to replace them. Wire ropes should be properly lubricated at all times.

In order to compensate for rope weight

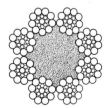

Rope lay, 8 × 19 rope

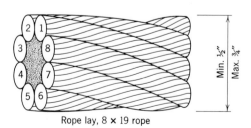

Fig. 25.10 General construction of typical elevator hoisting rope. The black section represents hemp core.

which in high rise elevators becomes an important factor, cables are attached to the bottom of the car and the counterweight, thus equalizing loads regardless of the cab position. These cables can be seen in Fig. 25.1.

Counterweights comprise a steel frame in which weights are placed, totalling car dead weight plus 40 percent of live load. Use of the counterweight provides lowered power costs and adequate traction for empty or loaded cars.

10. Safety Devices. The main brake of an elevator is mounted directly on the shaft of the elevator machine, (see Fig. 25.3). It controls the brake shoes which are forced against the brake drum by springs. The brake is released by the action of a d-c electromagnet and is set by the springs when the magnet is deenergized. When d-c machines are used, the elevator is first slowed down by dynamic braking action of the motor and the brake then operates to clamp the brake drum thus holding the car still at the floor.

A safety is designed to stop an elevator car automatically before the car's speed becomes excessive. The action of this device is controlled by a centrifugal fly ball or fly weight governor, (Fig. 25.11), which is independent of the other elevator machinery. At normal speeds the safety system has no effect on the operation of the elevator. On overspeed the governor will cut off the power to the d-c motor and set the brake. This usually stops the car, but, should the speed still increase, the governor actuates the two safety rail clamps, which are mounted at the bottom of the car, one on each side. These devices clamp the guide rails by wedging action bringing the car to a smooth stop.

Oil or spring buffers are always placed in the elevator pit. Their purpose is not to stop a falling car but to bring it to a partially cushioned stop if it should overtravel the lower terminal.

Electrical final-limit switches are located a few feet below and above the safe travel limits of the elevator car. If the car overtravels (down or up), these switches deenergize the traction motor and set the main brake.

11. Elevator Doors. The choice of car and hoistway door affects the speed and quality of elevator service considerably. Doors for most modern passenger elevators are power operated and synchronized with the leveling controls so that the doors are fully opened by the time a cab comes to a complete stop at the landing. The closing time however varies with the type of door and size of opening. The available types are shown in Fig. 25.12 along with typical applications. The 2-speed design is used where a car may be automatic or attendant operated; the slower speed being used in the former case for safety reasons and the higher speed in the latter case where the operator can visually determine that no passenger is blocking the doorway.

Detection of passengers on the car threshold can be accomplished electronically by beams across the doorway. Interruption of these beams will prevent a door from closing or will cause a door to reopen which has begun to close.

All automatic elevators, whether equipped with detection beams or not, are required by Code to have a safety edge device on the car doors that will cause the car and hoistway doors, which operate in synchronism, to reopen when the safety edge meets any obstruction.

12. Cabs and Signals. Possibly the only area in which the architect has a free hand in selection of equipment is in the decor of the cabs and the styling of hallway and cab signals. A normal elevator specification is a functional one which describes the intended operation of the equipment, and normally includes an amount to cover optional decor of the cabs. The type and functioning of signal equipment is also specified, but finish and styling are optional. Cab interiors may be finished in

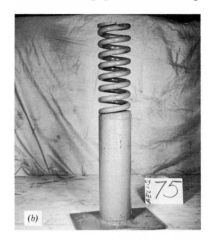

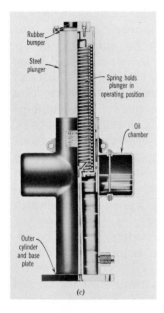

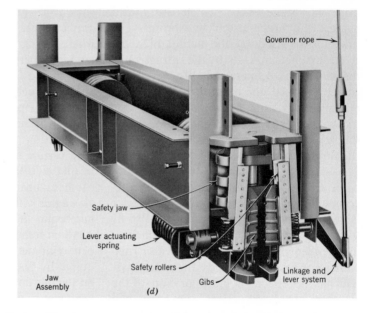

Fig. 25.11 Elevator Safety Devices. The elevator governor (a) which may be of the simple flyball type or the more complex unit illustrated, functions on car overspeed. The governor trips, clamping the governor rope (d) and releasing the safety jaws which exert a constant retarding force on the car rails, thus bringing the car to a gradual and safe stop. Buffers at the bottom of the car shaft are either of the spring type (b) or the oil type (c). (Westinghouse Electric Corp., Elevator Division)

wood paneling, plastic (Micarta or Formica), stainless steel, or almost any material desired. Floors may be tile, wood, or carpeting as selected. Illumination may be from ceiling fixtures, coves, or completely illuminated luminous ceiling, of standard or special design. For each bank of elevators, it is wise to furnish at least one set of

wall mats, to protect wall finishes when cars are being used to move tenant furniture.

The purpose of the hallway lantern is to signal the approach of a car. This is normally accomplished by a two color lantern to which may be added an audible signal to draw the attention of waiting persons.

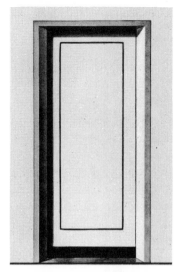

(a) Single–Speed
Small office or apartment

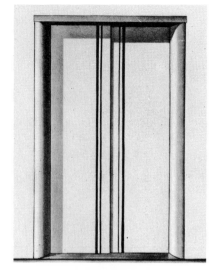

(c) Two–Speed
General commercial

(b) Center–Opening
Hospital

(d) Two–Speed Center–Opening
Department store

Fig. 25.12   Typical hoistway doors and applications.

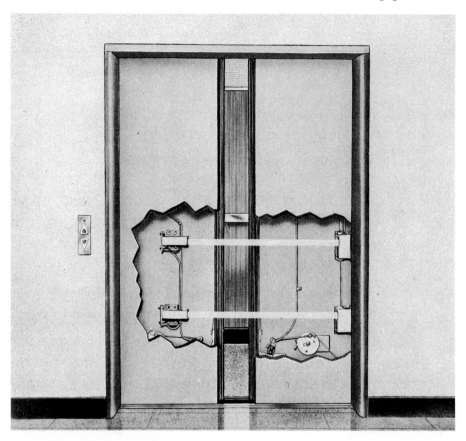

Fig. 25.13   Electric eye door protection is added to many installations to avoid annoyance caused by contacting the safety door edge.

If desired, the hallway lantern can be equipped with indication as well, which will visually show the exact position of the car in the hoistway and the direction of travel. This indicator, as well as the indicator normally installed over the door inside the car, operates from contacts in the machine room, thus eliminating tapes and chains.

The hallway car-call device, normally a push button, serves to signal the car and, when furnished with illumination, also can indicate the direction of car motion if the lantern device is not so equipped.

Although many designs are commercially standard, the architect may at his discretion design the lanterns, indicators, and push buttons to complement the building architecture. Several of the common types are illustrated in Fig. 25.14.

C. SYSTEMS OF ELEVATOR OPERATION AND SUPERVISION

13. Single Automatic Push-Button Control. This system is the simplest of the passenger-operated automatic control schemes since it handles only one call at a time, providing an uninterrupted trip for each call. A single corridor button at each level can register a call only when the car is not in motion. This control scheme is applicable only to a short-rise, inactive elevator, that is, one making 5 or fewer trips per hour. Such elevators are found in small apartment houses, residences, or small professional buildings.

14. Collective Control. With an increase in traffic, it is not possible to bypass waiting calls at landings (as the single-button control just described does) and maintain acceptable service. The control is therefore arranged to collect all waiting "up" calls on the trip up and all waiting "down" calls on the trip down, and is referred to, logically, as a *collective* control system. The control system "stores" all calls until they are answered, and automatically reverses the direction of travel at the highest and lowest calls. When all calls have been cleared the car will remain at the floor of its last stop awaiting the next call, and its

motor generator set will stop after several minutes. Pressure on any "up" or "down" button at any landing or any floor button in the car will start the m-g set and set the car into operation.

Collective control cars are normally arranged to be operated without attendants, although often a part-time attendent is desirable and manual controls may be provided accordingly. The attendant controls door closing, travel direction and can bypass landing calls when the car is full. (This is also known as "expressing" the car.)

Collective control is best adapted to locations where service requirements are moderate such as in apartment houses, small offices, and hospitals. Since these locations often require more than one car,

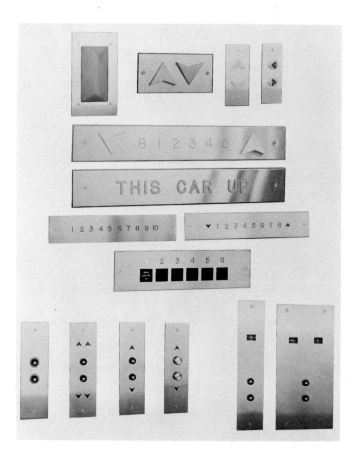

Fig. 25.14 Lanterns, push-buttons and indicators. (Armor Elevator Co.)

collective control is available for groups of 1 to 3 cars. This control scheme automatically assigns each landing call to the car best situated to answer it, prevents more than one car from answering a call, allows one car to be detached for freight duty while others serve passengers, and automatically parks all but one car at the ground floor, the other car acting as a free car until service calls require the use of the parked cars.

15. Electronic Group Supervisory Collective Dispatching and Control. Although collective control furnishes adequate and dependable elevator service where requirements are light to moderate, it is still basically a signal controlled system which weighs all calls equally and takes no cognizance of traffic patterns. Recognizing this shortcoming, elevator engineers after much developmental work evolved the traffic pattern controlled supervisory system found today in most office buildings and other locations with heavy traffic which follows a regular pattern.

The Otis Elevator Company and the Elevator Division of the Westinghouse Electric Corporation have been the pioneers in research and development of these group supervisory collective dispatching and control systems. The Otis system is referred to as Autotronic Elevatoring; the Westinghouse as the Selectomatic Elevator System.

Inspection of Fig. 25.15 shows that there are 2 peak periods; one up and one down, corresponding to the incoming and outgoing crowds. During the day traffic is balanced except for the noon lunch-hour peaks, and finally before and after working hours the traffic is light in both directions. This particular traffic pattern chart lends itself readily therefore to a 6-program system, viz. *up-peak, balanced, heavy-down, heavy-up, down-peak, and off-hours,* corresponding to the incoming rush, morning and afternoon off hours, lunch-out, lunch-return, homeward-rush, and non-working hours respectively. These programs may be selected by the starter at the lobby control panel or the control may be set to "Automatic Traffic Control" in which case the

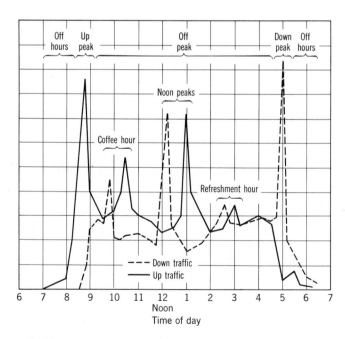

Fig. 25.15   Typical office building traffic chart—diversified tenancy.

system counts and times calls, weighs cars, and automatically selects a traffic pattern based on this data. This selection includes automatic establishment of zones within the building in order to minimize waiting time during peak periods of travel.

Programs other than the above are available which will satisfy almost any traffic pattern. These systems are generally designed around operatorless cars although the cars are normally equipped for manual operation as well.

Some special features of this control are:

1. Cars act as weighing platforms, giving "start" and "express" signals when loaded.
2. Doors open at full speed and close at reduced speed; all doors are equipped with safety edges.
3. When a car is delayed it is automatically dropped out of the control system, and registers a trouble call.
4. During off-hours cars are put into and taken out of service as required by traffic.

The most recent development along the lines of automation is the design of a control system which does not adhere and is therefore not bound to fixed traffic patterns, but develops an unlimited number of different traffic patterns, according to traffic conditions. This design is particularly suited to buildings with heavy irregular and erratic traffic such as in large hotels and urban apartment houses.

Detection devices record traffic calls, waiting times, and individual car loads and positions. This information is fed into a computer which controls all car movements, each car being controlled and dispatched individually. Thus cars can reverse in travel (down to an up call which was just passed, and up to a down call) to eliminate excessive and wasteful travel.

16. Control and Indication Panels. An indicator panel and a control panel (also called a starter's or traffic director's panel) is furnished with each group of elevators

and is usually mounted in an accessible and easily viewed location in the lobby. The functions of the various devices are indicated in Fig. 25.16.

A dial switch provides for manual control of traffic pattern when automatic control is not desired. Another dial switch can be provided to change the dispatching interval between up and down dispatching signals at the terminals for any position of

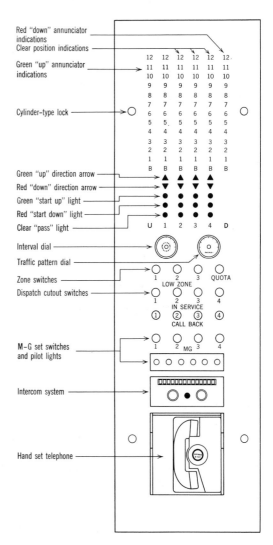

Fig. 25.16 Typical starter's control and indicator panel. Separate equipment is furnished for each group of elevators. Equipment for more than a single group may be assembled into a single fixture.

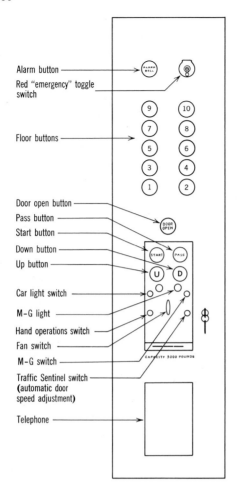

Fig. 25.17 Selectomatic-automatic car station with optional manual feature.

the traffic flow dial switch. Up and down manual dispatching buttons are used if required to dispatch a car in the up or down direction ahead of the schedule established by the automatic timing device. One zone switch is used per elevator in buildings utilizing a zone system to transfer cars individually to operate in the lower zone or the upper zone of the building as desired. Dispatching cutout switches are furnished for each car and used to disconnect individual cars from dispatch systems in the event it is desired to take any car out of service. Signal buttons (call back) are for prearranged signaling to car operators by prearranged code. Motor-generator pilot

lights indicate when each motor-generator set and its corresponding car are in or out of operation. Motor-generator switches are for starting and stopping the motor generators, and they cause doors of parked cars to open automatically when the car is put in service.

17. Car Panel. The car panel for a Westinghouse Selectomatic car is illustrated in Fig. 25.17. When control is transferred from automatic to manual-attendant a buzzer sounds every time a corridor call is registered, to alert the operator. The door closing is manually initiated and the doors operate at a higher speed than when on automatic, thus reducing time delays.

18. Location of Elevators and Elevator Lobbies. The elevator lobbies and shafts form one of the major space factors with which the architect is concerned. The elevator lobby on each floor is the focal point from which the corridors radiate for access to all rooms, stairways, service rooms, etc. Such lobbies obviously must be located one above the other. The ground-floor elevator lobby (also called the lower terminal) must be conveniently located with respect to main entrances; the modern equipment within or placed adjacent to this area should include public telephones, building directory, elevator starter service, elevator indicators, and control panels.

All lobbies should be adequate in area for the peak-load gathering of passengers to insure rapid and comfortable service to all. The number of people per floor contributing to the period of peak load for example, within a 15- to 20-min peak determines the required lobby area on the floor.

Approximately 4 sq ft of floor space per person should be provided at peak periods for waiting passengers at a given elevator or bank of elevators. The number of hallways leading to such lobbies should also provide about 4 sq ft per person approaching the lobby. This requires a check of human traffic through all approaches to elevator facilities. An ideal installation would provide a car "always waiting" at a given landing. Actually, excellent design provides an expected waiting period or interval of from 20 to 30 seconds at any landing.

The main lower terminal of elevator banks is generally on the street floor level, although some buildings place this terminal on the basement or mezzanine level, particularly when the elevations of the street entrances vary around the building so that one side of the building is on the mezzanine level while another main entrance is at a lower level. Such a situation is ideal for the use of escalators which will economically and rapidly carry large numbers of persons between levels thus making practical and efficient a single main lower elevator terminal. The upper terminal is usually the top floor of the building. In certain types of very tall buildings the lower zones (stories) are served by local elevators; the next zone by another bank of elevators which travel express through the lower zone, then local through the second zone, etc.

Occasionally, it is necessary in tall buildings to consider what number of elevators shall be installed to give local service to a zone of about half the floors above the street level; and what number shall be installed to give initial express service to the first floor of the upper-local-zone with local

service thereafter to the top floor. This consideration poses the question as to whether all elevator shafts should be designed to continue to the top floor, or whether the lower local-service elevator shafts should be terminated just above the last floor of that zone.

In general it is desirable to establish future maximum traffic conditions to all upper floors and extend shaftways according to these expected demands. It is also possible that escalators between certain upper floors might be anticipated for future local zone traffic, instead of extending elevator shafts.

One factor that has been considered as a result of electric power failures is the provision of escape doors in the lower portions of upper-zone elevator shafts in high-rise buildings. Provision is always made for emergency egress through the top of the elevator cab, but where no door is provided in the shaft, passengers are trapped in the car until power is restored. (A solution to this problem in existing buildings with such blind shafts is the use of a standby electric generator to supply power to stalled elevators).

19. General Considerations in Elevator Selection. In selecting the capacity and number of elevators and the type of elevator system for a given building, the building characteristics and the up- and down-

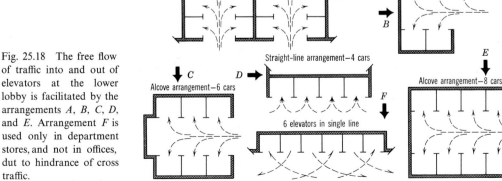

Fig. 25.18 The free flow of traffic into and out of elevators at the lower lobby is facilitated by the arrangements *A*, *B*, *C*, *D*, and *E*. Arrangement *F* is used only in department stores, and not in offices, dut to hindrance of cross traffic.

travel requirements of its population must be known or estimated. The class of work of the occupants and the type of building provide a basis for estimating the building population. Thus banks, large business offices, subdivided offices, department stores, apartment houses, and hospitals all suggest different traffic requirements.

Population estimates for office buildings are based on the available floor area, for apartment houses on the number of bedrooms, and for hospitals on the number of beds. Table 25.2 gives some typical values of floor area per person.

In the central business district in large

Table 25.2 Population of Typical Buildings for Estimating Elevator and Escalator Requirements

Office buildings	Sq ft per person
Diversified:	
Large lower floors	90 to 100*
Upper floors	100 to 125
Average use	100
Single purpose	75 to 90
Hotels	Persons per sleeping room
Normal use	1.3
Conventions	1.7
Hospitals	Visitors per bed†
General private	1.5
General public (large wards)	3 to 4
Apartment houses	Persons per apartment
One or two small bedrooms	3.0
One or two rooms "efficiency"	2.0
High rental; one or two bedrooms	2.0 to 3.0
Moderate rental housing	2.8
Low cost housing	4.0

* Density may vary for different floors. Clerical and stenographic area may have a population density as high as 50 sq ft per person.

† If visiting hours are restricted, visitor population will determine elevator requirements. If visiting is not restricted to only a certain few hours, staff requirements may determine elevator design. Where traffic is heavy, a combination of passenger cars and larger 'hospital' cars should be used to provide optimum service.

cities the service competition of similar types of buildings in the area must be considered. People should not be conscious of delays in elevator service. In first-class office building elevator installations the waiting period or interval should be not more than 25 to 30 secs. The "waiting time" or "interval" is defined as the time (in seconds) between cars leaving a terminal floor. Mathematically, for a given bank of elevators, it is the average roundtrip time of an elevator divided by the number of elevators in the bank which are operating. An interval as high as 40 secs is permissible in some office installations.

Another measure of the quality of the elevator installation is the passenger-carrying capacity. This is generally expressed as the percentage of the building population that can be carried one way in 5 min. In high-class installations this is approximately 13 percent, although this figure may be much greater in single-occupancy type buildings on a single schedule. Traffic studies are generally based on the morning up-peak period as this is the time of greatest demand on the elevator system.

In making a traffic study, building characteristics such as the number of floors, the floor heights, and the travel distance are generally known. The building population must be estimated as indicated above. If a particular type of elevator is then assumed, the average roundtrip time, the waiting interval, and the number of elevators required may be determined.

(a) Office Buildings, Hotels, and Industrial Buildings. The expected population may be estimated from Table 25.2. An interval of 30 secs is desirable, although slightly longer is acceptable in all except large structures in congested areas. A 5-minute capacity of 13 percent of building population is usual. The basic type of control is automatic electronic supervisory (Selectomatic or Autotronic), although collective control is satisfactory for small buildings with up to 3 cars. Table 25.3 lists

Table 25.3 Elevator Equipment Recommendations

Usage		Car Capacity (Pounds)	Minimum Car Speed* Feet per Min.	Car Travel Feet
Office Buildings			350–400	0 to 125
	Small Building	2500	500–600	126 to 225
	Medium Building	3000	700	226 to 275
	Large Building	3500	800	276 to 375
			1000	above 375
Hotels		2500		
		3000	as above	as above
Hospitals			150	0–60
			200	61–100
		3500	250–300	101–125
		4000	350–400	126–175
			500–600	176–250
			700	above 250
Apartment Houses†			100	0–75
		2000	200	76–125
		2500	250–300	126–200
			350–400	above 200
Retail Stores			200	0–100
		3500	250–300	101–150
		4000	350–400	151–200
		5000	500	above 200

* Geared equipment is used up to 350 fpm, gearless at higher speeds.

† FHA minimum requirements call for full-collective variable voltage control; minimum of 2 cars; and approximately 120 bedrooms per car, for all buildings exceeding 7 stories in height.

the characteristics of equipment usually used in these buildings.

The service requirements discussed herein do not consider freight cars, being based purely on passenger requirements. Freight car, dumbwaiter, and escalator application will be discussed in Chapters 26 and 27.

(b) *Apartment Houses.* Studies indicate that apartment house traffic depends not only upon population but also upon location and type of tenant. Houses with many children experience a school-hour peak; houses in midtown with predominantly adult tenancy exhibit evening peaks due to the homecoming working group and outgoing amusement traffic.

Normally a single elevator will suffice, although a second car functioning as a service and (or) passenger car is sometimes indicated, particularly in buildings taller than 6 stories. The cars may be banked or separated, as desired.

Self-service collective control is the general choice, with provision for attendant control in high-class buildings. With smaller cars and short rise, a swing-type manual corridor door is acceptable; in larger installations both the cab and corridor door should be the power-operated sliding type. Table 25.3 lists the preferred combinations of equipment for apartment applications.

Since peaks are not pronounced in apartment houses, a 5-minute carrying capacity of 7 to 8 percent is considered adequate. Also, due to the nature of the traffic, an interval of 60 to 80 seconds is acceptable.

(c) *Hospitals.* As mentioned in Table 25.2, the governing factor in the determination of elevator requirements may be either normal hospital traffic or visitors traffic, depending upon the visiting-hour schedule.

Due to the large amount of vehicular traffic such as stretcher carts, wheel chairs, beds, linen carts, laundry trucks, etc., the elevator cabs are much deeper than the normal passenger-type. This type of car when used for passenger service holds over 20 persons and therefore gives slow service. For this reason, it is occasionally advisable to utilize some normal passenger cars in addition to hospital-size cars, particularly in large hospitals.

The use of tray and bulk carts in food service imposes a considerable load on the elevators before, during, and after meals, and passenger service is seriously disrupted. To alleviate this congestion and

delay, many architects and hospital administrators investigate the use of dumbwaiter cars which will handle a $15\frac{1}{2}''$ x 20'' food tray. Dumbwaiters can also be used for transporting pharmaceuticals and other items.

Elevators should be grouped centrally, although separated by type of use. Car control is normally collective, manually controlled with optional self-service operation for the larger cars and self-service collective or fully automatic with manual option for the passenger size cars.

Population of the hospital may be estimated from Table 25.2. Experience has shown that a carrying capacity of 45 passengers in a 5-min period is adequate (estimating each vehicle as equivalent to 9 passengers).

Intervals should not exceed 1 minute. Car and corridor doors should be power-operated and cars must, of course, be self-

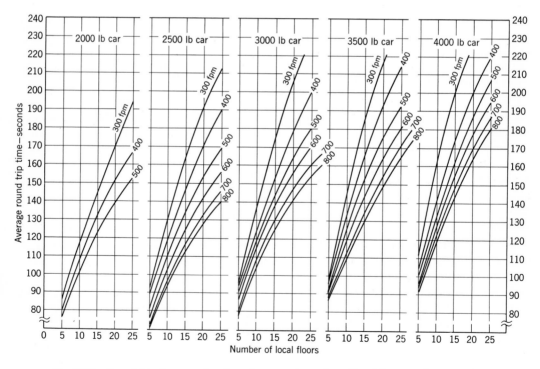

Fig. 25.19   Round-trip time as a function of car speed, number of local floors, and car capacity. Floor height is taken at 12 ft.

levelling. Recommended combinations of hospital equipment are shown in Table 25.3.

(*d*) *Retail Stores.* Retail stores present a unique problem in vertical transportation inasmuch as the objective is partially to transport persons to a specific level and partially to expose these persons to a display of merchandise. A combination of elevators and escalators is therefore normally used; the elevators for the use of persons heading for a particular place in the store; the escalators for "shoppers."

Elevators should be planned for between 10 and 20 percent of average store population. Table 25.3 lists standard store elevator equipment.

Control is normally manual collective with power operated doors. Cars are arranged in a straight-line pattern to facilitate loading and waiting.

20. Elevator Selection. As mentioned in Section 19 above, having established the building physical characteristics and population and having decided upon a desired interval and 5-min passenger capacity, it remains then only to select an elevator from the table of recommendations to determine the number of elevators required. To accomplish this, we have reference to the curves in Figs. 25.19 and 25.20 which show the relationship between average round-trip time and rise with parameters of capacity and elevator speed. The total average round-trip time is comprised of 4 factors; namely, time to accelerate and decelerate, time to open and close doors, time to load and unload, and running time. Door closing time is calculated for a 3 ft 6 in. bi-parting door closing at 1.25 ft per second.

These curves are applicable to all types of buildings except department stores, the traffic problems of which do not yield to solutions designed for maximum passenger transfer in minimum time.

The curves are shown for fully automatic operation. If the cars are to be attendant operated, the round trip time can be de-

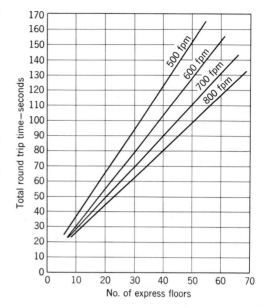

Fig. 25.20   Round-trip time as a function of car speed and number of express floors. All car capacities are approximately equal. Curves assume 12-ft floor height.

creased slightly due to faster door closing.

An example will best illustrate the use of the foregoing tables and curves:

EXAMPLE 25.1. An office building for which the following round-trip time analysis is typical, contains 28 rentable floors. Distance between floor levels is 12 ft. In this building it has been decided that the local floors are from the ground-to the fourteenth

Table 25.4   Car Passenger Capacity

Elevator Capacity Lbs	Maximum Passenger Capacity	Normal Passenger* Load per Trip
1200	7	6
2000	12	10
2500	16	13
3000	19	16
3500	22	18
4000	26	21

*The number of passengers carried on a trip during peak conditions is 80% of the car capacity.

floor, the express zone extending from the fifteenth to the twenty-eighth floor. The system is to have automatic leveling, power-operated doors, and completely automatic programmed operations. The estimated building population in the upper zone is 1200 people and 1500 in the lower zone. The maximum waiting interval is to be 30 seconds and the required passenger ca-pacity is 13 percent of population in 5 min.

The problem is to find the combination of elevator capacity, speed, and number of cars that will most economically satisfy the stipulated requirements. Since this build-ing, like most buildings above 20 stories in height, utilizes local and express zones, the problem really resolves into 2 separate problems, the solution of which follows.

SOLUTION.

(a) *Local Service, Floors 1–14.*

   (1) Total rise is 168 ft (14 floors at 12 ft)
   (2) Assuming a 3000 lb. attendant-operated car using gearless equipment, from Table 25.3 we tentatively select for the given rise a speed of 600 fpm.
   (3) Consulting Fig. 25.19 we find that for a 3000 lb. car and 600 fpm, average round-trip time is 132 sec for 14 local floors.
   (4) To calculate the 5-min capacity of this elevator:

   5 min = 300 sec

$$\frac{300 \text{ sec}}{132 \text{ sec round-trip}} = 2.27 \text{ round trips}$$

   From Table 25.4 there are 16 passengers per trip; therefore

   $2.27 \times 16 = 36$ passengers in 5 min per car

   (5) Total population in lower zone is 1500.

   Desired 5 min capacity = 13% of 1500 = 195 persons for all cars

   Therefore, no. of cars required $= \dfrac{195}{36} = 5.5$

   Rounding this off to the next largest integral number, we would use 6 cars.

   (6) Interval $= \dfrac{\text{Round-trip time}}{\text{No. of cars}} = \dfrac{132}{6} = 22$ sec

   Since this is less than the 30 sec maximum interval specified it is acceptable.

   Therefore, one solution is 6 cars, 3000 lb. capacity at 600 fpm.

   (7) Trying a 3500 lb. car, we obtain:

   (8) Round trip time   = 138 sec (from Fig. 25.19)
   (9) Car capacity   = 18 persons (from Table 25.4)

   (10) 5-min capacity $= \dfrac{300 \times 18}{138} = 39$ persons per car

   (11) No. of cars required $= \dfrac{\text{Total 5 min. capacity}}{\text{5 min. capacity per car}} = \dfrac{195}{39} = 5$ cars

   (12) Interval $= \dfrac{138}{5} = 27.6$ sec

It is apparent then that *5 cars is the minimum* that will satisfy the requirement in the local zone, since the maximum acceptable 30 sec. interval is approached with 5 cars and would be exceeded with four cars of any capacity and speed.

(*b*) *Express Floors 15th–28th*

   (1) Total Rise $= 28 \times 12 = 336$ ft
   (2) From Table 25.3, we select a 800 fpm speed, using a 2500 lb car.
   (3) Round-trip time is the sum of the round-trip time for the nonstop express zone (Fig. 25.20) and round-trip time for local floors (Fig. 25.19).

   Total round trip $= 33$ sec $+ 109$ sec $= 142$ sec

   (4) 5-min capacity $= \dfrac{300}{142} \times 13$ passenger/trip $= 27.4$

   5-min requirement $= 13\%$ of 1200 $= 156$ people

   (5) Required No. of cars $= \dfrac{156}{27.4} = 6$ cars

   (6) Interval $= \dfrac{142}{6} = 23.6$ sec

Therefore, one acceptable solution is 6–2500 lb 800 fpm express cars.

   Trying a 3000 lb. car we find

   (7) Total round-trip time $= 33 + 120 = 153$ sec

   (8) 5-min capacity $= \dfrac{300}{153} \times 16 = 31.4$ passengers per car

   (9) No. of cars $= \dfrac{156 \text{ persons}}{31.4 \text{ persons}} = 5$ cars

   (10) Interval $= \dfrac{153}{5} = 30.6$ sec—*which is acceptable.*

Finally, trying a 3500-lb car

   (11) Total round-trip time $= 33 + 125 = 158$ sec

   (12) 5-min capacity $= \dfrac{300}{158} \times 18 = 34.3$ passengers per car

   (13) No. of cars $= \dfrac{156}{34.3} = 4.6$, or 5 cars

   (14) Interval $= \dfrac{158}{5} = 32$—*which is unacceptable.*

We now have as a first solution:

(*a*) 6—3000 lb 600 fpm local cars and
      6—2500 lb 800 fpm express cars

or

(*b*) 5—3500 lb 600 fpm local cars and
      5—3000 lb 800 fpm express cars

As an alternate, the entire building should be calculated for local service.

    (1) Selecting 3000 lb. 800 fpm cars from Table 25.3, we obtain

    (2) Round-trip time = 160 seconds from Fig. 25.19

    (3) 5-min requirement = 13% of 2700 = 350 people

    (4) 5-min capacity $= \dfrac{300}{160}(16) = 30.0$ passengers per car

    (5) No. of cars $\quad = \dfrac{350}{30.0} = 11.6 = 12$ cars

    (6) Interval $\quad\quad = \dfrac{160}{12} = 13.3$ sec

As a rule-of-thumb, the minimum interval obtainable in seconds equals the maximum car capacity, in passengers. Thus, the minimum interval for a 3000 lb car is 19 sec which would therefore be the interval for the 12—3000 lb 800 fpm cars.

Since this interval is considerably below the 30 second maximum, we can try 3500 lb cars, as follows:

    (1) Round-trip time = 173 sec

    (2) 5-min capacity $\quad = \dfrac{300}{173}(18) = 31.2$ people

    (3) No. of cars $\quad = \dfrac{350}{31.2} = 11$ cars

    (4) Interval $\quad\quad = \dfrac{173}{11} = 15.7$ sec

But, as above, minimum interval = 22 sec from Table 25.4 and our rule-of-thumb.

Finally, for *4000 lb cars*

    (1) Round-trip time = 190 sec.

    (2) 5-min capacity $\quad = \dfrac{300}{190}(21) = 33.2$

    (3) No. of cars $\quad = \dfrac{350}{33.2} = 11$ cars

    (4) Interval $\quad\quad = \dfrac{190}{11} = 17.3$ sec

    Min interval = 26 sec. This solution is discarded in favor of the 11—3500 lb cars.

Summarizing then we can use for *all local service:*

12—3000 lb 800 fpm cars or
11—3500 lb 800 fpm cars
and for local-express service:

6—3000 lb 600 fpm and 6—2500 lb 800 fpm cars or
5—3500 lb 600 fpm and 5—3000 lb 800 fpm cars

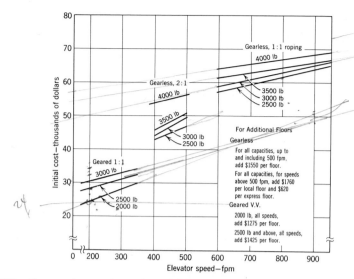

Fig. 25.21 Comparative cost figures for variable voltage-controlled elevator equipment. Cost data is for geared and gearless elevators in office buildings, general purpose buildings, hospitals, hotels, and industrial buildings with speeds of 200 to 800 fpm and with elevator passenger capacities from 2000 to 4000 lb. These curves are based on 6 floors (floor heights of 12′0″) upward. The cost data presented include cost of the complete elevator and its operating auxiliaries and control, including cab, entrances, and installation costs. It is emphasized that these cost data are for budget purposes only. Representatives of the manufacturers should be asked for specific quotations to be based on adequate specifications for a given proposed installation.

21. Economics of Elevator Selection. The final selection of a particular solution is made by the architect/engineer on the basis of several considerations, among which is first cost. Generally, gearless equipment is more expensive than geared, and costs vary directly with number, size and speed of cars. These relationships are shown graphically in Fig. 25.21. It must be emphasized that these figures are for comparative pricing only and that an actual quotation from a manufacturer should be obtained before arriving at a final decision. For a quick estimate, see Table 25.5. Applying the data shown in the curves to the problem at hand we obtain:

Express and Local Service:

(*a*) 6—3000 lb 600 fpm local:

basic elevator	$58,800	
additional floors		
(14 × 1760)	24,640	
	$83,440	
Cost of 6 cars		$500,640

6—2500 lb 800 fpm express:

basic elevator	62,000	
local floors		
(14 × 1760)	24,640	
express floors		
(14 × 620)	8,780	
	95,420	
Cost of 6 cars		572,520
Total Cost		$1,073,160

Similarly

(*b*) 5—3500 lb 600 fpm
           local $430,700
5—3000 lb 800 fpm
          express 483,100 $913,800

All Local Service:

(*c*) 12 cars 3000 lb 800 fpm $1,349,760
(*d*) 11 cars 3500 lb 800 fpm $1,217,480

We can thus readily see that the best solution economically (*b*) is probably also best

Table 25.5   *Office Buildings; Cost of Elevator and Electric Work*

Percent of Total Construction Cost

Item	Number of Stories		
	20 Sty.	35 Sty.	60 Sty.
Elevator Work	10.9%	11.9%	12.2%
Electric Work	13.3%	12.6%	12.2%

Based on 1963 National Averages

with respect to other considerations such as lobby arrangement and space, and penthouse and hoistway space.

22. Dimensions and Weights of Elevators. A set of standard dimensions for elevators has been agreed upon by the National Elevator Manufacturers Industry (NEMI). Typical layouts for elevators with gearless machines, capacities from 2500 to 4000 lb and speeds of 500 to 800 fpm are shown in

Table 25.6   *Some Approximate Dimensions of Gearless Elevator Equipment* *

Duty		Main Controller			Electronic Relay Panel			Selector			M-G Set		
Live Weight (lb)	FPM	W	D	H	W	D	H	W	D	H	W	D	H
3000 at	400												
2500	500	52	17	75	31	14	80	21	23	75	18	46	46
3000	500												
4000	400												
3500	500	52	17	86	31	14	80	21	23	75	18	46	46
4000	500												
3000	600												
3500	600	36	27	80	42	14	80	38	29	**	36	70	70
2500	700												
2500	800												
3000	800	36	27	80	42	14	80	38	29	**	44	75	75
3500	700												

* This table gives approximate dimensions in inches of the indicated equipment: W = width, D = depth, H = height.

** The height of selector depends on floors served since each floor adds 1 selector mechanism to the total height of the selector stack.

NOTES:

(1) The motor-generator set has a height of approximately the same dimensions as the length.

(2) If additional I-beams or a foundation is laid for the m-g set above the penthouse floor, then the height of the m-g set must be increased by the elevation of the extra foundation.

(3) The secondary level should have headroom of approximately 5 ft below the main elevator machine beams. The secondary level floor is designed and erected by other than the elevator manufacturing company.

(4) The double-wrap (secondary) sheave for gearless elevators is supported by the main elevator beams.

(5) The selector tape drive and the speed governor are normally supported on the secondary level, but occasionally are mounted to the penthouse floor.

(6) The penthouse floor and the secondary level floor must have removable trap doors and door supports if it is intended to raise and lower the main elevator machine through the elevator shaft.

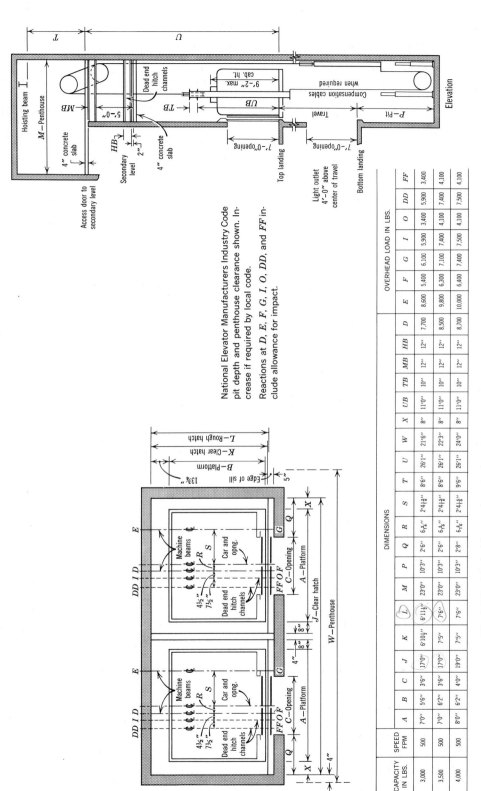

National Elevator Manufacturers Industry Code pit depth and penthouse clearance shown. Increase if required by local code.

Reactions at D, E, F, G, I, O, DD, and FF include allowance for impact.

Fig. 25.22 Typical layout data for general purpose gearless, variable voltage passenger elevators. 3000 to 4000 lbs; 500 fpm, 2:1 roping. (Westinghouse Electric Corp., Elevator Division)

CAPACITY IN LBS.	SPEED FPM	A	B	C	J	K	L	M	P	Q	R	S	T	U	W	X	UB	TB	MB	HB	D	E	F	G	I	O	DD	FF
																							OVERHEAD LOAD IN LBS.					
3,000	500	7'0"	5'6"	3'6"	17'0"	6'10½"	6'11½"	23'0"	10'3"	2'6"	6 5/16"	24 1/16"	8'6"	26'1"	21'6"	8"	11'0"	10"	12"	12"	7,700	8,600	5,400	6,100	5,900	3,400	5,900	3,400
3,500	500	7'0"	6'2"	3'6"	17'0"	7'5"	7'6"	23'0"	10'3"	2'6"	6 5/16"	24 1/16"	8'6"	26'1"	22'3"	8"	11'0"	10"	12"	12"	8,500	9,800	6,300	7,100	7,400	4,100	7,400	4,100
4,000	500	8'0"	6'2"	4'0"	19'0"	7'5"	7'6"	23'0"	10'3"	2'8"	6 5/16"	24 1/16"	9'6"	26'1"	24'0"	8"	11'0"	10"	12"	12"	8,700	10,000	6,400	7,400	7,500	4,100	7,500	4,100

561

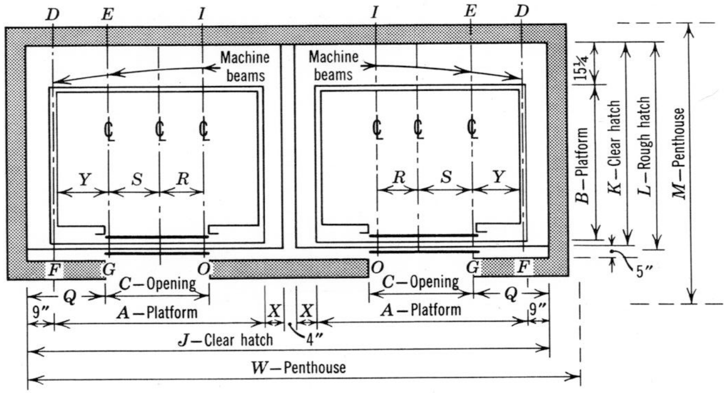

National Elevator Manufacturers Industry Std. pit depth and penthouse clearance shown. Increase if required by local code.

Reactions at D, E, F, G, I and O include allowance for impact.

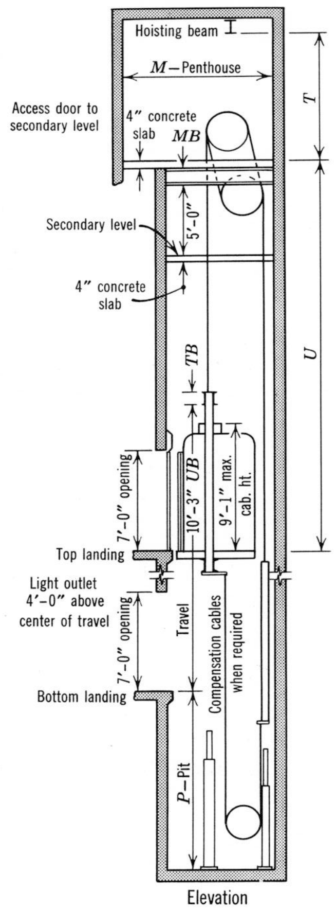

CAPACITY IN LBS.	SPEED FPM	DIMENSIONS																		OVERHEAD LOAD IN LBS.					
		A	*B*	*C*	*J*	*K*	*L*	*M*	*P*	*Q*	*R*	*S*	*T*	*U*	*W*	*X*	*Y*	*TB*	*MB*	*D*	*E*	*F*	*G*	*I*	*O*
2,500	700 800	7'0"	5'0"	3'6"	17'2"	6'4 1/2"	6'5 1/2"	23'0"	12'6"	2'6"	1'1 7/8"	2'0 1/8"	9'6" 10'6"	27'6" 29'10"	21'6"	8"	0	10"	15"	0	13,500 13,700	0	8,800 9,000	17,000 17,400	11,200 16,300
3,000	700 800	7'0"	5'6"	3'6"	17'2" 17'4"	6'10 1/2"	6'11 1/2"	23'0"	12'6" 12'6"	2'6"	1'1 7/8" 1'3 1/8"	2'0 1/8" 1'4 5/8"	9'6" 10'6"	27'6" 29'10"	21'6"	8" 9"	2'4 1/2"	10"	15" 14"	0 8,200	14,600 10,300	0 5,000	9,000 6,200	18,300 21,300	11,200 13,000
3,500	700 800	7'0"	6'2"	3'6"	17'4"	7'6 1/2"	7'7 1/2"	23'0" 24'0"	12'6" 13'0"	2'6"	1'3 1/8"	1'4 5/8"	10'6"	27'6" 29'10"	22'3"	9"	2'4 1/2"	10"	14"	8,800 9,100	11,300 11,500	5,200 5,300	6,400 6,700	23,800 24,800	14,100 14,500
4,000	700 800	8'0"	6'2"	3'10"	19'4"	7'6 1/2"	7'7 1/2"	23'0" 24'0"	12'6" 13'0"	2'8"	1'9 1/4"	1'7 3/4"	10'6"	27'6" 29'10"	24'0"	9"	2'0 1/2"	10"	14"	8,800 8,900	11,000 11,250	5,800 5,900	7,350 7,400	24,600 24,700	15,900 16,100

Fig. 25.23 Typical layout data for general purpose gearless variable voltage control passenger elevator. 2500 to 4000 lbs, 700 and 800 fpm, 1:1 roping. (Westinghouse Electric Corp., Elevator Division)

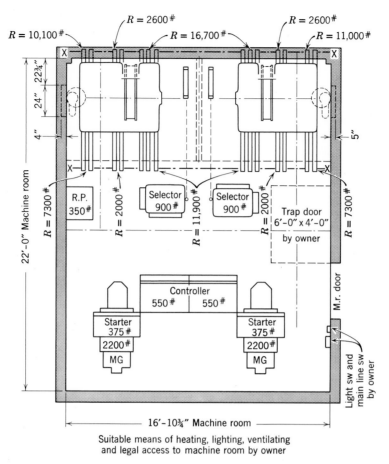

Fig. 25.24 Typical machinery room layout for 2500-lb, 500-fpm passenger elevator using gearless machines. Note supporting beams under elevator machines and the reaction loads (R) on various supporting beams (also see Figs. 25.22 and 25.23).

Figs. 25.22 and 25.23 with the accepted dimensions and weights. Other layouts are available for different values of capacity and speed and for geared machines. Figure 25.24 is a typical machinery room layout for 2 elevators.

As may be seen from Fig. 25.22, it is necessary, in providing for an elevator installation, to consider such factors as the depth of the pit, the dimensions of the hoistway, the clearance from the top of the hoistway to the floor of the penthouse, the size of the penthouse, and the loads which must be carried by the supporting beams. It should be noted that it may be necessary to deviate from the standard locations of penthouse

equipment. In that event it will be necessary to seek space allocations in the vicinity of the penthouse areas. Space variations may also arise because of special provisions of the local elevator code.

The penthouse floor and secondary level floor (respectively, containing the elevator traction machine and control panels, and the secondary sheave and selector tape drive) are located above the shaft of each elevator and need approximately 2 stories of additional height above the top of the support beam of a given elevator when it is standing at its top-floor location. The actual floor area required by the elevator traction machine, its motor-generator set,

Recommended Sizes and Capacities for Passenger Underslung Electric Elevators

Rated Capacity			Platform		Clear Hoistway	
Load pounds	Passengers	Speed fpm	(w) width	(d) depth	(W) width	(D) depth
1200	8	75	5'-0"	4'-0"	6'-9"	5'-3"
2000	13	100	6'-4"	4'-5"	8'-11½"	5'-9"
2500	16	100	7'-0"	5'-0"	8'-9½"	6'-4"
* 4000	27	75	5'-8"	8'-8"	8'-0½"	9'-1"

* Hospital-size elevator

Capacity pounds	Pit depth	Overhead height	Hoistway door opening	Sill
1200	5'-9"	12'-11"	3'-0" x 7'-0"	5½"
2000	5'-9"	12'-11"	3'-0" x 7'-0"	4"
2500	5'-9"	12'-11"	3'-0" x 7'-0"	4"
* 4000	6'-2"	16'-0"	4'-0" x 7'-0"	5½"

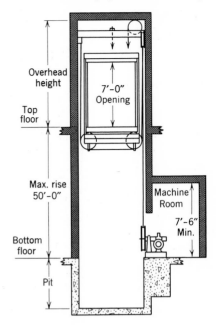

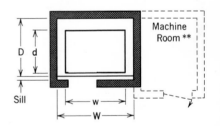

** Machine room can be located at either side or at rear of hoistway for all duties except the 4000# elevator for which the machine room can be at either side. Machine room dimensions vary with the type of installation and building conditions.

Fig. 25.25   Underslung electric elevators. (Otis Elevator Co.)

and control panels is roughly 2.0 times the area of the elevator shaft itself. The required area of the floor of the secondary level is no larger than the elevator shaft it serves. See Table 25.6 for approximate dimensional details and Fig. 25.24 for one of several possible arrangements of machinery in the penthouse and on the secondary floor levels.

The combinations of car capacity and speed shown in Figs. 25.22 and 25.23 are typical only. For actual recommendations consult Table 25.3 since rise determines the choice of car speed, and building proportion and usage affect car capacity. Where penthouse space is not available or not desirable and where traffic requirements allow use of a slow-speed elevator, the under-

Table 25.7 Analysis of Kinetic Energy of Typical Elevators
(Kinetic energy at rated load and speed in footpounds)

A	B	C	D	E	F	G	H	I
Traction-Machine Type, Hoist Motor and Control	Rated Duty	Rise in Ft	Machine	Car	Counter-weight	Ropes	Live Load	Total Col. D, E, F, G, H
Gearless 1:1 d-c motor, voltage control	2500 lb at 800 fpm	435	4180	15,250	18,200	10,000	6900	54,530
Gearless 2:1 d-c motor, voltage control	3000 lb at 500 fpm	200	2900	6,750	8,050	3,900	3250	24,850
Worm gear 1:1 d-c motor, voltage control	3500 lb at 250 fpm	125	6200	1,500	1,880	160	950	10,590
Worm gear 1:1 a-c motor, 1-speed rheostatic control	2500 lb at 150 fpm	100	2450	460	560	50	245	3,765

Adapted from *Standard Handbook for Electrical Engineers*.

slung arrangement shown in Fig. 25.25 may be used. Some dimensional data is also shown for this arrangement.

25. Maximum Structural Stresses. For purpose of structural design it is necessary to know the footpounds of kinetic energy which must be supported by the foundations, structural columns extending upward to the penthouse, and the main beams which support the penthouse floor and sub-

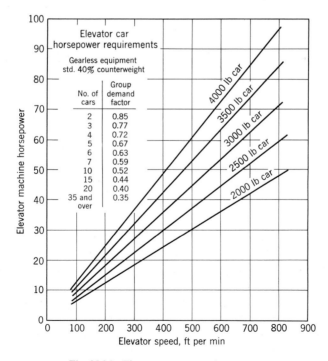

Fig. 25.26 Elevator power requirements.

floor. This kinetic energy is given for several typical elevators in Table 25.7. The weights given in columns D, E, F, G, and H include the actual dead weights of equipment when the elevator is not in motion plus the added weight caused by the momentum of all moving parts and passengers when the elevator is at top speed and is suddenly caused to stop rapidly by the safety devices.

26. Power Requirements. Although power requirements for elevators are generally not a major consideration in selection of equipment, it is desirable to be able to estimate horsepowers in order to size service equipment, switchgear, and feeders. Figure 25.26 gives the power requirements and group demand factors for gearless machines of different capacities and speeds. Geared machines are less efficient, taking approximately 25 percent more power than the equivalent gearless unit.

As an example of the use of the curves we can consider the elevators chosen in our office building study.

3500 lb 600 fpm local car

64 hp (70 hp motor)

Group demand for 5 cars = 0.67
Total power = 5 × 64 × 0.67
= 214 hp

Similarly for 5—3000 lb 800 fpm express cars

$$hp—5 \times 63 \times 0.67 = 211 \text{ hp}$$

The total demand hp requirement is therefore 425 hp.

Since electric power rates are readily available from the local utility, an estimate can easily be made of operating costs.

References and Bibliography

American Safety Code for Elevators, Dumbwaiters and Escalators.

26

Freight Elevators

1. General. The preceding chapter, which dealt with passenger traffic, had as its prime consideration the most economical solution to the problem of vertically transporting a given number of persons most expeditiously. The problem with respect to freight elevators is similar; to transport a given tonnage of freight efficiently, economically, and expeditiously.

Factors to be considered in freight elevator selection in addition to tonnage movement per hour are size of load, method of loading, and type of load, travel, type of doors, and speed and capacity of cars. These factors are interrelated so that the actual process of selection involves making assumptions on the basis of recommendation and then by trial, deciding on a solution, very much as was done for passenger elevators.

Since it is beyond the scope of this book to discuss in the same detail the selection of material handling elevators as was done for passenger elevators due to the large number of considerations involved, we will restrict ourselves in the following para-

Table 26.1 Standard Dimensions and Capacities

Standard Platform Size*		Standard Car Opening Size	Standard Capacity Rating in Pounds
Width	Depth		
5'4''	7'0''	5'0'' x 8'0''	2500, 3000
6'4''	8'0''	6'0'' x 8'0''	2500, 3000, 4000
8'4''	10'0''	8'0'' x 8'0''	4000, 5,000, 6000, 8000
8'4''	12'0''	8'0'' x 8'0''	5000, 6000, 8000, 10,000
10'4''	14'0''	10'0'' x 8'0''	10,000
10'4''	16'0''	Usually determined by load characteristics	12,000
10'4''	20'0''		14,000
12'4''	16'0''		16,000, 18,000, 20,000
Usually determined by load characteristics		Special	24,000, 30,000

* Inside car dimensions are 4'' less in width and 6'' less in depth than the standard platform size.

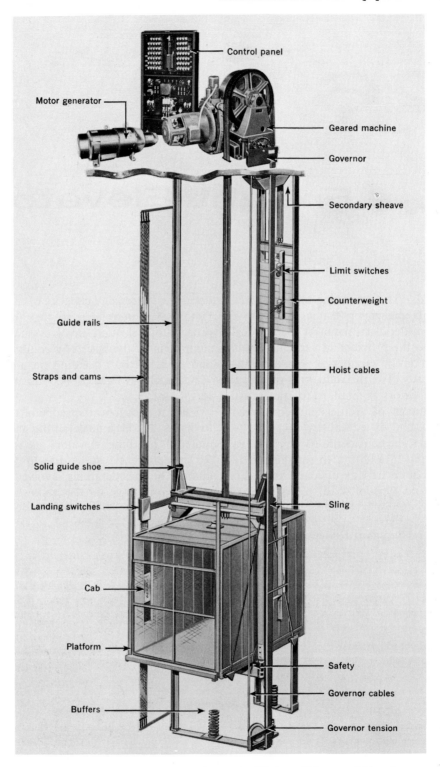

Fig. 26.1   Components of a typical freight elevator installation utilizing a variable voltage controlled geared traction machine. (Westinghouse Electric Corp.)

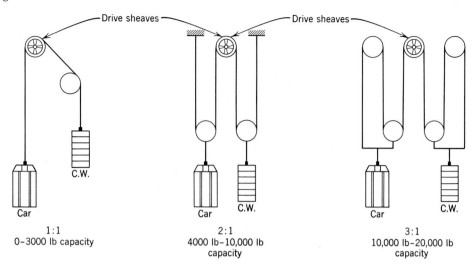

Fig. 26.2   Arrangements of roping for traction-type freight elevators.

graphs to descriptive material and recommendations. Also, since freight elevators form such an important link in industrial processes, a careful and detailed material flow study should be made before the freight elevators are selected. Elevator manufacturers, representatives can be very helpful in this regard. Table 26.1 shows some standard dimensions and capacities and Fig. 26.1 shows a section through a typical freight car shaft.

2. Description. Since speeds are generally between 50 and 200 fpm, a geared type machine is used almost universally. Roping is shown in Fig. 26.2 with the usual related capacities.

The preferred system of control is collective with variable voltage d-c which provides accurate control, smooth acceleration and deceleration, automatic leveling, and minimum maintenance. If, however, the car is used infrequently (less than 5 trips a day), economy is very important, and a rougher ride is tolerable, then a-c rheostatic control may be used. See Figs. 25.5 and 25.6.

Automatic leveling is also available on some rheostatically controlled machines with 2-speed motors. Table 26.2 shows the recommended speed for the 2 types of control and various rises.

3. Cabs and Doors. Cabs for freight service are normally built of heavy-gauge steel with a multilayer wooden floor, the entire unit being designed for hard service. A single guarded ceiling light fixture is normally provided.

Fig. 26.3   Typical freight cab with overhead gate. (Westinghouse Electric Corp.)

Table 26.2   Elevator Speed as a Function of Rise

Control System		Speed
Variable Voltage	*Rheostatic*	*fpm*
....	2 floors	50
....	3–4 floors	75
2–3 floors	5–8 floors	100
4–5 floors	....	150
6–10 floors	....	200

Rise*

* Where any one floor height exceeds 20 feet, use the next higher speed.

Cab and hoistway doors are normally vertical lift, center opening (cab door may be single, full height) manual or power operated. Both sets of doors are counter-weighted and open fully to give complete floor and head clearance.

4. Accessories. Governors, safeties, buffers, counterweights, guide rails, and other auxiliary equipment are similar to that for passenger elevators, previously described.

5. Sidewalk Elevators. Where material must be transported from the sidewalk level to one or more basement levels the choice of

Fig. 26.4   Typical hoistway doors. A combination of bi-parting hoistway doors and overhead cab gate is a common arrangement for freight cars. (Westinghouse Electric Corp., Elevator Division)

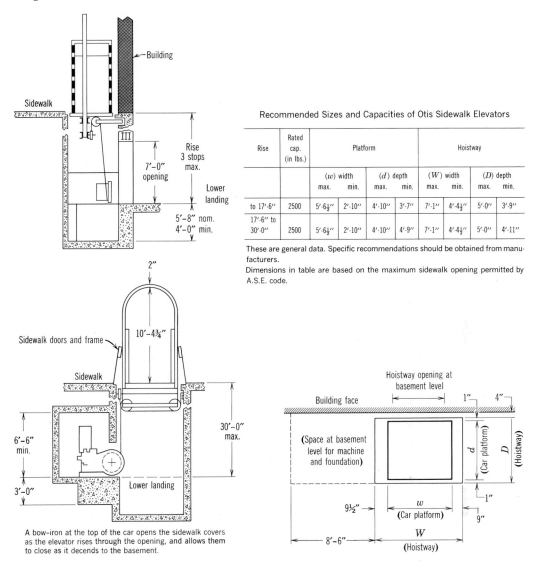

Recommended Sizes and Capacities of Otis Sidewalk Elevators

Rise	Rated cap. (in lbs.)	Platform				Hoistway			
		(w) width max.	min.	(d) depth max.	min.	(W) width max.	min.	(D) depth max.	min.
to 17'-6"	2500	5'-6½"	2'-10"	4'-10"	3'-7"	7'-1"	4'-4½"	5'-0"	3'-9"
17'-6" to 30'-0"	2500	5'-6½"	2'-10"	4'-10"	4'-9"	7'-1"	4'-4½"	5'-0"	4'-11"

These are general data. Specific recommendations should be obtained from manufacturers.

Dimensions in table are based on the maximum sidewalk opening permitted by A.S.E. code.

A bow–iron at the top of the car opens the sidewalk covers as the elevator rises through the opening, and allows them to close as it decends to the basement.

Fig. 26.5   Typical data—sidewalk elevators.

elevator, as the name infers, is the sidewalk elevator. These units operate normally at approximately 25 ft per min with a maximum rise of 30 ft. Rated capacity is 2500 lbs. Control of the car is normally by key switches or plug-in constant pressure push buttons. A bell sounds when the car is about to rise through the sidewalk, to warn pedestrians.

As shown in Fig. 26.5, the cab is actually a simple platform with a steel bow overhead which serves to open and close the sidewalk hatch covers.

Sidewalk elevators are normally used for basement freight loading in retail stores.

6. Light Duty Freight Elevators. The general purpose freight elevator has a minimum capacity of 3000 lbs. Where loads between

Sizes and Capacities of Otis Light-Duty Freight Elevators

Capacity pounds	Platform		Hoistway		Clear door width
	(w) Width	(d) Depth	(W) Width	(D) Depth	
1500	5'-4"	6'-0"	6'-11"	6'-8"	4'-5"
2000	6'-4"	7'-0"	7'-11"	7'-8"	5'-2"
2500	6'-4"	8'-0"	7'-11"	8'-8"	5'-2"

Opening height—7'0".
These data are general; specific recommendations should be obtained from manufacturers.

The car is normally equipped with horizontal folding gates, but vertical lifting gates are available where headroom permits.

SELF-SUPPORTING GUIDE RAILS

carry hoist ropes, sheaves, elevator car and full pay load, and transfer heavy vertical loads to pit. Rails are attached to the building at each floor and at top of the hoistway and steadying member carries governor and dead-end hitch. Maximum steadying load on the hoistway is less than 800 lbs.

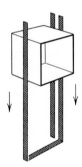

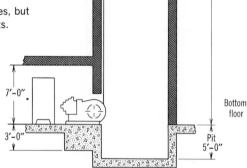

*These dimensions based on the use of a 7'-0" opening height as shown, and on the use of bi-parting hoistway doors and a folding gate on the car.

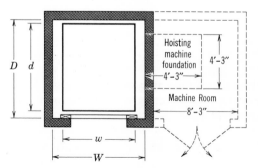

Fig. 26.6   Typical data—light-duty freight elevator.

Hoisting machine can be located at either side of hoistway.

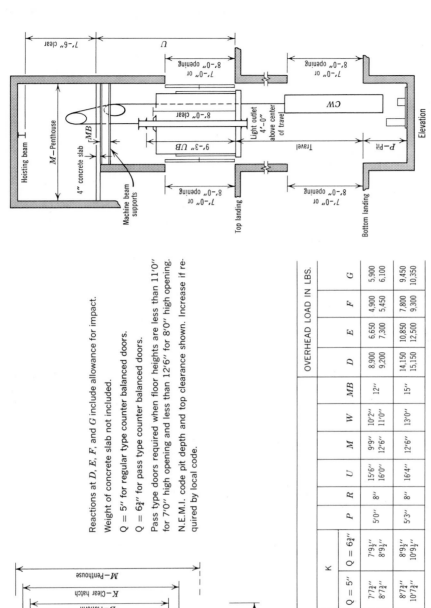

Reactions at D, E, F, and G include allowance for impact.

Weight of concrete slab not included.

Q = 5" for regular type counter balanced doors.

Q = 6¾" for pass type counter balanced doors.

Pass type doors required when floor heights are less than 11'0" for 7'0" high opening and less than 12'6" for 8'0" high opening. N.E.M.I. code pit depth and top clearance shown. Increase if required by local code.

CAPACITY IN LBS.	SPEED FPM	A	B	C	J	K		P	R	U	M	W	MB	OVERHEAD LOAD IN LBS.			
						Q = 5"	Q = 6¾"							D	E	F	G
3,000	50	5'4"	7'0"	5'0"	7'3"	7'7¾"	7'9½"	5'0"	8"	15'6"	9'9"	10'2"	12"	8,900	6,650	4,900	5,900
	100	6'4"	8'0"	6'0"	8'3"	8'7¾"	8'9½"			16'0"	12'6"	11'0"		9,200	7,300	5,450	6,100
4,000	200	6'4"	8'0"	6'0"	8'5"	8'7¾"	8'9½"	5'3"	8"	16'4"	12'6"	13'0"	15"	14,150	10,850	7,800	9,450
		8'4"	10'0"	8'0"	10'5"	10'7¾"	10'9½"							15,150	12,500	9,300	10,350

Fig. 26.7 Layout for 3000 and 4000 pound capacity, geared freight elevators. (Westinghouse Electric Corp., Elevator Division)

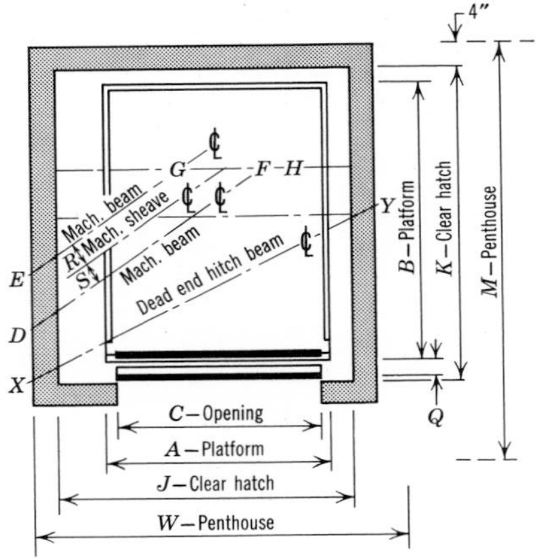

Front Opening

Reactions at D, E, F, G, H, X, and Y include allowance for impact.

Weight of concrete slab not included.

$Q = 5''$ for regular type counter-balanced doors.

$Q = 6\frac{3}{4}''$ for pass type counter-balanced doors.

Pass type doors required when door heights are less than 11′0″ for 7′0″ high opening and less than 12′6″ for 8′0″ high opening.

N.E.M.I. code pit depth and penthouse clearance shown. Increase if required by local code.

UB=11′0″ for 8000 and 10,000# cap.

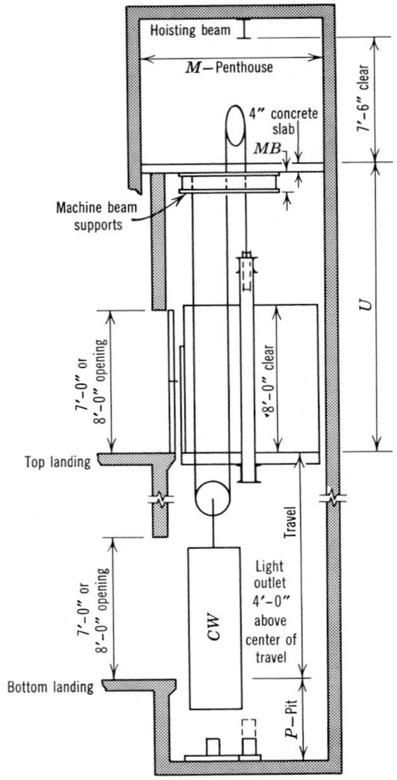

Elevation

CAPACITY IN LBS.	SPEED FPM	DIMENSIONS													OVERHEAD LOAD IN LBS.						
		A	B	C	J	K: Q = 5″	K: Q = 6¾″	S	P	R	U	M	W	MB	D	E	F	G	H	X	Y
4,000	100	8′4″	10′0″	8′0″	10′5″	10′7¾″	10′9½″	17″	5′0″	8″	15′8″	12′6″	12′3″	10″	10,250	6,500	4,050	3,900	4,300	6,100	6,150
5,000	100	8′4″	12′0″	8′0″	10′6″	12′7¾″	12′9½″	18″	5′0″	8″	16′1″	13′9″	11′1″	12″	11,350	6,900	5,500	5,100	5,050	6,950	7,550
5,000	200	8′4″	12′0″	8′0″	10′6″	12′7¾″	12′9½″	18″	5′3″	17″	16′4″	15′4″	14′0″	12″	14,400	7,700	11,500	6,400	0	7,300	9,100
6,000	50	8′4″	12′0″	8′0″	10′6″	12′7¾″	12′9½″	18″	5′0″	8″	15′10″	13′9″	11′1″	12″	11,650	7,250	5,700	5,400	5,400	7,150	7,600
6,000	100	8′4″	12′0″	8′0″	10′6″	12′7¾″	12′9½″	18″	5′0″	8″	16′3″	13′9″	11′1″	12″	13,150	7,050	10,600	5,900	0	6,700	8,300
6,000	200	8′4″	10′0″ 12′0″	8′0″	10′6″	10′7¾″ 12′7¾″	10′9½″ 12′9½″	18″	5′3″	17″	16′4″	15′4″	14′0″	12″	15,050	8,100	11,950	6,700	0	7,800	9,400
8,000	100	8′4″	12′0″	8′0″	10′10″	12′7¾″	12′9½″	20″	5′6″	8″	16′6″	13′9″	11′4″	15″	15,200	8,350	7,700	7,500	7,500	7,500	9,000
8,000	200	8′4″	12′0″	8′0″	10′10″	12′7¾″	12′9½″	20″	5′6″	17″	16′8″	15′4″	14′0″	15″	20,150	10,200	17,000	8,500	0	8,700	8,000
10,000	75	8′4″ 10′4″	14′0″	10′0″	12′11″	14′7¾″	14′9½″	21″	5′6″	8″	16′10″	15′4″	14′3″	15″	17,350	11,400	9,200	8,000	9,400	10,850	11,200
10,000	150	8′4″ 10′4″	14′0″	10′0″	12′11″	14′7¾″	14′9½″	21″	6′0″	17″	17′1″	15′4″	14′3″	15″	21,000	12,500	11,900	11,050	11,500	12,400	12,500

Fig. 26.8 Layout for 4000 to 10,000 pound capacity geared freight elevators.

1500 and 2500 lbs are encountered coupled with low rise, an economical installation can be made of light duty freight car with a semi-self-supporting framework as shown in Fig. 26.6. These units are designed with an underslung roping for rheostatic control and an operating speed of 25 fpm.

Usual applications are in small plants, light-duty warehouses, and stores. Loading of cars should be manual.

7. General Purpose Freight Elevators. These units are most widely used and are applicable to office buildings, garages, retail stores, and all but the heaviest of industrial requirements (above 10,000 pounds). Speeds vary with rise, as does the recommended control system (see Table 26.2). Gate and hoistway doors should correspond in type of operation, i.e., manual or power operated, although power operation is recommended where use is frequent. Typical layouts are shown in Figs. 26.7 and 26.8.

8. Freight Car Passenger Duty. In industrial buildings it is often desirable to utilize freight cars for passenger use. Providing this procedure is permitted by local codes, the following safety considerations obtain:

(*a*) Proper electric interlocks on doors to prevent car motion unless the doors are closed.

(*b*) Proper synchronization of the car and hoistway doors when power operated.

(*c*) Proper capacity use. See Table 26.3.

9. Cost Data. The installed cost of a freight elevator installation, as of a passenger elevator installation, is dependent upon many factors, principal among which are capacity, type of control, use, and type of door operation. Speed is not an independent variable since the range of speeds is limited to between 50 and 200 fpm and the rise and type of control fixes the operating speed. See Table 26.2.

Since exact pricing, as actual selection, is not covered in detail herein being considered outside our scope, it is our recommendation that a reputable manufacturer be consulted for such information. We can,

Table 26.3   Passenger Rating of Freight Elevators

Elevator Freight Rating	Platform Size	Elevator Passenger Rating	Number of * Passengers
3000	5'4" x 7'0"	2900 lbs	20
5000	6'4" x 8'0"	4350 lbs	33
8000	8'4" x 10'0"	8400 lbs	53
10000	8'4" x 12'0"	10500 lbs	66

* Passengers are calculated at 150 lbs each

however, here make some general remarks relative to pricing, as follows:

(*a*) Variable voltage controlled equipment is 50 to 100 percent higher in cost than rheostatic control.

(*b*) Above a basic 2-floor rise, the cost increases linearly with rise.

(*c*) Electric door operation can increase a car installation cost between 10 and 25 percent.

As an example of cost, and for the purpose of *comparative* pricing only, an 8000 lb, 75 fpm, 4 floor, manual door car with a-c rheostatic control and automatic leveling might cost $20,000; the same car with variable voltage control, 150 fpm and electrically operated doors might run $40,000.

10. Plunger Elevators. All of the foregoing elevators, both passenger and freight, have in common the characteristic that they are traction types, i.e., they are raised and lowered as a result of the tractive force of cables passing over a sheave. In contradistinction to these, the plunger elevator is raised and lowered quite simply, by means of a movable rod (plunger) rigidly fixed to the bottom of the elevator car. The absence of cables, drums, m-g sets, elaborate controllers and safety devices, and penthouse equipment make this system inherently inexpensive and often the indicated choice for low-speed, low-rise applications where construction of the plunger pit does not present difficulties and where absence of penthouse is desirable. (See Fig. 26.9.)

The system is hydraulic and operates very much the same as an hydraulic auto-

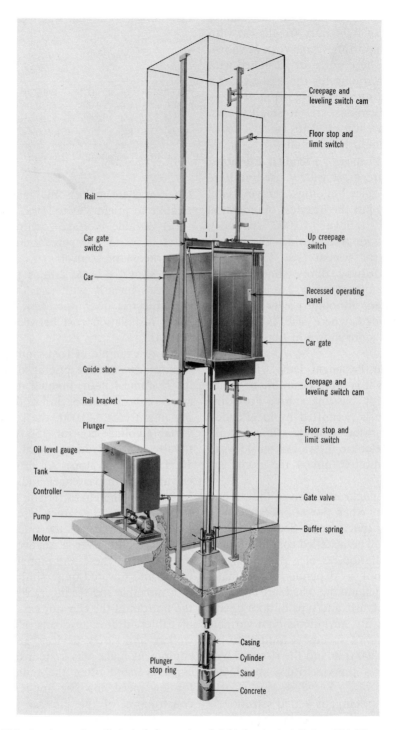

Fig. 26.9   A cutaway view of a typical plunger-type freight elevator installation. (Otis Elevator Co.)

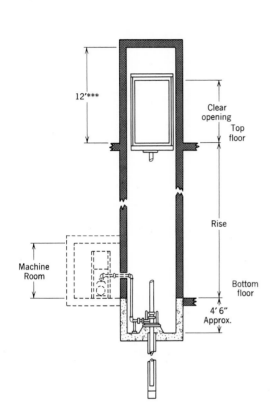

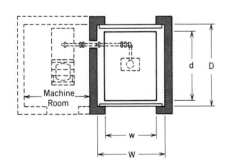

PASSENGER

CAPACITY in pounds	PLATFORM		CLEAR HOISTWAY		DOORS
	(w) width	(d) depth	(W) width	(D) depth	jamb opening
1,200	5'-0''	4'-0''	6'-5''	4'-10¾''	3'-0'' x 7'-0''
2,000	6'-4''	4'-5''	7'-8''	5'-2¼''	3'-0'' x 7'-0''
2,500	7'-0''	5'-0''	8'-4''	5'-9¼''	3'-6'' x 7'-0''
3,000	7'-0''	5'-6''	8'-4''	6'-3¼''	3'-6'' x 7'-0''
3,500	7'-0''	6'-2''	8'-4''	6'-11¼''	3'-6'' x 7'-0''
4,000	8'-0''	6'-2''	9'-4''	7'-0¾''	5'-0'' x 7'-0''
5,000	9'-0''	6'-0''	10'-4''	6'-10¾''	6'-0'' x 7'-0''

HOSPITAL ELEVATORS

3,500	5'-4''	8'-4''	6'-10''	9'-2¾''	3'-8'' x 7'-0''
4,000	5'-8''	8'-8''	7'-4''	9'-6¾''	4'-0'' x 7'-0''
4,500	5'-10''	9'-0''	7'-4''	9'-10¾''	4'-0'' x 7'-0''

FREIGHT

CAPACITY in pounds	PLATFORM		CLEAR HOISTWAY		DOORS
	(w) width	(d) depth	(W) width	(D) depth **	jamb opening
2,500	5'-4''	7'-0''	6'-8''	7'-11''	4'-3'' x 7'-6''
3,000	6'-4''	8'-0''	7'-8''	8'-11''	6'-0'' x 7'-6''
3,500	6'-4''	8'-0''	7'-8''	8'-11''	6'-0'' x 8'-0''
4,000	6'-4''	8'-0''	7'-8''	8'-11''	6'-0'' x 8'-0''
5,000	8'-4''	10'-0''	9'-8''	10'-11''	8'-0'' x 8'-0''
6,000	8'-4''	10'-0''	9'-8''	10'-11''	8'-0'' x 8'-0''
8,000	8'-4''	12'-0''	9'-8''	12'-11''	8'-0'' x 8'-0''
10,000	8'-4''	12'-0''	*11'-4''	12'-11''	8'-0'' x 8'-0''
12,000	10'-4''	14'-0''	*13'-4''	14'-11''	10'-0'' x 8'-0''
16,000	10'-4''	14'-0''	*13'-8''	15'-3''	10'-0'' x 10'-0''
20,000	12'-0''	20'-0''	*15'-4''	21'-3''	11'-8'' x 10'-0''

*These dimensions include space for double column guide rail supports, to be furnished by owner.

**Hoistway—front to back—large enough to allow for installation of a reverse or rear opening in the car.

***This dimension depends upon capacity, car height and local code requirements.

Fig. 26.10   Suggested sizes and capacities of plunger electric elevators. (Otis Elevator Co.)

mobile jack. Oil from a reservoir is pumped under the plunger thereby raising it and the car. The pump is stopped during downward motion, the car being lowered by gravity and controlled by action of by-pass valves which also control the positioning of the car during upward motion.

Control systems normally used are simi-

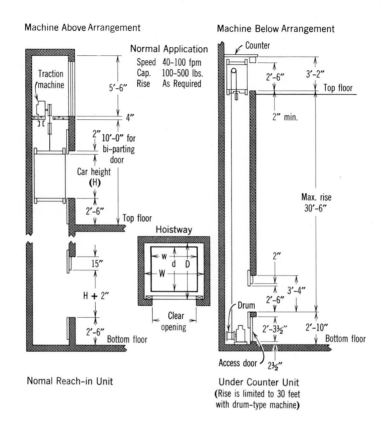

RECOMMENDED SIZES OF DUMBWAITERS

MAX. DUTY			CAR		HOISTWAY		
traction type machine		*drum type machine 2:1 roping	(w) width	(d) depth	(W) width	(D) depth without car gate	(D) depth with car gate
1:1 roping	2:1 roping						
400# @ 100 fpm	500# @ 50 fpm	400# @ 45 fpm	2'-0"	2'-6"	3'-2"	2'-11"	3'-0¼"
			2'-0"	3'-0"	3'-2"	3'-5"	3'-6¼"
			2'-6"	2'-6"	3'-8"	2'-11"	3'-0¼"
			2'-6"	3'-0"	3'-8"	3'-5"	3'-6¼"
			3'-0"	2'-6"	4'-2"	2'-11"	3'-0¼"
			3'-0"	3'-0"	4'-2"	3'-5"	3'-6¼"
400# @ 100 fpm	500# @ 50 fpm	400# @ 45 fpm	3'-6"	2'-6"	4'-8"	2'-11"	3'-0¼"
Under-Counter Dumbwaiter		300# @ 50 fpm	2'-6"	1'-8½"	3'-5"	2'-1½"	———

Standard car heights—3'-0", 3'-6", 4'-0"

Fig. 26.11 Recommended sizes of dumbwaiters.

lar to that for traction types; e.g., single pushbutton and collective, attended or non-attended. Automatic leveling may also be procured for applications where landing accuracy is important.

Figure 26.10 gives self-explanatory dimensional data for plunger installations.

11. Dumbwaiters. The use of dumbwaiters in various types of structures often provides the most convenient and economical means of transporting relatively small articles between levels. In department stores such units transport merchandise from stock areas to selling or pick-up counters; in hospitals dumbwaiters are often utilized for transporting food, drugs, linens and other necessary small items. In multilevel restaurants, office dining rooms, etc., dumbwaiters are almost always used for delivery of food from the kitchen and for return of soiled dishes.

Units will handle up to 500 lbs per load and travel at speeds of 45 fpm to 100 fpm. Control is normally "Call and Send" between 2 floors; for more than 2 floors multi-button or central dispatching control is available.

Figure 26.11 gives layout and dimensional data for selected dumbwaiters.

27

Electric Stairways

and Walks

1. General. The moving stairway is also referred to as an escalator, and as an electric stairway. Throughout this section all 3 names will be used. It was first operated at the Paris Exposition in 1900. In this country moving stairways now provide comfortable and rapid vertical transportation for many millions of persons.

The escalator not only delivers passengers comfortably, rapidly, and safely, but also it continuously receives and discharges its live load at a constant speed with practically no waiting periods at any landing. The many seconds of time which are lost by elevators are not present on traveling stairways. For example, time is not lost by acceleration, retardation, leveling, door operation, or operator's reactions; nor by pressing hall buttons, by passenger interferences in getting in or out of the cars, etc. One seldom sees a waiting passenger or congestion of passengers at the lighted comb plate of an escalator.

Instead of formal lobbies and hallways leading to a bank of elevators on each floor, the electric stairway is always in motion and inviting passengers to "take a ride." The corridors, aisles, and other passageways in existing buildings usually provide space for floor openings adequate for the installation of escalators. In contrast, it would in most cases be almost impossible to install an adequate bank of elevators in an existing building to meet the growing needs for vertical transportation. Elevator hoistways must be vertical from bottom to top floors; an escalator installation could be "staggered" at various appropriate locations. (See Fig. 27.1).

Figure 27.2 shows side views of a modern moving stairway. The outside balustrade is cut away at the lower and upper ends to show the general arrangement of the major parts and appurtenances.

The stairway is prepared for shipment by dividing the structural truss into 3 sections. The upper section of the truss is separated from the middle section at the locations near the arrows 22 and 8. A similar lower section is likewise separated at a closely corresponding line (hidden by the balustrade) near the arrow 23. The middle straight section may be any desired length to provide rises for floor heights of

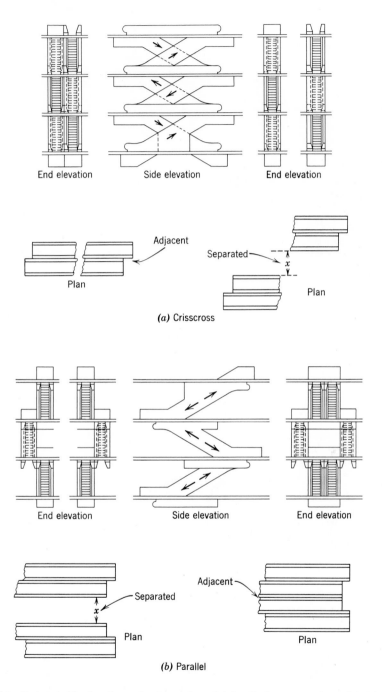

End elevation   Side elevation   End elevation

Adjacent

Plan

Separated

x

Plan

(a) Crisscross

End elevation   Side elevation   End elevation

Separated

x

Plan

Adjacent

Plan

(b) Parallel

Fig. 27.1   End and side elevations, showing various details of criss-cross and parallel stairways. Distance x may be chosen to suit architectural plans in new or existing buildings.

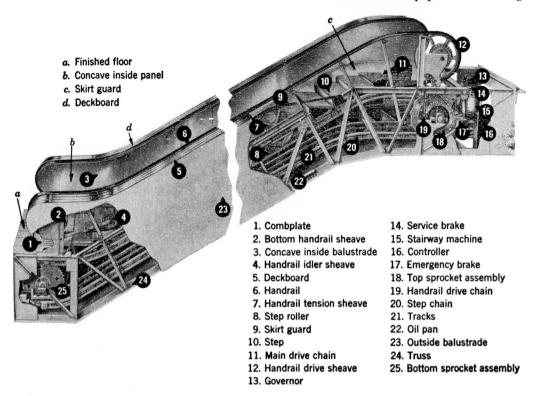

a. Finished floor
b. Concave inside panel
c. Skirt guard
d. Deckboard

1. Combplate
2. Bottom handrail sheave
3. Concave inside balustrade
4. Handrail idler sheave
5. Deckboard
6. Handrail
7. Handrail tension sheave
8. Step roller
9. Skirt guard
10. Step
11. Main drive chain
12. Handrail drive sheave
13. Governor
14. Service brake
15. Stairway machine
16. Controller
17. Emergency brake
18. Top sprocket assembly
19. Handrail drive chain
20. Step chain
21. Tracks
22. Oil pan
23. Outside balustrade
24. Truss
25. Bottom sprocket assembly

Fig. 27.2   Cutaway view of a modern escalator. (Westinghouse Electric Corp.)

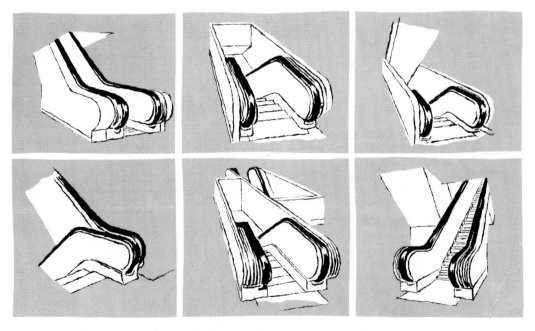

Fig. 27.3   Typical views of stairway landings, floor openings, and trims for escalators.

from 10 to 23 ft, for example. When the rise is over 20 ft an intermediate support is located between the 2 end supports of the stairway. Generally, the upper corners of the bottom and top ends of the truss, after assembly, carry the complete weight of the stairway mechanism and its live load.

Figure 27.3 illustrates various arrangements and views of the entrances of escalators.

2. Parallel and Crisscross Installations. Escalators may be installed so that the up-stairway and down-stairway crisscross each other as in Fig. 27.1a, or arranged in parallel as in b. The arrangements also may be such that the center lines of the pairs of stairways are close together (or adjacent); or that the center lines are far apart (or separated). These are clearly shown in the figure. Any up and down set of escalators may, in fact, be separated by many feet. This permits the sometimes desirable plan of forcing passengers to travel on a given floor (as in a department store) in order to display merchandise to create purchases.

The crisscross adjacent arrangement is considerably less costly than the parallel and is therefore generally chosen. Since both ends of the stairway are exposed, travel is easy. The parallel arrangement on the other hand is less efficient and relatively expensive, its major virtue being its impressive appearance.

3. Size, Capacity, and Speed. There are 2 sizes of escalator generally available, the 32 in. and the 48 in.—these dimensions being the distance between balustrades.

Actual step widths are 24 in. and 40 in. for the two sizes, respectively. Table 26.1 gives the carrying capacity and the floor dimensions of the 2 sizes of moving stairway. Normal speed is 90 ft per minute, the 120 fpm speed being utilized for "express" escalators. Installations at transportation terminals often utilize 2-speed escalators, for use during normal and rush hours.

Angle of incline is normally 30°. Since escalators are reversible, installations having major traffic in only one direction at a time, can utilize a single unit. Where heavy traffic is encountered in both directions simultaneously, obviously at least 2 escalators are required.

4. Components. The major components of an escalator installation are shown in Fig. 27.2 and in Figs. 27.4 through 27.10.

The *truss* is a welded steel frame which supports the entire apparatus.

The *tracks* are steel angles attached to the truss on which the step rollers are guided, thus controlling the motion of the steps.

The *sprocket assemblies, chains, and machine* provide the motive power for the unit, much like the simple chain drive of a bicycle. An emergency brake located on the top sprocket will stop a loaded escalator safely in the event of a break in the chain.

The *controller,* which consists of contactors, relays, and a circuit breaker, is normally located near the drive machine.

An emergency stop button wired to the controller and placed near or on the escalator housing will stop the drive machine

Table 27.1 *Characteristics of Standard Moving Stairways*

(For rises of 10 to 25 ft)

Step Width* (in.)	Passengers per Hour at 90' per Min	Passengers per Hour at 120' per Min	Approximate Floor Opening		Landings	
			Length	Width	Length	Width
32	5000	5750	20 to 25'	4'4"	6'0"	4'4"
48	8000	9200	20 to 25'	6'0"	6'0"	6'0"

* The steps have a 16" tread and 8" rise.

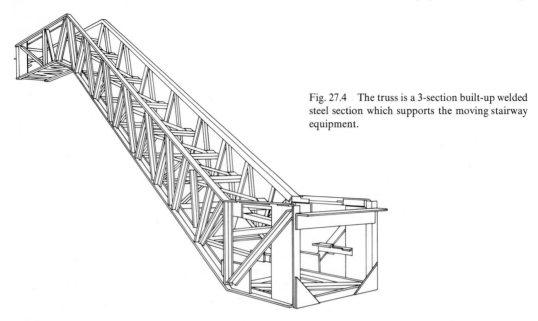

Fig. 27.4   The truss is a 3-section built-up welded steel section which supports the moving stairway equipment.

and apply the brake. Key-operated control switches at the top and bottom newels will start, stop, and reverse the stairway.

The *handrail* is driven by 2 sheaves and is powered from the top sprocket assembly. It provides stability to riding passengers, and a support for entering and leaving passengers.

The *balustrade assembly* is designed for maximum safety of persons stepping on or off the escalators. Handrails disappear at inaccessible points at newels.

5. Safety Features. Protection to passengers during normal operation is insured by a number of safety features associated with moving stairways:

(*a*) Handrails and steps travel at exactly the same speed (90 or 120 ft per min) to insure steadiness and balance on the up or down travel and to aid naturally in stepping on or off the combplates.

(*b*) The steps are large, steady, and are designed to prevent slipping.

(*c*) Step design and their leveling with the combplates at each landing insure against tripping as one enters or leaves the escalator.

(*d*) The balustrade includes all enclosures as furnished by the escalator manufacturers, as shown in Figs. 27.2, 27.3, and 27.10, including the deckboards, concave inside panels, skirt guards, handrail guards, handrails, and combplates. Details of these parts are designed to prevent catching of clothing and of packages being carried by passengers. Close clearances provide safety features near the combplates and step treads.

(*e*) Automatic controls of a service brake will bring the stairway to a smooth stop if electric power or mechanical parts should fail. Passengers would then walk the steps as they would any stationary stairway.

(*f*) In case of overspeed or underspeed an automatic governor shuts down the escalator, prevents reversal of direction (up or down), and operates the service brake.

(*g*)   Adequate illumination is provided at all landings at the combplates and completely down all stairways.

(*h*) An emergency stop switch is located near the combplate or in some unobstrusive location. Building employees and adult passengers may operate the switch to stop the

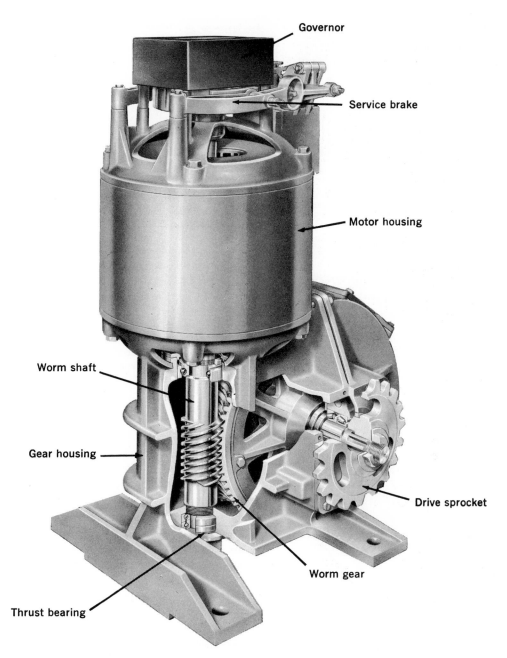

Fig. 27.5   Cutaway of machine and drive. (Westinghouse Electric Corp.)

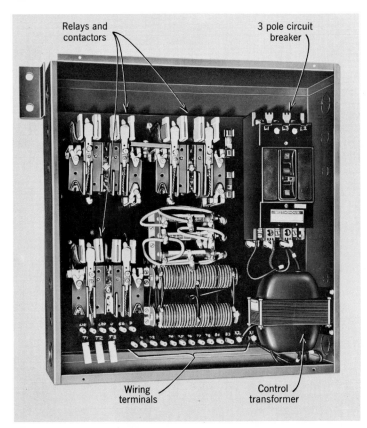

Relays and contactors

3 pole circuit breaker

Wiring terminals

Control transformer

Fig. 27.6 Typical control panel for an electric stairway. Control pushbuttons are mounted in a convenient and accessible location at the top and bottom of the stairway.

Fig. 27.7. Typical step assembly for electric stairway. Riser is 8″ high. Comb pattern is designed to prevent materials being caught between riser and tread. (Westinghouse Electric Corp.)

escalator. The electric controls also are arranged to shut down the stairway if by some accident it is caused to reverse its direction.

6. Fire Protection. Four methods of affording protection in case of fire near escalators are available: the rolling shutter, the smoke guard, the spray-nozzle curtain, and the sprinkler vent.

Fig. 3.2, p. 40, quite clearly illustrates how the wellway at a given floor level may be entirely closed off by the fire shutter, thus preventing draft and the spread of fire upward through escalator wells. The movement is actuated by temperature and smoke relays which automatically start the operation of the motor-driven shutters. The shutter in Fig. 3.2 is shown at the third-

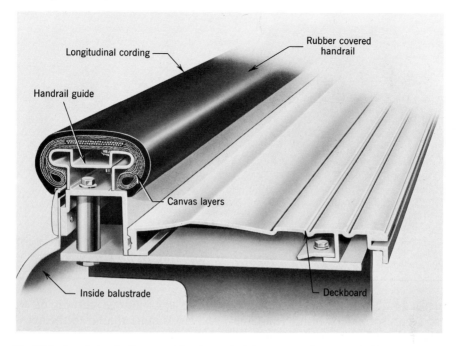

Fig. 27.8 Sturdy handrail construction is required by constant flexure. (Westinghouse Electric Corp.)

floor level, but other shutters may be installed at the tops of all horizontal wellway openings at any floor.

The smoke-guard method of protection, Fig. 27.11, consists of fireproof baffles surrounding the wellway and extending down-ward about 20 in. below the ceiling level. Smoke and flames rising upward to the escalator floor opening meet a curtain of water automatically released from the usual type of sprinkler heads shown at the ceiling level. The baffle is a smoke and

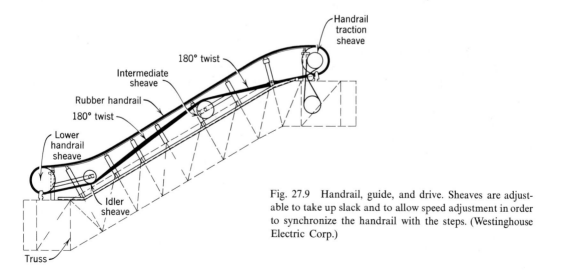

Fig. 27.9 Handrail, guide, and drive. Sheaves are adjustable to take up slack and to allow speed adjustment in order to synchronize the handrail with the steps. (Westinghouse Electric Corp.)

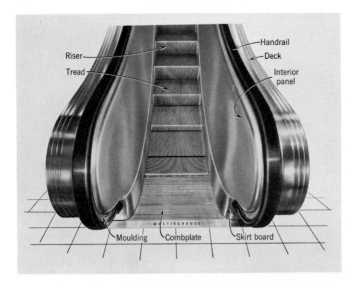

Fig. 27.10 Typical balustrade assembly of an electric stairway. (Westinghouse Electric Corp.)

flame deflector. The vertical shields between adjacent sprinklers insure that the spray from one will not cool the nearby thermal fuses and prevent the opening of adjacent sprinklers.

The spray-nozzle curtain of water (not shown) is quite similar to the above smoke-guard protection. Here closely spaced high-velocity water nozzles form a compact water curtain to prevent smoke and flame

Fig. 27.11 Smoke-guard method of fire protection for a 32-inch moving stairway, criss-cross type. Main baffle and typical stairway enclosures contain approximate dimensions. The escalator floor opening (per floor) is approximately 4'4" by 14'6".

rising through the wellways. Automatic thermal or smoke relays open all nozzles simultaneously.

The sprinkler-vent fire control is shown in Fig. 3.3, p. 41. The fresh air intake housed on the roof contains a blower to drive air downward through escalators floor openings while the exhaust fan on the roof creates a strong draft upward through an exhaust duct; this duct in turn draws air from the separate ducts just under the ceiling of each moving stairway floor opening. Three such separate wellway ducts are shown. Each duct has a number of smoke-pickup relays which automatically

start the fresh air fans. The usual spray nozzles on the ceiling near the stairways aid in quenching the fire.

Wellways and the entire escalator equipment can be protected against fire if they are enclosed between fireproof walls from floor to ceiling. The approaches to the stairs at each level are provided with lobbies with fireproofed swinging doors. These doors are self-closing and are held open by fusible links. Hot gases, smoke, or fire near these enclosures melt the fuses and allow the door springs to close the doors.

With the exception of the total-enclosure method, last mentioned, the operating

Illuminated
balustrade

Fig. 27.12 Illustrated is one of the many ways in which electric stairways are illuminated. Other methods include spot-lights at the balustrade interior panel, overhead general illumination and downlights over the stairs. (Westinghouse Electric Corp.)

floor areas near all escalators are not burdened with any apparatus connected with the protective equipment.

7. Lighting. Adequate illumination of a moving stairway, particularly at the landings, is important from decorative as well as safety standpoints since it is usually desirable to highlight the moving stair installation. Lighting consonant with the adjacent illumination is installed on the ceiling above the stairway with special emphasis on lighting of the combplates. A particularly effective and striking scheme is the use of an illuminated balustrade as illustrated in Fig. 27.12.

8. Miscellaneous Considerations. (*a*) Main floor locations should be chosen in the direct flow of traffic to assure maximum use.

(*b*) Vertical arrangements shall be made to accomplish specific purposes, such as exposure of merchandise, maximum passenger capacity, maximum accessibility to various areas, etc.

(*c*) The use of elevators and escalators should be considered together as a single problem in vertical transportation, as applied to the particular facility being designed. In this connection, particularly in case of modernization, Fig. 27.13 provides an interesting comparison.

(*d*) The aspect of reversibility of an electric stairway should be considered in applications where major traffic flow is unidirectional. Light traffic in the reverse direction can be handled by a normal fixed stair, adjacent to the escalator. Similarly,

a bank of 2 escalators can operate either both up, both down or 1 up and 1 down to handle variable traffic conditions in such areas as office buildings and transportation terminals.

9. Electric Power Requirements. Standard electric stairways are driven by 3-phase 60-cycle a-c induction motors at standard voltages (208—220—440 volts). Horsepower of driving motors are shown in a tabulation in Figs. 27.14 and 27.15.

It is recommended that no more than 4 escalators be served by a single electric feeder, and further that not all the escalators of an installation, whatever the number, be served from the same feeder.

10. Structural Design and Installation Data. The architect and his engineers must design the floor openings, stairway supports, and other structural work, and finishes. A typical moving stairway drawing, arranged for the information of the architect and the trained stairway erectors, is shown in Fig. 27.15. A careful review of all the details shown on these plans and indicated specifications picture the coordination necessary between the architect, engineer, and erection superintendent.

Outlined on these plans are the details for which the architects and engineers are responsible, including structural, mechanical, and electrical features. It will be seen that 2 "working points" are identified, between which a very strong steel wire is tightly stretched. From these 2 points all other measurements are made, i.e., to locate the center line of the truss sections; to place

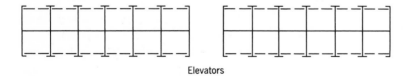

Elevators

Electric stairways

Fig. 27.13 Comparative space requirements. This diagram shows the marked savings in space requirements of electric stairways as compared to elevators. Both means of vertical transportation provide equivalent capacity.

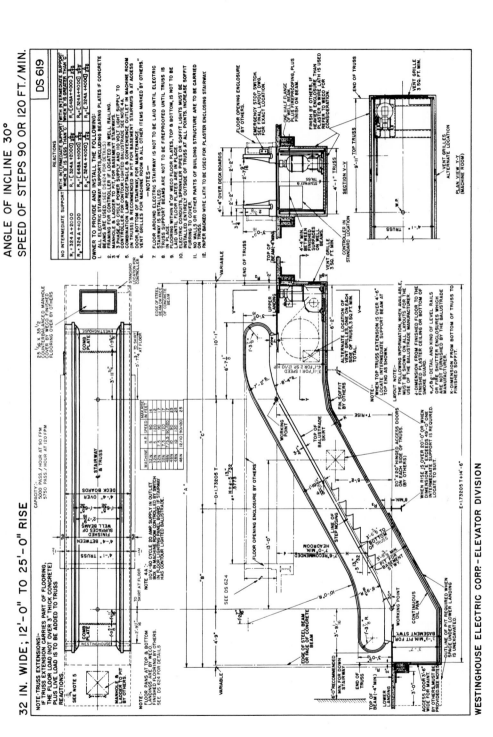

Fig. 27.14 Typical 32″ escalator erection drawing with dimensions and reactions for 32″ wide unit. Dimensions for the sprinkler vent equipment may be obtained from consulting engineer.

591

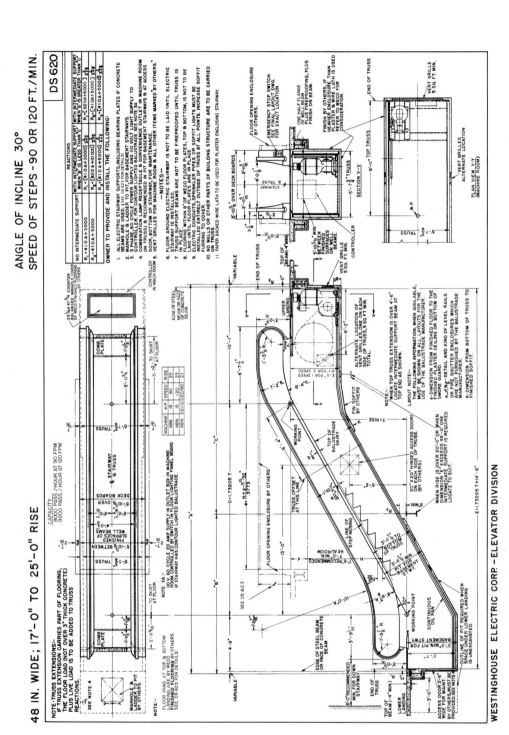

WESTINGHOUSE ELECTRIC CORP.-ELEVATOR DIVISION

Fig. 27.15 Typical escalator erection drawing with dimensions and reactions for a 48″ wide unit.

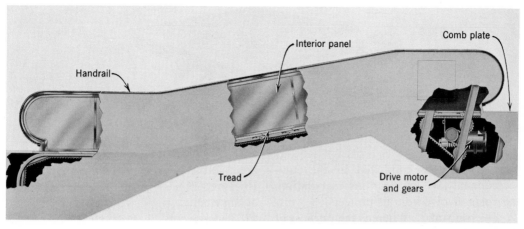

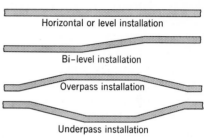

Fig. 27.16 Cutaway of an electric walk. Units are very similar to an electric stairway except that treadway pallets replace treads and risers. (Westinghouse Electric Corp.)

the lower and upper landing truss support beams, etc. Such plans as this one are available from all escalator manufacturers for any standard type of stairway.

11. Budget Estimating Data for Escalators. The cost of an escalator includes the cost of the associated mechanical and electrical equipment plus the shipping installation charges. The manufacturer provides expert engineering and a union field erector who supervises the installation which is done by unionized elevator and escalator mechanics.

The 32-in. and the 48-in. electric stairways are considered standard production models. These may be furnished from a 10-ft rise to a 25-ft rise, operating at 90 fpm or 120 fpm. On special orders other rises and speeds may be obtained.

The installation work furnished with the machine is mentioned in the specifications and dimensional information shown in Fig. 27.14 and 27.15.

A general average rule-of-thumb for quick estimating of costs for a 32-in. electric stairway, installed, is $30,000 for the first 10 feet of rise and $750 for each additional foot; the corresponding figure for a 48-in. stairway is $32,000, and $1000 for each additional foot. To these figures must be added the cost of builders' work, wellway protection, lighting, outside balustrades, and plaster. It is especially important that the assistance of experts in vertical

Table 27.2   Characteristics of Electric Walks

Normal Tread	Passengers per Hour		Maximum Incline	
(width)	*120' per min*	*180' per min*	*120 fpm*	*180 fpm*
27	6650	10,650	15°	8°
36	8800	14,000	15°	8°

Fig. 27.17   Electric walkway pallet which corresponds to the step in the electric stairway.

transportation be employed in the engineering analysis, specifications, installation, and costs involved on all projects.

12. Electric Walks. Whereas the purpose of electric stairways is to transport people vertically, "electric walks" are used to transport persons horizontally at any inclination from 0 to 15°. Typical applications are at display windows and exhibits where management desires that persons move smoothly through or past a particular area with no stopping or bunching, which tends to cause crowding and discomfort. Other applications are as connections between selling areas in a store, the walk serving as a moving invitation to the terminal area. Table 27.2 shows typical characteristics and Fig. 27.16 a typical cutaway and arrangements.

17. Components. Construction and operation of the electric walk is very similar to, but simpler than, that of the electric stairway. A flat pallet is utilized instead of a step (see Fig. 27.17) making the installation cheaper.

Units are available in various lengths, the design being flexible to fit the requirements. Because of their striking and avant-garde appearance, electric walks, both indoor and outdoor, are recommended for retail stores, exhibits of all kinds, and in modern transportation terminals.

28

Sound and Signal Systems

For the purpose of our discussion, sound and signal systems include all signal, communication, and control circuits operating on either a-c or d-c. The function of these circuits is the rapid and accurate transmission of information required for the proper and efficient operation of the particular facility. Since the signal and communication fields perhaps more than any other offer a variety of solutions to any particular design problem, the equipment details depend in large measure on the specific manufacture. For this reason our discussion will be functional only.

Residential Systems. Modern residences utilize a variety of signal apparatus which greatly enhance their functional value. Figure 28.1 shows a residence which has been provided with what would be considered adequate but by no means excessive sound and signal equipment for a residence of this size.

1. Residential Fire Alarm. It is now generally recognized that a fire-alarm system is as much a requirement of a residence as of an industrial or commercial building. The purpose of such a system is to provide sufficient time for evacuation of the building and for appropriate counter-measures to be initiated. The basic elements of the system are the central panel, the audible alarm devices, and alarm-initiating devices. The alarm-initiating devices are available in either manual (hand-pull) or automatic form. The manual devices, also known as fire-alarm stations, are not applicable to residential work for obvious reasons. The automatic devices, (see Fig. 28.3) also known as thermostats or detectors, are set to operate at either a fixed temperature, an excessive rate of temperature rise, or a combination of both. Systems other than residential utilizing only manual stations are known as manual fire-alarm systems. Systems utilizing automatic sensing devices either alone or in combination with manual stations are known as automatic fire-alarm systems.

The function of the central panel is to energize the audible devices (bells and gongs) upon receipt of a signal from the detectors, whereupon the bells and gongs will continue to sound until the emergency condition is cleared or until they are manu-

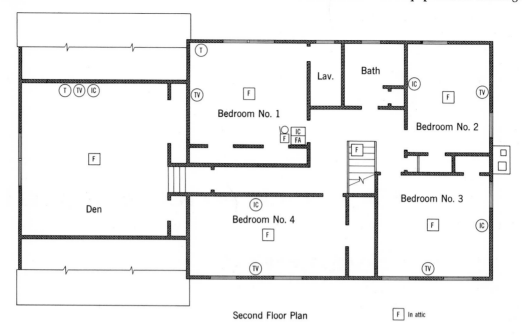

Second Floor Plan   F In attic

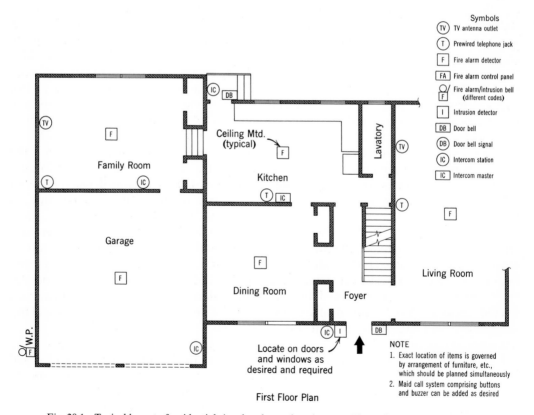

Fig. 28.1   Typical layout of residential signal and sound equipment. (Floor plan courtesy of Brisby Builders, Metuchen, N.J.)

ally silenced at the control panel. Other functions which the panel may be designed to serve are: shut-off of oil and gas lines, shut-off of attic fan to prevent fire spread, and turning on of lights, both inside and outside. In order to assure system operation even in the event of a power interruption, most systems are provided with a standby battery.

(a) *System Design.* Detectors are rated by temperature and coverage, for example, 135 F and 200 sq ft, and are normally located on the ceiling in all rooms and stairwells, including the attic and the basement. Due to high ambient temperatures, the units installed in the kitchen, attic, and basement near the heating unit are normally rated at 190 to 200 F while the units in the other rooms are usually set at 135 F. The bell or gong is located so as to waken sleeping occupants, e.g., in the master bedroom or bedroom corridor. A switched outside bell can be added to alert neighbors during periods that the residence is unoccupied by turning the switch to "on" when the family leaves.

(b) *System Arrangements.* A system which is normally de-energized and carries no current except when functioning is called an open-circuit system. (See Fig. 28.4a). Such a system is the simplest and most economical type but has the disadvantage of not indicating a broken wire or other malfunction which will render the system inoperative.

Figure 28.4b shows a closed circuit system. This arrangement will set off the alarm bells in the event of trouble in the equipment, but since this type of "false alarm" is to an extent undesirable, a further refinement in the form of a trouble bell and (or) light can be added (at approximately 50 percent cost increase) which will then indicate to the occupants an equipment failure without ringing the fire-alarm bells. This feature is known as supervision, and such a system is known as closed-circuit supervised system.

(c) *Equipment.* Detectors and alarm bells and gongs are generally surface-mounted. Control cabinets may be flush-mounted where installed in finished areas or surface-mounted in unfinished areas.

Since the detector circuits and bell cir-

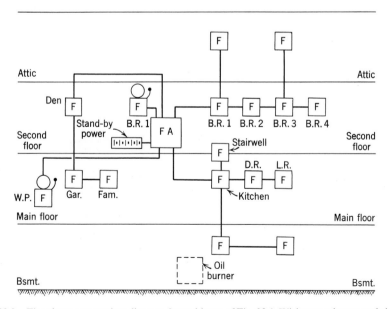

Fig. 28.2   Fire alarm system riser diagram for residence of Fig. 28.1. Wiring may be run and circuits arranged as desired, to effect the required operation.

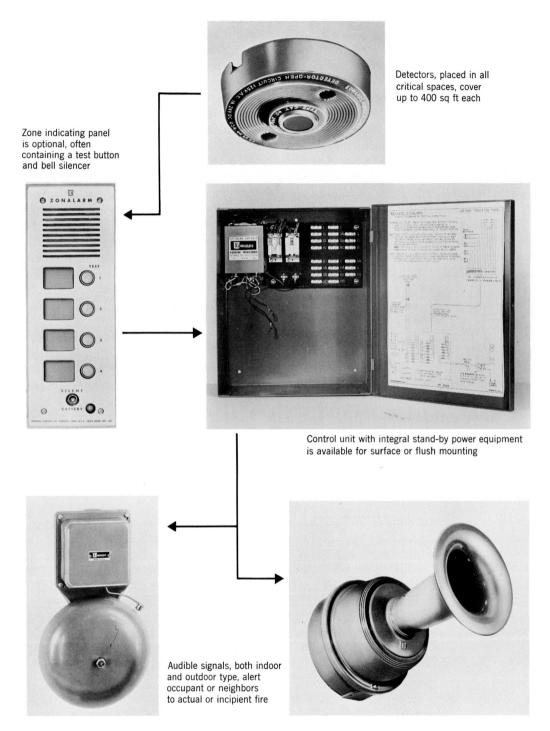

Detectors, placed in all
critical spaces, cover
up to 400 sq ft each

Zone indicating panel
is optional, often
containing a test button
and bell silencer

Control unit with integral stand-by power equipment
is available for surface or flush mounting

Audible signals, both indoor
and outdoor type, alert
occupant or neighbors
to actual or incipient fire

Fig. 28.3   Typical residential fire alarm equipment. (Courtesy of Edwards Co.)

cuits operate at low voltage and carry very little current, wiring is normally twisted pair No. 18 or No. 20 AWG bell wire, installed concealed in walls and ceilings.

2. Residential Intrusion Alarm System. An increasing number of private residences in the moderate-price class are utilizing intrusion (burglar) alarm systems, often in conjunction with fire-alarm equipment, due to the resultant economy.

Basically, an intrusion alarm system is similar to a fire-detection system except that instead of thermal detection, devices such as metallic tape, micro and magnetic switches are used to detect door and window motion, glass breakage, etc. A manual switch at the end of a long cord is also often provided so that the resident may at will set off the alarm in the event he hears an intruder and wishes to frighten him off and alert the neighbors.

The system may employ the same audible signals as the fire system or other units, as designed. A further refinement in both the intrusion alarm and the fire alarm is the use of annunciation to indicate which circuit, detector or switch has operated. This type of installation is indicated only for very large single or estate-type residences with multiple outbuildings. Figure 28.5 shows a typical system and Fig. 28.6 typical annunciator panels.

Although rarely done except with the largest residences, intrusion alarm systems can be continuously supervised by connection with central stations of companies whose business is such supervision, and who will either respond directly to an alarm call or notify local police authorities of any illegal entry.

3. Residential Door Bell and Button Systems. Door bells are perhaps the oldest and certainly the most common residential signal. The basic elements of an electric door bell system comprise a bell transformer, door buttons, and an audible signal device (see Fig. 28.7). Chimes and bells are available with up to 3 different signals to differentiate between the various entrances of the residence. The door button is often combined with an outdoor intercom station.

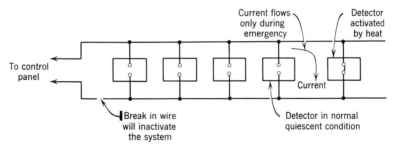

Fig. 28.4 Wiring of open and closed circuit systems, showing the inherent advantage of closed-circuit wiring.

(a) Wiring of an open–circuit fire–alarm system

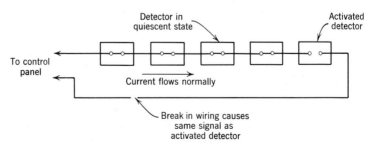

(b) Wiring of a closed–circuit fire–alarm system

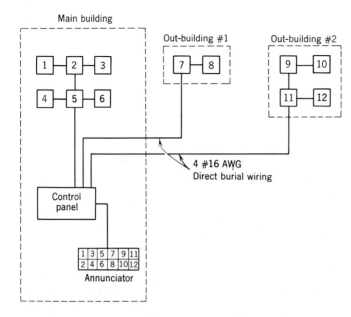

Fig. 28.5 Schematic wiring diagram of an alarm system for a multi-building installation. Numbers may indicate circuits or individual devices.

Maid-call systems utilizing call buttons and multiple drop annunciators are basically similar to the simple door bell systems but are, of course, applicable only to homes employing a household staff.

4. Residential Television Antenna System. The availability of compact television receivers and the increasingly large number of multi-set American homes have made the central television antenna system a desirable feature of the modern residence. Systems with more than 2 outlets generally require a booster amplifier (except in strong signal areas), and are known as amplified systems.

The function of the system is to supply a television signal at each wall outlet, so that a receiver may be operated at more than one location and that two or more receivers may operate simultaneously. Figure 28.8 shows a schematic arrangement of a typical system and Fig. 28.9 some commercial outlets.

The operation of the system is simply

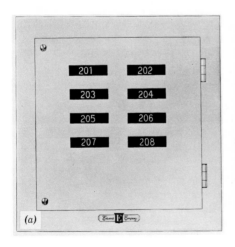

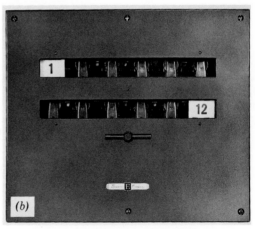

Fig. 28.6 Typical annunciator panels. (*a*) Illuminated type. (*b*) Drop type. (Edwards Co., Inc.)

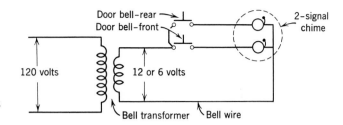

Fig. 28.7 Typical doorbell system; schematic wiring diagram.

to amplify the signal received by the antenna and by means of special cable to distribute these amplified signals in a concealed cable to the various wall outlets. The type and location of antenna, gain (amplification) of the amplifier, type of cable and necessity for color reception are variables which, being dependent on the specific installation, are best left to a competent and reliable local television company.

5. Residential Inter-Communication and Sound System. The pronounced public demand for step-saving conveniences has resulted in the wide acceptance of the home "intercom." (See Figs. 28.10 and 28.11.) Although available with various features, the basic systems comprise 1 or more master and several remote stations, one of which monitors the front door allow-

ing it to be answered from various points within the home. In general, master stations allow selective calling, while remote stations operating through the masters are nonselective. The systems are particularly useful when left in the open (monitor) position for remote "baby sitting." The applicability of such systems to residences with outbuildings should be immediately apparent. Since wiring is low-voltage and low-power, multiconductor color-coded intercom cable is generally used, run concealed within walls, attics, and basements.

With the advent of high-fidelity music systems, many manufacturers have incorporated a tuner (AM, FM, or both) into the home intercom system so that music can be "piped" to each of the stations within the home. Since these stations generally utilize inexpensive 5″ to 7″ speakers, the

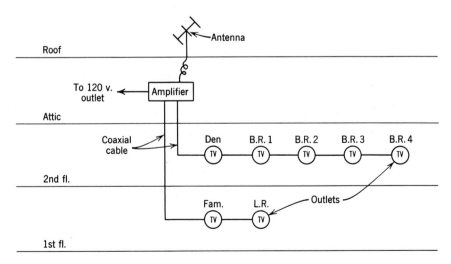

Fig. 28.8   TV antenna system for the residence of Fig. 28.1.

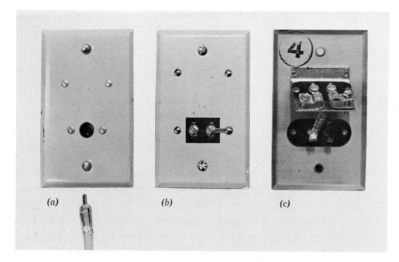

Fig. 28.9 Typical TV wall outlets. Outlet (*a*) is a coaxial type which requires professional skill to make up the jack connection shown; (*b*) is of the screw type allowing tenants to make their own installation; (*c*) is a rear view of outlet (*b*). (Bell Television Inc.)

results can only be construed as high-fidelity by an unknowledgeable home owner or an overzealous manufacturer.

A music system can be readily installed in the home as a separate entity. The design, components, and arrangement of such a system is however a highly specialized field and the advice of experts should be sought if the results are to be gratifying.

6. System Components. An examination of the residential equipment shows that each system comprises 3 basic elements—

the signal generation, the signal processing, and the translation of the electric signal into a usable and recognizeable form. Table 28.1 lists the systems discussed above and subsumes under each functional category the component parts.

Multiple-Dwelling Systems. The types and design of the various sound, signal, and alarm systems employed in multiple-dwelling buildings such as apartment houses, hotels, motels, and dormitories are to some extent governed by local ordnances and

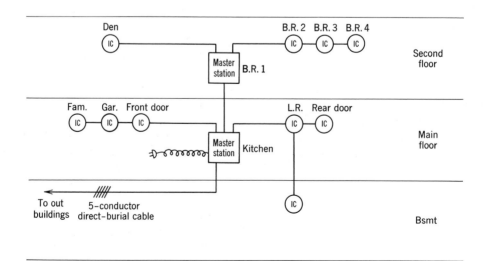

Fig. 28.10   Intercom wiring for the residence of Fig. 28.1.

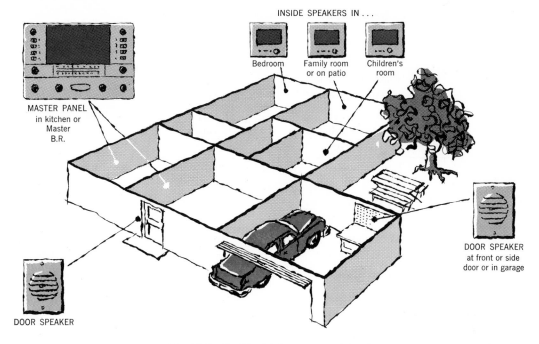

INSIDE SPEAKERS IN . . .

Bedroom

Family room
or on patio

Children's
room

MASTER PANEL
in kitchen or
Master
B.R.

DOOR SPEAKER
at front or side
door or in garage

DOOR SPEAKER

Fig. 28.11   Residential intercom equipment.

codes but in general are functionally similar to the systems discussed above for individual residences.

7. Multiple-Dwelling Fire Alarm System. A hotel fire-alarm system will generally be of the supervised closed-circuit coded type, utilizing manual stations generally, with automatic stations in boiler rooms, storerooms, and other unsupervised or heat-producing areas, with a connection to the building sprinkler system, if one exists. In such a system, operation of any station will sound on all the bells in the building, one to four rounds of a ringing code distinctive to that particular station. This allows immediate identification of the station so that authorized personnel can proceed without delay to the location of the trouble, while the building occupants are evacuating. An auxiliary circuit can be added to such a system which will trip the city fire-alarm box. Such connections, however, are rigidly controlled by local ordinance.

A code usually comprises 3 digits, e.g., 2-3-2, with a pause between the individual ringing groups. The first number will identify the building or zone, the second number of rings the floor or area, and the third the particular station. For a single building without zones or wings the first digit is common to all stations, or may be omitted entirely. A punch recorder at the control panel will record on punched-paper tape the signal code which is sounded thus making an indelible record for use of arriving firemen or for future reference.

In a common-coded system, all gongs ring the same code. Such an arrangement is used to evacuate the premises.

Sprinkler systems are normally provided with waterflow transmitters which will trip the fire-alarm system and simultaneously indicate on an annunciator the particular transmitter involved. Another common feature which is often included where a general alarm would cause disruption of activities, confusion, or even panic, is pre-signalling. With this arrangement an alarm is sounded first only in a specific preselected location such as the engineer's office in a

Table 28.1   *Elements of Residential Signal Systems*

System Type	Signal Generator	Signal Processor*	Signal Transducer
Fire alarm	Temperature detectors, manual stations	Control cabinet(s)	Bells, gongs
Intrusion alarm	Door and window switches, electric eyes	Control cabinet	Bells, gongs, and lights
Door bell, maid call	Push button	Transformer	Buzzer, chime annunciator
TV antenna	TV station and house antenna	Amplifier	TV set
Intercom	Microphone, speaker—mike	Amplifier	Speakers in various stations
Music distribution	Phono, tuner	Amplifiers	Speakers

* The proper wiring and switching is included under this title in all cases.

large hotel. The general alarm is sounded only after it has been determined by the investigating party that a need for it exists or after sufficient time has elapsed to have allowed such an investigation to be made. The application and advantages to such a system are obvious. Various types and combinations of sensing, zoning, and coding equipment are available to meet the exact requirements of the most complex installations—but the fundamental arrangement of sensor, control and supervision, and transducer remains unchanged. Figures 28.12 and 28.13 show a typical hotel floor plan and the related building riser diagram.

Smaller hotels, motels, and dormitories often utilize a larger number of automatic detectors, placing them in individual rooms and closets and connecting them to a non-coded (continuous ringing) or a common-coded supervised zoned system. Manual corridor stations and sprinkler transmitters

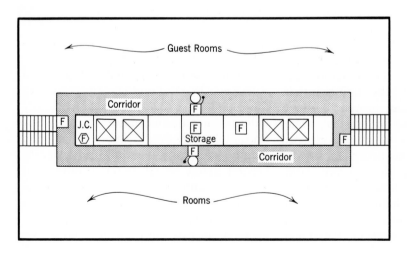

Fig. 28.12 Typical hotel floor plan. Bells are so placed that an alarm will be audible in all parts of the building. Stations are normally installed at all points of egress, such as stairwells and main-floor exits. A typical location for sprinkler alarm transmitter would be in a janitor's closet (J.C.) or electric closet. Automatic temperature detectors are properly located in storage and mechanical spaces.

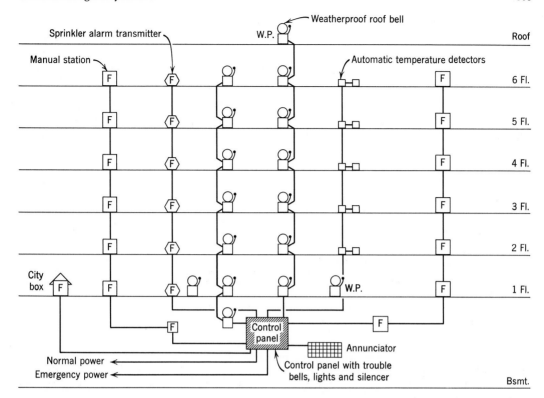

Fig. 28.13   Fire alarm riser diagram for hotel of Fig. 28.12. Normal wiring uses a maximum of 10 stations per alarm circuit and 20 bells per ringing circuit. Presignal bells (not shown) and control panel would be located in the building engineer's office and/or manager's office. The tie to the city box is governed by local fire department regulations.

are connected to the system. Such a system acts as, and is generally referred to as, an evacuation fire-alarm system.

8. Multiple Dwelling Lobby Intercom. Apartment houses, residences, and hotels combine the functions of the intrusion alarm and doorbell systems in the familiar lobby telephone system. Until recently this system was limited to, and generally comprised, a series of push buttons in the lobby and an intercom speaker or telephone with which to communicate with apartments and residents. At the other end, the tenant had a speaker microphone plus a lobby door-opener button. This system was often combined with a housephone system connecting these same apartment stations to a selective master station in the superintendent's apartment. A fairly recent innovation has been

the addition of closed-circuit television to the lobby tenant system, enabling the occupant not only to converse with, but actually to see, the caller. Such a system will increase the electrical contract cost for an average apartment house from 7 to 10 percent. Figure 28.14 and 28.15 illustrates some of the equipment currently available.

Larger hotels with attended desks utilize a housephone system between the rooms and lobby. The house phone system is normally connected through an attended switchboard so that phones may be used for "inside" (intercom) calls as well as for outside calls, as ordinary telephones.

9. Multiple Dwelling Antenna System. All modern multiple residences supply each room with 1 or more TV FM jack outlets. The master antenna systems feeding these are entirely similar to the residential type discussed except for size and electronic design of the components.

10. Music-Paging Systems. Large hotels often utilize music-paging systems consisting generally of a microphone at the hotel desk and telephone operator's board connected via an amplifier to strategically located loudspeakers which, intruding upon every public area in the hotel, broadcast continually their urgent messages. These ubiquitous systems also suffuse nondescript music through the elevators, coffee shops, lobby, lounges, etc., during the times when paging messages are lacking.

School Systems. The proper operation of a modern school requires that flexible and efficient signal and communications equipment be available to the administrative and teaching staff. Such equipment, engineered to meet the needs of the individual institutions, will do much toward optimum utilization of staff and student time.

11. School Fire Alarm System. Although personal safety and prevention of property loss combine to form the raison d'etre of all fire-alarm systems, the former consideration far outweighs the latter in the instance of school buildings, particularly of the elementary grades. For this reason a general schoolwide alarm causing an immediate evacuation of the premises is the primary requirement of the system. For this reason

also, presignalling is rarely used. Consideration also must be given to maintaining the uniqueness of the sound of the fire-alarm gongs to allow no possibility of confusion with the program gongs.

The system employed almost universally calls for a closed-circuit supervised arrangement, noncoded or common-coded in the case of smaller schools, and individually coded in the instance of large or multibuilding institutions. For a multiple-building school, the circuitry is generally arranged to sound an evacuation alarm in the affected building, only i.e., in the building containing the manual or automatic station which set off the alarm. The signal also is transmitted to administrative areas in other buildings.

Since regular fire alarm drills are mandatory in all schools, the system circuitry must be arranged to allow for this type of testing. Systems which are connected to the city fire-alarm circuits must be provided with a lockout to allow use of the equipment in a fire drill without turning in an alarm. As with other systems, manual stations are placed on each floor at egress points, such as stairways, with automatic stations in the boiler room, kitchen, some laboratories, shop classrooms, and selected storage areas. It is also advisable to connect any sprinkler flow transmitters to the alarm system to effect building evacuation while

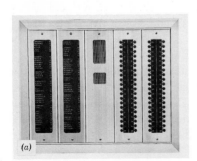

Fig. 28.14   The components of a common apartment house lobby intercommunication system are (*a*) the lobby unit, utilizing a tenant register, wall speaker-microphone and apartment pushbuttons or (*b*) a register (not shown) combined with pushbuttons and handset, and (*c*) the apartment units. The button marked "door" electrically releases the lobby door, allowing the visitor to enter the building. (Auth Electric Co., Inc.)

Fig. 28.15 (a) In an apartment house lobby the caller is viewed by a camera behind a one-way mirror. (b) The picture is transmitted to the apartment occupant. (c) In another installation, the lobby attendant views simultaneously the person at the rear delivery entrance and the interior of the self-service elevator on a two-screen monitor installation. (Courtesy of Bell Television Inc.)

utilizing, in larger schools, a central sprinkler annunciator panel which will indicate the particular transmitter involved. This accomplishes the same purpose as coding of fire-alarm stations.

12. School Clock and Program Systems. The clock and program system commonly used in educational institutions is in reality a combination of 2 separate and distinct systems, i.e., a clock system and a program system. They are normally combined because a program system requires timing facilities which the clock system offers. However, for the sake of clarity in our discussion we will consider the functions separately.

The function of the clock system is simply to indicate the correct time on the various room and corridor clocks in the system.

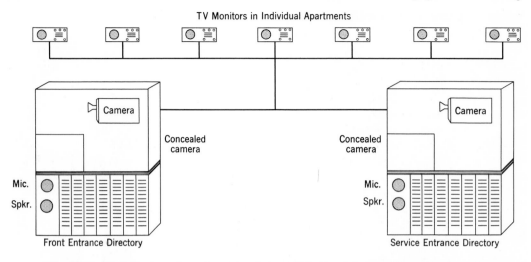

Fig. 28.16   Block diagram of apartment closed-circuit TV system, connected in conjunction with speaker system.

This can be accomplished in four ways—3 employ a master clock and 1 does not. The synchronous, wired master clock system utilizes a master clock which transmits over separate wiring (3 wires) power and correcting signals to the secondary clocks which are driven by synchronous motors. The correcting signal is generally sent hourly and every 12th hour. The entire system, as with all systems employing masters, depends upon the proper function of the master clock for accuracy. (See Fig. 28.17.)

A system which utilizes the power wiring for the transmission of correcting signals from the master clock to the secondary clocks is the electronic system. The individual clocks are powered locally and receive a high frequency correcting signal over the power wires. The outstanding advantage of this system is the elimination of a physical (wiring) connection between master and secondary clocks thus making it particularly attractive in renovation work or in multiple-building schools.

The minute impulse system also utilizes a master and secondary units, the latter being driven by a d-c signal from the master, transmitted at minute intervals, rather than by individual synchronous motors. A cor-

recting signal is also normally transmitted hourly. This system uses a 2-wire connection between units and master.

The 1 system which does not employ a master clock utilizes clocks with dual motors; 1 synchronous for normal drive and 1 high-speed motor for correction. These clocks depend upon their synchronous motors and the constancy of the 60-cycle power supply for accuracy. The high-speed correcting motors merely speed up the clock hands to correct for loss of time due to power interruption. This resetting is centrally controlled, either manually or automatically. The system is separately wired, thus allowing for ease of intentional corrections, such as is required for daylight-saving time.

The function of a program system is to delineate audibly the various time periods into which the school day and week are divided. A single-circuit unit is utilized in the instance of an institution which operates entirely on 1 schedule, such as an elementary school on a morning period—lunch—afternoon period regimen. However, for schools employing different schedules for its various parts, program instruments are available offering up to 6 different program schedules.

The program instrument, as the unit is normally known, comprises a timing device which drives up to 6 wheels or drums, providing individual minute-interval, 24-hour and weekly control. Plugs or pins inserted into the various drums activate contacts and relays which in turn control the audible devices. Provision is usually made as well for manual control of individual circuits. In certain units a cross-connecting board is furnished which allows a completely flexible arrangement of programs and circuits.

The audible devices may be bells, gongs, buzzers, horns, or, in the case of a school equipped with a classroom sound system, a tone which is reproduced on the classroom speakers.

When convenient, the clock and program equipment are combined into a single unit, with some monetary savings and no loss in flexibility. (See Fig. 28.18.)

13. School Television Antenna Systems have found limited use to date, but all signs point to burgeoning use in the future. Their principal function at present is to bring into the classroom or auditorium applicable portions of such educational or cultural material as is being broadcast. Although the amount of such material is at present very limited, even in large urban areas, educational TV stations are multiplying and will perhaps one day be of considerable use to education. Classroom outlets obviate the necessity for congregating large groups of students in assembly halls, and increase the

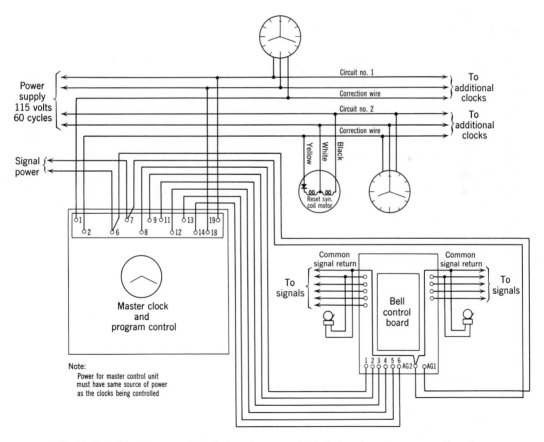

Fig. 28.17 Wiring diagram of a typical synchronous, wired, clock and program system. (Stromberg Time Corp.)

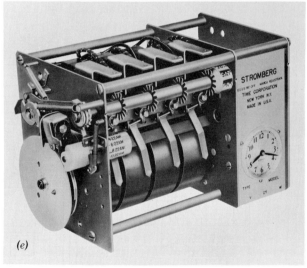

Fig. 28.18   Typical school clock and program equipment. (*a*) Surface type-round clocks. (*b*) Semi-flush square clock (*c*) Central operations panel (*d*) Interior of master and program unit. (*e*) Program control unit. (*f*) Master time and program control for electronic, wired synchronous, or impulse systems. (Stromberg Time Corp.)

system cost only slightly in proportion to their usefulness.

The system design is similar to that discussed above for dwellings except that the equipment is designed for the UHF educational channels in addition to the usual VHF channels. These remarks, of course, apply to antenna systems only which receive broadcast material and not to internal, closed-circuit TV systems.

14. School Intercommunication Systems of various types are to be found in the well-equipped buildings. Intercoms using telephone equipment are often used to link the main office to those of the principal, assistant principal, custodian, departmental offices, classrooms (occasionally), etc. Hand sets are utilized, and, depending upon the number of offices, each set is either equipped with buttons or arranged for dialing. Oc-

casionally desk and wall-type speaker-microphones are used in place of hand sets. (See Fig. 28.19.)

Where desired, the intercom function can be integrated with the outside telephone equipment. This arrangement is offered by practically all public telephone companies using telephone company equipment and wiring exclusively. In large institutions, manual or automatic switchboards are often required and the architect/engineer is advised to determine space requirements for this and auxiliary equipment during the preliminary stage of job design.

15. School Sound Systems. The integrated sound-paging-radio system designed for school use, offers several modes of operation and considerable flexibility.

Its function, of course, is to provide a means for distributing recorded (records,

Fig. 28.19 Typical dial intercom equipment. Equipment of any capacity is available for outright purchase or lease. Dial-type switchboards are usually designed to be readily expandable, and can be installed in any convenient location. (*a*) Dial-type wall unit; (*b*) push-button desk unit; (*c*) Relay and switching rack. (Dukane Corp.)

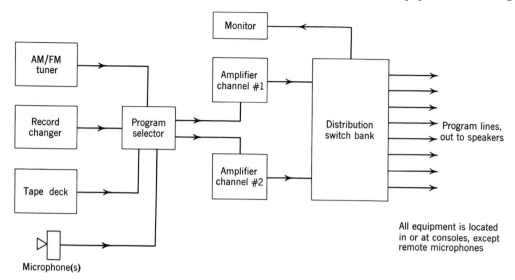

Fig. 28.20   Block diagram of a two-channel sound system.

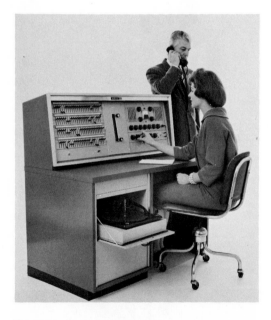

Fig. 28.21 Typical school sound system console. Upper
drawer contains phonograph equipment; lower drawer
may contain tape deck or record storage. Classroom
selectors occupy the left section, AM—FM tuner the
center, and amplifier and intercom controls the right
section of the desk portion. Voice communication uses a
microphone and monitor speaker or a handset as shown.
(Dukane Corp.)

tapes), broadcast (AM/FM) or live sound to
preselected areas of the school. Thus a simple system might provide a record player
and single microphone input, and a single
channel to all of the speakers in the school,
whereas a complex system can be arranged
to operate with, three simultaneous input
signals, for example, distributed to 6 different areas of the school. Increasing
flexibility, as might be expected, very materially increases the cost of the system. See
block diagram Fig. 28.20.

The system consists of a control-console,
which houses most of the input units,
amplifiers, and switching devices, and the
remote loudspeakers, with related volume
controls where required. The input units
may comprise 1 or more AM/FM tuners,
multispeed turntables or record changers,
tape deck, and microphones. One microphone is normally located at the console
with others in the principal's office, auditorium, school office, or other selected location. If desired, mike outlets can be spotted
around the school and a single mike and
stand supplied to be plugged in at any of

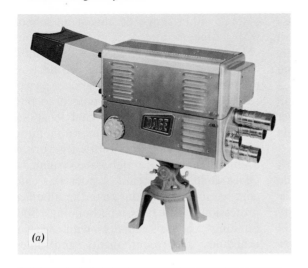

Fig. 28.22 A complete closed-circuit television system. (*a*) The camera; (*b*) the portable camera control unit; (*c*) the central console (the illustrated unit can handle three cameras simultaneously); (*d*) the monitor. Necessary auxiliaries such as lighting, coaxial and power cables, etc., are not shown. (*e*) A typical studio illustrating the arrangement use of these components. (Dage; RCA)

these points. Loudspeakers, located in classrooms, gymnasium, auditorium, cafeteria, and outdoors receive the amplified signal through the switching mechanisms located in the console. It is the function of these switches to deliver, according to their set-ting, the program material to the various loudspeaker circuits, which are also called program lines. Thus, using a system with multiple amplifiers, music can be piped to the cafeteria, an important radio address to senior classrooms and teachers lounge, and instructions to an outdoor gym class or team practice. An all-call feature also allows announcements to reach all speakers in the system simultaneously. The intercom system discussed above can be incorporated into the sound system to allow conversation between classrooms and the console or other points, although it is often kept entirely separate.

The console is usually built in a desk arrangement and it is advisable to provide sufficient space for it at the normal location of the person whose responsibility operation of it will be. Often an alcove of 30–50 sq ft is reserved for it and a library of recordings.

Loudspeakers may be in flush or surface baffles, at the discretion of the designer. Gymnasium, cafeteria, and auditorium units are normally flush-mounted in the ceiling. For large areas such as these it is well to provide a volume control, enclosed in a recessed wall box with a locking cover.

16. School Closed-Circuit TV System. Though now limited, the use of closed-circuit television promises to increase rapidly in coming years and considerably affect teaching techniques. This equipment allows lectures to be heard and witnessed in individuai classrooms, demonstrations to be seen in close-up by all, etc. Because of its great potential, many far-sighted educators and administrators are having the equipment installed, or at least making provision for future equipment in the form of empty conduit systems. Advances in TV technology have brought the price of a simple

system within range of almost all schools with designs arranged for future additions.

Basically the system comprises 1 or more cameras, a control console, wiring, and monitoring equipment. The cameras as well as the monitors can be arranged to plug into special outlets at selected locations. Thus a single camera and several monitors can take the place, with a little leg work, of a considerably more elaborate system.

Office Building Systems. Under this category we include systems found in all office, professional, and sales-type buildings. Such buildings house tenants with varying schedules and requirements and unless large, do not have a full-time custodian. These factors then must be considered in the design of the low-voltage systems for such buildings.

17. Office Building Fire-Alarm Systems. Fire detection is of great concern in this type of structure since it is empty much of the time and loss of records by fire can seriously impair a company's operations for a very considerable time. For this reason the fire-alarm system which in office buildings is generally a common-coded closed-circuit supervised one, often utilizes various types of automatic detection in addition to the usual manual station at egress points. This automatic detection may take the form of the combination type renewable thermostatic elements with which we are familiar, plus more sophisticated devices such as smoke detectors (Figs. 28.23, 28.24).

One type of smoke detection, commercially available for some years, is the photo-

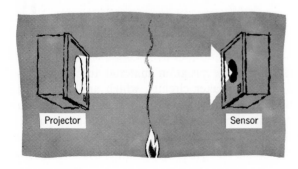

Fig. 28.23 Principle of smoke detection. Smoke detection is useful in spaces where occupants may be asleep, since smoke poisoning may occur before temperature-sensitive detectors operate. A principal drawback to the extensive use of this type of equipment in residences is the relatively high cost.

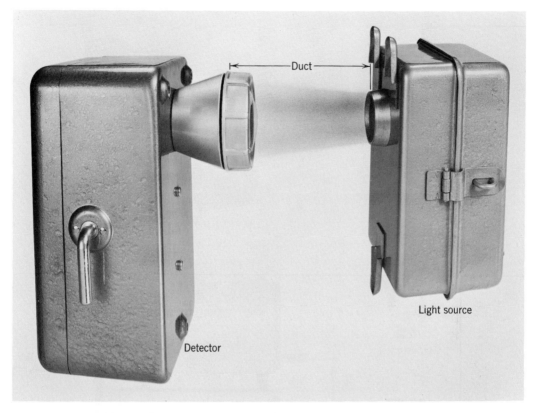

Fig. 28.24   Smoke detection equipment. This type of equipment is often used on air-conditioning ductwork to detect the presence of smoke. When the detector operates an alarm is sounded, and the system fans and blowers are shut down to prevent the spread of smoke and fire. (Acme Fire Alarm Co.)

electric system which detects a change in the intensity of a light beam, such as would be caused by smoke in the room. Another extremely sensitive type utilizes the fact that particles in the air in the area of an incipient fire will affect an ionization chamber. This type often operates before smoke is detectable by a photo-electric system. These devices, when placed in areas which are not normally occupied, such as record storage areas, stockrooms, etc., and in ventilation and air-conditioning ducts, can do much to give early, and, hopefully, ample, warning of a fire. Figure 28.25 shows several of the automatic detectors now in commercial use.

In addition to alarm devices, office structure often utilize built-in automatic fire-fighting equipment such as sprinkling, although these are used sparingly in many locations since water can be as ruinous to records as fire. Another more recent system utilizes a carbon-dioxide deluge to smother a fire without causing water damage. This system is also extensively utilized in the floating floors commonly found in computer installations. Needless to say, these various fire-quenching systems are connected into the alarm system, and, if extensive, also to an annunciator so as to immediately pinpoint the location of the trouble.

18. Office Building Watchmen's Tour Systems. In order that surveillance of unoccupied office premises be conducted on a regular basis, some type of watchmen's

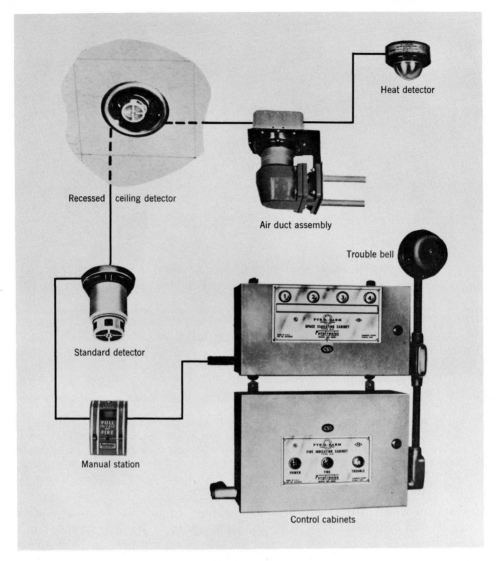

Heat detector

Recessed | ceiling detector

Air duct assembly

Trouble bell

Standard detector

Manual station

Control cabinets

Fig. 28.25   Commercial installations often include ionization-type smoke detectors combined with heat detectors and manual stations. Sprinkler transmitters (not shown) are also frequently utilized. (Acme Fire Alarm Co.)

clock, or tour system, is generally installed. The simplest type which is nonelectric comprises a number of small cabinets, each containing a key, placed at intervals around the interior and exterior of the building. The watchman uses these keys to operate a special clock which he carries about, thus recording the exact time at which he "clocked-in" at any specific location.

Electrical systems are available which permit constant supervision and are particularly effective where more than one man is on duty. Such systems show on a panel the location and progress of the watchman, by means of lights which glow when the device at each location is operated. Since part of the effectiveness of these systems lies in the timing of the tour, a system can be

(b)

(a)

Fig. 28.26 Watchmens tour equipment. (*a*) Main control unit contains: Telephone communication between watchman's stations and main control unit, watchman's clock with recording dial to provide a permanent record of each tour, elimination of compulsory tour feature, and individual coded signals from each watch station. (*b*) Patrol Station; in addition to watchman's key hole, outer door is usually provided with a telephone jack and bull's eye lamp.

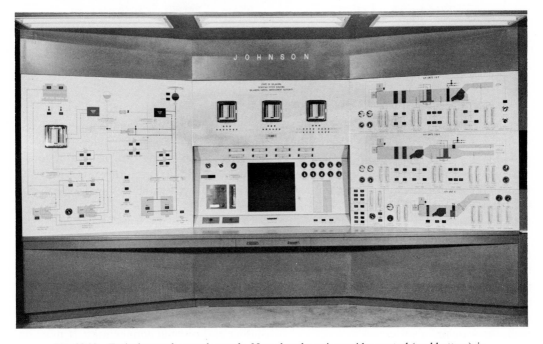

Fig. 28.27 Typical central control console. Note that the unit provides control (pushbuttons), indication (meters), and system arrangement diagrams of the major building systems so that normal and emergency procedures can be initiated with no delay. The size of the board and the number of controlled and metered parameters is governed by considerations of necessity and economy. (Johnson Service Company)

Fig. 28.28   Sketch of composite alarm system. All alarms can be monitored by a single man at this type of console. These would include fire, intrusion, sprinkler, and such special units as liquid levels, flame-failure, gas detection, etc.

arranged to sound an alarm if a particular station is not operated within a specific time period.

Telephone jacks spaced at points along the guard's route allow him to communicate with the supervising office or other point, without interrupting his scheduled tour.

For protection of areas housing extremely valuable items or documents, an intrusion alarm system utilizing the radar principle may be employed. This equipment detects *any motion* within the protected area. Such spaces are obviously excluded from the watchman's tour.

19. Office Building Communication Systems. A large number of communication systems are available to the modern office which will reproduce visually and (or)

audibly almost any signal, generated remotely as well as locally. Since these systems are complex and are usually tailored to the individual requirements, we will restrict our discussion to the less esoteric types.

In addition to the usual types of phone and desk intercom systems, the telephone companies have generally made available systems which to a large extent do away with PBX boards by allowing direct dialing of extension phones from outside, in addition to the more usual "inside" intercom dialing and outside connections. It must be borne in mind by the architect that such automatic equipment requires considerable space for relay racks, switching equipment, cable splicing, etc. Similarly the space requirements for such equipment as Facsimile, Telautograph, Teletype, central dictation, etc., should be determined in consultation with manufacturers.

In all but the simplest systems it is generally advisable that the architect leave the selection, design, and location of equipment to the consulting engineer within whose responsibility such work lies.

20. *Office Supervisory Data-Control Centers.* As the modern office building mechanical and electrical systems increased in complexity a need began to be felt for a central point of supervision, control, and data collection from which an operator could survey an entire building's functioning. From such a point the water, air-conditioning, heating, ventilating, electrical, and other systems could be controlled manually and automatically with much greater accuracy than if no such central control point were available.

In addition, data on temperatures, pressures, flow, current, voltage, and all the many parameters of mechanical systems could be made instantly available so that operational decisions could be made more accurately. Also all systems could be monitored here and all alarms instantly acted upon.

Such centers, generally called supervisory control and data centers, are now being installed in many large office buildings and represent an excellent example of the application of signal and control equipment to increase the efficiency of the mechanical and electrical building equipment.

Industrial Building Systems. All industrial facilities ranging from the taxpayer loft, housing a small hand-assembly plant to the immense steel manufacturing plant require a variety of signal and alarm equipment. Although, as in the case of commercial structures, a detailed analysis of the equipment is out of place here, it behooves the building designer to be sufficiently familiar with this area to know generally the function, operation, and availability of this type of equipment.

21. *Industrial Building Fire-Alarm Systems.* Plant systems are normally coded, closed-circuit, and supervised with the control panel and the various annunciators located in the plant engineer's office, guard house, or both. Automatic detection is usual, in conjunction with manual alarms in the same manner as for office buildings. Due to the high ambient noise level in many locations in plants, horns are substituted for bells since ordinary gongs or vibrating bells would be inaudible.

22. *Industrial Building Watchmen's Tour Systems.* The watchmen's equipment is similar to that described above, and except in the smallest installations, is of the supervised type. This supervisory equipment is generally placed in the guard house, which would also house any burglar alarm equipment. (See Fig. 28.28.)

23. *Industrial Building Clock and Program Systems.* The function of the clock system is self-evident, and may be any of the 4 types discussed above, as applicable.

Program equipment may be used to delineate the working and rest periods, start

Fig. 28.29 Typical pocket-type paging equipment. Audio reproducer is provided with lapel clip for easy positioning while receiver unit can be placed in any pocket. The unit operates on the induction principle and receives a nonselective voice message; other units operate on radio frequency and receive a selective call signal or a nonselective voice message. (Dukane Corp.)

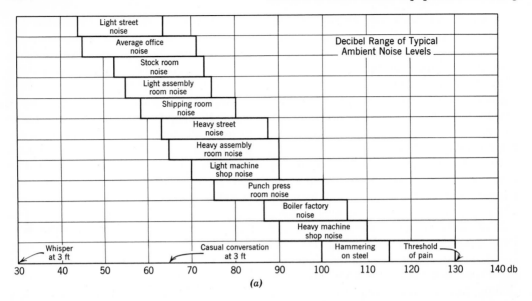

(a)

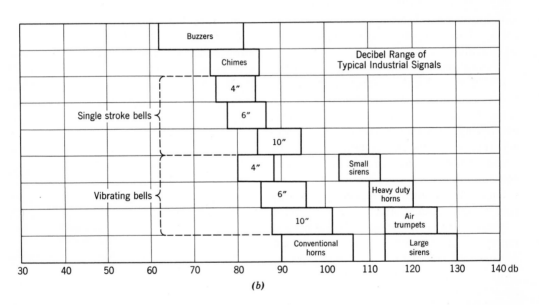

(b)

and finish of a particular process, periodic tests, etc. Audible devices may be any combination of bells, horns, gongs, or buzzers applicable to the area being designed.

24. Industrial Building Paging Systems. All of the time-saving and efficiency potential which result from the proper use of the various signal and communication equipment available can be lost if there is no recipient for the information transmitted. Furthermore, sometimes a decision must be reached quickly to avoid costly delay, reruns, etc. These factors combine to make rapid and accurate paging an extremely important function in a manufacturing operation, particularly of the larger variety.

The various types of paging systems fall into two general categories and several sub-

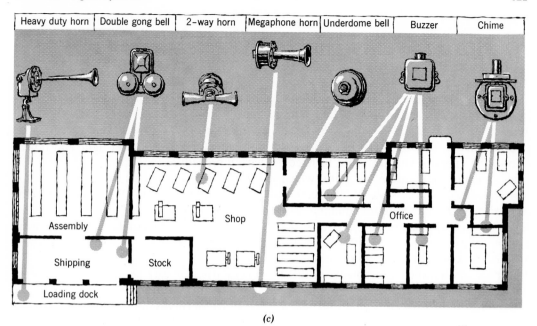

| Heavy duty horn | Double gong bell | 2-way horn | Megaphone horn | Underdome bell | Buzzer | Chime |

(c)

Fig. 28.30   Decibel range of typical industrial noise levels shown in chart (a) can be compared with decibel ratings of typical industrial signals shown in chart (b) to facilitate selection. Suggested locations are shown in plan (c) of a typical small industrial installation. (Reprinted by permission from Vol. 5, No. 5. of *Actual Specifying Engineer,* Copyright 1961 Domestic Engineering Co.)

categories: they are either visual, audible, or both, and are either common or selective.

The simplest visual and audio-visual types comprise flashing lights, which may be combined with buzzers or bells, either or both of which are generally coded.

Such systems are nonselective in that they impinge upon the senses of all the building occupants—an obvious disadvantage.

More sophisticated systems utilize a small pocket device which is carried by each person likely to be paged, i.e., maintenance men, plant engineers, executives, etc. By means of either direct radio transmission or of electric fields induced by induction loops installed throughout the building an *individual* pocket device can be alerted—the call being either a buzz or a voice call. In some systems, the alerted person then listens to his message directly, whereas on others, it is necessary for him, once having been paged, to go to a phone and call in to a cen-

tral paging desk to receive his message. In either case, the improvement over the light-bell-buzzer systems is considerable.

In any of these systems, it is necessary to have a paging operator and a coding board at which the paging calls originate. Often, in a small factory, paging is handled by the regular phone operator.

25. Industrial Building Music and Sound Systems.   Environmental and other psychological research have shown the effectiveness of soothing background music in certain rest and work situations. These conclusions led to the installation of speaker systems in many industrial areas including manufacturing, shops, cafeterias, and lounges which blanket the area with music. These same speakers are connected to a record player or tape input at a console, or alternatively, receive their signal from commercial sources specializing in this field.

The systems are usually arranged so that

a microphone can be switched in for the purpose of making general announcements over these same loudspeakers.

26. Industrial Building Closed-Circuit Television. Closed-circuit television found its first extensive use in industrial plants and this usage still accounts for a large portion of proprietary TV system sales. The application of TV to industrial processes allows the operator to "see" into furnaces, mills, machine tools, and other points which were previously inaccessible to his eye, thus improving control, product quality, etc. This type of application is of course the responsibility of a specialist but it is well for the architect and engineer to keep in mind the space and power requirements of these systems.

27. Electric Wiring for Signal and Sound Systems. The requirements for wiring of signal and sound systems are found in the National Electric Code, 1962 Edition, Articles 700, 725, 800, and 810.

Although the details of these requirements will not be reproduced here, being readily available in the referenced Articles, some of the general rules and considerations are listed below.

(*a*) *All wiring and material should be in strict accordance with manufacturers instructions.*

(*b*) Wiring for power supply of signal equipment follows normal light and power wiring procedure.

(*c*) Wiring for systems whose power is not strictly limited (class 1), follows normal wiring procedure.

(*d*) Signal system conductors should generally be kept separate from light and power wiring.

(*e*) Particular care should be taken in installation of special cables, wires, etc., as these are normally more sensitive to rough handling than normal building wiring.

(*f*) Ground connections should be well made and then double checked, as a poor ground can materially affect the quality of signal system performance.

29

Acoustics

W. Ranger Farrell, of Bolt, Beranek, and Newman, Consultants in Acoustics

1. General Information. Architectural acoustics is the technology of sound control associated with building design and, as such, deals with making "wanted" sounds clearly heard and "unwanted" sounds (noise) undisturbing. In all acoustics problems there is a source from which the sound emanates, a path along which it travels, and finally a receiver who (or sometimes which) perceives the sound. It is the source and (or) the path which the architect modifies to control the sound, but it is of great importance to note that it is the receiver who determines whether the degree or quality of control is satisfactory.

Although broad and general dissertations on acoustics may make interesting reading, it is the author's opinion that they are of little practical use to the reader. It is the purpose of this chapter to outline design procedures in as usable fashion as possible within the limited space. The reader will find, however, that without some preliminary "brushing up" on arithmetic and some memorization of formulas and acoustic terminology, he will soon find himself lost in unfamiliar territory. To avoid this, it is suggested that the reader get out his high school arithmetic book and review the use of logarithms to the base 10 and the use of positive and negative exponents $(10^{\pm n})$.*

2. The Generation of Sound. Sound is generated when an object oscillates to-and-fro, thus imparting kinetic energy into the adjacent air particles. This energy must be conserved and thus a wave is set into motion, the energy being transmitted from one particle to the next, and so on, in succession progressing away from the source.

3. Wave Velocity and Wave Length. The wave length of sounds of various frequencies of sounds we hear range from about $\frac{1}{2}$ in. to about 50 ft. Since under normal conditions sound waves always travel through air at essentially the same velocity, a simple relationship exists.

$$\lambda = \frac{c}{f} \qquad (29.1)$$

---

* One need not concern oneself with the logs of numbers less than unity but should be familiar with manipulations involving negative exponentials of 10.

where λ = wave length, ft,

   c = velocity of sound in air =
       1140 ft/sec,

   f = frequency, cps (cycles per
       second).

4. Specification of Sound. Sound is a 3-dimensional phenomenon. It can have different amounts of intensity (corresponding to different loudnesses), can occur at different frequencies (corresponding to pitch), and in either of these respects can vary with time. All three of these dimensions must be simultaneously specified before the sound is fully defined. Fortunately, many sounds do not vary with time and, even when they do, it is possible to assume a steady condition by taking some stated form such as an average or the highest or lowest levels reached at any time.

(*a*) *Intensity.* Assuming a steady emission of sound energy (power) from the source, one can observe that in free space the energy will spread itself thinner as it travels farther from the source (see Fig. 29.1).

From this figure one can deduce several things. There is an intensity at any point around a source which is emitting power. This is expressed as the power being emitted, divided by the area over which it has spread, or

$$I = \frac{P}{A} \qquad (29.2)$$

It is customary in acoustics to use a mixed system in which power (P) is expressed in watts, area (A) in square centimeters (cm²), and thus intensity (I) in watts/cm². One can also see in the special (though not unusual) case where the waves radiate freely in a spherical pattern that

$$I = \frac{P}{4\pi r^2} \qquad (29.3)$$

because the surface area of a sphere is $4\pi r^2$. Since, in our calculation, we usually express the distance (r) from the sound source in English, unit equation 29.3 may be written

$$I = \frac{P}{930 \times 4\pi r^2} \qquad (29.4)$$

because 1 ft² = 930 cm².

From Fig. 29.1 one can derive a useful and classic formula for finding the relationship between the intensities (I_1 and I_2) at two distances (r_1 and r_2) from the same source. This formula is traditionally called "inverse square law":

$$\frac{I_1}{I_2} = \frac{r_2{}^2}{r_1{}^2} \qquad (29.5)$$

Sound intensities which we can hear extend to as low as 10^{-16} watt/cm² which, because it is the least an average person can hear, is called our "threshold" of hearing. They also extend upwards to 10^{-7} watt/cm² (shouting at a distance of 6 or 7 ft) or even 10^{-3} watt/cm² (an intensity at which we

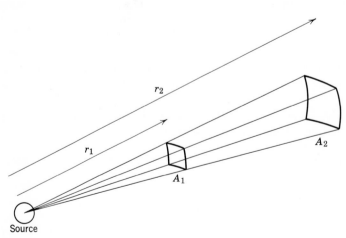

Fig. 29.1   The same total energy passes through A_1 and A_2.

experience pain). Notice that (a) these are very small numbers, and (b) they cover an energy ratio of 10,000,000,000,000:1 (see Table 29.1).

Not only is the scale of the numbers small and the scope broad but also our ears respond in a special "nonlinear" way to the intensity. If we are subjected successively to sounds of intensities, 1×10^{-14}, 2×10^{-14}, 3×10^{-14}, 4×10^{-14}, 5×10^{-14}, etc., we would notice that the change from 1×10^{-14} to 2×10^{-14} was a greater change than that from 4×10^{-14} to 5×10^{-14} in terms of the detected "loudness" change.

Intensity, though a useful quantity when discussing wave motion and energy radiation and "spreading," has the practical disadvantages of employing awkwardly small numbers and failing to conform directly to our hearing experience. It would be convenient to have a scale for acoustic measurement in which (a) "zero" was the least amount of sound we could hear, (b) the numbers were whole numbers rather than very small fractional numbers, and (c) any convenient change, say 10 units, corresponded to a given change in loudness, say, doubling the loudness. For example, a change from 20 to 30 would give the same

increase in loudness as a change from 70 to 80.

(b) **Intensity Level (IL, db).** Such a scale can be achieved by using a function of the logarithm of the intensity, defined by the formula:

$$IL = 10 \times \log \frac{I}{I_0} \qquad (29.6)$$

where IL = the intensity level, db,
I = intensity in watts/cm^2,
$I_0 = 10^{-16}$ watt/cm^2 (the least intensity audible to the average human ear).

Intensity level (IL) is that term which fulfills the three requirements given in the previous paragraph. The unit is the decibel (db)—the prefix "deci" indicating that the logarithm is multiplied by 10 to reduce the occurrence of decimal points.

It can be seen from formula 29.6 and Table 29.1 that, if the intensity at a listener's ear is equal to 1×10^{-16} watt/cm^2, the ratio of the intensities (I/I_0) is equal to unity and the intensity level equals zero. This is the least amount of sound that the average listener can hear. Table 29.1 shows some absolute values of IL and Table 29.2 shows some relative values.

Table 29.1   Comparison of Decimal, Exponential and Logarithmic Statements of Various Acoustic Intensities

| Intensity (watts/cm$_2$) | | Intensity Level— | |
Decimal Notation	Exponential Notation	Logarithmic Notation	Examples
10000	10^{+4}	200 db	
1000	10^{+3}	190 db	
0.001	10^{-3}	130 db	Painful
0.0001	10^{-4}	120 db	
0.00001	10^{-5}	110 db	75-piece orchestra
0.000001	10^{-6}	100 db	
0.0000001	10^{-7}	90 db	Shouting at 5 ft
0.0000000000001	10^{-13}	30 db	Quiet unoccupied office
0.00000000000001	10^{-14}	20 db	Rural ambient
0.000000000000001	10^{-15}	10 db	
0.0000000000000001	10^{-16}	0 db	Threshold of hearing

Table 29.2　Subjective Loudness Changes and Corresponding Intensity Level Changes

Change in Level, db	Subjective Change in Loudness
3	Barely perceptible
5	Perceptible
7	Clearly perceptible
10	Twice or half as loud
20	Four times or one quarter as loud

Intensity level (*IL*) may be equated to another acoustic term, sound pressure level (*SPL*). Because sound *intensity* cannot be measured and sound *pressure* can, the acoustical engineer prefers to use sound pressure level. If the reader finds references to *SPL* in the literature, he need only remember that $SPL = IL$, at least for temperatures and barometer pressures near normal.

(*c*) *Acoustic Power Level* (***PWL, db***). Another useful acoustical quantity is the acoustic power level. This is the term in units of decibels which corresponds directly to the power (*P*, watts) of a source. Power level is defined as

$$PWL = 10 \times \log \frac{P}{10^{-13}} \text{ db} \quad (29.7)$$

where P = the acoustic power in watts radiated from the source,
10^{-13} = reference power, watts.*

PWL is a quantity independent of the environment and the distance from the source. For this reason manufacturers of a device or machine publish power levels, but what we are interested in is *IL*. Thus, it is desirable to be able to calculate *IL*:

$$IL = PWL - 20 \log r - 11 \text{ db} \quad (29.8)$$

where IL = the intensity level at distance r,
PWL = the power level with 10^{-13} = reference power,
r = distance from the source, ft.

Formula 29.8 applies only for "free field" or spherical radiation of a nondirectional source. When the source is in a room or enclosure, see equation 29.13. The complexities introduced by directional sources (i.e., those that "beam" sound energy in one direction rather than truly spherically) are beyond the scope of this discussion. For more complete discussion, see Refs. 3 and 9.

(*d*) *Frequency.* The second dimension of sound which must be specified is frequency or the number of pressure fluctuations per second caused by the passage of sound waves. Our ears can detect sound at frequencies between approximately 20 cps and 20,000 cps. A sound having energy at one and only one frequency is called a pure tone. A pure tone is seldom encountered. Most of the sounds with which we are familiar (machine noises, voice, musical instruments, etc.) contain some acoustic energy over a wide range of frequencies. A sound having a preponderance of energy at the lower frequencies will tend to have a rumbling sound, as in the case of a subway train passing beneath a building. Sounds having a preponderance of energy in the higher frequencies tend to have a hissing sound. Most of the sounds with which we communicate to each other have a preponderance of energy in the middle frequencies. To specify both frequency and sound level at the same time, it is necessary to give an indication of the "spectrum" of the sound. This can be done in tabular or graphical form. Fig. 29.2 shows several typical acoustical spectra in which *PWL* is plotted as a function of frequency.

It is customary, for convenience in making acoustical measurements, to measure the sum of the energy in each of several groups or "bands" of frequencies. These bands may be of any width, but Fig. 29.3*a*, *b*, *c*, and *d* show examples of the four most commonly used bandwidths. Figure 29.3*a* shows a "spectrum scale" in which the levels at each of the frequencies from 20 to 20,000

---

* 10^{-12} watt is also used occasionally as a reference power. When this is the case, the power levels must be increased 10 db for use in the formulas of this chapter.

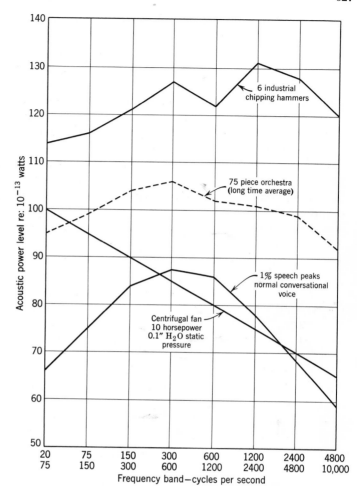

Fig. 29.2 Four typical acoustic power level spectra.

are indicated individually. For most measurements this is more detail than required, and the measurement is too time-consuming. Thus, we usually measure over wider intervals of frequency. Levels measured in "octave bands" of frequencies are shown in Fig. 29.3d. In octave bands, the upper frequency is twice that of the lower. Figures 29.3b and 29.3c show levels measured in half and one-third octave bands which also are frequently used.

(e) *Time Variation.* Some sounds which we deal with in architectural acoustics do not vary as a function of time. For example, a constantly operating ventilating fan or a ceiling diffuser makes a steady-state noise. Its spectrum can be plotted, as shown in

Fig. 29.2. Many other sounds such as voice, music, or traffic do vary as a function of time. In such a case one must plot or tabulate some clearly defined spectrum such as the peak (highest) intensity levels or the average intensity level, which the source generates. For example, the voice power levels of Fig. 29.2 are those which will be exceeded only 1 percent of the time in average conversation.

5. Sounds Outdoors. Although the propagation of sound outdoors may not appear to be of immediate importance in architectural acoustics, outdoor noise sources such as aircraft may frequently prove loud enough to disturb activities within or immediately adjacent to a building. Conversely, the noise made by building equipment such as cooling towers may be sufficiently loud to disturb neighbors in a nearby apartment building. For this reason it is desirable to have some basic understanding of outdoor sound propagation.

For preliminary evaluation of an outdoor noise problem assuming a nondirectional source, one needs to know only the power level radiated by the source as a function of frequency and time; from this one can establish the intensity level of sound at the appropriate distance (see formula 29.8). The power radiated by the source may be estab-

lished from measurements, published data, or theoretical calculations. If *IL* data are available at some known distance from the source, it may be necessary to apply the inverse square law (formula 29.5) to find the intensity at the distance of interest. Basically, in free field, the sound level drops by 6 db with each doubling of distance.

A number of factors other than spherical radiation may affect the level of sound outdoors. For example, if the sound source is on the ground, the intensity of the sound will be distributed over a hemisphere rather than a sphere, and thus the intensity will

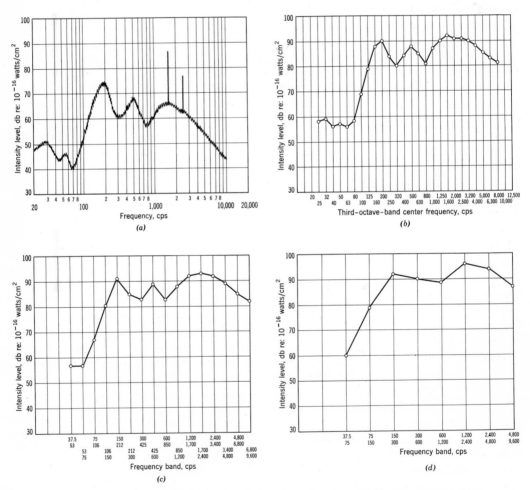

Fig. 29.3   Spectra of a noise measured and plotted as a function of 4 different frequency band widths. (*a*) 1 cps wide bands; (*b*) $\frac{1}{3}$ octave wide bands, (*c*) $\frac{1}{2}$ octave wide bands and (*d*) full octave bands.

be double that for spherical radiation. This would increase the *IL* calculated from formula 29.8 by 3 db. In other cases, such as fresh-air intake grilles (from the basement of a very tall building), the sound radiated may be concentrated on one quarter of a sphere, thus giving levels of 6 db higher than free spherical spreading. In each of these special but common cases of "directivity" of the source, the level will fall off 6 db with each distance doubling as before.

Other factors, such as moisture in the air, the presence of trees, wind, temperature gradients, etc., will affect outdoor sound propagation to some extent but they can be ignored except when great distances (i.e., over 1000 ft) are involved. Barrier walls (such as solid fences) are an influence only when the wall is high, wide, and near the source, or near the listener. These effects, however, are discussed in detail in Refs. 3, 5, and 9.

6. Sound in Enclosures. Sound, when it originates within an enclosure, such as a room, will spread out in that enclosure until it impinges on the surfaces, where it must either be absorbed or reflected. The percentage of energy transmitted is so small that it has little effect on the space within which the sound originates although, as will be discussed, it may be very important in the surrounding spaces. The percentage absorbed or reflected will significantly affect what one hears within the space. Specifically, if little energy is absorbed, two effects will be noticeable. Intermittent sounds will be mixed together (which may make speech *less* intelligible or music *more* pleasant) any steady sounds will "add up" (making restaurants or offices noisier).*

(*a*) *Sound Absorption.* It is useful to be able to quantitize these effects. If all of the enclosing surfaces are completely efficient sound absorbers, there will be no mixing of sounds (no reflections) and, if given the power *P*, the resulting intensity may be calculated by formula 29.3 or 29.4. Most materials, however, do not absorb all the

sound energy. To define this

$$\alpha = \frac{I_a}{I_i} \qquad (29.9)$$

where I_i = intensity impinging on the material, watts/cm²,
I_a = intensity absorbed by the material, watts/cm²,
α = absorption coefficient (no units).

Thus α is a measure of absorption efficiency. If $\alpha = 1.0$, all the impinging energy is absorbed and if $\alpha = 0.0$ all is reflected. If 1 ft² of material absorbs 10 percent of the impinging energy ($\alpha = 0.10$), 10 ft² will absorb as much as 1 ft² having complete efficiency. Thus we can determine the sound absorption provided by a material by

$$\text{Sound absorption} = S\alpha \qquad (29.10)$$

where S = surface area, ft²,
α = absorption coefficient.

Since α is a ratio and thus unitless, and S is in square feet, $S\alpha$ should be in square feet. Actually, sound absorption units are called sabins in honor of W. C. Sabine, a pioneer in architectural acoustics.

Most rooms are constructed of several materials each having different absorption coefficients (α) and thus it becomes necessary to use

$$\Sigma S\alpha = S_1\alpha_1 + S_2\alpha_2 + \cdots S_n\alpha_n \qquad (29.11)$$

where $\Sigma S\alpha$ = the total absorption in the room, sabins
S_1, S_2 etc. = the areas (ft²) of each material,
α_1, α_2 etc. = the coefficients of each material.

Table 29.3 gives the absorption coefficients of many typical building materials. Notice that α varies for different materials and is different at different frequencies for each material.

Special manufactured products provide

---

* The latter effect will be discussed under "Noise Reduction."

Table 29.3   Coefficients of General Building Materials and Furnishings

Complete tables of coefficients of the various materials that normally constitute the interior finish of rooms may be found in the various books on architectural acoustics. The following short list will be useful in making simple calculations of the reverberation in rooms.

	Coefficients					
Materials	125 cps	250 cps	500 cps	1000 cps	2000 cps	4000 cps
Brick, unglazed	.03	.03	.03	.04	.05	.07
Brick, unglazed, painted	.01	.01	.02	.02	.02	.03
Carpet, heavy, on concrete	.02	.06	.14	.37	.60	.65
Same, on 40 oz hairfelt or foam rubber	.08	.24	.57	.69	.71	.73
Same, with impermeable latex backing on 40 oz hairfelt or foam rubber	.08	.27	.39	.34	.48	.63
Concrete Block, coarse	.36	.44	.31	.29	.39	.25
Concrete Block, painted	.10	.05	.06	.07	.09	.08
Fabrics						
Light velour, 10 oz per sq yd, hung straight, in contact with wall	.03	.04	.11	.17	.24	.35
Medium velour, 14 oz per sq yd, draped to half area	.07	.31	.49	.75	.70	.60
Heavy velour, 18 oz per sq yd, draped to half area	.14	.35	.55	.72	.70	.65
Floors						
Concrete or terrazzo	.01	.01	.015	.02	.02	.02
Linoleum, asphalt, rubber or cork tile on concrete	.02	.03	.03	.03	.03	.02
Wood	.15	.11	.10	.07	.06	.07
Wood parquet in asphalt on concrete	.04	.04	.07	.06	.06	.07
Glass						
Large panes of heavy plate glass	.18	.06	.04	.03	.02	.02
Ordinary window glass	.35	.25	.18	.12	.07	.04
Gypsum Board, $\frac{1}{4}''$ nailed to 2x4's 16" o.c.	.29	.10	.05	.04	.07	.09
Marble or Glazed Tile	.01	.01	.01	.01	.02	.02
Openings						
Stage, depending on furnishings				.25 — .75		
Deep balcony, upholstered seats				.50 — 1.00		
Grills, ventilating				.15 — .50		
Plaster, gypsum or lime, smooth finish on tile or brick	.013	.015	.02	.03	.04	.05
Plaster, gypsum or lime, rough finish on lath	.02	.03	.04	.05	.04	.03
Same, with smooth finish	.02	.02	.03	.04	.04	.03
Plywood Panelling, $\frac{3}{8}''$ thick	.28	.22	.17	.09	.10	.11
Water Surface, as in a swimming pool	.008	.008	.013	.015	.020	.025
Air, Sabins per 1000 cubic ft					2.3	7.2

	Values in Sabins per sq ft of Seating Area or per Unit					
Absorption of Seats and Audience	125 cps	250 cps	500 cps	1000 cps	2000 cps	4000 cps
Audience, seated in upholstered seats, per sq ft of floor area	.60	.74	.88	.96	.93	.85
Unoccupied cloth-covered upholstered seats, per sq ft of floor area	.49	.66	.80	.88	.82	.70
Unoccupied leather-covered upholstered seats, per sq ft of floor area	.44	.54	.60	.62	.58	.50
Wooden Pews, occupied, per sq ft of floor area	.57	.61	.75	.86	.91	.86
Chairs, metal or wood seats, each, unoccupied	.15	.19	.22	.39	.38	.30

very efficient sound absorption. Photographs of some such products are shown in Fig. 29.4 and absorption coefficients are given in Ref. 6. The absorbing effect of audiences and seats can have a major effect on the total absorption. Audience and upholstered seat absorption is calculated on the basis of the floor area covered including narrow aisles (up to 7 ft 0 in. for center aisles and 3.5 ft for perimeter aisles).

(b) Reverberation. The prolongation of sound experienced in rooms having sound-absorbing surfaces of low efficiency is caused by the persistence of the sound energy within the room for some period of time after the source has stopped. Typically, it will take between 0.4 sec (in small rooms with significant absorption) and 3.0 sec (in large, hard-finished churches) for a loud sound to diminish (or decay) to inaudibility.

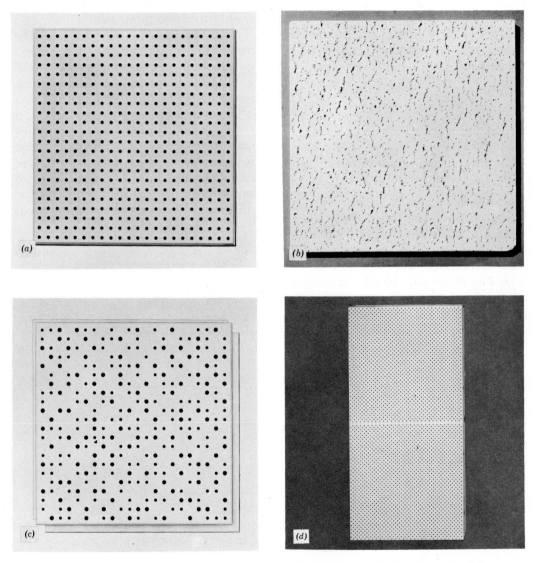

Fig. 29.4 Prefabricated tiles. (a) Regular perforated; (b) Fissured; (c) Random perforated; (d) Metal pan.

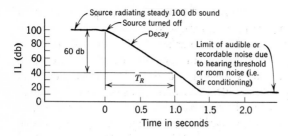

Fig. 29.5   Typical reverberation decay.

This decay time is called the reverberation time (T_R) and is defined as the time required for the sound to decay 60 db. Figure 29.5 shows an *IL*-vs.-time plot of a typical decay. For most rooms the reverberation time can be approximately calculated by the formula:

$$T_R = \frac{0.049 \times V}{\Sigma S\alpha_f} \qquad (29.12)$$

where 0.049 = a dimensional constant,
   V = room volume, ft³,
   $\Sigma S\alpha_f$ = total absorption, sabins, at frequency f^*

Reverberation criteria are discussed later in this chapter. Absorption coefficients of various materials are available (Ref. 6) and room dimensions can be obtained from plans or measurements.

(*c*) *Ray Diagrams.* Ideally, in every auditorium, concert hall, or theater, each listener should hear the performance at relatively the same loudness and without any of the disturbing effects to be discussed in the next three sections. Ray diagramming is a design procedure for analyzing reflected sound distribution throughout a hall.

Figure 29.6 shows a ray diagram. The rays are drawn normal (perpendicular) to the spherically propagating sound waves. The angles made between the reflecting panel and the incident and relected rays are always equal ($\angle A = \angle A$ and $\angle B = \angle B$). Thus, in addition to the direct sound, each listener is receiving reflected sound energy. It is as though there were additional sound sources, the *real* one and numerous "image sources."

Figures 29.7*a, b,* and *c* show the applica-

---

* Since the absorption coefficient α for almost all materials will vary at different frequencies, it is necessary to calculate T_R at each important frequency. In noncritical room problems, a single calculation at 500 cps is often sufficient. For more critical rooms calculations at 125, 250, 500, 1000, and 4000 cps are made. In broadcast studios, calculations below 125 cps may also be important.

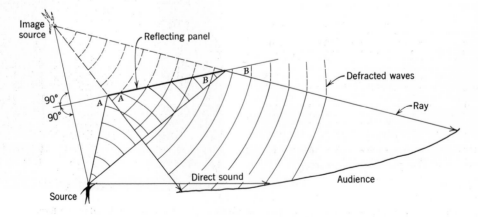

Fig. 29.6   Sound reflection analysis by ray diagram technique showing reflection off a single panel.

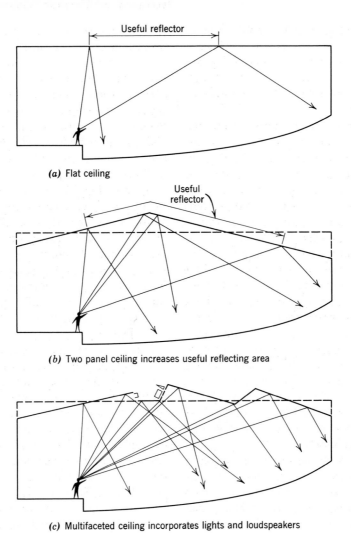

(a) Flat ceiling

(b) Two panel ceiling increases useful reflecting area

(c) Multifaceted ceiling incorporates lights and loudspeakers

Fig. 29.7   Lecture room section showing the use of ray diagrams.

tion of a ray diagram analysis to a lecture room. In Fig. 29.7a the stage height and seating slope are arranged to provide visual line of sight and the ceiling height is established by reverberation requirements, esthetics, cost, etc. It can be seen that less than half of the ceiling is providing useful reflection. By dividing the ceiling into two panels (Fig. 29.7b), people in the rear of the room perceive the direct source plus two image sources and the useful reflecting area is increased by 50 percent. In Fig. 29.7c, the shape has been further refined to include a lighting slot and a loudspeaker grille.

Although a useful design tool, ray diagrams have certain restrictions. The final design must always be a compromise between ray diagrams for various "speaking positions" on the stage. Thus a parabaloid may be a "perfect" shape for one source position but will be very poor for other positions. Furthermore, the panels must be large (the least dimension must be greater than or equal to the wave length of the lowest frequency of concern (see formula 29.1), or most of the energy will be diffracted (see Fig. 29.6).

(d) **Echoes.** An echo is caused when reflected sound at sufficient intensity reaches a listener approximately $\frac{1}{17}$ sec (0.07 sec or 70 msec) or more after he hears the direct sound. This occurs whenever the reflected sound path is more than 70 ft longer than the direct path.

Echoes, even if not distinctly discernable, are undesirable in rooms. They are annoying and make speech less intelligible. The relative annoyance is dependent on the time delay and loudness relative to the direct sound, which, in turn, are dependent on the size, position, shape and absorption of the reflecting surface.

Typical echo-producing surfaces in an auditorium are the back wall and the ceiling above the proscenium. Figure 29.8 shows these problems and suggests remedies. Note that the energy which produced the echoes can be redirected to places where it becomes useful reinforcement. If echo control by absorption alone were used on the ceiling and back wall, that energy would be wasted. The rear wall, since its area cannot be reduced too far, may have to be made more sound-absorptive to reduce the loudness of the reflected sound.

(*e*) *Flutter.* A flutter is perceived as a buzzing or clicking sound, and it is comprised of repeated echoes traversing back and forth between two nonabsorbing parallel (flat or concave) surfaces. Flutters often occur between shallow domes and hard, flat floors. The remedy for a flutter is either to change the shape of the reflectors, their parallel relationship, or add absorption. The

solution chosen will depend on reverberation requirements, cost, or esthetics.

(*f*) *Focusing.* Concave domes, vaults, or walls will focus reflected sound into certain areas of rooms. This has several disadvantages. For example, it will deprive some listeners of useful sound reflections and also (if the reflecting surface is far enough away) will increase the intensity of echoes or flutters.

(*g*) *Standing Waves.* Standing waves and flutters are very similar in principle and cause, but are heard quite differently. When an impulse (such as a hand clap) is the energy source, a flutter will occur between two parallel walls. When a steady pure tone is the source, a standing wave will occur, but only when the parallel walls are spaced apart at some integral multiple of a half wave length.

When the parallel walls are exactly one-half wave length apart, the tone will sound very loud near the walls and very quiet halfway between the walls. This is owing to the fact that at the center the reflected waves traveling in one direction are exactly one-half wave length away from those traveling in the other, and thus equal *but opposite in pressure,* which results in total cancellation. Standing waves are important only in rooms small with respect to the wave lengths generated (smallest room dimension <30 ft for music or <15 ft for speech).

If one speaks (or plays a musical instrument) standing near a wall of a room, let us

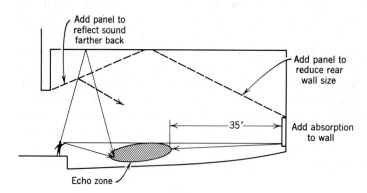

Fig. 29.8 Auditorium section showing the causes of and remedies for two typical echoes.

say about 8 ft by 8 ft, one would notice an abnormal and sometimes unpleasant loudness in the sound at about 280 cps. Thus, when a musician plays a scale, one note may seem far louder than the adjacent ones, and listeners in one section of the room will hear a different quality of sound than those in other sections. This effect *must* be avoided for music performance but is merely an annoyance in rooms designed for speech use. This is one of the reasons that one finds music rehearsal rooms, broadcast studios, etc., with nonparallel walls and undulating ceilings. These irregularities direct sound energy towards the absorbing materials of the room and cause the standing waves to degenerate.

7. Sound Amplification Systems. Sound amplification systems consist of a signal source (microphone, movie projector sound head, record unit), a control unit (ranging from a simple volume control up to a complete control console), amplifier(s), and the loudspeakers. Such systems will be required

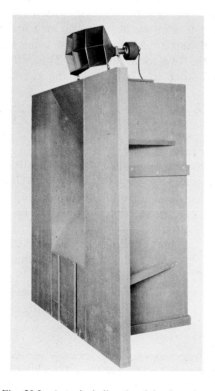

Fig. 29.9 A typical directional loudspeaker.

for voice amplification in large rooms or low-ceiling dead rooms, and in all rooms in which movies or recordings are to be played. Whether or not a room requires reinforcement by sound amplification depends on its size, shape, reverberation time, freedom from noise, and other factors. A basic choice must be made by the sound system designer —whether to use a "central" single loudspeaker cluster or a distributed loudspeaker system.

Whenever possible, the loudspeakers should be installed centrally, just above and slightly in front of the visual source, i.e., lecturer. This position causes the amplified sound to arrive at the same time as the live sound and to come from the appropriate direction.

With a central loudspeaker in close proximity to the microphone, we must prevent amplified sound from being picked up by the microphone, which causes the familiar ringing or squealing called "feedback." The loudspeakers should be highly "directional." Directional loudspeakers (which beam the sound) must be *large* relative to the wave length of the lowest frequency they are to radiate. This is important to the architect because he must provide space to accommodate units which are often 7 ft wide, 9 ft high, and 3 ft front-to-back (see Fig. 29.9).

Directionality, besides preventing feedback, may also be important when the loudspeakers are being used to increase intelligibility in highly reverberant spaces. Thus in a church where music criteria require that $T_R = 2.0$ sec or more, directional loudspeakers "aim" the sound into the absorptive congregation or audience rather than into the upper harder portions of the enclosure.

In rooms with very low ceilings or deep under-balcony seating areas, a central position may not be practical. Such situations require "distributed" systems consisting of many small loudspeakers (i.e., 8-in. diameter-cone type) mounted so that they point straight down from the ceiling. In a room having a 12 ft high, flat ceiling, for example, speakers should be spaced about 8 ft on centers both ways. Distributed systems have little directional realism, and if the room is much over 60 ft long, an artificial echo may occur owing to the immediate arrival of the amplified sound even at very remote seats if the live sound is loud enough or the ceiling is hard and sound-reflecting. Tapeloop time-delay units can control this problem.

The amplifier(s) may be located in any convenient position, such as a projection booth. The control unit (usually a preamplifier in small systems and a control console in large systems) *must* be located where the operator can hear the amplified sound and, preferably, near the back of the room. If the controls are in a booth, the "port" must be large (4 ft high by 6 ft wide) to provide adequate monitoring.

Microphones of high quality will minimize feedback by smooth response. Omnidirectional, cardioid pattern and ultradirectional microphones are available to serve a variety of pickup conditions.

8. Noise Reduction. It is often important to reduce annoying or disturbing noises to acceptable levels within the room in which the noise source is located. It is sometimes possible to do this by increasing the amount of absorption on the room surfaces. In situations where the source need not be in the same space, a greater reduction can be achieved by erecting a barrier.

(a) By Absorption. If one places one's ear next to a continuously operating nondirective noise source in a room and then moves away, one will detect that the noise level drops until one is several feet from the source. Beyond that point it will not change, but will remain nearly constant with increasing distance. Near the source, in the region known as the "direct sound field," the IL will follow formula 29.8. In the remainder of the room away from the source known as the "reverberant field," the level is dominated by the many repeated reflections from the room surfaces, and the IL is given by

$$IL = PWL - 10 \log \Sigma S\alpha + 6 \text{ db} \quad (29.13)$$

Thus, if one increases the absorption in the

room, the IL will be reduced in the reverberant field. This approach to noise control is limited to spaces where the listener (*a*) *will not* be very near a noise sound, (*b*) in offices, stores, or restaurants, where there are numerous noise sources extending throughout the room, (*c*) where reverberation criteria are not applicable, and (*d*) where it is not important to propagate sounds to an audience. It is extremely important to note that the increase of surface-absorptive treatment will have no effect at all on the direct sound field.

(b) By Barriers. Frequently a noise source can best be controlled by completely enclosing it with solid impervious materials; that is, by placing it in a separate room. In buildings we rarely can get sufficient noise reduction unless we house unrelated activities in separate rooms. The selection of dividing partitions or floor constructions on the basis of sound isolation is a very important aspect of architectural acoustics.

The acoustical isolating property of a barrier is called its transmission loss (*TL*). Noise reduction (*NR*) rather than *TL*, however, is what we observe and measure in the field, and it takes into account other aspects of the two-room situation. The *NR* is the difference in IL between the two rooms.

$$NR = IL_1 - IL_2 = TL - 10 \log \frac{S_w}{\Sigma S\alpha_2}$$
$$(29.14)$$

where NR = noise reduction,* db,
IL_1 and IL_2 = sound pressure levels in the source and receiving rooms respectively, db, re: 10^{-16} watt/cm^2,
TL = transmission loss,* db,
S_w = surface area of the transmitting wall, ft^2
$\Sigma S\alpha_2$ = the total sound absorption of the receiving room, sabins.

---

* Notice that *NR* and *TL*, since they are ratios of two variables, ($NR = 10 \log I_1/I_2$ and $TL = 10 \log P_t/P_i$) do not utilize a reference level, whereas $IL = 10 \log IK$, where K = constant = $1/10^{-16}$ watt/cm^2.

The *TL* is a function of the weight, stiffness, edge-mounting condition, and other physical properties of the barrier alone. *NR*, or the level difference, is a function of the size ($l \times w$) of the barrier and the absorption of the receiving room *as well as* the *TL* of the barrier. The applicability of *TL* is that it is a common denominator to which all measurements can be reduced, and, thence, from which all predictions can be derived.

Transmission loss values vary, as do most other acoustical values, with frequency; in general the *TL* increases (provides more sound isolation) at higher frequencies. Materials of greater mass (density in lb/ft³ × thickness in feet) provide greater isolation than lighter ones except that too great a stiffness can often greatly offset the advantage of great weight.

Actual values of *TL* as a function of frequency are available from theoretical calculations (see Ref. 5), field measurements (see Refs. 5 and 11), or laboratory measurements (see Refs. 1 and 7). Some examples of field-measured transmission loss are given in Fig. 29.10.

Many attempts have been made to simplify sound-isolation calculations by use of average *TL* figures and other "one-number" schemes. Unless such schemes are directly related to the problem being analyzed, it seems better to do a full 8-octave or 11-half-octave band-frequency calculation, time consuming though it may be.

Acoustical testing laboratories measure noise reduction (*NR*) between two special rooms through sample partitions, and from this obtain the transmission loss for the sample. Tests are made at 11 half-octave intervals from 125 cps to 4000 cps (see ordinate, Fig. 29.3*b*). Formerly all 11 results were averaged for each sample. Currently, 1414 cps and 2828 cps are omitted, giving what is called the "nine frequency" average. Still another "one-number" scheme, the "sound transmission class" or "STC" is obtained by a procedure outlined in Appendix A of Ref. 1. It is not recommended that these be used, even for rank-ordering barriers, if the results are important.

Sound transmission does not always occur along the most direct or obvious route. Frequently, an effective partition is erected to the height of a lightweight suspended ceiling, permitting sound to pass through the ceiling "plenum" space. Such transmission is said to travel along a "flanking path." Other common flanking paths are through leaks near windows, pipes, or electrical boxes, or through two doors and a corridor.

(c) Impact Sound Transmission and Structure-Borne Sound Transmission. Two special categories of sound transmission through barriers are "impact" sound transmission and "structure-borne" sound transmission. Both are similar in that the source of the sound is in mechanical contact with the barrier. Impact sound occurs when an object hammers directly on the source side of the barrier (i.e., footfall) and structure-borne sound occurs when a vibrating device (fan, radio, or cello) is in continuous rigid contact with the barrier.

Both of the latter kinds of sound transmission can be significantly reduced by interposing a resilient material between the source and the barrier. For example, carpeting can reduce footfall noise, and springs can isolate fan vibrations. An alternative (or additional) remedy is to erect a second barrier in the receiving room just inside the transmitting barriers of the receiving room as, for example, by installing a resiliently suspended plaster ceiling to reduce footfall from above. A method of rating impact noise barriers is given in Ref. 15.

Noise Control for Mechanical Equipment. With the increasing use of air conditioning, the problem of noise in buildings increases each year. Mechanical noise reaches occupancy spaces in one or more of at least four specific ways: (1) When the mechanical equipment room is adjacent to the occupancy space, the noise in the equipment room may be transmitted through the common walls or ceilings; (2) the noise may travel through the air in supply or return ducts; (3) when the equipment is rigidly attached to the structure, vibration may

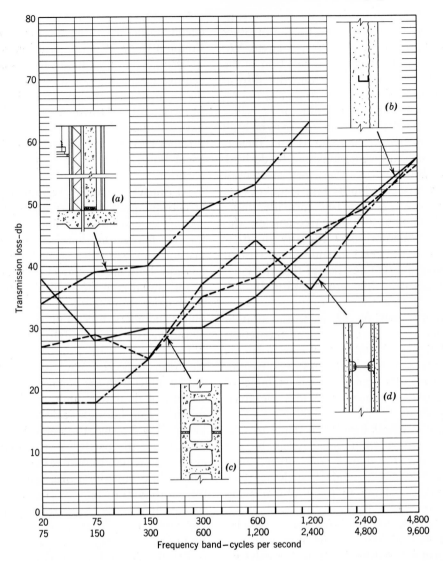

Fig. 29.10   4 typical partition and their sound transmission loss curves: (a) 4 in. masonry with separately framed plaster skins, (b) $2\frac{1}{2}$ in. solid plaster, (c) $\frac{5}{8}$ in. plaster on mineral lath on metal studs, and (d) 4 in. masonry block.

travel through the structure and be radiated into the air of occupancy rooms; and (4) grilles, fan-coil units, induction units, etc., located directly in the room may themselves generate annoying noise.

Airborne sound transmission through equipment room walls is dealt with as outlined in the Section 18.2. Fortunately, more and more manufacturers are providing sound power level data for their equipment

and the calculation becomes routine with the use of formulas 29.13 and 29.14.

Duct-borne noise can be controlled by the use of duct linings and prefabricated mufflers. The noise reduction provided by linings and mufflers is usually designated "attenuation." A procedure for calculating the required attenuation is given in the chapter on "Noise Control" in the current edition of ASHRAE Guide (Ref. 8).

Structure-borne sound transmission from rotating or reciprocating equipment can usually be reduced by the proper mounting of the equipment. Steel spring and rubber pad mounts are available for the basic support of the machine itself. Mounts should be selected which are equally "soft" up and down and side to side. The isolation efficiency of mounts for simply supported systems is usually indicated by the amount they deflect under static loading. Current good practice utilizes springs having deflections of more than 1 in. and often uses deflections of 4 in. to 6 in. for powerful, low-rpm equipment. In addition to the basic support, it is essential to provide resilient couplings in pipes, ducts, electric conduits, and all other possible "short-circuiting" paths.

Noise-producing equipment within occupancy spaces can be divided into those in which air passage generates the noise (grilles, induction units) and those which are electrically powered (fan coil units, package a-c units). Responsibility for quiet operation of the former should be in the hands of the mechanical engineer. The primary requirement for low air-diffusion noise is to avoid large pressure drops at the device. Pressure drops in excess of approximately 0.2 to 0.3 in. are likely to cause disturbing noise levels. The noise levels of electrically powered equipment are primarily the responsibility of the manufacturer, although the engineer can do much by enforcing a tightly worded specification of maximum acceptable *PWL* as a function of frequency.

10. Criteria. All of the previous discussion has merely shown ways of establishing noise levels, degree of isolation, reverberation time, noise reduction, etc. Some of these characteristics of sound fields, such as echoes, flutters, etc., are basically undesirable and should be eliminated. Other characteristics such as reverberation time can be either too great, too small, too short, or too long. Criteria are goals based on measurable quantities (speech intelligibility,

etc.) or are subjective judgments, or opinions (reverberation times for music appreciation, etc.). The following covers a few of many such acoustic criteria.

(*a*) *Hearing Damage.* Sound pressure levels in excess of 130 db even for short periods of time may cause permanent loss of hearing. Continuous exposure (over many 40-hr work-weeks) to levels in excess of 85 db may also damage our auditory mechanism. When such conditions exist, a careful study should be made to evaluate the seriousness of the risk. Shorter exposures to loud noises may cause pain in the ears and, thus, we may refer to a "threshold of pain."

(*b*) *Threshold of Hearing.* On the other end of the sound level scale, 0 db is, by definition, our "threshold of hearing." In actual fact this is only true at 1000 cps and most listeners can hear slightly lower sound levels at 4000 cps (about -5 db) and have trouble hearing $+40$ db at 20 cps and $+10$ db at 8000 cps.

Young people, in general, hear more acutely than older people. Deafness can be caused by illness or exposure to high noise levels. Also, an artificial threshold is created by the presence of masking noise. If, for example, an air conditioner creates a 30-db steady level, it would not be possible to hear a 10-db signal. If the signal in this case is an intermittant tone (at a single frequency) we might hear it at 15 or 20 db.

(*c*) *Comfort and Annoyance.* Between levels inducing audibility and pain lies the area in which the science of psychology rather than physiology must be brought to bear. After a pleasant evening listening to the hi-fi (at levels often in excess of 90 db), one may well be angered and kept awake by a dripping faucet (the levels of which may never exceed 25 db). One must examine the listener's tolerance in terms of the information conveyed by the sound and in terms of the listener's conditioning to the sound.

Fortunately, most people respond similarly to broad-band steady noises which do not convey information, and it is possible to set down quantitative criteria. The most commonly used criteria consist of a family of curves called noise criteria or NC curves. These are shown on Fig. 29.11, and are further described in Ref. 11. In Table 29.4 the criteria are related to typical occupancies for which each is suitable.

A typical noise spectrum has been superimposed on the NC curves to illustrate their use. If an intensity level spectrum equal to the "typical spectrum" on Fig. 29.2 were to exist in a room, the room noise would just meet an NC-30 criterion since the spectrum is tangent to the NC-30 curve in the 300/600 octave band. On this basis we can predict

that the room would serve as a satisfactory office (from Table 29.4) but would be too noisy for a recording studio.

When a noise is disturbing, one form of design goal is to reduce the noise to inaudibility. This seldom means reducing the noise down to the threshold of hearing. It usually involves reduction to levels equal to or somewhat lower than the background noise in the space. Thus, if one is disturbed by a machine noise entering an office one measures or predicts the IL with the machine turned on and with it off, and uses the difference between the two levels as the required noise reduction. If the noise is intermittent or contains strong pure tone com-

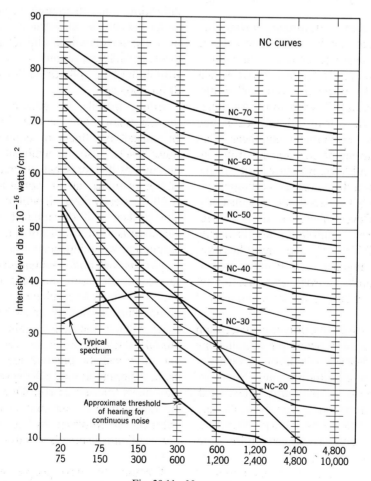

Fig. 29.11 Nc curves.

Table 29.4 Noise Criteria Suitable for Various Types of Spaces

Type of Space	Recommended Noise Criterion
Broadcast studios	NC 15–20
Concert halls	NC 15–20
Legitimate theaters (500 seats, no amplification)	NC 20–25
Music rooms	NC 25
Schoolrooms (no amplification)	NC 25
TV studios	NC 25
Apartments and hotels	NC 25–30
Executive office	NC 25–35
Assembly halls (amplification)	NC 25–30
Homes (sleeping areas)	NC 25–35
Motion picture theaters	NC 30
Hospitals	NC 30
Churches	NC 30
Courtrooms	NC 30
Libraries	NC 30
Restaurants	NC 45
Coliseums for sports only (amplification)	NC 50

ponents, it is wise to reduce it an additional 5 db to 10 db, and if it is both intermittent and has pure-tone components it should be reduced 10 db to 20 db below the ambient.

(*d*) **Reverberation Time Criteria.** Different room uses require different reverberation times. Figure 29.12 shows optimum reverberation times for various room uses. The times indicated are for optimum conditions at 500 cps and higher. Longer times are acceptable at lower frequencies and for music even highly desirable.

(*e*) **Speech Intelligibility.** Speech intelligibility varies under varying conditions. For example, a long reverberation time can cause loss of intelligibility. The same thing is true for high ambient noise, echoes, or a badly designed loudspeaker system. The most effective method of measuring intelligibility is to read a carefully selected set of phonetically balanced nonsense syllables (see Ref. 2) to a test audience and then to compute the ratio of correct answers to the total syllables read. This ratio is called the

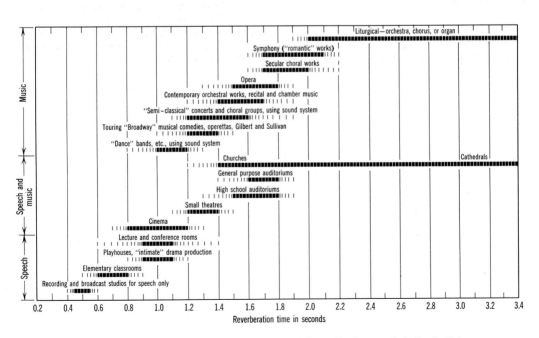

Fig. 29.12 Optimum reverberation (500/1000 cps) for auditoriums and similar facilities.

Articulation Index (AI). If the AI is greater than about 0.5, the intelligibility of sentences should be nearly perfect.

(*f*) *Criteria for Music Listening.* In addition to the reverberation and noise conteria mentioned above, there are a number of other criteria for the judgment of the quality of music rooms. These are described in Ref. 4. Foremost among these is "intimacy" which is a function of the time at which the first reflected sounds reach a listener's ear after the direct sound. The optimum condition is when that initial time delay is less than 0.02 sec.

Reverberation time is also important for excellent music listening. Optimum for most symphonic performances is a midfrequency reverberation time of 2.0 sec and about 2.4 sec at low frequencies.

(*g*) *Speech Privacy.* Speech privacy, as applied to offices, hotel rooms, etc., is judged on the basis of the *intelligibility* of speech transmitted. Most people (about 80 percent) feel that their room is "private" if the AI of the transmitted speech is below 0.05. This condition may exist and the speech may still be audible (Ref. 10).

References

1. *Laboratory Measurement of Air-Borne Sound Transmission Loss of Buildings, Floors, and Walls, ASTM E90-61T,* American Society for Testing Materials, New York.
2. *Acoustic Measurements,* Beranek, L. L., John Wiley and Sons, New York, 1949.
3. *Acoustics,* Beranek, L. L., McGraw-Hill Book Company, Inc. New York, 1954.
4. *Music, Acoustics, and Architecture,* Beranek, L. L., John Wiley and Sons, New York, 1962.
5. *Noise Reduction,* Beranek, L. L., McGraw-Hill Book Company, New York, 1960.
6. *Sound Absorption Coefficients of Architectural Acoustical Materials,* Acoustical Materials Association, Bulletin XXII, A.I.A., No. 39-b, (1962).
7. *Building Materials and Structures Report 144, Sound Insulation of Wall and Floor Constructions,* U.S. Department of Commerce, National Bureau of Standards (December 1, 1958).
8. *Guide and Data Book,* ASHRAE, 1963 Edition, Chapter 14.
9. *Handbook of Noise Control,* Harris, Cyril M., McGraw-Hill Book Company, New York, 1957.
10. *Speech Privacy Analyzer* (November 1961), available from Owens Corning Fiberglas.
11. *Acoustics, Noise and Buildings,* Parkin, P. H., and Humphreys, H. R., Faber and Faber, Ltd., London, 1958.
12. *Acoustical Designing in Architecture,* Kundsen, V. O., and Harris, C. M., John Wiley and Sons, New York, 1950.
13. *Design for Hearing,* Progressive Architecture (May 1959), pp. 143–206.
14. *The Use of Architectural Acoustical Material: Theory and Practice, AIA No. 39-A,* American Institute of Acoustics, New York.
15. *Impact Noise Control in Multi-Family Dwellings, FHA No. 750,* Federal Housing Administration, Washington 25, D.C.

Appendix A

Table of Contents of the National Electrical Code 1961

Principal Tables

Index